The Elements of

NUCLEAR REACTOR

THEORY

by

SAMUEL GLASSTONE

Consultant, United States Atomic Energy Commission

AND

MILTON C. EDLUND

Physicist, Oak Ridge National Laboratory

TWELFTH PRINTING

D. VAN NOSTRAND COMPANY, INC.

PRINCETON, NEW JERSEY

TORONTO NEW YORK LONDON

D. VAN NOSTRAND COMPANY, INC.
120 Alexander St., Princeton, New Jersey (*Principal office*)
24 West 40 Street, New York 18, New York

D. VAN NOSTRAND COMPANY, LTD.
358, Kensington High Street, London, W.14, England

D. VAN NOSTRAND COMPANY (Canada), LTD.
25 Hollinger Road, Toronto 16, Canada

Library of Congress Catalogue Card No. 52–12438

First Published November 1952

*Reprinted February 1954, May 1955,
November 1955, August 1956, February 1957,
August 1958, November 1960, June 1962,
October 1963, February 1965,
August 1966*

FOREWORD

by

Gordon Dean, Chairman
U. S. Atomic Energy Commission

Nothing is more essential to the Nation's atomic energy program than our resources of trained scientists and engineers. As the AEC project has expanded, the need for more and more trained personnel has been ever present. The established educational organizations of the Nation have eagerly sought ways and means to provide the proper training for present-day students who wish to study nuclear science and engineering, but to some extent the educators have been hampered by the lack of informational material available.

In order to provide the essential information in the important field of nuclear reactor theory, the AEC engaged Dr. Samuel Glasstone, a scientist, educator, and textbook writer of established reputation, to assist in the preparation and presentation of the information that could be gathered from all sources, including the files and facilities of the project. In so doing, he participated in the activities of the Oak Ridge School of Reactor Technology and collaborated with the staff, chiefly Mr. Milton C. Edlund, who conducted the course in nuclear reactor theory. The text prepared by these men has been reviewed by a number of scientists and engineers within the atomic energy program. The AEC Office of Classification also checked the final manuscript to ascertain that its publication would in no way prove harmful to national security. The scientific evaluation and presentation of the information, however, are wholly the work of the authors.

The Atomic Energy Commission takes pride in offering this book as an aid to further education and training in the field of nuclear science.

FOREWORD

by

Alvin M. Weinberg, Research Director
Oak Ridge National Laboratory

The field of nuclear reactor theory is unique among physical theories in that it is a subject of extreme practical importance whose principles have not been written down in fairly complete, coherent fashion. Parts of the theory have been the subjects of several monographs and books, notably Soodak and Campbell's *Elementary Pile Theory* and the MIT volumes, *The Science and Engineering of Nuclear Power*. However, because of previous secrecy restrictions there has been, up to now, no more or less complete exposition of the subject from a single unified point of view.

The present volume by Glasstone and Edlund is the first attempt at presenting the whole field in one reasonably complete work. The book bears resemblance to the Soodak and Campbell volume since both are based on courses in reactor theory at Oak Ridge — the older on Soodak's lectures in the original Clinton Laboratories Training School, the newer on Edlund's lectures in the recently reconstituted Oak Ridge School of Reactor Technology. The fuller treatment in the Glasstone-Edlund book is mainly a reflection of the broader scope of the training given to embryo nuclear engineers in the new school as compared with the old.

While it is too early to say with certainty, it seems very probable that reactor technology will remain an extraordinarily important engineering field. The theory of nuclear reactors is of course central to an understanding of this field. To the authors who have given so much effort to the preparation of this text deep gratitude is therefore due not only from the coming generation of nuclear engineers, but also from the many original contributors to the theory who, because of day-to-day pressures, have never been able to accomplish the task which Messrs. Glasstone and Edlund have done so admirably.

PREFACE

This book is intended as an introduction to the subject of nuclear reactor theory for the use of physicists, engineers, and others who are being brought into the reactor program for the first time. Because of the varying backgrounds of the readers, there is a considerable range in the scope and difficulty of the material. Some readers will consequently wish to omit certain chapters, and this can frequently be done without affecting the fundamental development of the subject.

The present form is a revision of the preliminary draft, issued in 1950, that was developed from lectures given by M. C. Edlund at the Oak Ridge School of Reactor Technology. The authors wish to take this opportunity to acknowledge their indebtedness to the many scientists whose cooperative efforts in connection with the Manhattan Project led to the development of the ideas discussed in this book. Mention may be made in particular of the contributions of R. F. Christy, C. Eckart, E. Fermi, F. L. Friedman, L. W. Nordheim, P. Morrison, G. Placzek, L. Szilard, E. Teller, A. M. Weinberg, J. A. Wheeler, E. P. Wigner, and G. Young.

The authors' thanks are also due to a number of colleagues, who read the preliminary draft, and, in particular, to A. M. Weinberg for his helpful advice and valuable criticism.

SAMUEL GLASSTONE
MILTON C. EDLUND

CONTENTS

CHAPTER | PAGE

I. NUCLEAR STRUCTURE AND STABILITY 1

II. NUCLEAR REACTIONS. 16

III. PRODUCTION AND REACTIONS OF NEUTRONS. 33

IV. THE FISSION PROCESS 62

V. THE DIFFUSION OF NEUTRONS 90

VI. THE SLOWING DOWN OF NEUTRONS 137

VII. THE BARE HOMOGENEOUS THERMAL REACTOR (Sources Determined by Fermi Age Theory) 191

VIII. HOMOGENEOUS REACTOR WITH REFLECTOR: THE GROUP-DIFFUSION METHOD 225

IX. HETEROGENEOUS (NATURAL URANIUM) REACTORS 250

X. TIME BEHAVIOR OF A BARE THERMAL REACTOR 290

XI. REACTOR CONTROL 314

XII. GENERAL THEORY OF HOMOGENEOUS MULTIPLYING SYSTEMS . . 345

XIII. PERTURBATION THEORY. 372

XIV. TRANSPORT THEORY AND NEUTRON DIFFUSION 384

INDEX 405

Chapter I

NUCLEAR STRUCTURE AND STABILITY*

CHARACTERISTICS OF ATOMIC NUCLEI

PROTONS AND NEUTRONS

1.1. The operation of nuclear reactors depends on various types of interaction of neutrons with atomic nuclei. In order to understand the nature and characteristics of these reactions, it is desirable to review briefly some of the fundamental aspects of nuclear structure and nuclear energy.

1.2. An atom consists of a positively charged nucleus surrounded by a number of negatively charged electrons, so that the atom as a whole is electrically neutral. In the processes taking place in a reactor, leading to the release of atomic energy, it is only the atomic nuclei which are involved, and the electrons may be neglected. Chemical energy, such as is obtained by the combustion of coal and oil, results in a rearrangement of the atoms due to a redistribution of the electrons. Atomic energy, on the other hand, is a consequence of the redistribution of the particles within the atomic nuclei. For this reason, the term *nuclear energy* is frequently used as a more precise alternative to the historic name, atomic energy.

1.3. Atomic nuclei are built up of two kinds of primary particles, called *protons* and *neutrons*, respectively. Because they are the units of which the nuclei are composed, and for other reasons, protons and neutrons are often referred to by the general term *nucleon*. Both protons and neutrons can be obtained in the free state, i.e., outside atomic nuclei, and their individual properties can thus be studied.

1.4. The proton carries a single unit positive charge, equal in magnitude to the electronic charge. This particle is, in fact, identical with the nucleus of a hydrogen atom, i.e., a hydrogen atom without its single electron. Hence, the

---

* General references to these topics are H. A. Bethe, "Elementary Nuclear Theory," John Wiley and Sons, Inc., 1947; D. Halliday, "Introductory Nuclear Physics," John Wiley and Sons, Inc., 1950. A more elementary treatment is given by S. Glasstone, "Sourcebook on Atomic Energy," D. Van Nostrand Co., Inc., 1950.

mass of a proton is taken as equal to the mass of a hydrogen atom minus the mass of an electron.   Thus, expressed in *atomic mass units* or amu,*

$$\text{Mass of hydrogen atom} = 1.00813 \text{ amu}$$
$$\text{Mass of proton} = 1.00758 \text{ amu.}$$

1.5. The neutron, which is of fundamental importance in connection with the release of nuclear energy, is electrically neutral and carries no charge.   Consequently, it does not suffer electrical repulsion when it approaches an atomic (positively charged) nucleus from outside, as does a charged particle, such as a proton.   The mass of a neutron is somewhat greater than that of a proton, and even of a hydrogen atom; thus,

$$\text{Mass of neutron} = 1.00897 \text{ amu.}$$

Methods for the production of neutrons and a discussion of their interaction with atomic nuclei will be given later.

Atomic Number and Mass Number

1.6. For a given element, the number of protons present in the atomic nucleus, which is the same as the number of positive charges it carries, is called the *atomic number* of the element.   It is usually represented by the symbol Z, and it is equal, apart from a few exceptions, to the number of the element in order of increasing atomic weight.   Thus, the atomic number of hydrogen is 1, of helium 2, of lithium 3, and so on up to 92 for uranium, the element with the highest atomic weight existing in nature to any appreciable extent.   A number of heavier elements, of which plutonium, atomic number 94, is important in connection with the release of nuclear energy, have been made artificially.

1.7. The total number of protons and neutrons in an atomic nucleus is called the *mass number* of the element and is indicated by A.   The number of protons is equal to Z, as stated above; hence, the number of neutrons in a given atomic nucleus is $A - Z$.   Since both neutron and proton have masses which are close to unity on the atomic weight scale, it is evident that the mass number is the integer nearest to the atomic weight of the species under consideration.

Isotopes and Nuclides

1.8. It is the atomic number, i.e., the number of protons, and not the atomic weight, that determines the chemical nature of an element.   This is because the chemical properties depend on the electrons, and the number of the latter in an atom is equal to the atomic number.   Consequently, atoms with nuclei containing the same number of protons, i.e., with the same atomic number, but with different numbers of neutrons, i.e., with different mass numbers, are essentially

* The atomic mass unit is defined in terms of the mass of the atom of O^{16}, the main isotope of oxygen.   The weight of this atom is taken to be exactly 16 atomic mass units.

identical chemically, although they frequently exhibit marked differences of nuclear stability. Such species, having the same atomic number but different mass numbers, are called *isotopes*.

1.9. Most elements present in nature exist in two or more stable isotopic forms, which are virtually indistinguishable chemically, although their mass numbers and atomic weights are different. Altogether, some 280 stable isotopes have been identified as occurring naturally, and in addition some 50 unstable species are found in nature. Another 700 or more unstable species have been obtained artificially by various nuclear reactions. In order to distinguish among the different isotopes of a given element, it is usual to indicate the mass number together with the name or symbol of the element. Thus, the isotope of uranium of mass number 238 may be represented as uranium-238, U-238, or U^{238}.

1.10. The element uranium, which is at present the most important for the release of nuclear energy, exists in nature in at least three isotopic forms, with mass numbers 234, 235, and 238, respectively. The proportions in which the isotopes occur in natural uranium and the weights of the respective atoms in atomic mass units are given in Table 1.10. It is seen that uranium-238 is by far the most abundant isotope, but all natural uranium contains a little over 0.7 per cent of uranium-235. The proportion of uranium-234 is so small that it is usually neglected in the study of nuclear reactors.

TABLE 1.10. ISOTOPIC COMPOSITION OF NATURAL URANIUM

Mass Number	Per Cent	Isotopic Mass (amu)
234	0.006	234.11
235	0.712	235.11
238	99.282	238.12

1.11. Although the majority of elements exist naturally as a mixture of isotopes, about 20 occur as single species only. For this and other reasons, it has been found desirable to introduce the term *nuclide*. It is used to describe an atomic species characterized by the composition of its nucleus, i.e., by the numbers of protons and neutrons it contains. An isotope is consequently one of a group of two or more nuclides having the same number of protons, i.e., the same atomic number, but different numbers of neutrons. An element like fluorine, of which only one species exists in nature, is said to form a single stable nuclide.

RADIOACTIVITY

RADIOACTIVE ISOTOPES

1.12. It was stated above that a number of unstable isotopes (or unstable nuclides) are found in nature. Actually, the naturally occurring elements of highest atomic weight, such as polonium, thorium, radium, and uranium, consist entirely of unstable nuclides or *radioactive isotopes*. These substances undergo spontaneous change, referred to as radioactive disintegration or radio-active decay, at definite rates.   The decay is accompanied by the emission from the atomic nucleus of an electrically charged particle, either an *alpha particle*, which is a helium nucleus, or a *beta particle*, which is an electron.   Frequently, the products of decay are themselves radioactive, expelling either an alpha or a beta particle.   After a number of stages of disintegration, an atomic species with a stable nucleus is formed.

1.13. In many instances, when a nucleus suffers radioactive decay, the product (or daughter) nucleus is not in its lowest energy state or ground state. In other words, the product nucleus is in an *excited state*, having energy in excess of the ground state.   Within a very short time, perhaps 10^{-15} sec of its formation, the excited nucleus emits the excess (or excitation) energy in the form of radia-tion called *gamma rays*.   These rays are similar in character to X-rays; they are highly penetrating and have wave lengths in the range of 10^{-8} to 10^{-11} cm or less. The greater the excitation energy of the nucleus, the shorter the wave length of the gamma radiation.

1.14. Although the elements of highest atomic number, from polonium (atomic number 84) onward, exist only in unstable, radioactive forms, thallium (81), lead (82), and bismuth (83) occur in nature largely as stable isotopes, and also to some extent as unstable isotopes.   With a few exceptions, which are not important here, the elements below thallium, as found in nature, consist entirely of stable nuclides.   However, in recent years there have been produced, by various nuclear reactions, unstable, i.e., radioactive, isotopes of all the known elements.

1.15. For reasons which will be apparent shortly (§ 1.45, *et seq.*), if a particular nuclide is to be stable, the ratio of neutrons to protons in its nucleus must lie within a certain limited range.   This may be seen from Fig. 1.15, in which the number of neutrons (ordinates) is plotted against the number of protons (abscis-sas) present in each of the known stable atomic nuclei.   It is apparent that the points lie within a relatively narrow band, corresponding to a restricted stability range of neutron-to-proton ratios for any given mass (or atomic) number.   As the mass number, i.e., the sum of the neutrons and protons, increases, the neu-tron-to-proton ratio for stability increases steadily from 1.00 to about 1.56. For each mass (or atomic) number there is a relatively small variation in the ratio within which stable nuclides occur.

RADIOACTIVE CHANGE

1.16. When the numbers of neutrons and protons in the nucleus of a given atomic species are such that the ratio lies outside the stability range for that mass number, the nuclide will be radioactive.   The unstable nucleus will undergo spontaneous change in the direction of increased stability.   Should the nucleus contain more neutrons or, what is the same thing, fewer protons, than are required

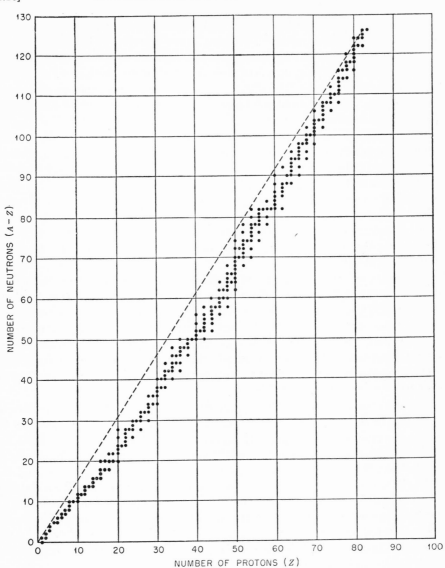

FIG. 1.15. Numbers of neutrons and protons in stable nuclei

for stability, a neutron will be spontaneously converted into a proton and at the same time a negative electron, i.e., a negative beta particle, will be expelled; thus,

Neutron → Proton + Negative Beta Particle ↑

	Charge	0	+1	−1
	Mass	1	1	0

The charge and mass on the left-hand side, i.e., the neutron, are seen to balance those on the right-hand side, i.e., proton + negative beta particle. It may be mentioned that there are reasons for postulating that another particle, called a *neutrino*, having essentially zero mass and no charge, is also formed and carries off some of the energy liberated in the radioactive transformation.

1.17. The result of the change depicted above, is, effectively, to replace a neutron by a proton, so that the atomic number of the product (or daughter) element is one unit greater than that of the parent element, although its mass number is unchanged. In other words, the radioactive (negative beta) change leads to the formation of an isotopic form of another element with the same mass number as the parent element. In this new species the neutron-to-proton ratio will be less than in the nucleus of the parent, because the change of a neutron to a proton means a decrease in the number of neutrons and an accompanying increase in the number of protons. Hence, in general, the daughter nucleus will tend to be more stable than the parent. It may not be entirely stable, however; in this event, it will also be radioactive, expelling a negative beta particle and forming an isotope of still another element. After one, two, or more stages, in each of which a neutron is replaced by a proton and a negative beta particle is emitted, a stable species is formed.

1.18. A nuclide will also be unstable if the number of neutrons is too small, or the number of protons is too large, for the neutron-to-proton ratio to be within the stability range for the particular mass number. Now, however, a proton will be converted into a neutron, and at the same time a positive electron or positron, i.e., a positive beta particle, will be ejected; thus,

$$\text{Proton} \rightarrow \text{Neutron} + \text{Positive Beta Particle} \uparrow$$

	Proton	Neutron	Positive Beta Particle
Charge	+1	0	+1
Mass	1	1	0

The product nucleus will then have an atomic number one unit lower than its parent, although the mass number will be the same. As in the case considered above, the daughter may still be somewhat unstable, and then it also will be radioactive. In any event, after one or more stages of positive beta decay, a stable nucleus having a neutron-to-proton ratio within the stability range will be formed.

1.19. There are two other ways in which a nuclide with a ratio of neutrons to protons that is too low for stability can become more stable. One is by the emission of an alpha particle (§ 1.12), and the other is by the nucleus capturing a negative electron from outside the atom, thus reversing the process described in § 1.16. In each case the change is associated with an increase in the neutron-to-proton ratio. Since neither of these modes of radioactive decay is important in connection with nuclear reactors, it is unnecessary to consider them in further detail.

RATE OF RADIOACTIVE DECAY

1.20. For a given radioactive species, every nucleus has a definite probability of decaying in unit time; this decay probability is characteristic of the particular species and has a constant value which cannot be changed in any known way. It is the same irrespective of the chemical or physical state of the element at all accessible temperatures and pressures. In a given specimen, the rate of decay at any instant is always directly proportional to the number of radioactive atoms of the isotope under consideration present at that instant. Thus, if N is the number of the particular radioactive atoms (or nuclei) present at any time t, the decay rate is given by

$$\frac{dN}{dt} = -\lambda N, \tag{1.20.1}$$

where λ is called the *decay constant* of the radioactive species. Upon integration between any arbitrary zero time, when the number of radioactive nuclei of the specified kind present is N_0, and a time t later, when the number of these nuclei remaining is N, it is readily found that

$$N = N_0 e^{-\lambda t}. \tag{1.20.2}$$

1.21. A convenient method for representing the rate of radioactive decay is by means of the *half life* of a particular nuclide. It is defined as the time required for the number of active nuclei (or the activity) to decay to half its initial value. This means that if, in (1.20.2), N is set equal to $\frac{1}{2}N_0$, the corresponding time is the half life T; thus,

$$e^{-\lambda T} = \tfrac{1}{2}$$

or

$$T = \frac{\ln 2}{\lambda} = \frac{0.6931}{\lambda}, \tag{1.21.1}$$

so that the half life is inversely proportional to the decay constant. The half lives of known radioactive species range from a small fraction of a second to billions of years.

1.22. The reciprocal of the decay constant, represented by t_m, is the *mean life* or average life of the radioactive species; thus,

$$t_m = \frac{1}{\lambda}. \tag{1.22.1}$$

It can be shown that the mean life is equal to the average life expectancy of the nuclei present at any time.

NUCLEAR BINDING ENERGIES

NUCLEAR FORCES

1.23. The remarkable fact about atomic nuclei is not that some show partial instability and are radioactive, but rather that they exhibit any stability at all.

It might be thought, upon first consideration, that a system of closely packed (positively charged) protons, such as exists in an atomic nucleus, would fly apart because of the electrostatic repulsion of the charges. The stability of atomic nuclei is evidently related, at least partly, to the presence of neutrons in addition to protons.

1.24. The existence of the stable nucleus of deuterium, the isotope of hydrogen of mass number 2, consisting of a neutron and a proton, shows that attractive neutron-proton forces must be involved. In addition, there is good evidence that at close range, as in an atomic nucleus, there are forces of attraction between protons themselves as well as between neutrons. For example, the definite stability of the helium-3 nucleus, containing one neutron and two protons, indicates the existence of proton-proton forces of attraction within the atomic nucleus. However, although it is accepted that attractive neutron-neutron, proton-proton, and neutron-proton forces exist, little is known of the nature of such forces. The subject of nuclear stability cannot yet be satisfactorily treated from a theoretical standpoint, and so a semi-empirical approach, based on nuclear masses, will be used here.

Mass Defect and Binding Energy

1.25. If there were no energy changes, due to the operation of nuclear forces, the mass of a nucleus would be equal to the sum of the masses of its constituent Z protons and $A - Z$ neutrons (§ 1.7). The total mass of the atom as a whole would then be the sum of these quantities plus the mass of Z electrons. Since a proton and an electron make up a hydrogen atom, it may be supposed that the mass of an atom of any nuclide of atomic number Z and mass number A should be equal to the mass of Z hydrogen atoms plus that of $A - Z$ neutrons, i.e., to $Zm_H + (A - Z)m_n$, where m_H and m_n are the masses of a hydrogen atom and of a neutron, respectively.

1.26. Actual determinations of individual atomic masses show that they are always *less* than the values calculated in this manner. The difference between the calculated mass and the experimental mass M, called the *mass defect*, is represented by

$$\text{Mass defect} = Zm_H + (A - Z)m_n - M. \tag{1.26.1}$$

This mass defect represents the mass which would appear in the form of energy in the hypothetical process of assembling a particular atom from the requisite number of electrons, protons, and neutrons. The same amount of energy would, of course, have to be supplied to the atom in order to break it up into its constituent particles. Hence, the energy equivalent of the true mass defect is taken as a measure of the *binding energy* of the particular atomic species.

1.27. In order to determine the energy equivalent of the mass defect, use is made of the Einstein mass-energy relationship

$$E = mc^2, \tag{1.27.1}$$

where E is the energy equivalent of the mass m, and c is the velocity of light. If m is in grams, and c in cm per sec, i.e., 3×10^{10} cm per sec, E will be in ergs. For present purposes, it is more useful to express m in atomic mass units, where 1 amu $= 1.67 \times 10^{-24}$ gram*; equation (1.27.1) then becomes

$$E(\text{ergs}) = m(\text{amu}) \times 1.49 \times 10^{-3}. \tag{1.27.2}$$

1.28. In atomic studies it has become the practice to express energies in *electron volt* units. The electron volt, i.e., 1 ev, is the energy acquired by any charged particle carrying a unit (electronic) charge when it passes without resistance through a potential difference of 1 volt. From the known magnitude of the electronic charge, it is found that

$$1 \text{ ev} = 1.60 \times 10^{-12} \text{ erg}. \tag{1.28.1}$$

Consequently, (1.27.2) can be written as

$$E(\text{ev}) = m(\text{amu}) \times 9.31 \times 10^{8}.$$

Actually, the electron volt is too small a unit for many purposes, and the *million electron volt* unit, i.e., 10^{6} ev, abbreviated to Mev, is used; hence,

$$E(\text{Mev}) = m(\text{amu}) \times 931, \tag{1.28.2}$$

so that 1 atomic mass unit is equivalent to 931 Mev.

1.29. Returning to equation (1.26.1) for the mass defect, it follows from the arguments presented above that the binding energy is given by

$$\text{Binding energy in Mev} = 931[Zm_{\text{H}} + (A - Z)m_{\text{n}} - M], \tag{1.29.1}$$

where m_{H} is 1.00813 amu, m_{n} is 1.00897 amu, and M is the isotopic mass in amu. In this derivation the binding energy of the electrons to the nucleus has been neglected or, rather, it has been regarded as included in the Zm_{H} term. In any event, the electron binding energy is a very small fraction of the total. Consequently, (1.29.1) may be taken as giving a measure of the net binding energy of the constituent nucleons, i.e., protons and neutrons, in the nucleus of the atom under consideration.

1.30. By means of (1.29.1) the binding energies have been calculated for all nuclides whose isotopic weights are known with sufficient accuracy. If the binding energy is divided by the mass number, i.e., by the total number of nucleons in the nucleus, there is obtained the mean *binding energy per nucleon* for the given nuclide. The results have been plotted against the respective mass numbers in

* This is one-sixteenth part of the actual mass in grams of an O^{16} atom.

Fig. 1.30. It will be seen that with the exception of a few light nuclei, the values fall on, or in close proximity to, a single curve. The mean binding energy per nucleon in the elements of low mass number is low, but over a considerable range it is close to 8 Mev. The total binding energy is then approximately proportional to the mass number, i.e., to the number of nucleons in the nucleus.

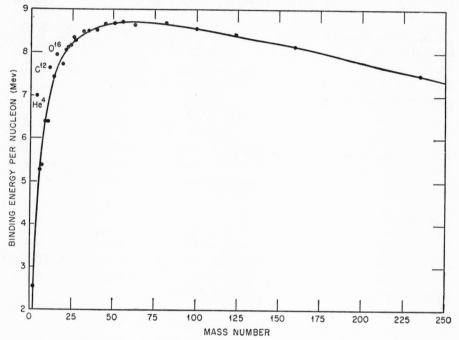

Fig. 1.30. Binding energy per nucleon of stable nuclides

LIQUID DROP MODEL OF NUCLEUS

1.31. It has been found useful in certain respects to regard an atomic nucleus as somewhat similar in character to a drop of incompressible liquid. Just as the forces responsible for surface tension tend to maintain a liquid drop in a spherical form which resists distortion, it is believed that nuclear forces have a similar effect on the atomic nucleus. This point of view has been especially valuable in the consideration of nuclear fission.

1.32. In a liquid the forces between molecules are short-range forces; that is to say, they operate only between any given molecule and such others as are immediately adjacent to it. Hence, in a liquid, there is no appreciable interaction between more distant molecules. Similar considerations are apparently applicable to the forces operating between the nucleons in an atomic nucleus. This view is supported by the binding energy data given above. If nuclear forces had long-range character, so that each nucleon interacted with every other nucleon, the total binding energy would increase roughly as the square of the number of nucleons. Actually, the total binding energy is almost directly proportional to the number of nucleons, as stated in § 1.30.

1.33. Further evidence for the short-range character of nuclear forces is provided by determinations of nuclear radii. Three main methods have been used for this purpose. The first method, applicable to radioactive nuclides of high mass number which emit alpha particles, depends on the rates of decay and the energies of the alpha particles expelled. The second method is based on the difference in the binding energies of mirror nuclei, i.e., pairs of nuclei in which the neutron and proton numbers of one member of the pair are the proton and neutron numbers, respectively, of the other member. Finally, there is a method for determining nuclear radii which can be used, at least in principle, for any species, irrespective of its stability or mass number. This involves measurement of the scattering cross sections of fast neutrons (§ 3.38, *et seq.*).

1.34. The values obtained by different methods for a given nuclide are generally in good agreement with each other. Except for the elements of lowest mass number, the results can be expressed, to a fair approximation, by the formula

$$R = 1.5 \times 10^{-13} A^{\frac{1}{3}} \text{ cm,} \qquad (1.34.1)$$

where R is the radius of a nucleus of mass number A. The fact that the nuclear radius is approximately proportional to the cube root of the mass number is of great importance. The volume of the nucleus is consequently directly proportional to the mass number and, hence, to its actual mass. This means that all atomic nuclei containing the same constituents, namely, neutrons and protons, have essentially the same density. The constancy of the nuclear density, irrespective of the number of nucleons, is just what is to be expected if the nucleus behaves like a liquid with short-range forces operating between the constituent particles.

SEMI-EMPIRICAL CALCULATION OF BINDING ENERGIES

1.35. The liquid-drop model of the atomic nucleus can be used, in default of a complete theory of nuclear forces, to derive a semi-empirical expression for the binding energy. This is done by considering, in what is undoubtedly an oversimplified manner, the various factors which are believed to contribute to nuclear binding. The appropriate weighting constants are then derived from theoretical considerations where possible and from experimental data where the theory is still inadequate.

1.36. If the forces in the nucleus are like those in a liquid drop, each nucleon will, in the first place, be strongly attracted by those in its immediate vicinity, but will be unaffected by the others. This leads to an attractive contribution to the energy which is proportional to the number of nucleons in the nucleus. The *attractive energy* will thus vary as the mass number A, and it can consequently be represented by

$$\text{Attractive energy} = a_1 A, \tag{1.36.1}$$

where a_1 is a constant.

1.37. In stating that the attractive energy is proportional to the mass number, it is tacitly assumed that every nucleon has the same access to other nucleons. Actually, those at the surface of the nucleus will be less tightly bound than those in the interior, so that the attractive energy, as given by (1.36.1), has been overestimated by an amount which depends on the surface area. The larger this area, the greater will be the number of nucleons which are not completely surrounded by others. The amount whereby the attractive energy has been overestimated may thus be regarded as proportional to the surface area of the nucleus. It is frequently referred to as the *surface tension effect*, because it is due to a factor similar to that which causes surface tension in a liquid. Since, according to (1.34.1), the nuclear radius is proportional to $A^{\frac{1}{3}}$, the surface area varies as $A^{\frac{2}{3}}$, and hence

$$\text{Surface tension effect} = -a_2 A^{\frac{2}{3}}, \tag{1.37.1}$$

where a_2 is a constant.

1.38. In stable nuclei there is a tendency for groups of neutron-proton pairs to form. For example, the most stable species, such as He^4, C^{12}, and O^{16} (see Fig. 1.30), are those consisting of equal numbers of neutrons and protons. Most nuclei, however, especially the heavier ones, have an excess of neutrons over protons. This excess is necessary in order that the attractive neutron-neutron and neutron-proton forces may compensate for the electrostatic repulsion between protons. At the same time, a degree of instability is introduced because the excess neutrons occupy a number of nuclear energy levels that contain no protons. The presence of more neutrons than protons in the nucleus means that the estimate of the attractive energy given by (1.36.1) is too large. The appropriate correction can be made by a *composition term*, expressed by

$$\text{Composition term} = -a_3 \frac{(A - 2Z)^2}{A}, \tag{1.38.1}$$

where a_3 is a constant and $A - 2Z$ is the excess of neutrons over protons in the nucleus.*

1.39. The sum of the three terms derived above probably represents essentially the net attractive energy in the nucleus. It is necessary now to examine the *repulsive energy* due to the mutual electrostatic repulsion of the protons. The potential energy of a uniformly charged sphere is proportional to Z^2/R, where Z is the number of unit charges, i.e., the atomic number in the present case,

---

* See E. Fermi, "Nuclear Physics," page 22, University of Chicago Press, Chicago, 1950.

and R is the radius of the sphere.   As applied to the nuclear binding energy, the electrostatic repulsion can be represented by

$$\text{Repulsive energy} = -a_4 \frac{Z^2}{A^{\frac{1}{3}}}, \tag{1.39.1}$$

where the nuclear radius R has been replaced by $A^{\frac{1}{3}}$, to which it is proportional; as in the other expressions, a_4 is a constant.

1.40. Finally, consideration must be given to the influence of the odd and even character of the numbers of protons and neutrons.   When these are both even, i.e., even-even type, the nucleus is exceptionally stable, and when they are both odd, i.e., odd-odd type, the system is particularly unstable.   This may be attributed to the stabilizing effect of the pairing of nucleon spins, which is possible when there are even numbers of both protons and neutrons.   Consequently, in an even-even nucleus there is an additional positive contribution to the binding energy, whereas in an odd-odd nucleus, having a neutron and a proton with unpaired spins, there is a corresponding negative (or repulsive) effect.   Purely empirical considerations, based on binding energies calculated from the isotopic mass by (1.29.1), show that the *spin effect* contribution can be represented by

$$\text{Spin effect} = \pm \frac{a_5}{A^{\frac{3}{4}}}, \tag{1.40.1}$$

where the plus sign applies to even-even nuclei and the minus sign to odd-odd nuclei.   For odd-even (or even-odd) nuclei the spin term is zero.

1.41. Upon combining the various contributions to the binding energy, as given in the preceding paragraphs, it follows that the total binding energy (B.E.) of a nucleus may be represented by

$$\text{B.E.} = a_1 A - a_2 A^{\frac{2}{3}} - a_3 \frac{(A - 2Z)^2}{A} - a_4 \frac{Z^2}{A^{\frac{1}{3}}} \pm \frac{a_5}{A^{\frac{3}{4}}}, \tag{1.41.1}$$

where a_5 is zero for odd-even nuclei.   Of the five constants in this equation, a_4 can be obtained from electrostatic theory, but the others must be derived empirically as follows.

1.42. Differentiation of (1.41.1) with respect to Z, with A constant, leads to

$$\frac{d(\text{B.E.})}{dZ} = 4a_3 \frac{A - 2Z}{A} - 2a_4 \frac{Z}{A^{\frac{1}{3}}},$$

and, consequently, a maximum in the binding energy occurs when

$$4a_3 \frac{A - 2Z}{A} = 2a_4 \frac{Z}{A^{\frac{1}{3}}}. \tag{1.42.1}$$

This equation should express the relationship between the mass number A and the atomic number Z of the most stable nuclei, as these will have the largest binding energy for each mass number.   Since a_4 is known, as stated above, a_3

can be determined by finding the value which, when inserted in (1.42.1), will best represent a plot of A against Z for the most abundant naturally occurring nuclides. Actually, no single constant is adequate for the whole range of mass numbers, and so a compromise has to be made in assessing the best value of a_3 to be used in (1.41.1).

1.43. With a_3 and a_4 known, the values of a_1 and a_2 can be determined from the known binding energies, calculated from the isotopic weights of any pair of odd-even nuclei, since a_5 is then zero. Finally, the value of a_5 is estimated from the binding energies of even-even nuclei, since only a very few stable odd-odd nuclei are known, and these are of low mass number.

1.44. Upon inserting the constants derived in the manner explained above, (1.41.1) for the binding energy, expressed in Mev, becomes

$$\text{B.E. (Mev)} = 14.0A - 13.0A^{\frac{2}{3}} - 19.3\frac{(A - 2Z)^2}{A} - 0.585\frac{Z^2}{A^{\frac{1}{3}}} \pm \frac{33}{A^{\frac{3}{4}}}. \quad (1.44.1)$$

The relative effects of the various terms on the net binding energy can best be seen by using (1.44.1) to calculate the values for nuclides of low, medium, and high mass number. The results for $_{20}Ca^{40}$, $_{47}Ag^{107}$, and $_{92}U^{238}$ are given in Table 1.44; the experimental values of the total binding energies obtained from the known isotopic weights are included for comparison. The agreement between the calculated and observed values is satisfactory, since the constants in (1.44.1) are given only to three significant figures.

TABLE 1.44.   CALCULATION OF BINDING ENERGIES

	$_{20}Ca^{40}$	$_{47}Ag^{107}$	$_{92}U^{238}$
Attraction of nucleons	560	1500	3330
Surface effect	−152	−293	−501
Composition effect	0	−30.6	−236
Electrostatic repulsion	−68.4	−272	−799
Spin effect	3.2	0	0.5
Calculated binding energy	343	904	1790
Experimental binding energy	341	907	1785
B.E. per nucleon	8.5	8.4	7.5

NUCLEAR FORCES AND STABILITY

1.45. The results derived above may be used to provide a qualitative interpretation of the fact that for any mass (or atomic) number there is a limited stability range for the neutron-to-proton ratio (§ 1.15). As stated earlier, the actual value of this ratio increases from 1.00 for low mass numbers to about 1.56 for elements of high atomic weight. Since the neutron-neutron, proton-proton, and neutron-proton attractive forces are approximately equal, a neutron-to-proton ratio close to unity is to be expected for stability; this is the case for nuclei of low mass number.   However, as the atomic number increases, the electrostatic repulsion between protons begins to have an increasingly important effect.   The electrostatic forces are long-range in character, and each proton repels, and is repelled by, all the other protons.   Thus, as seen in § 1.39, the repulsive energy varies as $Z^2/A^{\frac{1}{3}}$, and so it increases rapidly with increasing atomic number.

1.46. In order to overcome the increasing repulsion of the protons and maintain stability in the heavier elements, the nuclei must contain an increased proportion of neutrons.   The additional nucleon-nucleon attractive forces then partly compensate for the growing proton-proton repulsion.   Consequently, the neutron-to-proton ratio in stable, heavier nuclei is greater than unity.

1.47. There is, however, a limit to the number of neutrons which can be present for a stable system of given mass (or atomic) number, because, as explained in § 1.38 in connection with the so-called composition term, an excess of neutrons over protons introduces some instability.   This fact determines the upper stability limit for the neutron-to-proton ratio.   The lower limit, on the other hand, arises because increasing the number of protons would lead to instability due to increased electrostatic repulsion.   The fact that the stability range for the neutron-to-proton ratio is relatively small can thus be understood.

Chapter II

NUCLEAR REACTIONS*

RATES OF NUCLEAR REACTIONS

COMPARISON OF NUCLEAR AND CHEMICAL REACTIONS

2.1. Under suitable laboratory conditions atomic nuclei can be made to react with other nuclei, especially those of the lightest elements, namely, hydrogen (protons), deuterium (deuterons), and helium (alpha particles). Atomic nuclei can also interact with neutrons, electrons, and gamma radiation. However, at ordinary temperatures the rates of nuclear reactions, i.e., the number of nuclei in a given volume reacting in a specified time, are very much less than for chemical reactions involving atoms or molecules. There are essentially two reasons for this marked difference in reaction rate between chemical processes and nuclear processes.

2.2. In the first place, the small size of the nucleus, whose diameter is of the order of 10^{-12} cm, as compared with 10^{-7} or 10^{-8} cm for the whole atom or molecule, means that nuclear collisions or encounters are much less frequent than atomic (or molecular) collisions. There are special circumstances, to be referred to below (§ 2.9), in which a nucleus or nuclear particle of low mass and energy can behave as if it had a diameter approaching that of the whole atom. The rates of nuclear reactions are then greatly increased over the usual values.

2.3. The second factor responsible for the relatively low rate of interaction of one nucleus with another is the coulombic repulsion between them, arising from their positive electrical charges. The repulsion energy is proportional to $Z_1 Z_2 / R$, where Z_1 and Z_2 are the charges, i.e., the atomic numbers, of the interacting nuclei, and R is the distance between their centers. Since the two nuclei must approach each other to within distances of about 10^{-12} cm before they can interact, the repulsive energy which must be overcome is very large, especially for nuclei of high atomic number. Even for nuclei of low atomic number, e.g., hydrogen and helium, the coulombic energy is of the order of millions of electron volts.

---

* See general references to Chapter I, also H. A. Bethe, *Rev. Mod. Physics*, **9,** 69 (1937); E. P. Wigner, *Amer. J. Physics*, **17, 3** (1949); and references in the text.

2.4. For chemical reactions, on the other hand, the energies required to permit interaction of the electronic fields are rarely more than a few electron volts. At ordinary temperatures, there is an appreciable probability that a pair of colliding atoms or molecules will possess this amount of kinetic energy. The reaction then takes place at an easily detectable rate. The probability that at ordinary temperatures two colliding nuclei will possess kinetic energy of a million electron volts is extremely small. Hence, not only is the number of encounters between atomic nuclei less than for atoms or molecules, under equivalent conditions, but the probability of interaction occurring upon collision is also considerably less. The rates of reactions between nuclei are thus very much less than for chemical reactions between atoms or molecules.

2.5. There are two ways in which nuclear reactions can be made to take place more readily. First, by increasing the temperature to several million degrees, the interacting nuclei will acquire sufficient kinetic energy to overcome their mutual electrostatic repulsion or coulomb barrier. Such nuclear processes, referred to as *thermonuclear reactions*, take place in the sun and stars; they represent the energy source of these celestial bodies. Second, in the laboratory, reactions involving atomic nuclei are studied by bombarding various materials with light nuclei, e.g., protons, deuterons, or alpha particles, which have been accelerated until they have kinetic energies in the vicinity of a million electron volts or more.* Cyclotrons and other devices are used for this purpose. Reactions of nuclei with highly accelerated electrons, and with gamma rays and X-rays of high energy, have also been achieved.

INTERACTION OF NEUTRONS WITH NUCLEI

2.6. Although the foregoing nuclear processes are of great interest, they are not important in connection with the present discussion of nuclear reactors. As stated earlier, these devices involve interaction of atomic nuclei with neutrons, and such reactions differ in one important respect from those considered above. Since the neutron has no electric charge, it does not have to overcome any appreciable repulsive force in approaching an atomic nucleus. Consequently, even the so-called "slow" neutrons, having the same mean kinetic energy as ordinary gas molecules, e.g., about 0.03 ev at ordinary temperatures (§ 3.10), can readily interact with atomic nuclei.

2.7. The probability of interaction between a nucleus and a neutron is, in fact, generally greater for slow neutrons than for fast neutrons with energies of the order of several thousand or more electron volts. An explanation of this fact, in classical terms, might be that, in an encounter with a nucleus, a slow-moving neutron spends, on the average, more time in the vicinity of the nucleus than does a fast-moving neutron. The chances of interaction would thus be expected to be larger in the former case. However, in quantum mechanics, the collision

---

* At 1 Mev kinetic energy, the equivalent temperature is about 8×10^9 degrees.

between a neutron and a nucleus is regarded as the interaction of a neutron wave with the nucleus. As will be shown below, the effective wave length of the neutron is inversely proportional to its velocity. Hence, the wave length of a slow neutron is greater than that of a fast neutron, and the probability of interaction with a nucleus is increased correspondingly.

NEUTRON WAVE LENGTH

2.8. According to the wave theory of matter, all particles are associated with waves, called *matter waves* or *de Broglie waves,* the wave length λ being given by

$$\lambda = \frac{h}{mv}, \tag{2.8.1}$$

where h is Planck's quantum theory constant, i.e., 6.62×10^{-27} erg sec, m is the mass of the particle, and v is its velocity. Let E be the kinetic energy of the particle, then $E = \frac{1}{2}mv^2$, and (2.8.1) may be written as

$$\lambda = \frac{h}{\sqrt{2mE}}. \tag{2.8.2}$$

If m is in grams, E in ergs, and h is in erg sec, the wave length will be in centimeters. If m is expressed in amu units, which are 1.67×10^{-24} gram (§ 1.27), and E in electron volts, i.e., 1.60×10^{-12} erg, (2.8.2) becomes

$$\lambda = \frac{4.05 \times 10^{-9}}{\sqrt{2mE}} \text{ cm.} \tag{2.8.3}$$

2.9. For a neutron, which is the particle of special interest here, m is approximately unity in amu, and hence the expression for the neutron wave length becomes

$$\lambda = \frac{2.86 \times 10^{-9}}{\sqrt{E}} \text{ cm,} \tag{2.9.1}$$

where E is the neutron energy in electron volts. For fast neutrons of energy about 1 Mev, the wave length is seen from (2.9.1) to be of the order of 10^{-12} cm, which is the same magnitude as the diameter of a nucleus. If the neutron energy is about 0.03 ev, however, λ is found to be about 1.7×10^{-8} cm. Thus, a slow neutron might have an effective diameter approaching that of the whole atom.* Even if the energy were 1000 ev, the neutron wave length (or effective diameter) would be of the order of 10^{-10} cm; this is still much larger than a nuclear diameter. The conditions under which slow neutrons thus behave as if they were almost as large as a whole atom, and hence have a relatively large probability of interacting with atomic nuclei, will be described in § 2.31, *et seq.*

---

* It is because slow neutrons have equivalent wave lengths of the order of 10^{-8} cm that, like X-rays, they can be diffracted by crystals.

THE COMPOUND NUCLEUS MODEL

MECHANISM OF NUCLEAR REACTIONS

2.10. Before considering various types of interaction of neutrons with atomic nuclei, a brief review will be given of some of the general features of nuclear reactions. In the first place, two broad classes of such reactions may be distinguished, depending on the energy of the particle, called the *incident particle* or *projectile*, which impinges on an atomic nucleus, called the *target nucleus*. In a nucleus the constituent nucleons are tightly bound, the degree of binding being measured by the average interaction energy per nucleon. As seen in § 1.30, this interaction (or binding) energy is of the order of 8 Mev per nucleon for nuclei of medium or high mass number. If the kinetic energy of the incident particle is roughly equal to or greater than the average interaction energy between nucleons in the target nucleus, i.e., about 10 Mev or more, the incident particle interacts with only a single nucleon or with a small number of nucleons. Since the operation of nuclear reactors generally depends on the interaction with matter of neutrons of energies considerably less than 10 Mev, this type of process need not be discussed further.

2.11. When the kinetic energy of the incident particle is less than the mean interaction energy per nucleon, the incident particle may be regarded as interacting with the nucleus as a whole. In these circumstances, the model of the *compound nucleus*, advanced independently by Bohr and by Breit and Wigner (§ 2.38, *et seq.*),* is applicable. According to this model, a nuclear reaction is considered to occur in two stages. First, the incident particle is absorbed by the target nucleus to form a compound nucleus; then, after the lapse of a short time, the latter disintegrates expelling a particle (or a photon†) and leaving another nucleus, called the residual nucleus or *recoil nucleus*. The two stages may thus be written as follows:

(1) *Formation of Compound Nucleus*
    Target nucleus + Incident particle → Compound nucleus

(2) *Disintegration of Compound Nucleus*
    Compound nucleus → Recoil nucleus + Ejected particle.

It should be noted that the compound nucleus may well be a nucleus of a familiar atomic species, or it may be one which is unstable. In any event, the disintegration stage (2) described above is due to the fact that the compound nucleus when formed in stage (1) is in an unstable, high-energy state (§ 2.16).

---

* N. Bohr, *Nature*, **137**, 344 (1936); G. Breit and E. P. Wigner, *Phys. Rev.*, **49**, 519 (1936). The experimental evidence for the formation of a compound nucleus in nuclear reactions is largely due to W. D. Harkins (1935).

† A photon may be regarded as an "atom" or "particle" of radiation. According to quantum theory, the energy quantum carried by a photon is equal to $h\nu$, where h is Planck's constant (§ 2.8), and ν is the frequency of the radiation.

2.12. In order that the compound nucleus may be considered as a separate entity, its lifetime must be long compared to the time required for the incident particle to traverse a distance equal to the nuclear diameter. The time required for a slow neutron, having a speed of about 10^5 cm per sec, to cross a distance of about 10^{-12} cm is of the order of 10^{-17} sec. Actually, after capture, an initially slow neutron will acquire additional kinetic energy and, hence, will move more rapidly. The time of transit is thus less than the 10^{-17} sec, just estimated. It will be seen shortly (§ 2.29) that the mean lifetime of the excited compound nucleus in many reactions with heavy nuclei is about 10^{-14} sec. Since this is less than the transit time by a factor of 1000, at least, the condition for the occurrence of the compound nucleus as a separate entity is satisfied.

EXCITATION ENERGY OF COMPOUND NUCLEUS

2.13. When a target nucleus captures an incident particle, the resulting compound nucleus is invariably in a higher energy, i.e., excited, state (§ 2.16). The excitation energy, i.e., energy above the ground state, is equal to the kinetic energy of the captured particle plus its binding energy in the compound nucleus. That this is so may be seen by considering the case of the capture of a neutron (n^1) of zero kinetic energy by a nucleus X of mass number A.

2.14. The formation of the compound nucleus Y, of mass number $A + 1$, may be represented as

$$X^A + n^1 \rightarrow [Y^{A+1}]^*,$$

where the asterisk indicates an excited state of the Y^{A+1} nucleus. Suppose now that the excited compound nucleus emits the excitation energy and thereby passes into its normal or ground state; thus,

$$[Y^{A+1}]^* \rightarrow Y^{A+1} + E_{ex},$$

where E_{ex} is the excitation energy, i.e., the difference in energy between the excited and ground states. Next, imagine a neutron of zero kinetic energy to be removed from the ground state of Y^{A+1}, leaving the ground state of the nucleus X^A. The energy which must be supplied is the binding energy E_b of the neutron in the compound nucleus; thus,

$$Y^{A+1} \rightarrow X^A + n^1 + E_b.$$

Upon combining the three stages, as a result of which the original condition is restored, it is seen that the excitation energy E_{ex} of the compound nucleus is equal to E_b, the binding energy of the neutron, which is about 5 to 8 Mev. It readily follows that, if the neutron possesses kinetic energy, as it invariably does, the excitation energy is equal to the binding energy plus the kinetic energy of the neutron.

2.15. The situation may be represented diagrammatically by means of a potential energy curve, as in Fig. 2.15, where the energy of the system of target nucleus and neutron of zero kinetic energy is plotted against the distance between these particles. At the extreme right, at B, the target nucleus and neutron are far apart and may be regarded as being quite independent. At the extreme left, at A, on the other hand, the target nucleus and the neutron may be regarded as being completely fused so as to form the *ground state* of the compound nucleus. The vertical distance between A and B represents the binding energy of the neutron in the compound nucleus. This amount of energy would have to be supplied in a process starting from the ground state of the compound nucleus at A and ending with the separated target nucleus and neutron at B.

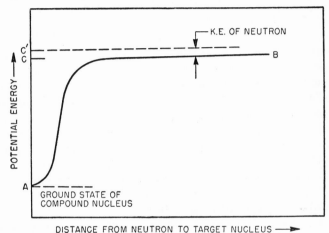

Fig. 2.15.   Potential energy of target nucleus-neutron system

2.16. If a neutron of zero kinetic energy is gradually brought up to a target nucleus, there is no attraction or repulsion, and the energy of the system remains equal to that at B. Eventually, when the nucleus has completely absorbed the neutron, the energy state of the compound nucleus is at C. This nucleus is evidently in an excited state, the excitation energy being equal to AC, which is the same as the neutron binding energy. If the captured neutron has kinetic energy, the state of the compound nucleus is indicated by the line C', so that the excitation energy is given by AC'. It can be seen, in general, that when a compound nucleus is formed by neutron capture, the excitation energy, i.e., the (internal) energy in excess of the ground state of the compound nucleus, is equal to the binding energy of the neutron plus its kinetic energy.

2.17.   It may be pointed out that the foregoing conclusion is strictly true only when the target nucleus has infinite mass. In general, because of the conservation of momentum in a capture collision between a nucleus and a neutron, the compound nucleus will acquire some kinetic energy, even though the target nucleus was at rest. Consequently, only part of the energy of the neutron appears as internal, i.e., excitation, energy of the compound nucleus. For target nuclei of appreciable mass number, however, virtually the whole of the kinetic energy of the neutron is transferred to the internal energy of the nucleus. Throughout the subsequent discussion, it will be assumed that this condition holds.

STATISTICAL DISTRIBUTION OF ENERGY IN NUCLEUS

2.18. Immediately after its formation, the excitation energy of the compound nucleus may be regarded as being concentrated on the captured particle. But, as a result of interactions within the nucleus, the additional energy is rapidly shared among the nucleons. This distribution occurs in a statistical manner. Thus, at a given instant, the excitation energy may be shared between two or more nucleons, while at a subsequent instant it may be shared by other nucleons or it may be concentrated on one of the nucleons. In the course of time, one particular nucleon or combination of nucleons in the compound nucleus may acquire sufficient energy to permit it to escape. This corresponds to the disintegration stage referred in § 2.11.

2.19. Because of the large number of ways that the excitation energy may be shared among the nucleons, the probability that a single nucleon will acquire sufficient energy to permit escape from the compound nucleus during the time required for a captured particle to traverse the nucleus is usually small. Consequently, the average life of the compound nucleus will be long in comparison with the time required for a neutron to cross it.

2.20. An important consequence of the relatively long lifetime of the excited compound nucleus is that, for a given excitation energy, the manner in which the compound nucleus breaks up is independent of its mode of formation. If the lifetime of the compound nucleus is sufficiently long, the distribution of the excitation energy will depend only on the total excitation energy, the number of nucleons, and the energy levels of the compound nucleus. The mode of formation is thus "forgotten" by the compound nucleus as a result of the statistical manner in which the excitation energy is shared.

2.21. Because of its relatively long lifetime, there is a possibility that the excited compound nucleus will rid itself of its excess energy by the emission of radiation. Nuclear processes in which a particle is captured and the excess energy is emitted as radiation are called *radiative capture* reactions. The conditions for such reactions are especially favorable when a slow neutron is captured. In the majority of instances, although not always, the only process for which the compound nucleus has sufficient energy is the re-emission of a slow neutron. In other words, this stage would involve reversal of the capture process. However, before the redistribution of energy among the nucleons results in a particular neutron acquiring enough energy to escape from the compound nucleus, the excess (excitation) energy of the latter is emitted as gamma radiation, i.e., radiation of 10^{-10} to 10^{-11} cm wave length.*

2.22. In certain reactions involving heavy atomic nuclei, the capture of a suitable particle results in the formation of an excited state of a compound nucleus so unstable that it splits up into two smaller nuclei. This is the process of *fission*, which is of fundamental importance for the operation of nuclear reactors. It will be referred to again in § 3.35 and discussed more fully in Chapter IV.

Nuclear Energy Levels

2.23. The existence of definite nuclear energy† levels or quantum states is supported by various types of experimental evidence. In particular, mention may be made of the emission of gamma rays of definite energy (or wave length) in many radioactive processes. The nuclear energy levels are quite analogous to the familiar atomic or electronic energy levels which permit an interpretation of atomic spectra. However, since the forces acting between nucleons are not completely understood, it has not yet been possible to apply quantum mechanics to the study of nuclear energy levels with the same degree of success as has been done in connection with the problem of electronic energy levels. Nevertheless, certain aspects of the subject can be considered.

2.24. From various studies it has been concluded that the energy levels of atomic nuclei are relatively far apart for the low energy states, i.e., near the ground state, but become closer and closer as the internal energy of the nucleus increases. At very high energies, about 15 to 20 Mev or more, the energy levels are so close that they may be regarded as virtually continuous.

2.25. For nuclei with mass numbers in the medium range, namely, from about 100 to 150, the separation (or spacing) of the levels near the ground state is in the vicinity of 0.1 Mev. However, when the energy is in the region of 8 Mev above the ground level, as in a compound nucleus formed by the capture of a slow neutron, the level spacing is only 1 to 10 ev. For light nuclei, the energy levels are somewhat farther apart; the separations are of the order of 1 Mev near the ground state and roughly 10,000 ev when the internal energy is about 8 Mev above the ground level.

Lifetime and Level Width

2.26. To every excited quantum state of a nucleus there may be ascribed a *mean lifetime*, τ; this is the period of time, on the average, that a nucleus will remain in the given excited state before undergoing a change, e.g., emission of a particle or of radiation. Correspondingly, each quantum state has a *level*

---

* It can be shown from Planck's equation ($E = h\nu$) that the wave length λ in cm is equal to $1.24 \times 10^{-10}/E$, where E is the energy, expressed in Mev, emitted by the nucleus in one step (cf. § 2.11, footnote).

† The energy under consideration is internal energy of the nucleus, and not kinetic energy of the nucleus as a whole.

width Γ, which may be regarded as an indication of the indefiniteness involved in the determination of the energy of the particular state.* From the Heisenberg uncertainty principle the mean lifetime and the level width are related by

$$\tau\Gamma \approx \frac{h}{2\pi},$$ (2.26.1)

where h is Planck's constant. The level width has the dimensions of energy and is usually expressed in electron volts. Making use of the conversion factor in § 1.28, it follows that

$$\tau\Gamma \approx 0.7 \times 10^{-15},$$ (2.26.2)

where τ is in seconds and Γ in ev.

2.27. Since a compound nucleus in a given excited state can frequently undergo change in several ways, e.g., emission of a neutron, proton, alpha particle, or radiation, it is necessary to define a *partial level* width for each type of process. If τ_i is the mean lifetime of the particular quantum state, assuming the process i to be the only possible way in which excitation energy could be lost, then the partial level width Γ_i for this process is given by

$$\tau_i\Gamma_i \approx \frac{h}{2\pi},$$ (2.27.1)

as in (2.26.1). The total level width Γ for the given quantum state is then the sum of the partial level widths for all the possible processes which the compound nucleus in that state can undergo; thus,

$$\Gamma \approx \sum_i \Gamma_i.$$ (2.27.2)

2.28. The level width has a simple and interesting physical significance: it is proportional to the probability that the compound nucleus, in the given energy state, will undergo change per unit time. As was seen in connection with radioactive disintegration (§ 1.22), the mean life of an unstable species is equal to the reciprocal of the decay constant, the latter representing the probability of decay per unit time. Since, by (2.26.1), the total level width is inversely proportional to the mean lifetime of the compound nucleus, the level width is related to the total probability that the latter will decay (or change) in unit time. Similarly, the partial level width Γ_i is a measure of the probability that the given excited quantum state will undergo the process i per unit time.

2.29. Level widths of about 0.1 ev have been observed for heavy nuclei which have captured neutrons of low energy, e.g., an electron volt or less. The mean lifetime of the compound nucleus, in such cases, is found from (2.26.2) to be about 7×10^{-15} sec. As stated earlier, this is relatively long in comparison with the time required for a neutron to travel a distance equal to the nuclear diameter (§ 2.12).

---

* This "indefiniteness" has nothing to do with the accuracy of the experimental methods. It is something fundamental to all measurements and may be considered as arising from the interaction of the measuring device with the system being measured.

2.30. At high excitation energies, such as would result from the capture of a particle having a large kinetic energy, the level width is increased and the mean lifetime of the compound nucleus is correspondingly decreased. Thus, if Γ is 1000 ev, the mean lifetime would be 0.7×10^{-18} sec, which is of the same order as the time of transit of a nucleon. In these circumstances, the compound nucleus model, based on an exchange of energy among the nucleons, would break down. At the same time, the level width would exceed the spacing between the energy levels, especially for the nuclei of moderate mass (§ 2.25). In other words, as far as experimental measurements were concerned, the energy levels would appear to overlap.

RESONANCE ABSORPTION

Conditions for Resonance

2.31. In experimental studies of nuclear reactions, by bombarding different target elements with various projectiles, such as protons, neutrons, etc., it has been found that, when the incident particles have certain specific energy values, there is a sharp increase in the reaction rate. In other words, for certain energy values the probability that the incident particle will be captured and a compound nucleus formed is exceptionally large. This phenomenon, which is very marked in connection with nuclear reactions involving slow neutrons, is attributed to what is called *resonance*. For elements of moderate and high mass numbers, resonance absorption frequently occurs with neutrons of energy between roughly 1 ev and 10 ev. Uranium-238, for example, exhibits resonance absorption of neutrons with energies in the electron volt range.

2.32. It is generally accepted that a marked increase in the rate of the given nuclear reaction occurs when the energy of the incident particle is such that the resulting excited state of the compound nucleus is very close to one of the quantum states of the latter. This is what is meant by resonance absorption. The effect may be illustrated by considering Fig. 2.32, the lines

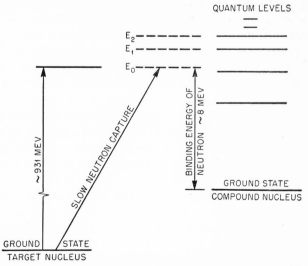

FIG. 2.32.   Compound nucleus formation and energy levels

at the right indicating (schematically) the quantum levels of the compound nucleus. The line marked E_0, in the middle, represents the energy of the target nucleus plus that of a neutron with zero kinetic energy. Thus, the energy E_0 corresponds to that at the point C in Fig. 2.15; it is above the ground state by an amount equal to the binding energy of the neutron in the particular compound nucleus (§ 2.16).

2.33. An examination of Fig. 2.32 indicates that the energy E_0 does not correspond to any of the quantum levels of the compound nucleus. However, if the neutron has a certain amount of kinetic energy, sufficient to bring the energy of the system of target nucleus plus neutron up to E_1, the energy of the compound nucleus will correspond to that of one of its quantum states. When the neutron has kinetic energy $E_1 - E_0$, resonance absorption is said to occur. Similarly, there will be resonance absorption of neutrons with kinetic energy $E_2 - E_0$, so that the total energy E_2 of the system is equivalent to another quantum level of the compound nucleus, as seen in Fig. 2.32.

2.34. According to quantum mechanics, the only states of a system which can be stable (or quasi-stable) are the definite quantum states. The probability of the formation of a compound nucleus in a given reaction will be greatest when its energy corresponds to that of one of its quantum states. Thus, when resonance absorption occurs the rate of the particular reaction will be markedly increased.

2.35. Experimentally, at least, as was seen in § 2.26, the energies of the quantum levels of a nucleus are not sharply defined. Each level has a certain level width; and, more or less corresponding to this width, there is a spread of particle energies over which resonance absorption is observed. If the conditions are such, for example at high energies, that the level width is greater than the separation of the quantum levels, the spread will be so large that adjacent regions will overlap. In these circumstances, the concept of resonance absorption, like the compound nucleus model (§ 2.30), becomes inapplicable.

2.36. It was mentioned in § 2.25 that the separation of the energy levels of a nucleus of moderate or high mass number in the 8-Mev region is about 1 ev to 10 ev. Hence, it is to be expected that resonance absorption will be observed for neutrons having certain kinetic energies of this order of magnitude. Further, when there are two or more resonance absorption regions, they will be separated by roughly similar energy values. If the neutron has a large amount of energy, e.g., about 1 Mev or more, the compound nucleus will have some 9 Mev of energy in excess of the ground state. In this region the level widths are frequently large enough, compared with the separations, to make the resonance concept invalid.

2.37. For nuclei of low mass number the spacing of the energy levels in the 8-Mev region is larger than for species of moderate or high atomic weight. Hence, resonance absorption should occur only if the neutron has energy of the order of 10,000 ev, i.e., 0.01 Mev. Resonance effects of this kind have been observed, but the increased absorption is not very marked because, as will be seen later, there is a general tendency for the rate of absorption of neutrons to decrease as their energy increases.

THE BREIT-WIGNER FORMULA

2.38. By applying the methods of wave mechanics to the compound nucleus concept, Breit and Wigner (§ 2.11) derived an expression for the rates of nuclear reactions, including resonance absorption. The results are expressed in terms of a quantity called the *nuclear cross section*, represented by the symbol σ, which will be considered in some detail later (§ 3.38). For the present it is sufficient to state that the cross section is a measure of the probability of the occurrence of a particular nuclear reaction under prescribed conditions. It is a specific property of that reaction for incident particles of a given energy.

2.39. Consider a nuclear reaction represented, in general, by

$$a + X \rightarrow [\text{Compound Nucleus}]^* \rightarrow Y + b,$$

where a is the incident particle, X the target nucleus, Y the residual nucleus, and b the ejected particle. Let Γ_a and Γ_b be the level widths representing the probabilities of the emission of the particles a and b, respectively, by the compound nucleus in a specific quantum state (§ 2.28); the total level width Γ is then the sum of the partial widths, as stated in § 2.27. If E is the total energy, both internal and kinetic, of the incident particle, and E_r is the energy value which would give exact resonance with the specified quantum level of the compound nucleus, then the *Breit-Wigner formula* for the variation, with the energy of the incident particle, of the nuclear cross section σ for the given reaction is represented (approximately) by

$$\sigma \approx \frac{\lambda^2}{4\pi} \cdot \frac{\Gamma_a \Gamma_b}{(E - E_r)^2 + \frac{1}{4}\Gamma^2}, \tag{2.39.1}$$

where λ is the equivalent wave length of the incident particle as derived from its mass and velocity by the de Broglie equation (2.8.1).* For simplicity, a factor allowing for the angular momenta of the nuclei and the spins of the particles has been omitted; it is generally of the order of unity.

2.40. The Breit-Wigner equation (2.39.1) is frequently referred to as the "one-level" formula. It applies to energies in the vicinity of any quantum level, provided the latter is sufficiently widely separated from adjacent levels so that the resonances do not interfere with one another. A one-level Breit-Wigner formula, with the appropriate values of Γ_a, Γ_b, Γ, and E_r, will then apply to each resonance region or quantum state. When the resonances overlap, because of the small separation of the quantum levels, a more complex equation must be used, but for present purposes the one-level formula is adequate.

* In determining λ from the de Broglie equation, the mass m should be the "reduced mass" of the incident particle and the target nucleus. For nuclei of moderate or high mass number this is essentially the same as the mass of the incident particle.

APPLICATIONS OF BREIT-WIGNER EQUATION

2.41. In applying the Breit-Wigner equation to the resonance absorption of neutrons, a matter of particular interest in connection with nuclear reactors, the particle a is a neutron. Since this has no internal energy, E in (2.39.1) becomes merely the kinetic energy of the neutron. Further, by (2.8.2), the wave length λ is proportional to $1/\sqrt{E}$, where E is the kinetic energy. Hence, when the incident particle is a neutron,

$$\lambda^2 = \frac{k}{E}, \qquad (2.41.1)$$

where k is a constant.

2.42. The level width Γ_b, representing the probability of the ejection of the particle b, is believed to be independent of the energy of the incident particle, but Γ_a, which is a measure of the probability of the re-emission of the latter, can be shown to be proportional to its velocity. If a is a neutron, so that E is merely the kinetic energy, it follows, therefore, that

$$\Gamma_a = \Gamma_n = k'\sqrt{E}, \qquad (2.42.1)$$

where k' is a constant. Upon inserting (2.41.1) and (2.42.1) into the Breit-Wigner equation (2.39.1), and combining the constants into A, it follows that

$$\sigma = \frac{A}{\sqrt{E}} \cdot \frac{\Gamma_b}{(E - E_r)^2 + \frac{1}{4}\Gamma^2}. \qquad (2.42.2)$$

This expression gives the variation of the cross section for neutron absorption with the energy E of the neutron, in the vicinity of a particular resonance widely separated from others. The quantities A, Γ_b, E_r, and Γ are then constants.

2.43. An examination of (2.42.2) reveals a number of interesting qualitative features. When the neutron kinetic energy E is considerably less than the value E_r required for exact resonance, $(E - E_r)^2$ is large and almost constant. Since the kinetic energy E is proportional to v^2, where v is the neutron velocity, (2.42.2) then reduces to the form

$$\sigma \approx \frac{B}{v}, \qquad (2.43.1)$$

where B is a composite constant. Thus, at neutron energies that are small compared to the first resonance energy, the neutron absorption cross section should be inversely proportional to the neutron velocity. As expected from the Breit-Wigner treatment, a low-energy range, in which the neutron absorption cross section is proportional to $1/v$, generally called the "$1/v$ region", is often observed for slow neutrons (§ 3.68).

2.44. As the neutron energy E is increased and approaches E_r, it is evident from (2.42.2) that σ should increase rapidly, since $E - E_r$ becomes smaller. When E is equal to E_r the absorption cross section will be a maximum. Subsequently, when E exceeds E_r, the cross section will decrease, at first sharply and then more slowly, with increasing neutron energy. This means that, if σ is plotted as a function of E, there will be a fairly sharp peak, the maximum of which corresponds to the resonance energy E_r (Fig. 2.44). Such peaks, called

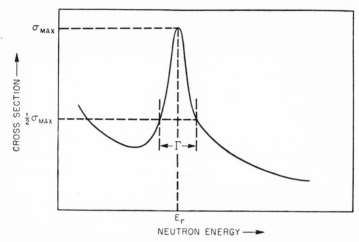

Fig. 2.44.   Resonance peak for neutron absorption

resonance peaks, are of frequent occurrence, as will be seen later. It will be noted from (2.42.2) that if Γ_b does not vary greatly with energy, the maximum value of the absorption cross section, which is given by

$$\sigma_{max} \approx \frac{A}{\sqrt{E_r}} \cdot \frac{\Gamma_b}{\frac{1}{4}\Gamma^2},\qquad (2.44.1)$$

is approximately inversely proportional to the square root of the energy. Thus, the cross section at the resonance absorption maximum will tend to be small when the resonance energy is large, and vice versa.

2.45. It can be readily shown from (2.42.2) and (2.44.1) that, when the neutron absorption cross section σ is equal to $\frac{1}{2}\sigma_{max}$, the width in ev of the resonance peak is equal to Γ, the total level width. For this reason, Γ is sometimes called the *half width* of the resonance peak.

2.46. Another special case of interest arises when the total width Γ of a particular level is large compared to $E - E_r$. Then $(E - E_r)^2$ in the denominator of (2.42.2) may be neglected in comparison with $\frac{1}{4}\Gamma^2$, and the expression for the neutron absorption cross section becomes

$$\sigma \approx \frac{A}{v} \cdot \frac{\Gamma_b}{\frac{1}{4}\Gamma^2},\qquad (2.46.1)$$

so that the cross section is again inversely proportional to the neutron velocity. In other words, the $1/v$ law for neutron absorption will apply either (a) when the level width Γ is small and the neutron energy E is appreciably less than E_r

(§ 2.43), or (*b*) when the level width Γ is large compared to $E - E_r$.   An example of the latter type of behavior will be given in § 3.77.

2.47. It should be noted that, when Γ is large compared to E_r, there is no cross section maximum and no resonance peak in the plot of σ against E.   The absorption cross section decreases steadily with increasing neutron energy, in accordance with (2.46.1).   In these circumstances, it is not the practice to speak of resonance capture of neutrons.

SCATTERING OF NEUTRONS

THE NATURE OF SCATTERING

2.48. A possibility that has not been considered so far is that the particle expelled in a nuclear reaction is identical with the incident particle captured. In the course of the redistribution of energy among the nucleons in the compound nucleus there is always a possibility that a particle of the same type as the incident particle will acquire enough energy to leave the nucleus.   In general, the expelled particle will have less kinetic energy than the incident particle, some or all of its energy having been transferred to the target nucleus.   A process in which the overall result is merely the transfer of energy from one particle (or nucleus) to another is called *scattering*.   The scattering of neutrons by atomic nuclei plays a highly important part in the operation of nuclear reactors.   Consequently, some general aspects of the subject will be considered here, and a more extended treatment will be given in Chapter VI.

2.49. There are two types of scattering processes, namely, inelastic scattering and elastic scattering.   In inelastic collisions momentum is conserved, but kinetic energy is not, whereas in elastic collisions both momentum and kinetic energy are conserved.

INELASTIC SCATTERING

2.50. When a neutron undergoes *inelastic scattering*, it is first captured by the target to form a compound nucleus; a neutron of lower kinetic energy is then expelled, leaving the target nucleus in an excited state.   Thus, in inelastic scattering some (or all) of the kinetic energy of the neutron is converted into internal or excitation energy of the target nucleus.   This energy is subsequently emitted in the form of gamma radiation, the target nucleus thereby returning to its ground state.

2.51. It was noted in § 2.25 that the spacing of nuclear energy levels near the ground state is about 0.1 Mev for nuclei of moderate or high mass number, but it is larger for nuclei of low mass number.   Consequently, a neutron must possess at least 0.1 Mev of energy if it is to be involved in an inelastic collision process.   If the scattering material has a low mass number, the required neutron energy is even higher.   In nuclear reactors, the neutrons initially have high energies in the Mev range, and hence inelastic scattering then occurs to some extent. However, as will be seen later, the energy of the neutrons is soon reduced to values at which inelastic scattering is not possible.

Elastic Scattering

2.52. The situation in regard to elastic scattering is quite different. In this type of collision kinetic energy is conserved. Some (or all) of the kinetic energy of the neutron appears, after the collision, as kinetic energy of the initially stationary target nucleus. The process may be regarded as essentially a "billiard ball" type of collision, which may be treated by the laws of classical mechanics, based on the principles of the conservation of energy and momentum. In each collision with an essentially stationary nucleus, the neutron will transfer part of its kinetic energy to the nucleus; the amount of energy transferred will depend upon the angle through which the neutron is scattered. For a given scattering angle, the fraction of the neutron energy transferred will be greater the smaller the mass of the scattering nucleus (see Chapter VI).

2.53. From the theoretical standpoint, there are two aspects of elastic scattering of neutrons to be considered. First, there is *resonance scattering*, when the energy of the captured neutron is such that the excited compound nucleus formed is at, or close to, one of its quantum states. Second, there is what is called *potential scattering*, which occurs for neutrons with energies on either side of the resonance level. In the language of wave mechanics, potential scattering is treated as being due to the interaction of the neutron wave with the potential at the nuclear surface. Effectively, the incident neutron then does not enter the target nucleus and there is no compound nucleus formation.

2.54. In resonance scattering of neutrons, a compound nucleus is formed which can be treated by the Breit-Wigner method and an expression derived for the corresponding cross section. As a rough indication of the behavior, it may be assumed that (2.39.1) is applicable, and since the particles a and b are both neutrons, this becomes

$$\sigma \approx \frac{\lambda^2}{4\pi} \cdot \frac{\Gamma_n^2}{(E - E_r)^2 + \frac{1}{4}\Gamma^2}, \qquad (2.54.1)$$

where E is the kinetic energy of the incident neutrons. In this case, the level width Γ_n is essentially the same for the incident and outgoing neutrons, and each is proportional to $\sqrt{E}$, by (2.42.1); hence Γ_n^2 is proportional to E. Further, since λ^2 is inversely proportional to E, by (2.41.1), it is seen that $\lambda^2\Gamma_n^2$ is approximately constant; consequently, (2.54.1) becomes

$$\sigma \approx \frac{A}{(E - E_r)^2 + \frac{1}{4}\Gamma^2},$$

where A is a constant. When E is equal to E_r, the resonance scattering cross section will be a maximum, but when $E \ll E_r$, i e., the neutron energy is appreciably less than the resonance value, it is evident that the cross section will be independent of the neutron energy.

2.55. Except near resonance, the resonance scattering is usually much less than the potential scattering, and the cross section for the latter does not vary greatly with the neutron energy. Although the resonance scattering at or near resonance does depend on the neutron energy, the variations are not great and the cross sections are of the same order of magnitude as for potential scattering. Consequently, it is generally accepted that the total elastic scattering cross section is independent of the kinetic energy of the incident neutrons. This is especially true for neutrons with energies less than about 0.1 Mev when scattered by nuclei of fairly low mass number, a situation of common occurrence in the study of nuclear reactors.

Chapter III

PRODUCTION AND REACTIONS OF NEUTRONS

PRODUCTION OF NEUTRONS

Alpha Particles and Light Nuclei

3.1. The neutron was first identified as a result of the interaction of alpha particles, emitted by radioactive material, with the light elements beryllium, boron, and lithium.   Subsequently it was found that other elements of low atomic number expel neutrons when bombarded by alpha particles.   In the case of beryllium, for example, the reaction may be represented by

$$_4\text{Be}^9 + {}_2\text{He}^4 \rightarrow {}_6\text{C}^{12} + {}_0n^1,$$

where the subscript gives the atomic number, i.e., the nuclear charge, and the superscript the mass number in each case.*   Since a neutron has a mass of unity but no charge, it is represented by the symbol $_0n^1$. The sum of the atomic numbers, i.e., the total number of protons, must be the same on each side of the equation.   Similarly the mass numbers, i.e., the total number of nucleons, must balance.

3.2. A combination of an alpha emitter, such as radium or polonium, and a light element, such as beryllium or boron, makes a very simple, compact, and useful source of neutrons for laboratory purposes.   A mixture of 5 grams of beryllium and 1 gram of radium, for example, emits about 10 to 15 million neutrons per sec.   Because of its long radioactive half life, about 1600 years, a radium-beryllium neutron source is virtually constant and permanent.   Its chief disadvantages are the high cost of the radium and the strong gamma radiation which it emits.   Polonium is frequently employed, with beryllium, in place of radium; the cost and gamma radiation are greatly reduced, but so also is the life of the neutron source.

---

* The reaction may be written in the abbreviated form $\text{Be}^9(\alpha, n)\text{C}^{12}$.   In this method of representation, the first symbol, i.e., Be^9, is the target nucleus; then, in the parentheses, are the incident particle (α) and the ejected particle (n); and, finally, the symbol of the residual nucleus, i.e., C^{12}, is given.   Reactions are frequently described in terms of the particles involved; thus, an (n, γ) reaction is one in which a neutron is captured and gamma radiation emitted.   The symbol p is used to indicate a proton, i.e., a hydrogen nucleus.

3.3. The neutrons produced by the action of alpha particles on beryllium have moderately high energies, the minimum being about 5 Mev and the maximum extending up to 12 Mev or more, depending on the energy of the incident particles. The sources described above are thus polyenergetic, the energy spectrum covering the range from about 5 Mev to 12 Mev. There may be, in addition, neutrons of energy lying outside this range which are produced by reactions due to gamma rays from the alpha-particle emitter, as will be seen in the next paragraph.

Photoneutron Sources

3.4. If monoenergetic neutrons, i.e., neutrons of (approximately) the same energy, are required, use may be made of certain *photonuclear reactions*. These are reactions in which gamma rays interact with a nucleus, transferring energy to the latter; the excited nucleus so formed may then eject a particle, such as a neutron. *Photoneutron sources*, as they are called, involve reactions represented by the symbol (γ, n), since the gamma-ray photon (§ 2.11) is the incident particle and a neutron is expelled.

3.5. Two (γ, n) processes which are possible with gamma radiation from available radioactive substances are the following:

$$_4\text{Be}^9 + {}_0\gamma^0 \rightarrow {}_4\text{Be}^8 + {}_0n^1$$

and

$$_1\text{H}^2 + {}_0\gamma^0 \rightarrow {}_1\text{H}^1 + {}_0n^1.$$

In the former, the target element is beryllium* and in the latter it is deuterium, the heavier (stable) isotope of hydrogen, having mass number 2. These reactions are of special interest in connection with the operation of nuclear reactors, as will be indicated later (§ 4.80).

3.6. The minimum threshold energy of the gamma rays necessary to bring about these (γ, n) reactions is 1.6 Mev for the beryllium reaction and 2.21 Mev for the deuterium reaction. Thus, gamma rays with energies less than these amounts will be unable to produce neutrons by the respective reactions. Any energy of the gamma ray in excess of the threshold energy will appear mainly as kinetic energy of the emitted neutron, some being carried off by the recoil nucleus. Since gamma rays from a given radioactive source usually have a definite energy, so also will the emitted neutrons; consequently, when the latter are produced by the photonuclear (γ, n) reaction, they are essentially monoenergetic.

3.7. Possible sources of gamma radiation for use with neutron sources are the naturally occurring elements radium and mesothorium. The artificially produced isotopes Na^{24}, Ga^{72}, Sb^{124}, and La^{140} are considerably cheaper, although

---

* The Be⁸ nucleus, indicated in the equation, is highly unstable and breaks up, almost instantaneously, into two He⁴ nuclei.

they have much shorter half lives.   The target material can be beryllium metal or heavy water, i.e., water enriched in the heavier isotope of hydrogen.   The lowest energy of neutrons obtainable in this manner is 0.03 Mev from the Sb^{124}-Be reaction, and the highest is 0.88 Mev from the MsTh-Be process.

3.8. A simple and convenient source of approximately monoenergetic neutrons is available from the Isotopes Division of the Atomic Energy Commission. It consists of a rod of antimony, containing the radioactive Sb^{124} isotope, surrounded by a beryllium metal cup.   When newly prepared, the system emits neutrons of roughly uniform energy, 0.03 Mev, at the rate of about 8 million per sec.   The Sb^{124} has a half life of 60 days, and when the activity has decayed to such an extent that the neutron source has become appreciably weakened, it can be regenerated by exposure of the antimony rod to neutrons in a nuclear reactor.

USE OF ACCELERATORS

3.9. In addition to the relatively compact neutron source described above, there are various methods for producing neutrons, especially of fairly uniform energy, by using incident particles which have been accelerated by means of a cyclotron or, better, by a Van de Graaff machine, since the latter more readily yields particles of uniform energy.   The action of accelerated protons, i.e., hydrogen nuclei, on lithium, or of deuterons, i.e., deuterium nuclei, on targets of lithium, beryllium, or deuterium (as "heavy" ice or "heavy" paraffin) results in the formation of neutron beams of fairly uniform energy.   The actual energy depends on that of the incident particles used, as well as on the particular process employed.

SLOWING DOWN OF NEUTRONS

SCATTERING AND MODERATION

3.10. All the sources described above yield neutrons of fairly high kinetic energy, usually in the Mev range.   Such neutrons are referred to as *fast neutrons*. It was mentioned in § 2.52 that, as a result of elastic scattering collisions, neutrons can be deprived of some (or all) of their kinetic energy and are thereby slowed down.   *Slow neutrons*, and particularly neutrons with energies in the vicinity of 0.03 ev at ordinary temperatures, called thermal neutrons (§ 3.13), are of importance in connection with nuclear reactors.

3.11. It will be seen in Chapter VI that, for a given scattering angle, the fractional decrease in the kinetic energy of a neutron in an elastic collision is greater the smaller the mass number of the scattering nucleus.   This means that fast neutrons are slowed down most effectively by scattering in a medium containing nuclei of low mass number.

3.12. The slowing down of neutrons plays a significant part in most nuclear reactors, and the material used for the purpose is called a *moderator*.   The process of slowing down neutrons as a result of scattering collisions is sometimes referred to as *moderation*. A good moderator is consequently a material which reduces the speed of fast neutrons in a small number of collisions; it will obviously consist of atoms of low mass number. Thus, ordinary water (H_2O), heavy water (D_2O), beryllium, and carbon have been used as moderators in various reactors.*

3.13. After a number of scattering collisions, the velocity of a neutron is reduced to such an extent that it has approximately the same average kinetic energy as the atoms, or molecules, of the medium in which it is undergoing elastic scattering. As will be seen below, the energy depends on the temperature of the medium, and hence it is called *thermal energy*. Neutrons whose energies have been reduced to values in this region are designated *thermal neutrons*, and the process of reducing the energy of a neutron to the thermal region is known as *thermalization*. Neutrons with energies above thermal values are sometimes referred to as *epithermal neutrons*.

MAXWELL-BOLTZMANN DISTRIBUTION

3.14. Thermal neutrons may strictly be defined as neutrons that are in thermal equilibrium with the atoms (or molecules) of the medium in which they are present. A particular thermal neutron undergoing collisions with the nuclei of the medium may gain or lose energy in any one collision. But, if a large number of neutrons diffusing in a nonabsorbing medium are considered, there is no net energy change for all the neutrons. The kinetic energies of the neutrons will then be distributed statistically according to the Maxwell-Boltzmann distribution law, as derived from the kinetic theory of gases; thus,

$$\frac{dn}{n} = \frac{2\pi}{(\pi kT)^{\frac{3}{2}}} e^{-\frac{E}{kT}} E^{\frac{1}{2}} dE, \tag{3.14.1}$$

where dn is the number of neutrons with energies in the range from E to $E + dE$, n is the total number of neutrons in the system, k is the Boltzmann constant, and T is the temperature on the Kelvin scale.

3.15. Since most media absorb neutrons to some extent, and the absorption cross sections, apart from resonance peaks, increase with decreasing energy, the Maxwell-Boltzmann distribution does not apply. The greater absorption of the slow neutrons results in an increase in the average energy above that to be expected from (3.14.1), the extent of the deviation increasing with the distance from the neutron source. This phenomenon is called *hardening*. However, provided the medium is not too strongly absorbing, the Maxwellian distribution may be assumed to be valid for thermal neutrons.

---

* A good moderator must not absorb neutrons to any great extent; consequently, the light elements lithium and boron, which absorb slow neutrons very strongly, are not used as moderators.

3.16. In conformity with a symbolism to be used later (§ 3.50), let $n(E)$ be the number of neutrons of energy E per unit energy interval.* Then $n(E)\, dE$ is the number of neutrons having energies in the range from E to $E + dE$; this is equivalent to dn in (3.14.1), and hence the latter may be written as

$$\frac{n(E)}{n}\, dE = \frac{2\pi}{(\pi kT)^{\frac{3}{2}}}\, e^{-\frac{E}{kT}}\, E^{\frac{1}{2}}\, dE,$$

or

$$\frac{n(E)}{n} = \frac{2\pi}{(\pi kT)^{\frac{3}{2}}}\, e^{-\frac{E}{kT}}\, E^{\frac{1}{2}}, \qquad (3.16.1)$$

where the left-hand side represents the *fraction* of the neutrons having energies in the range from E to $E + dE$ per unit energy interval. The right-hand side of the equation can be evaluated for various E's at a given temperature, and the plot obtained in this manner of $n(E)/n$ against the kinetic energy E of the neutrons is represented in Fig. 3.16.

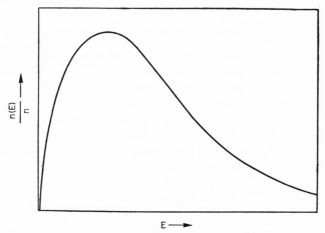

FIG. 3.16.   Maxwell-Boltzmann distribution of energy

3.17. In the study of thermal neutrons, it has become the practice to state the energy as kT for the particular temperature T. Actually, this represents the kinetic energy corresponding to the most probable velocity per unit velocity.† The average kinetic energy of thermal neutrons, according to the Maxwell equation, is $\frac{3}{2}kT$.

---

* The volume of the system is usually taken as 1 cm³, but for present purposes the volume is immaterial.

† Since $E = \frac{1}{2} mv^2$, where v is the velocity, the Maxwell equation (3.16.1) can be written as

$$\frac{n(v)}{n} = 4\pi \left(\frac{m}{2\pi kT}\right)^{\frac{3}{2}} v^2 e^{-\frac{mv^2}{2kT}}.$$

If this is differentiated with respect to v and the result set equal to zero, the most probable velocity per unit velocity is found to be equal to $(2kT/m)^{\frac{1}{2}}$. The corresponding kinetic energy is then kT.

3.18. Expressing energy, as usual, in electron volts, the Boltzmann constant k has the value 8.61×10^{-5} ev per degree; consequently, it is possible to write for thermal neutrons

$$\text{``Energy of thermal neutrons''} = 8.61 \times 10^{-5}T \text{ ev.} \qquad (3.18.1)$$

A number of values for a series of temperatures are recorded in Table 3.18; at ordinary temperature, i.e., about 25°C or 298°K, the "energy of thermal neutrons" is approximately 0.025 ev.

TABLE 3.18. "ENERGIES" AND "SPEEDS" OF THERMAL NEUTRONS AT VARIOUS
TEMPERATURES

Temperature		"Energy" (ev)	"Speed" (cm/sec)
(° K)	(° C)		
300	27	0.026	2.2×10^5
400	127	0.034	2.6
600	327	0.052	3.1
800	527	0.069	3.6
1000	727	0.086	4.0

3.19. The speed v of a neutron in cm per sec is related to its kinetic energy E by the equation

$$v = 13.8 \times 10^5 \sqrt{E} \text{ cm per sec,} \qquad (3.19.1)$$

where E is expressed in electron volts. This result may be combined with (3.18.1) to give the "speed of thermal neutrons" as a function of the temperature; thus,

$$\text{``Speed of thermal neutrons''} = 1.28 \times 10^4 \sqrt{T} \text{ cm per sec.}$$

At room temperature, T is about 295°K and the "speed of thermal neutrons" is then found to be 2.22×10^5 cm per sec. Values for several temperatures are given in Table 3.18.

REACTIONS OF SLOW NEUTRONS

TYPES OF CAPTURE REACTIONS

3.20. Apart from scattering, slow neutrons undergo four types of capture reactions with atomic nuclei; these involve either (a) the emission of gamma radiation, (n, γ); (b) the ejection of an alpha particle, (n, α); (c) the ejection of a proton, (n, p); or (d) fission, (n, f). Of these, the radiative capture, i.e., (n, γ), process is the most common, for it occurs with a wide variety of nuclides from low to high mass numbers. The (n, α) and (n, p) reactions with slow neutrons are limited to a few elements of low mass number, whereas fission by slow neutrons is restricted to certain nuclei with high mass number.

RADIATIVE CAPTURE

3.21. In radiative capture reactions, the target nucleus captures a slow neutron and produces a compound nucleus in an excited state (§ 2.14). The excess energy is then emitted in the form of one or more gamma rays, leaving the compound nucleus in its normal or ground state. The process may thus be represented by

$$Z^A + n^1 \rightarrow [Z^{A+1}]^* \rightarrow Z^{A+1} + \gamma,$$

where A is the mass number and Z is the atomic number of the target nucleus; the symbol $[Z^{A+1}]^*$ represents the compound nucleus in the excited state. The residual nucleus or product is Z^{A+1}, i.e., a nucleus having the same atomic number as the target nucleus, but with a mass number one unit greater.

3.22. Since the capture of a neutron by a nucleus, followed by emission of gamma radiation, must be associated with an increase in the neutron-to-proton ratio, the product of an (n, γ) reaction is likely to be radioactive, especially if the ratio of neutrons to protons in the target nucleus is already near the upper limit of stability for the given atomic number. As seen above, the latter remains unchanged in the radiative capture of a neutron, while the number of neutrons increases by unity. If the product nucleus is unstable, it will usually be a negative beta emitter, since this mode of decay means that the extra neutron is replaced by a proton (§ 1.16). In cases of this kind, the occurrence of the neutron capture reaction can be detected experimentally by the resulting radioactivity. The procedure is frequently used in various measurements with slow neutrons (§ 3.60, *et seq.*).

3.23. The simplest (n, γ) reaction occurs with hydrogen as the target nucleus; thus,

$$_1H^1 + _0n^1 \rightarrow [_1H^2]^* \rightarrow _1H^2 + \gamma,$$

the product being deuterium. It will be seen that this process is exactly the reverse of that given in § 3.5, for the action of gamma rays on deuterium as a source of neutrons. Since the minimum or threshold energy in that case is known to be 2.21 Mev, it follows that the energy of the gamma radiation resulting from the (n, γ) reaction with hydrogen will have at least this value. The emission of such radiation, of relatively high energy and penetrating power, when neutrons pass through materials containing hydrogen, has been confirmed experimentally. Cognizance must be taken of this fact when such substances, e.g., concrete, water, etc., are used in connection with nuclear reactors, either as a means for slowing down neutrons, as a coolant, or as a shield to prevent the escape of neutrons.

3.24. When a slow neutron is absorbed in an (n, γ) reaction, the excitation energy of the compound nucleus above its ground state is approximately equal to the binding energy of the neutron in the compound nucleus, as was seen in § 2.14. Consequently, if the excited compound nucleus passes directly to the ground state by the emission of gamma radiation, the energy of the latter should be equal to the binding energy of the neutron.   For example, in the case of the (n, γ) reaction with hydrogen referred to above, the binding energy of the neutron in the compound nucleus, i.e., in deuterium, is known to be about 2.21 Mev from the nuclear masses.   This is in complete agreement with the measured energy of the radiation in the $H^1(n, \gamma)H^2$ reaction, and with the threshold energy for the reverse process.   With heavier target nuclei the slow-neutron (n, γ) reaction leads to the formation of compound nuclei with higher excitation energies, and the so-called *capture gamma rays* may have energies of about 8 to 9 Mev.

3.25. The radiative capture of neutrons has been used extensively for the production of isotopes by exposing stable nuclides to the action of slow neutrons in a reactor.   Over a hundred (n, γ) reactions leading to beta-emitting isotopes have been reported.   Two of these, in which rhodium-103 and indium-115, respectively, are the target nuclei, i.e.,

$$_{45}Rh^{103} + {}_0n^1 \rightarrow {}_{45}Rh^{104} \text{ (44 sec) } + \gamma$$
$$_{49}In^{115} + {}_0n^1 \rightarrow {}_{49}In^{116} \text{ (54 min) } + \gamma,$$

are of particular interest since the beta activities of the products are used for the detection of neutrons of more or less specific energies, as will be described in § 3.84.   The half life of the radioisotope formed as product is given in each case.

3.26.   Perhaps the most notable of all (n, γ) reactions with slow neutrons is that undergone by uranium-238; thus,

$$_{92}U^{238} + {}_0n^1 \rightarrow {}_{92}U^{239} + \gamma.$$

The product, uranium-239, has a half life of 23 min, emitting negative beta particles (electrons), represented by $_{-1}\beta^0$ (charge -1, mass essentially zero); thus,

$$_{92}U^{239} \rightarrow {}_{93}Np^{239} + {}_{-1}\beta^0,$$

the daughter being an isotope of an element of atomic number 93, called neptunium (Np), which does not exist in nature to any detectable extent.   Neptunium-239, with a half life of 2.3 days, is itself beta active, decaying by the process

$$_{93}Np^{239} \rightarrow {}_{94}Pu^{239} + {}_{-1}\beta^0$$

to form the isotope Pu^{239} of the element of atomic number 94, called plutonium (Pu).

3.27. The element plutonium occurs naturally in the merest, almost undetectable, traces.*   Nevertheless, plutonium-239, which is in a sense an isotope of an artificial element, is being produced in appreciable quantities in nuclear re-

---

* Such amounts of plutonium-239 as do exist in nature are believed to be formed as a result of the capture of neutrons by uranium-238 and subsequent two-stage decay of the product, as described in § 3.26.

actors, as the result of the radiative capture of neutrons by uranium-238. The immediate product then undergoes two relatively rapid stages of beta decay, as stated above, forming the alpha emitter plutonium-239. The latter has a half life of 24,000 years and is consequently relatively stable. It is an important substance from the standpoint of the release of nuclear energy, being used in atomic bombs.

3.28. A series of processes similar to those just described is initiated by the (n, γ) reaction with thorium-232; thus,

$$_{90}\text{Th}^{232} + {}_0n^1 \rightarrow {}_{90}\text{Th}^{233} + \gamma$$

the isotope thorium-233 being formed. This is known to have a half life of 23 min, and the product resulting from negative beta decay is protactinium-233, i.e.,

$$_{90}\text{Th}^{233} \rightarrow {}_{91}\text{Pa}^{233} + {}_{-1}\beta^0.$$

The Pa^{233} is also a beta emitter, with a half life of 27.4 days, the decay process being

$$_{91}\text{Pa}^{233} \rightarrow {}_{92}\text{U}^{233} + {}_{-1}\beta^0,$$

so that the daughter element is a new isotope of uranium which does not occur in nature, at least to any appreciable extent. It is radioactive, emitting alpha particles and having a half life of 1.63×10^5 years. Thus, bombardment of thorium-232 by neutrons, and allowing time for the product to decay through two stages of beta activity, leads to the formation of the relatively stable uranium-233. This isotope, like the artificially produced plutonium-239 described in the preceding paragraph, is of significance in connection with the release of nuclear energy.

EMISSION OF ALPHA PARTICLES AND PROTONS

3.29. Slow-neutron reactions accompanied by the emission of a charged particle, e.g., an alpha particle or a proton, are rare. The reason is that before a positively charged particle can be expelled from a nucleus it must acquire sufficient energy to overcome an electrostatic potential barrier, in addition to the energy needed for its detachment from the compound nucleus. Part of the requisite energy is provided by the addition of the neutron to the target nucleus; the remainder must be supplied by the kinetic energy of the neutron.

3.30. Since the kinetic energy of a slow neutron is very small, it is apparent that (n, α) and (n, p) reactions, with slow neutrons, can occur only when the electrostatic repulsion which the charged particle must overcome is small. This is the case for elements of low atomic number, and hence it is with a few species of this kind that (n, α) and (n, p) reactions with slow neutrons have been observed.

3.31. The (n, α) reactions may be written in the general form

$$Z^A + n^1 \rightarrow [Z^{A+1}]^* \rightarrow (Z-2)^{A-3} + {}_2\text{He}^4,$$

where ${}_2\text{He}^4$ represents an alpha particle, i.e., a helium nucleus, with a mass number of 4 and an atomic number of 2. The recoil nucleus now has a mass number three units less and an atomic number two units less than the target nucleus. The absorption of slow neutrons by lithium-6 (Li^6), the rarer, naturally occurring isotope of lithium, and by boron-10 (B^{10}), the less common isotope of boron, leads to the emission of alpha particles. Both of these reactions have a special interest in the present connection.

3.32. The (n, α) reaction of boron-10 with slow neutrons may be represented by

$${}_5\text{B}^{10} + {}_0n^1 \rightarrow {}_3\text{Li}^7 + {}_2\text{He}^4,$$

the recoil nucleus being the stable isotope lithium-7. This reaction is accompanied by the liberation of 2.5 Mev of energy, which is shared between the alpha particle and the nucleus. Both particles are therefore ejected, in opposite directions, with high velocities, so that they produce considerable ionization in their passage through a gas. It will be seen later that the (n, α) process with boron-10 is significant in several respects. It is utilized, for example, in an important method for the detection and counting of slow neutrons (§ 3.80), and also in the control of nuclear reactors (§ 4.73).

3.33. The other (n, α) reaction, which takes place readily with slow neutrons, is

$${}_3\text{Li}^6 + {}_0n^1 \rightarrow {}_1\text{H}^3 + {}_2\text{He}^4.$$

The residual (recoil) nucleus is here H^3, a hydrogen isotope of mass number 3 called *tritium*. The isotope is radioactive, having a half life of about 12 years, and emitting a negative beta particle. Tritium has attracted attention because of its possible use in connection with the so-called "hydrogen bomb," as well as for other reasons.

3.34. The general representation of (n, p) reactions is given by

$$Z^A + n^1 \rightarrow [Z^{A+1}]^* \rightarrow (Z-1)^A + {}_1\text{H}^1,$$

so that the product has the same mass number as the target nucleus, but its atomic number is one unit less. A few isotopes of low atomic number, notably nitrogen-14, sulfur-32, and chlorine-35, undergo (n, p) reactions with slow neutrons; thus,

$${}_7\text{N}^{14} + {}_0n^1 \rightarrow {}_6\text{C}^{14} + {}_1\text{H}^1$$
$${}_{16}\text{S}^{32} + {}_0n^1 \rightarrow {}_{15}\text{P}^{32} + {}_1\text{H}^1$$
$${}_{17}\text{Cl}^{35} + {}_0n^1 \rightarrow {}_{16}\text{S}^{35} + {}_1\text{H}^1.$$

These processes can be carried out by exposing the respective elements to slow neutrons in a nuclear reactor. The products are all radioactive, emitting beta particles; they have found many applications in investigations which make use of radioactive isotopes as tracers.

Nuclear Fission

3.35. Another type of reaction caused by neutrons, which will be considered in more detail in Chapter IV, is *nuclear fission*.   In the fission process the nucleus absorbs a neutron and the resulting compound nucleus is so unstable that it immediately breaks up into two more or less equal parts.   Some nuclei, such as uranium-233, uranium-235, and plutonium-239, will readily undergo fission with slow neutrons, but others require fast neutrons.   There are many different ways in which fission of a particular nucleus takes place, but in only a small proportion of the fissions does the nucleus break up in a symmetrical manner.   This and other aspects of fission will be treated more fully below.

REACTIONS WITH FAST NEUTRONS

Capture and Fission Reactions

3.36. Reactions of fast neutrons with matter, other than scattering and fission, are not of major importance for the study of nuclear reactors; hence, they will be referred to only briefly here.   Provided the energy is available, the expulsion of a charged particle from the excited compound nucleus is more probable than the emission of radiation.   Thus, (n, α) and (n, p) reactions of nuclei with fast neutrons, with energies of 1 Mev or more, frequently occur more readily than the (n, γ) reaction.   If neutrons of sufficiently high energy are used as projectiles, two or more nucleons may be expelled from the compound nucleus. For incident neutrons of energy of about 10 Mev, it is possible for two neutrons or a neutron and a proton to be emitted.   Such reactions, which are not uncommon, are designated $(n, 2n)$ and (n, np), respectively.   If the neutron energy is still higher, processes such as $(n, 3n)$, $(n, 2np)$, etc., are possible.

3.37. Several nuclei which do not undergo fission by slow neutrons suffer this reaction as a result of the capture of fast neutrons.   Thus, uranium-238 and thorium-232 require neutrons of about 1 Mev energy to cause fission at an appreciable rate.   By the use of neutrons of very high energy, e.g., 100 Mev or more, the fission of a number of normally stable nuclei, such as bismuth, lead, thallium, mercury, gold, etc., has been achieved.   Such fission, however, does not appear to have any immediate practical interest.

NEUTRON CROSS SECTIONS

Significance of Cross Section

3.38. The description of the interaction of neutrons with atomic nuclei can be made quantitative by introducing the concept of *cross section*, defined in general terms in § 2.38.   If a given material is exposed to the action of neutrons, the rate at which any particular nuclear reaction occurs depends on the number of neutrons, their velocity, and the number and type of nuclei in the given material.   The cross section of a target nucleus for any given reaction is a property of the nucleus and of the energy of the incident neutron.

3.39. Suppose a uniform beam of I neutrons per cm² impinges perpendicularly, in a given time, on a layer one atom thick of target material containing N_a atoms per cm², and let C be the number of individual nuclear processes, e.g., neutron captures, occurring per cm², in that time.   The nuclear cross section σ for a specific reaction is then defined as the average number of individual processes occurring per incident neutron in the beam per nucleus; thus,

$$\sigma \equiv \frac{C}{N_a I} \text{ cm}^2 \text{ per nucleus.} \qquad (3.39.1)$$

Because nuclear cross sections are frequently in the range of 10^{-22} to 10^{-26} cm² per nucleus, it is the general practice to express them in terms of a unit of 10^{-24} cm² per nucleus, called a *barn*.   Thus, a cross section of 1.8×10^{-25} cm² per nucleus would be written as 0.18 barn.

3.40. The significance of the cross section may be seen by rearranging (3.39.1); thus, consider the form

$$N_a \sigma = \frac{C}{I}. \qquad (3.40.1)$$

If every neutron falling on the target reacted, then I would be equal to the number of nuclei taking part in the reaction; hence the right-hand side of (3.40.1) would represent the fraction of the incident neutrons which succeed in interacting with the target nucleus.   Consequently, $N_a\sigma$ may be regarded as the fraction of the surface which is capable of undergoing the given reaction; hence, of 1 cm² of surface, $N_a\sigma$ cm² is effective.   Since the 1 cm² of surface contains N_a nuclei, the quantity σ cm² is the *effective area per single nucleus* for the reaction.   It is this interpretation of σ that leads to the use of the term "cross section," although, as will shortly be apparent, it is related to the geometrical nuclear cross section only in certain special cases.

3.41. In the foregoing treatment, for purposes of defining the cross section, only the surface of the target material was considered.   In order to determine cross sections experimentally, the attenuation of the neutron beam through a target of finite thickness is measured.   For the present, the effect of scattering will be neglected.   Consider a 1 cm² area, enclosed by the dotted lines in Fig. 3.41, of a slab of material x cm thick, and let I_0 be the number of incident neutrons striking this area from the left.   If N is the number of target nuclei per cm³ of material, then the number present in a thin layer dx, parallel to the surface, will be $N\,dx$ nuclei per cm².   This is equivalent to the quantity designated by the symbol N_a above.   Hence, by (3.40.1), $N\,dx\sigma$ is the fraction of the neutrons falling on this layer which react; this may be set equal to $-dI/I$, where $-dI$ is the decrease in the neutrons per cm^2 as a result of passing through the thickness dx of target material. Consequently,

$$-\frac{dI}{I} = N\sigma\, dx \qquad (3.41.1)$$

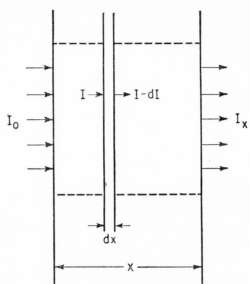

FIG. 3.41.   Neutron attenuation in passage through a slab

and integration over the thickness x of the material gives

$$I_x = I_0 e^{-N\sigma x}, \qquad (3.41.2)$$

where I_0 is the number of incident neutrons falling on a given area and I_x is the number which succeed in passing through x cm of the material over the same area. The experimental method for determining cross sections for nuclear reactions involving neutrons makes use of (3.41.2), as will be seen in § 3.58.

MACROSCOPIC CROSS SECTIONS

3.42. The cross section σ for a particular process, which applies to a single nucleus, is frequently called the *microscopic cross section* to distinguish it from $N\sigma$, called the *macroscopic cross section* of the material for that process. Thus, representing the latter by Σ, the definition is

$$\Sigma \equiv N\sigma \; cm^{-1}, \qquad (3.42.1)$$

where N is the number of nuclei per cm^3; it is consequently the total cross section of the nuclei in 1 cm^3 of the material. It will be noted that the macroscopic cross section has the dimensions of a reciprocal length.

3.43. Replacing N_0 in (3.41.1) by Σ, in accordance with (3.42.1), it is seen that

$$-\frac{dI}{I} = \Sigma \, dx.$$

Since $-dI/I$ is the fraction of neutrons absorbed in the path dx, it is evident that $\Sigma \, dx$ is the probability that neutrons will be absorbed in the path dx.

3.44. If ρ is the density of the absorbing material in grams per cm^3, and A is its atomic weight, if an element, then ρ/A is the number of gram atoms per cm^3. The number of atomic nuclei per cm^3 is then obtained upon multiplying by N_0, the Avogadro number (6.02×10^{23}), which gives the number of individual atoms (or nuclei) per gram atom; thus,

$$N = \frac{\rho}{A} N_0 \tag{3.44.1}$$

and hence

$$\Sigma = \frac{\rho N_0}{A} \sigma. \tag{3.44.2}$$

If the material under consideration contains several nuclear species, then the macroscopic cross section is given by

$$\Sigma = N_1\sigma_1 + N_2\sigma_2 + \cdots + N_i\sigma_i + \cdots, \tag{3.44.3}$$

where, in general, N_i is the number of nuclei per cm^3 of the ith kind present and σ_i is the microscopic cross section for the given process. For a compound, A in (3.44.1) must be replaced by the molecular weight M, and the result multiplied by the number ν_i of the absorbing atoms of the ith kind per molecule, to obtain N_i. The value of Σ is then given by (3.44.3); thus,

$$\Sigma = \frac{\rho N_0}{M} (\nu_1\sigma_1 + \nu_2\sigma_2 + \cdots + \nu_i\sigma_i + \cdots).$$

MEAN FREE PATH AND RELAXATION LENGTH

3.45. By introducing (3.42.1) into (3.41.2) it follows that

$$I_x = I_0 e^{-\Sigma x} \tag{3.45.1}$$

or

$$\frac{I_x}{I_0} = e^{-\Sigma x}. \tag{3.45.2}$$

The quantity I_x/I_0 is the fraction of incident neutrons which succeed in penetrating the thickness x of material without undergoing the reaction being considered. Hence $e^{-\Sigma x}$ may be regarded as the probability that a neutron will penetrate to a point x without being involved in the reaction. Since the probability that reaction will occur between x and $x + dx$ is given by $\Sigma \, dx$ (§ 3.43), the average distance λ a neutron will travel before being absorbed is given by

$$\lambda = \frac{\int_0^\infty xe^{-\Sigma x}\,\Sigma\,dx}{\int_0^\infty e^{-\Sigma x}\,\Sigma\,dx} = \frac{1}{\Sigma}\text{ cm,} \qquad (3.45.3)$$

the integrals in numerator and denominator being standard forms.

3.46. The average distance λ calculated above is called the *mean free path* for the given nuclear reaction. It has, of course, the dimensions of length, since Σ is a reciprocal length. Replacing Σ in (3.45.2) by $1/\lambda$, the result is

$$\frac{I_x}{I_0} = e^{-x/\lambda}. \qquad (3.46.1)$$

If x is set equal to λ, then $I_x/I_0 = e^{-1}$, so that λ may also be regarded as the distance in which all but a fraction $1/e$ of the incident neutrons are absorbed.

3.47. When a neutron can take part in several different processes with a given target nucleus, there will be a different cross section and mean free path for each process. The equations derived above are quite general and will apply to all the reactions in which neutrons are absorbed. It is then possible to define a total cross section for neutron absorption which is the sum of the individual cross sections. An equation of the form of (3.46.1) will give the total attenuation of neutrons due to absorption in a thickness x of medium through which they pass. In this case, the quantity λ, which is equal to the reciprocal of the total macroscopic absorption cross section, is sometimes called the *relaxation length* of the neutrons in the given medium. It is the distance in which the intensity of the neutron beam is reduced to a fraction $1/e$ of its initial value due to absorption of neutrons in the medium if there were no scattering.

RATES OF NEUTRON REACTIONS

3.48. Suppose a neutron moves with a velocity v cm per sec, and λ cm is the mean free path for a given reaction; then, on the average, v/λ is the probability that a neutron will interact per second. If the *neutron density*, i.e., the number of neutrons per cm³, of the beam is n, then the number of neutron interactions is nv/λ per cm³ per sec. Since λ is equal to $1/\Sigma$, this number can be written as Σnv, where Σ is the macroscopic cross section for a given process. In other words, it follows that

Number of neutrons involved in a given process $= \Sigma nv$ per cm³ per sec,   (3.48.1)

a result of considerable importance. In the study of nuclear reactors, for example, it is frequently necessary to know the number of neutrons of velocity v absorbed per cm³ per sec; this is equal to $\Sigma_a nv$, where Σ_a is the total macroscopic absorption cross section for these neutrons.

3.49. The product nv, expressed as neutrons per cm² per sec, is a significant quantity called the *neutron flux* and represented by the symbol ϕ. It is the sum of the distances traveled by all the neutrons in one cubic centimeter in one second and is therefore sometimes called the *track length*.   Upon substituting ϕ for nv in (3.48.1), it follows that

Number of neutrons involved in a given process = $\Sigma\phi$ per cm^3 per sec.   (3.49.1)

In general, if Σ_a is the macroscopic absorption cross section for all processes, then $\Sigma_a\phi$ is the total number of neutrons absorbed by all nuclear processes per cm^3 per sec.   This result will find frequent use in later sections.

POLYENERGETIC NEUTRON SYSTEMS

3.50. In the derivations given above, it has been assumed, for simplicity, that all the neutrons have the same velocity, but this is not true in many nuclear reactor problems.   As brought out in the preceding chapter, and considered further below, the cross section for a particular reaction varies with the energy, or speed, of the neutron.   This introduces a complication for which due allowance must be made.   If $n(E)$ is the number of neutrons of energy E per cm^3 per unit energy interval, then $n(E)\,dE$ is the number of neutrons in the energy range from E to $E + dE$.   The total neutron flux ϕ, for neutrons of all energies (or velocities), is then given by

$$\phi = \int_0^\infty n(E)v \, dE \text{ per cm}^2 \text{ per sec,} \qquad (3.50.1)$$

where the integration limits of zero and infinity are meant to be formal only, the implication being that integration is carried over the whole range of neutron energies.   The velocity v corresponding to the kinetic energy E is defined by $v = \sqrt{2E/m}$, where m is the mass of the neutron.

3.51. An alternative form of (3.50.1) may be obtained by letting $\phi(E)$ represent the flux per unit energy of neutrons having energy E; then $\phi(E)\,dE$ is the flux of neutrons in the energy range from E to $E + dE$.   The total neutron flux is then

$$\phi = \int_0^\infty \phi(E) \, dE \text{ per cm}^2 \text{ per sec.} \qquad (3.51.1)$$

Similarly, the corresponding form of (3.48.1) for a polyenergetic neutron system is

$$\text{Number of neutrons involved in a given process} = \int_0^\infty \Sigma(E)n(E)v \, dE \qquad (3.51.2)$$

$$= \int_0^\infty \Sigma(E)\phi(E) \, dE \text{ per cm}^3 \text{ per sec,} \qquad (3.51.3)$$

where $\Sigma(E)$ is the macroscopic cross section for the process for neutrons of energy E.

3.52. When the neutrons have a range of energies, an average macroscopic cross section $\bar{\Sigma}$ for a particular process may be defined so that, by analogy with (3.49.1),

$$\begin{array}{l} \text{Number of neutrons involved} \\ \text{in a given process} \end{array} \equiv \bar{\Sigma}\phi \text{ per cm}^3 \text{ per sec,}$$

where ϕ is the total neutron flux given by (3.50.1). It follows, therefore, upon introducing (3.50.1) and (3.51.2), or (3.51.1) and (3.51.3), that

$$\bar{\Sigma} = \frac{\int_0^\infty \Sigma(E)n(E)v\,dE}{\int_0^\infty n(E)v\,dE}$$

$$= \frac{\int_0^\infty \Sigma(E)\phi(E)\,dE}{\int_0^\infty \phi(E)\,dE} \text{ cm}^{-1}. \tag{3.52.1}$$

The corresponding average mean free path $\bar{\lambda}$ is expressed by

$$\bar{\lambda} = \frac{\int_0^\infty \lambda(E)\phi(E)\,dE}{\int_0^\infty \phi(E)\,dE} \text{ cm,} \tag{3.52.2}$$

where $\lambda(E)$, the mean free path for neutrons of energy E, is equal to $1/\Sigma(E)$ for the given process. It may be noted that, in general, $\bar{\lambda}$ will not be equal to $1/\bar{\Sigma}$.

3.53. For thermal neutrons having a Maxwell-Boltzmann distribution, $n(E)$ in the foregoing equations would be defined by (3.16.1), with n equal to the total number of neutrons per cm³. Because of absorption, however, the actual distribution of thermal neutrons is not strictly in accordance with the Maxwell-Boltzmann equation, as indicated in § 3.15. Nevertheless, for a weak absorber, the Maxwell-Boltzmann distribution would represent a very good approximation. The same would be true if the absorption cross section were essentially independent of the neutron energy. If the absorber obeys the $1/v$ law (§ 2.43), the absorption cross section may be expressed by $\sigma_a(E) = (a/E^{\frac{1}{2}})$, and the average cross section is then

$$\bar{\sigma}_a = \frac{\int_0^\infty \sigma_a(E)n(E)v\,dE}{\int_0^\infty n(E)v\,dE} = \frac{a\int_0^\infty n(E)\,dE}{\int_0^\infty n(E)E^{\frac{1}{2}}\,dE}.$$

The ratio of the integrals is seen to be the reciprocal of the average value of $E^{\frac{1}{2}}$; that is, it is equal to $1/\overline{E^{\frac{1}{2}}}$, and so

$$\bar{\sigma}_a = \frac{a}{\overline{E^{\frac{1}{2}}}}.$$

The approximate average absorption cross section for polyenergetic neutrons in the case of a $1/v$ absorber is thus the value at the velocity $\overline{E^{\frac{1}{2}}}$. For a thermal neutron distribution satisfying the Maxwell equation (3.16.1), it is found that

$$\overline{E^{\frac{1}{2}}} = \sqrt{\frac{4kT}{\pi}}.$$

Consequently, the average absorption cross section for thermal neutrons having a Maxwellian distribution, if the absorber obeys the $1/v$ law, is precisely the value of the cross section at the energy equal to $4kT/\pi$. If $\sigma_a(kT)$ is the absorption cross section for neutrons of energy kT (§ 3.17), then it is readily seen that

$$\bar{\sigma}_a = \frac{\sqrt{\pi}}{2} \sigma_a(kT),$$

provided the $1/v$ law holds.

SCATTERING PROPERTIES

CROSS SECTIONS AND MEAN FREE PATH

3.54. The results obtained above (§ 3.38, *et seq.*) are quite general, being applicable both to the absorption of neutrons and to scattering, in which the incident neutron is not lost, as in absorption reactions, but is only deprived of some, or all, of its energy. The cross section σ_s for scattering is defined by an expression similar to (3.39.1), where C is now the number of neutrons scattered out of the beam of I neutrons per cm² by the N_a nuclei. The macroscopic scattering cross section Σ_s is equal to $N\sigma_s$, where, as before, N is the number of nuclei per cm³ of the scattering material.

3.55. In applying the arguments of § 3.41 to the scattering of neutrons, there is a change in the significance of the term I_x; it is now the number of neutrons which have escaped scattering, and not merely the number which succeed in passing through the material. Actually, the number of neutrons passing through in the x-direction is greater than I_x, since many neutrons will be scattered in this direction. However, bearing in mind the correct interpretation of I_x, equations (3.41.2) and (3.45.2) apply to scattering. The quantity I_x/I_0 is the fraction of the neutrons which have escaped scattering, so that $e^{-\Sigma_s x}$ is the probability that a neutron will penetrate to a point x without being scattered, and $\Sigma_s \, dx$ is the probability that scattering will occur in the interval between x and $x + dx$. The scattering mean free path λ_s, which is the average distance a neutron travels before being involved in a scattering collision, can then be obtained from (3.45.3) as

$$\lambda_s = \frac{1}{\Sigma_s}. \tag{3.55.1}$$

3.56. For a neutron of velocity v cm per sec, the number of scattering collisions will be, on the average, v/λ_s per sec, and the total number of neutrons scattered per cm³ per sec is nv/λ_s, or $nv\Sigma_s$, where n is the number of neutrons per cm³.

As in § 3.49, it follows that the number of neutrons scattered per cm³ per sec is $\Sigma_s\phi$, where ϕ is the neutron flux. The scattering cross sections do not vary so greatly with energy* as do absorption cross sections; nevertheless, when a beam of polyenergetic neutrons is being considered, the total number of scattering collisions per cm³ per sec will be given by an expression analogous to (3.51.3). Average values of the macroscopic scattering cross section and of the mean free path are given by (3.52.1) and (3.52.2).

DETERMINATION OF CROSS SECTIONS

TRANSMISSION METHOD

3.57. The most direct procedure for the measurement of cross sections, which gives the total of absorption and scattering cross sections, is the *transmission method*. The experimental arrangement consists of a neutron source S and a detector D, between which is placed a slab A of the material being investigated (Fig. 3.57). By means of a suitable collimating shield, the neutron beam passing

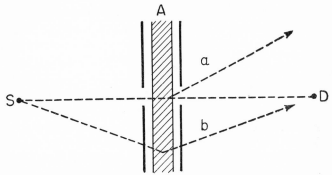

FIG. 3.57.   Transmission method for determination of cross sections

through to the detector is restricted to a relatively small solid angle. The purpose of the shield is to prevent, as far as possible, neutrons which have been scattered in the material from reaching the detector. This will be evident from a consideration of the dotted lines showing possible paths of scattered neutrons. If the aperture in the shield is small, the neutrons in general will not be scattered into the detector, as shown at a. However, if the aperture had been larger, there is a possibility that scattered neutrons would reach the detector, as indicated at b.†

---

* The potential scattering cross section σ_s for neutrons (§ 2.53) should theoretically be equal to $4\pi R^2$, where R is the "effective" radius of the scattering nucleus.

† It is assumed here that the slab is not too thick, so that the neutrons are not scattered more than once within the slab; otherwise, neutrons such as a might be scattered into the detector. It is on account of the scattering of neutrons that the exponential equation (3.41.2) for the attenuation of neutrons is not altogether valid.

3.58. With the arrangement suggested above, the neutrons reaching D will be those which have escaped absorption and have not been scattered. If I_0 is the neutron intensity measured at D with the slab of material removed, and I_x is the value when the slab of thickness x is interposed between the source and the detector, then insertion of these results in (3.41.2) will permit the total (microscopic) cross section for absorption and scattering to be calculated. Alternatively, (3.45.1) may be used to give the total macroscopic cross section.

3.59. The scattering cross section can be determined by having the neutron detector in such a position that it can be reached by scattered neutrons only. This may be achieved by placing the detector at an angle approaching 90° from the incident beam; then only those neutrons which have been scattered through this angle will be counted. From the result obtained the total number of neutrons scattered through all angles by a known thickness of material can be calculated and hence the cross section can be evaluated. The difference between the total cross section obtained in § 3.58 and the scattering cross section gives the absorption cross section for all processes.* The method just described for obtaining scattering cross sections requires a strong neutron source, since the proportion of neutrons scattered is small, and only a fraction of these enter the detector placed at a selected angle.

ACTIVATION METHOD

3.60. If a particular neutron absorption reaction leads to the formation of a radioisotope (§ 3.22), the amount of which can be estimated from its radioactivity, it may be possible to determine the cross section for that reaction by what is known as the *activation method*. A thin foil of the material under investigation is exposed to the neutrons for a known time; it is then removed from the neutron flux and its activity is measured. If the target material is thin, the neutron density or flux may be regarded as constant throughout, and this simplifies the treatment of the results.

3.61. According to (3.49.1), the number of neutrons absorbed per cm^3 per sec, in a given process, is $\Sigma_a\phi$, where Σ_a is the macroscopic cross section for that process and ϕ is the neutron flux. If V cm^3 is the volume of the absorbing foil, the rate of absorption is $V\Sigma_a\phi$ neutrons per sec. Since each neutron absorbed results in the production of a radioactive nucleus, the rate of formation of the active species is $V\Sigma_a\phi$ nuclei per sec. However, the decay of the radioactive nuclide occurs to some extent while it is being produced. If λ is the radioactive decay constant (§ 1.20), the net rate of increase of the active species at any instant is given by

$$\frac{dN}{dT} = V\Sigma_a\phi - \lambda N, \qquad (3.61.1)$$

---

* It should be noted that for neutrons of sufficiently high energy, where absorption is of the same order as, or smaller than, scattering, this method is inapplicable, since it involves the difference of two almost equal numbers containing experimental inaccuracies.

where N is the number of active nuclei present after T sec of exposure of the foil to the neutron flux ϕ.

3.62. The solution of the linear differential equation (3.61.1), noting that $N = 0$ when $T = 0$, is

$$N = \frac{V\Sigma_a\phi}{\lambda}(1 - e^{-\lambda T}). \tag{3.62.1}$$

The activity A of the foil measured by a counter is equal to $N\lambda$, which is the rate of emission of charged particles (or photons), so that

$$A = V\Sigma_a\phi(1 - e^{-\lambda T}). \tag{3.62.2}$$

If exposure to neutrons is continued for some time, so that T is large, and $e^{-\lambda T}$ is small compared with unity, (3.62.2) becomes

$$A_\infty = V\Sigma_a\phi. \tag{3.62.3}$$

The quantity designated A_∞ is called the *saturation activity*, and for a given neutron flux and foil it is directly proportional to the absorption cross section. It is the maximum or limiting activity the foil can acquire in the specified neutron flux.

3.63. After removal of the activated foil from the neutron flux, it continues to decay, and at any subsequent time t the activity is

$$\begin{aligned} A_t &= V\Sigma_a\phi(1 - e^{-\lambda T})e^{-\lambda t} \\ &= V\Sigma_a\phi[e^{-\lambda t} - e^{-\lambda(T+t)}]. \end{aligned} \tag{3.63.1}$$

By determining the activity of the foil in a counter, after a period T of exposure to neutrons and a delay t before counting, and making allowance for decay during the process of counting, it is possible to evaluate the saturation activity $V\Sigma_a\phi$ from (3.63.1). If the neutron flux ϕ to which the foil is exposed and the volume of the foil are known, it is possible to determine the macroscopic cross section Σ_a for the process leading to the species whose activity was measured. The neutron flux may be determined directly by means of a suitable counter (§ 3.84). Alternatively, the procedure just described, using a foil with a known absorption cross section, may be employed for the measurement of neutron flux. Once the latter, from a given source, is known, it may be utilized for the determination of absorption cross sections of other materials.

3.64. It should be noted that the cross section obtained by use of the activation method not only refers to a particular process, but also to a specific isotopic constituent of the target material. For example, if silver is exposed to the action of slow neutrons, an active species, with a half life of 2.3 min, is formed. This has been identified as Ag^{108} formed by the (n, γ) reaction of slow neutrons with the stable isotope Ag^{107}. Hence, if the activity having a half life of 2.3 min is studied, the results will give the cross section for the (n, γ) reaction of the silver-107 isotope. Measurements made by the transmission procedure, described in § 3.57, *et seq.*, give an average value for both stable isotopes, of mass numbers 107 and 109.

RESULTS OF CROSS SECTION MEASUREMENTS

VARIATION OF CROSS SECTION WITH NEUTRON ENERGY

3.65. The problem of a complete determination of cross sections for neutron reactions is a very complex one; not only do the values vary from one isotope to another of the same element, and change with the nature of the reaction, but they are also markedly dependent on the velocity, or energy, of the incident neutrons. Although the energy dependence of neutron absorption cross sections has been determined in many cases, the data have been obtained with the naturally occurring form of the target material, often consisting of two or more isotopes. In certain instances, where one isotope has a much larger absorption cross section than another, the former has been identified and its contribution estimated. The fact that the absorption cross sections are generally the total for all possible processes is not serious, because for nearly all elements, other than those of low atomic weight, the (n, γ) reaction takes place almost exclusively for neutrons of energy less than several Mev. A few exceptional cases (§ 3.32 to § 3.34) are known, and then appropriate allowance can be made.

3.66. In order to study the effect of neutron energy on the cross section, it is necessary to have monoenergetic neutron sources. Some of these were described earlier, but they mostly refer to neutrons with energies of several thousand electron volts, at least. In the low-energy range, neutrons of specific energies can be obtained from polyenergetic beams by the use of devices called *velocity selectors*. With their aid, neutrons of any desired velocity, in the range from a fraction of an ev to about 1000 ev, can be studied.

3.67. With the exception of hydrogen in the unbound state, for which the value is as high as 20×10^{-24} cm^2, i.e., 20 barns,* the scattering cross sections of nearly all elements lie in the range from about 1 to 10 barns for neutrons of low energy. With increasing energy, the cross sections decrease somewhat, and for high-energy (40 to 100 Mev) neutrons they approach the geometrical cross section, πR^2, where R is the radius of the nucleus. The value of R is given, with a fair degree of accuracy, especially for the elements of higher atomic number, by the expression $1.5 A^{\frac{1}{3}} \times 10^{-13}$ cm, where A is the mass number (§ 1.34). Hence, for an element of mass number 125, for example, the limiting value of the scattering cross section is about 2 barns.

3.68. For many nuclides, especially those of mass number exceeding 100, an examination of the variation of the absorption (or total) cross sections with the energy of the neutrons reveals the existence of three regions, in agreement with the general conclusions reached from the Breit-Wigner formula (§ 2.39, *et seq.*). There is, first, a low-energy region where the cross section decreases steadily with increasing neutron energy. The absorption cross section σ_a in this slow-

---

* In the bound state, as in solid paraffin, the scattering cross section increases to 80 barns for neutrons of very low energy (§ 3.80).

neutron region is inversely proportional to the square root of the neutron energy, as indicated by (2.43.1). Since the energy is kinetic in nature, σ_a is inversely proportional to the neutron velocity; this is the $1/v$ region referred to in § 2.43.

THE RESONANCE REGION

3.69. Following the $1/v$ region for slow neutrons, the elements under consideration exhibit a *resonance region* (§ 2.44). This is characterized by the occurrence of peaks where the absorption cross section rises fairly sharply to high values for certain neutron energies, and then falls again. Some elements, cadmium and rhodium, for example, have only one resonance peak in the electron volt region, whereas others, such as indium, silver, iridium, and gold, have two or more peaks. The cross sections of cadmium and indium, as functions of the neutron energy, are shown in Fig. 3.69. The scales are logarithmic in both direc-

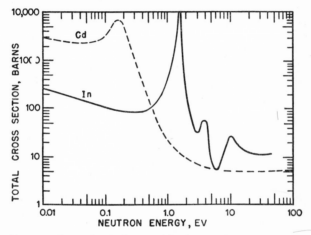

FIG. 3.69.   Cross sections of cadmium and indium as functions of neutron energy

tions, and so the $1/v$ region, at the left side of the figure, appears as a straight line. The resonance peak for cadmium occurs at 0.18 ev and the absorption cross section is then about 7200 barns. The main peak for indium is for neutrons of 1.44 ev energy, with a cross section exceeding 20,000 barns. There are also two lower resonance peaks at somewhat higher energies, about 4 and 10 ev.

3.70. Since the resonance peaks are found in regions of relatively low neutron energies and with elements of higher mass number, the reactions taking place must be of the (n, γ) type. As pointed out earlier, for other processes, such elements would require neutrons having energies in the Mev range. The behavior of certain nuclides of low mass number undergoing (n, α) reactions with slow neutrons will be referred to below (§ 3.76).

3.71. The resonance peaks for (n, γ) reactions at low energies are usually sharp and narrow. This is in agreement with the Breit-Wigner treatment of resonance absorption.   The partial level width Γ_γ for gamma-ray emission is apparently small, of the order of 0.1 ev, and since other reactions of the compound nucleus are not very probable for slow neutrons, the total level width Γ will also be small.   It was shown in § 2.45 that the so-called half-width of the resonance peak should be equal to the total level width.   The resonance peaks should thus be relatively narrow, as they are in Fig. 3.69.

3.72. Another point of interest is the high values of the resonance absorption cross sections.   These are frequently of the order of 10,000 barns, i.e., 10^{-20} cm², compared with an actual ("geometrical") nuclear cross section of about 2 barns, i.e., 2×10^{-24} cm².   Since the cross section may be thought of as the effective area of the nucleus as far as a given reaction is concerned (§ 3.40), it is apparent that the effective area can be much larger than the actual area.

3.73. An interpretation of this result can be found in the wave theory of matter.   Thus, according to (2.9.1), a neutron with energy of 1 ev has a wave length of 2.9×10^{-9} cm.   The neutron can consequently be regarded as a wave which can engulf many nuclei if the required energy conditions, namely, those for resonance, are fulfilled.   The effective area of the nucleus for absorption of a neutron may then well approach a value of $(10^{-9})^2$, i.e., 10^{-18} cm².

3.74. The same general conclusion may be reached from the Breit-Wigner equation (2.39.1) by setting E equal to E_r; the corresponding value of the cross section, i.e., the maximum of the resonance peak, is then

$$\sigma_{\max} \approx \frac{\lambda^2}{\pi} \cdot \frac{\Gamma_a \Gamma_b}{\Gamma^2}. \tag{3.74.1}$$

If $\Gamma_a \Gamma_b / \Gamma^2$ is taken to be about 0.1, then since the wave length λ is 2.9×10^{-9} cm for a neutron of 1 ev energy, the value of $\sigma_{\max}$ might be roughly 10^{-19} cm², i.e., about 10^5 barns.*

Fast-Neutron Region

3.75. Beyond the resonance region the nuclear cross sections decrease steadily with increasing neutron energy.   This represents what may be called the *fast-neutron region*.   The cross sections are usually low, being less than 10 barns in most cases and becoming even smaller at energies in the Mev range.   For a neutron of 1-Mev energy the equivalent wave length is 2.9×10^{-12} cm, by (2.9.1), and hence the absorption cross sections are likely to be of the same order as the scattering cross sections.

Large Level Widths

3.76. A type of variation of cross section with neutron energy, different from that described above, has been observed with a few nuclei of low mass number for

---

* Because of accepted conventional usage, the symbol λ is employed in this chapter to represent mean free path, radioactive constant, and neutron wave length.   However, the proper significance should be clear from the context, in each case.

reactions in which a charged particle is expelled.   Examples of this behavior are to be found in the (n, α) reactions with B^{10} and Li^6, referred to earlier.   The dependence on neutron energy of the cross section for the (n, α) reaction with boron, mainly due to the boron-10 isotope, is shown in Fig. 3.76.   The logarithmic plot

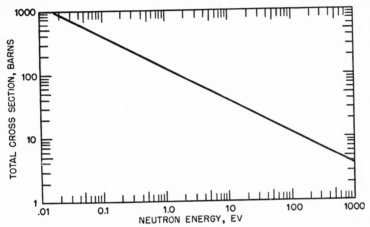

FIG. 3.76.   Cross section of boron as function of neutron energy

of σ against E is essentially linear from about 0.01 ev to 0.1 Mev, although the data in the figure go only to 1000 ev.   This means that the $1/v$ law holds at energies well beyond those found for (n, γ) reactions, in fact beyond the usual resonance region.

3.77.   The interpretation of this result may also be found in the Breit-Wigner formula.   When the excited compound nucleus has sufficient excess energy to make emission of a charged particle possible, the probability that the process will occur is large.   In other words, the partial level width Γ_α is large and, consequently, so also will be Γ, the total width.   In these circumstances, the quantity $(E - E_r)^2$ in the Breit-Wigner equation may be neglected in comparison with $\frac{1}{4}\Gamma^2$ over a considerable energy range.   The cross section will then vary inversely as the square root of the neutron energy, or inversely as its velocity, as shown in § 2.46.   The extension of the $1/v$ region over such a large range of energies in the (n, α) reaction with boron (and lithium) may thus be explained by the large level width.

ELEMENTS OF LOW MASS NUMBER

3.78.   It is important to point out that not all elements exhibit the types of behavior described above.   Most nuclides of low mass number, as well as several of high mass number, do not exhibit resonance absorption, at least not to any appreciable extent.   The total neutron cross sections, including both absorption and scattering, are small, of the order of a few barns, over the whole energy range, from thermal values to several Mev.*   Were it not for this fact the construction of nuclear reactors would be a virtual impossibility.

THERMAL NEUTRON CROSS SECTIONS

3.79. Because of their special interest in connection with the design and operation of thermal nuclear reactors, the scattering and absorption cross sections of a number of substances for thermal neutrons are given in Table 3.79.†

TABLE 3.79.   THERMAL NEUTRON CROSS SECTIONS

Element or Compound	Total σ (barns)	Absorption σ_a (barns)	Scattering σ_s (barns)
H	20–80	0.32	20–80
D_2O	15.3	0.00092	15.3
He	1.56	0.008	1.55
Be	6.9	0.009	6.9
B	722	718	3.8
C	4.8	0.0045	4.8
N	12.7	1.5	11.2
O	4.2	<0.0009	4.2
F	4.0	≤0.01	4.0
Na	4.5	0.46	4.0
Al	1.6	0.22	1.35
S	1.6	0.47	1.1
Ca	4.4	0.4	4.0
Fe	13.5	2.5	11.0
Ni	22	4.5	17.5
Zr	8.4	0.4	8.0
Cd	3500	3500	6.5
In	193	191	2.2
Pb	8.5	0.2	8.3
Bi	9	<0.01	9

3.80. It will be noted that the scattering cross section for hydrogen is quoted as 20 to 80 barns; the value depends upon whether the atom is in the free state or is bound in a molecule, and also upon the precise thermal neutron energy.   In the bound state, as in paraffin, for example, the scattering cross section of hydrogen changes rapidly with the neutron energy at low energies, as is indicated by the experimental curve in Fig. 3.80.   At neutron energies of the order of 10 ev, the scattering cross section is about 20 barns, which is probably close to the thermal value for free atoms, but the observed cross section increases to about 80 barns for very slow neutrons.

---

* The most notable exceptions are, of course, Li[6] and B[10].

† The results are taken mainly from "Nuclear Data," NBS Circular 499, National Bureau of Standards, U. S. Department of Commerce, 1950; see also, R. K. Adair, *Rev. Mod. Phys.*, **22,** 249 (1950); H. Pomerance. *Phys. Rev..* **83,** 641 (1951).

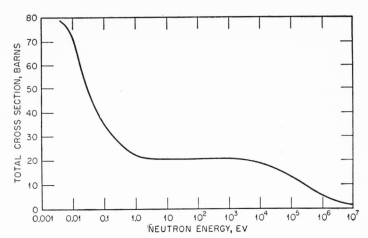

FIG. 3.80.   Cross section of hydrogen in paraffin as function of neutron energy

3.81. At low neutron energies, when E is small in comparison with the resonance energy E_r, the Breit-Wigner equation (2.54.1) for resonance scattering reduces to

$$\sigma \approx \frac{\lambda^2}{4\pi} \cdot \frac{\Gamma_n{}^2}{E_r{}^2},\qquad(3.81.1)$$

provided the total level width Γ is also small in comparison with E_r.   The neutron wave length λ is here proportional to $1/\mu v$ (cf. § 2.39, footnote), where μ is the reduced mass of the scattering system and v is the velocity of the neutron. It can be shown * that Γ_n is proportional to $\mu^2 v$, and so it follows from (3.81.1) that for any atomic species, the scattering cross section for low neutron energies should be proportional to μ^2.

3.82. If the energy of the incident neutron is larger than the binding energy of the hydrogen atom in a molecule, i.e., about 3 or 4 ev, the proton will behave essentially as if it were free in the collision.   The reduced mass of the scattering system, defined by

$$\frac{1}{\mu} = \frac{1}{\text{H}} + \frac{1}{n},\qquad(3.82.1)$$

where H represents the effective mass of the proton and n is the mass of the neutron, is then equal to $\frac{1}{2}$ in atomic mass units.   On the other hand, if the neutron energy is small compared with the binding energy of the hydrogen atom in a relatively large molecule, such as paraffin, the effective mass of the hydrogen is large and the reduced mass, as given by (3.82.1), is then approximately unity. Since the scattering cross section for neutrons of low energy is proportional to μ^2, it follows that for bound hydrogen the cross section should increase fourfold

---

* Cf. H. A. Bethe, *Rev. Mod. Phys.*, 9, 69 (1937); see also J. G. Beckerley, "Neutron Physics," AECD–2664, pages 14, 36.

as the neutron energy decreases, as has been found experimentally (Fig. 3.80). According to this argument, the lower value of 20 barns, i.e., for neutrons of about 10 ev, represents the scattering cross section for free hydrogen atoms.

DETECTION AND COUNTING OF NEUTRONS

SECONDARY IONIZATION COUNTERS

3.83. Neutrons produce very little direct ionization in their passage through a gas, and so they cannot be detected directly in such instruments as a Geiger counter or a cloud chamber. The operation of these and similar devices depends on the presence of ions produced by the entry of a particle; hence they will not respond to neutrons directly. Nevertheless, instruments of this kind can be adapted to detect and count neutrons by utilizing certain secondary effects of these neutral particles.

3.84. The most common method for counting slow neutrons makes use of the (n, α) reaction with B^{10}, for which the cross section is large. As seen in § 3.32, a Li^7 nucleus and an alpha particle are formed; both have relatively high energies and they produce considerable ionization in their paths. In order to take advantage of this process, a counter containing boron or a compound of boron is employed. A proportional counter, for example, may contain boron trifluoride as part of the filling gas, or the walls may be lined with a thin coating of elemental boron or of a solid compound, such as boron carbide. Since it is really the B^{10} isotope which is effective in the (n, α) reaction, better results are obtained if the boron compound used contains a larger than normal proportion of this isotope.

3.85. In a counter tube of proper design each neutron entering will produce sufficient secondary ionization to permit it to be counted without difficulty. If the area of the surface covered with boron is known, the slow neutron flux can be determined.

3.86. Another type of neutron detector and counter makes use of the fission reaction (§ 3.35). Slow neutrons cause fission of the uranium-235 nucleus, and the nuclear fragments which result have considerable ionizing effect. A simple device for observing slow neutrons thus consists of an ionization chamber of which one electrode is coated with uranium oxide, preferably somewhat enriched in the uranium-235 isotope. Again, each neutron entering the chamber and striking the coated electrode can be counted.

3.87. When fast neutrons are being studied, it is the general practice to make use of the ionization in the track of a light nucleus, e.g., a proton, recoiling after being struck by a high-energy neutron. For this purpose a proportional counter may be filled with hydrogen. Preferably, argon or one of the heavier inert gases is used as the filling gas and a thin sheet of a hydrogenous material, such as paraffin, is placed at one end of the chamber. Fast neutrons striking the paraffin cause protons to be ejected with relatively high energy; the latter produce ionization in their paths through the counter and so can be detected. Instruments of this type have been developed for determining the energy of the fast neutrons as well as counting them.

ACTIVATION DETECTORS

3.88. As indicated in § 3.63, the activation method can be applied to the determination of neutron flux. This procedure is often very convenient because thin foils, which cause little disturbance of the neutron density, can be placed in regions not accessible to counters. Further, the use of cadmium in combination with indium provides a means of distinguishing between neutrons of different energies. An examination of Fig. 3.69 shows that indium, with a resonance peak at 1.44 ev neutron energy, has a high absorption cross section, 100 barns or more, for neutrons of energy less than about 2 ev. On the other hand, cadmium has a resonance peak at 0.18 ev, and the cross sections are high for energies less than about 0.5 ev. When indium is exposed to neutrons it becomes radioactive, but cadmium does not.

3.89. The foregoing facts are utilized in the following manner. First, an indium foil is exposed to neutrons for a known time and the activity measured in the usual manner; this is then used to calculate the saturation activity (§ 3.63), and from the known average absorption cross section, the flux of neutrons with energy less than about 2 ev can be evaluated. The indium foil is then completely surrounded by cadmium foil and once more exposed to the neutrons. Because of the strong absorption by cadmium of neutrons with energies below about 0.5 ev, essentially the only neutrons reaching the indium will be those with energies in excess of this amount. Consequently, the indium foil will now be sensitive to neutrons in the range of 0.5 to 2 ev, approximately, and their flux can be determined from the saturation activity of the foil. The difference between the results obtained without a cadmium shield and with cadmium gives the flux of neutrons of energy less than about 0.5 ev.

Chapter IV

THE FISSION PROCESS*

CHARACTERISTICS OF THE FISSION REACTION

INTRODUCTION

4.1. Although many nuclear reactions were known prior to 1939, they were all of the type in which a relatively light particle or a gamma-ray photon was expelled, so that the atomic and mass numbers of the product nucleus were not very different from those of the target. In that year, however, there was discovered the process of fission, mentioned in § 2.22 and § 3.35, whereby a uranium nucleus, after capture of a neutron, splits into two parts which differ considerably from the target element. From the standpoint of the utilization of atomic energy, the importance of the fission reaction lies in two facts. First, the process is associated with the liberation of relatively large amounts of energy and, second, the reaction initiated by neutrons is also accompanied by the liberation of neutrons. Consequently, it is possible under suitable conditions, which will be discussed in this book, for the process to be self-sustaining, and for energy to be generated continuously.

4.2. The theoretical interpretation of fission and its application in nuclear reactors will be considered later; but first the essential phenomena will be described. Uranium-235, which is present to the extent of 0.712 per cent in natural uranium, undergoes fission with thermal neutrons, as well as with those of higher energy. The same is true for the artificially produced isotopes plutonium-239 and uranium-233 (§ 3.35). On the other hand, uranium-238 and thorium-232, which are the most abundant isotopes of these elements as found in nature, require fast neutrons, of at least 1 Mev energy, to induce fission to an appreciable extent. It is of interest to note that natural uranium apparently undergoes

---

* A detailed history of the discovery of fission and the development of the first chain reactor by E. Fermi and his collaborators is given by H. D. Smyth, "Atomic Energy for Military Purposes," U. S. Government Printing Office, 1945; see also L. A. Turner, *Rev. Mod. Phys.*, **12**, 1 (1940); S. Glasstone, "Sourcebook on Atomic Energy," D. Van Nostrand Co., Inc., 1950, Chapters XIII and XIV.

fission spontaneously, at a definite rate.   Thus, in a gram of ordinary uranium, about 23 nuclei suffer spontaneous fission per hour, on the average.*

4.3. In addition to uranium and thorium, other common elements of high, and even of moderate, atomic number exhibit fission, but only by the use of incident particles of very high energy.   Fission processes of this kind, although of considerable general interest, do not appear to have any application in the field of nuclear energy, since these high-energy particles are not produced by the reaction, and hence the process cannot be self-sustaining.

Emission of Neutrons

4.4. When a nucleus of high atomic number undergoes fission, splitting into two more or less equal parts, called *fission fragments*, the neutron-to-proton ratios of these fragments fall near the dotted line in Fig. 1.15.   This is a straight line joining the origin to the points representing nuclides of high atomic number, such as those which are capable of undergoing fission.   Because the fission fragment nuclei are roughly similar in size, it follows that their neutron-to-proton ratios must lie somewhere near the middle of the dotted line.   Nuclei of this kind obviously contain too many neutrons for them to be stable; they can approach stability, however, either by ejecting one or more neutrons, or by conversion of a neutron into a proton with the simultaneous emission of a negative beta particle.

4.5. On account of the foregoing considerations, the possibility that neutrons might be expelled in the fission of uranium was soon realized and verified experimentally.   It has been found that, in the fission of uranium-235 by slow neutrons, an average of 2.5 ± 0.1 neutrons are emitted for each nucleus suffering fission, i.e., for each neutron absorbed in a fission reaction.   The number is not an integer because, as will be seen below, the uranium nucleus splits in many different ways, and although the number of neutrons expelled in any individual act of fission must obviously be zero or integral, the average may well not be an exact whole number.

4.6. The neutrons emitted as a result of the fission process can be divided into two categories, namely, *prompt neutrons* and *delayed neutrons*.   The prompt neutrons, which are over 99 per cent of the total fission neutrons, are released within an extremely short interval of time, about 10^{-14} sec, of the fission process. The evidence indicates that they are not released directly from the compound nucleus which results when a uranium-235 nucleus, for example, captures a slow neutron.   It appears that the compound nucleus first breaks up into two nuclear fragments, each of which has too many neutrons for stability, as well as the excess (excitation) energy, at least 6 Mev or so, required for the expulsion of a neutron. The excited, unstable nucleus consequently expels one or more neutrons within a

---

* The apparent spontaneous fission of uranium may be due, at least in part, to interaction with neutrons from cosmic radiation and from other sources.

very short time after its formation.   The instantaneous gamma rays accompanying fission are apparently emitted at the same time.

4.7. The energies of the prompt neutrons cover a considerable range, probably from over 10 Mev down to thermal values; the majority, however, have energies of about 1 or 2 Mev.   The energy distribution, represented schematically in Fig. 4.7, is referred to as the fission neutron spectrum or, in brief, as the *fission*

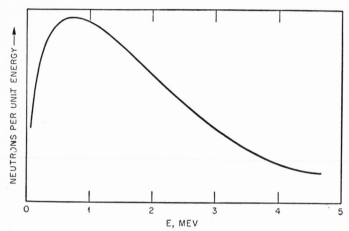

FIG. 4.7.   Fission neutron energy spectrum

spectrum.   Within the energy range from 0.1 to 10 Mev, which includes practically all fission neutrons, the fission spectrum is given, to a fair degree of accuracy, by

$$s(E) = 0.484e^{-E} \sinh \sqrt{2E},$$

where $s(E)$ is the number of fission neutrons per unit energy normalized to one fission neutron; E is the neutron energy in Mev.   In the center-of-mass system of the fission fragment and the prompt neutron, the fission spectrum would probably be approximated by a Maxwell-Boltzmann distribution (§ 3.14), but in the laboratory system this is disturbed by the motion of the fission fragments, and by the fact that the neutron emission probability is a function of its energy.

4.8. Whereas the expulsion of the prompt neutrons ceases within a very short time, the delayed neutrons are emitted, with gradually decreasing intensity, over a period of minutes.   The delayed neutrons accompanying fission fall into five, and possibly more, groups.   The rate of decay of the neutron intensity in each group is exponential in nature, as it is for radioactive change in general.   By observing the decay of the delayed neutrons after fission has ceased, it has been found possible to associate a specific half life with each group.   The characteristic properties of the five definitely established groups of delayed neutrons are given in Table 4.8;* these include the half life T_i, the mean life t_i, i.e., $T_i/0.693$,

* D. J. Hughes, J. Dabbs, A. Cahn, and D. Hall, *Phys. Rev.*, **73,** 111 (1948).

the decay constant λ_i, i.e., $1/t_i$, the fraction β_i which the group constitutes of the total (prompt and delayed) fission neutrons, and the neutron energy, in each case. The last two columns apply only to the slow-neutron fission of uranium-235; the total fraction of delayed neutrons is seen to be roughly 0.0075. The same five groups of delayed neutrons are also formed when plutonium-239 suffers fission, but the proportions and energies are different from those recorded here.

TABLE 4.8.   PROPERTIES OF DELAYED NEUTRONS IN SLOW-NEUTRON FISSION OF
URANIUM-235

Half Life T_i (sec)	Mean Life t_i (sec)	Decay Constant λ_i (sec^{-1})	Fraction β_i	Energy (Mev)
0.43	0.62	1.61	0.00084	0.42
1.52	2.19	0.456	0.0024	0.62
4.51	6.50	0.151	0.0021	0.43
22.0	31.7	0.0315	0.0017	0.56
55.6	80.2	0.0124	0.00026	0.25

4.9. The properties of the delayed neutrons have an important bearing on the time-dependent behavior of nuclear reactors, and hence an explanation of their origin is of interest. By making rapid chemical separations of the fission fragments and their radioactive decay products, it has been found that neutrons decaying with the 55.6-sec half life follow the chemistry of bromine, whereas those of 22.5-sec half life follow that of iodine. It does not appear probable that the neutrons are expelled directly from the nuclei of isotopes of bromine or iodine, for if sufficient energy, about 6 to 8 Mev, were available to permit the removal of a neutron, the process would be virtually instantaneous, with a half life of the order of 10^{-14} sec. The conclusion to be drawn, therefore, is that the emission of delayed neutrons occurs in an indirect manner from the bromine or iodine isotopes, as follows.

4.10. One of the products of fission is a bromine isotope of high mass number, probably Br^{87}; the nucleus contains too many neutrons for stability and is consequently a negative beta emitter. The half life of the Br^{87} is 55.6 sec, which is the same as the half life of one of the groups of delayed neutrons, and its decay product is Kr^{87}. The latter can evidently be formed in a highly excited state, with sufficient energy to permit it immediately to eject a neutron and leave a stable Kr^{86} nucleus (Fig. 4.10). Any excess energy available, after removal of the neutron, appears as kinetic energy of the latter (see last column of Table 4.8). The observed rate of emission of neutrons is thus determined by the rate of formation of the neutron emitter Kr^{87}, and this is dependent on the decay of the precursor Br^{87}. Like all radioactive species, the latter decays in an exponential manner, the half life in this case being 55.6 sec, and hence the neutron emission falls off at the same rate.

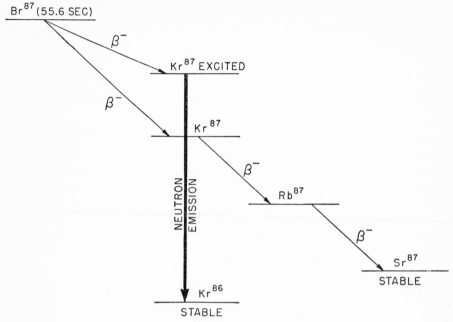

FIG. 4.10.   Interpretation of delayed neutron emission

4.11. The precursor of the group of delayed neutrons with a half life of 22.5 sec is apparently I^{137}.   It is known to have a half life of this magnitude and when it decays, by the emission of a negative beta particle, the product is Xe^{137}.   The latter can presumably be in a state of high internal energy, so that it instantaneously expels a neutron to form stable Xe^{136}.   Here again the emission of the neutron is delayed because the rate of formation of the Xe^{137} from which it originates depends on the rate of decay of the precursor I^{137}.   The other three groups of delayed neutrons are undoubtedly produced in an analogous manner, although the precursors in these cases have not yet been definitely identified.

THE FISSION PRODUCTS

4.12. The discovery of fission was made as a result of the detection of elements of moderate atomic weight, such as barium and lanthanum, when slow neutrons interact with uranium.   Since lanthanum has an atomic number of 57, whereas that of uranium is 92, the other fission fragments* must presumably be bromine,

---

* The term *fission fragments* or primary fission products is used here to refer to the nuclei formed directly in fission or after emission of the prompt neutrons.   The expression fission products, without qualification, is intended to include the fission fragments and the products of their radioactive decay.

atomic number 35.   The fission process in this case might then be represented by
the equation $_{92}U^{235} + {}_0n^1 \rightarrow {}_{57}La^{147} + {}_{35}Br^{87} + 2_0n^1,$

using plausible mass numbers and assuming two neutrons to be emitted per fission.   It will be noted that the two fragments, although considerably lighter than
the uranium nucleus, have mass numbers which are appreciably different from
each other.   That the uranium nucleus tends to break up in an unsymmetrical
manner was first indicated by the fact that the fission fragments were observed
to fall into two groups with different ionizing powers and presumably different
energies.   The ratio of the kinetic energies was found to be about 1.45, and consequently, if momentum is conserved, the masses of the respective fragments
must be inversely related to this ratio.

   4.13. A more detailed investigation of slow-neutron fission has shown that
uranium-235 splits up in more than 30 different ways, for more than 60 primary
products have been identified.   The range of mass numbers is from 72, probably
an isotope of zinc (atomic number 30), to 158, possibly an isotope of samarium
(atomic number 62).   In Fig. 4.13, the mass numbers of the products are plotted

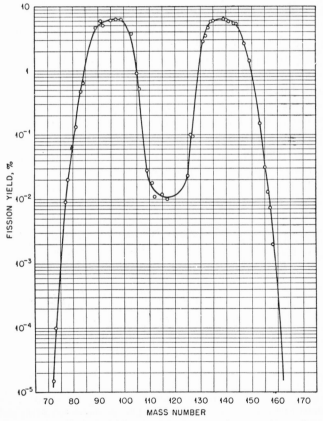

FIG. 4.13.   Fission yields of products of various mass numbers

against the corresponding *fission yields*, the fission yield being defined as the proportion (or percentage) of the total nuclear fissions yielding products of a given mass number.* Since the observed fission yields range from 10^{-5} to over 6 per cent, they are plotted on a logarithmic scale. It should be noted that as two nuclei result from each act of fission, the total fission yield for all mass numbers adds up to 200 per cent. Incidentally, the reason why mass numbers, rather than atomic numbers, are considered is because the fission fragments are probably all radioactive, decaying by the loss of a negative beta particle. The atomic numbers, consequently, change with time, but the mass numbers are unaffected by the beta decay.

4.14. An examination of Fig. 4.13 shows that, in accordance with the conclusions drawn from the energies of the fission fragments, the masses of nearly all the products fall into two broad groups, a "light" group, with mass numbers from 80 to 110, and a "heavy" group, with mass numbers from 125 to 155. There are some products in the intermediate range, from 110 to 125, but altogether these represent no more than a per cent or so of the fissions. The most probable type of fission, comprising nearly 6.4 per cent of the total, gives products with mass numbers 95 and 139. It is apparent from these results that the thermal-neutron fission of uranium-235 is far from symmetrical. If the compound nucleus had split into two equal fragments, the mass of each would be 117 or 118; only 0.01 per cent of the nuclei undergoing fission break up in this manner.

4.15. One of the most significant properties of the fission products is their radioactivity. As seen in § 4.4, the fragments formed, when a uranium nucleus splits up into two nuclei of somewhat similar mass, have neutron-to-proton ratios that are too high for stability. Even if a prompt neutron is expelled, the ratio of neutrons to protons will, in most cases, still be outside the stability range for the particular mass number. Consequently, all or nearly all the fission fragments are radioactive, emitting negative beta particles. The immediate decay products are also frequently radioactive, and, although some decay chains are longer and some shorter, each fragment is followed, on the average, by three stages of decay before a stable species is formed. An important decay chain, because of its high yield (6.3 per cent) and also because it contains the barium and lanthanum which led to the recognition of the fission of uranium, is the following:

$$_{54}\mathrm{Xe}^{140} \xrightarrow{16\,\mathrm{s}} {}_{55}\mathrm{Cs}^{140} \xrightarrow{66\,\mathrm{s}} {}_{56}\mathrm{Ba}^{140} \xrightarrow{12.8\,\mathrm{d}} {}_{57}\mathrm{La}^{140} \xrightarrow{40\,\mathrm{h}} {}_{58}\mathrm{Ce}^{140} \text{ (stable).}$$

4.16. Since there are probably some 60 different radioactive nuclides produced in fission and each is, on the average, the precursor of two others, there are about 180 radioactive species present among the fission products after a short time. Although it is possible theoretically to express the rate of decay of this complex

---

* Similar curves, but with the maxima and minima displaced somewhat from Fig. 4.13, have been obtained for the slow-neutron fission of plutonium-239 and uranium-233.

mixture in terms of the fission yields and the radioactive decay constants, it is quite impractical. The rate of decay of the fission products is, therefore, represented by an empirical equation, which is probably accurate within a factor of two or less.* From about 10 sec after fission has taken place, the rates of the emission of beta particles and of gamma-ray photons per fission are as follows:

$$\text{Rate of emission of gamma-ray photons} \approx 1.9 \times 10^{-6}t^{-1.2} \text{ per sec} \qquad (4.16.1)$$

and

$$\text{Rate of emission of beta particles} \approx 3.8 \times 10^{-6}t^{-1.2} \text{ per sec}, \qquad (4.16.2)$$

where t is the time after fission in days. Taking the mean energy of the gamma rays as 0.7 Mev, and that of the beta particles as 0.4 Mev, the total rate of energy emission for both beta and gamma radiation is about $2.7 \times 10^{-6}t^{-1.2}$ Mev per sec per fission, with each type of radiation contributing an approximately equal amount. For practical purposes it is useful to express the result in terms of watts per gram of uranium-235 undergoing fission; this is found to be

$$\text{Rate of dissipation of beta and gamma energy} = 1.1 \times 10^{3}t^{-1.2} \text{ watts per gram,} \qquad (4.16.3)$$

at t days after fission. It will be seen below that about 5 per cent of the energy released in the fission of uranium-235 is initially present as latent beta and gamma energy of the fission products. The rate at which this is released is consequently of some significance during the steady-state operation of a nuclear reactor, and also after shut-down.

Energy of Fission

4.17. The fission process is remarkable for the magnitude of the energy released; this is about 200 Mev for each nucleus reacting, compared with a maximum of 20 Mev or so for other nuclear reactions.† The magnitude of the fission energy can be calculated in several ways, perhaps the most direct being to use the masses of the reacting species and of the fragments formed. The isotopic weight of uranium-235 is 235.124 amu and the mass of a neutron, on the same scale, is 1.00897, making a sum of 236.133 amu for the total mass of the interacting particles. As stated in § 4.14, the fission products obtained in greatest yield have mass numbers of 95 and 139, which add up to 234; it may be assumed, therefore, that in this case two neutrons are liberated in the fission process. An examination of the masses of stable nuclides shows that the isotopic weights corresponding to the mass numbers 95 and 139 are 94.945 and 138.955, respectively.

* Cf. K. Way and E. P. Wigner, *Phys. Rev.*, **73**, 1318 (1948).
† In chemical reactions, the energy released is never greater than a few electron volts for each atom or molecule reacting.

These, together with 2×1.00897 for the masses of the two fission neutrons, add up to a total mass, after fission, of 235.918. The difference between this and the mass of the interacting particles is converted into energy of the fission process; thus,

$$\text{Mass converted into energy} = 236.133 - 235.918$$
$$= 0.215 \text{ amu.}$$

From (1.28.2) it is seen that 1 amu is equivalent to 931 Mev; consequently,

$$\text{Energy released per fission} = 931 \times 0.215$$
$$= 198 \text{ Mev.}$$

4.18. The energy calculation made above was for a particular mode of fission, and the actual energy will be the weighted mean for the 30 or more different ways in which the uranium-235 nucleus splits. However, as seen earlier, the great majority of the fissions yield products with mass numbers in a fairly limited region, and for all these the mass converted into energy, and hence the energy released, is approximately the same. It may be accepted, therefore, that 195 to 200 Mev of energy are released for every uranium-235 nucleus suffering fission.

4.19. The reason for the large magnitude of the fission energy will be apparent from an examination of Fig. 1.30, which shows that the binding energy curve has a broad maximum. In the mass number range from about 80 to 150, which is that of the majority of the fission products, the binding energy per nucleon has an average value of 8.4 Mev. For higher mass numbers the value decreases and has fallen to 7.5 Mev per nucleon for uranium. This means that in the products formed by fission the binding energy is about 0.9 Mev per nucleon greater than in the original uranium nucleus. Since the latter contains some 230 nucleons, the total difference in binding energy is about 200 Mev and this is the energy released in the fission process.

4.20. The large energy of fission is thus to be ascribed to the fact that in the fission products the nucleons are more firmly bound than they are in the nucleus which suffers fission. That is to say, more energy would be released in assembling the fission product nuclei from their constituent protons and neutrons than would be the case for the uranium nucleus. Consequently, when the latter breaks up into two parts, with mass numbers in the range from 80 to 150, there will be a liberation of energy. It can be seen from (1.29.1) that a smaller isotopic mass M would mean a higher binding energy. This is reflected in the total mass of the uranium nucleus and a neutron being greater than the total mass of the fission products, as noted in § 4.17. The differences in mass and in the binding energy are thus equivalent; they are, in fact, both consequences of the same fundamental factor, namely, the forces acting between the nucleons in the different nuclei.

4.21. Consideration of the various energy terms in Table 1.44 shows that the decreased binding energy per nucleon for elements of high atomic number, which is related to the large value of the fission energy, is due mainly to the marked increase in the electrostatic repulsion of the protons. This, ultimately, is also the reason why fission has been observed to take place most readily with the elements of highest atomic number, as will be apparent from the discussion given below.

4.22. The energy data will shortly be expressed in terms of more practical quantities. In the meantime something must be said about the experimental determinations of the fission energy. From the extent of the ionization produced by the fission fragments it has been estimated that this energy is 162 Mev. On the other hand, direct calorimetric measurement of the energy liberated as heat gave a value of 175 Mev. The explanation of the apparent disagreement between these figures and the difference from the calculated 195 Mev of energy is that the ionization measurement gives only the kinetic energy of the fission fragments. But the heat liberated includes also some other forms of energy which are associated with the fission process.*

4.23. According to the latest estimates, the total amount of energy released by the fission products when they have decayed completely is about 21 Mev. Of this, about 5 Mev is beta energy, 5 Mev is gamma energy, and the remainder is carried off by the neutrinos which accompany the beta emission (§ 1.16). In addition, some 6 Mev of the fission energy are associated with the neutrons which are released, and 6 Mev appear in the form of the so-called instantaneous gamma radiation produced within an extremely short period (§ 4.6). A complete energy balance, indicating the approximate distribution of the energy per fission, is given in Table 4.23. The kinetic energy of the fission products appears imme-

TABLE 4.23. DISTRIBUTION OF FISSION ENERGY

Kinetic energy of fission fragments	162 Mev
Beta decay energy	5
Gamma decay energy	5
Neutrino energy	11
Energy of fission neutrons	6
Instantaneous gamma-ray energy	6
Total fission energy	195 Mev

diately as heat, and the neutron energy and instantaneous gamma-ray energy are degraded in a very short time. The beta and gamma energies of the fission products, however, are released gradually as these radioactive nuclides decay. Consequently, in the early stages of the operation of a nuclear reactor only about 174 Mev of energy are produced per fission, but this will increase gradually, and,

---

* For review of energy distribution of fission fragments, see J. L. Fowler and L. Rosen, *Phys. Rev.*, **72**, 926 (1947); D. C. Brunton and G. C. Hanna, *Canad. J. Res.*, A, **28**, 190 (1950).

when the fission products decay as fast as they are being formed, it will attain a maximum of 184 Mev, i.e., 195 Mev minus the energy carried off by the neutrinos.

4.24. Making use of the conversion units, 1 Mev $= 1.60 \times 10^{-6}$ erg $= 1.60 \times 10^{-13}$ watt sec, it is seen that the fission of a single uranium-235 nucleus is accompanied by the liberation of about 3.2×10^{-11} watt sec. In other words, it requires 3.1×10^{10} fissions to release 1 watt sec of energy, so that fissions at the rate of 3.1×10^{10} per sec would yield 1 watt of power. Since 1 gram of uranium contains $6.02 \times 10^{23}/235 = 2.6 \times 10^{21}$ atoms, the energy produced by its complete fission would be 8.3×10^{10} watt sec, which is 2.3×10^{4} kilowatt hours or nearly 1 megawatt day. Thus, the fission of all the atoms in 1 gram of uranium-235 per day would yield 1 megawatt of power. Similar values apply to the fission of uranium-233 and plutonium-239.

MECHANISM OF NUCLEAR FISSION

4.25. Whenever the mass of a nucleus exceeds that of the fragments into which it can be divided, the former will tend to be unstable with respect to the latter, since the process of subdivision would be accompanied by a loss of mass and a consequent liberation of energy. This condition certainly applies to all elements of mass number exceeding about 100, and hence for such elements spontaneous fission is theoretically possible. The reason why it is not observed is that the nucleus must acquire a certain *critical energy* or *activation energy* before it can break up. For species with mass numbers below about 210, this energy is so high that fission can occur only by bombardment with neutrons or other particles having energies exceeding 50 Mev.

4.26. Some understanding of the problem of critical energy may be obtained by considering the liquid-drop model of the atomic nucleus, referred to in Chapter I. Consider a drop of liquid to which a force is applied so that it is set into oscillation; the system passes through a series of stages, some of which are depicted in Fig. 4.26. The drop is at first spherical as at A; it is then elongated

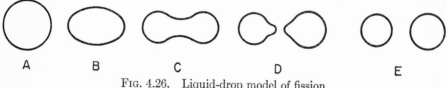

FIG. 4.26.   Liquid-drop model of fission

into an ellipsoid as at B. If insufficient energy is available to overcome the force of surface tension, the drop will return to its original form, but if the deforming force is sufficiently large, the liquid acquires a shape similar to a dumbbell, as at C. Once it has reached this stage it is unlikely to return to the spherical form, but it will rather split into two droplets. These will, at first, be somewhat deformed, as at D, but finally they will become spherical, as shown at E.

4.27. The situation in nuclear fission is believed to be analogous to that just considered. A target nucleus combines with a neutron to form a compound nucleus; the excitation energy of the latter is then equal to the binding energy of the neutron plus any kinetic energy the neutron may have had before capture (§ 2.16). As a result of this excess energy, it may be said that the compound nucleus undergoes a series of oscillations, in the course of which it passes through a phase similar to Fig. 4.26*B*. If the energy is insufficient to cause further deformation beyond *B,* the intranuclear forces will compel the nucleus to return to its original spherical form, and the excess energy will be removed by the expulsion of a particle from the excited compound nucleus.

4.28. However, if the nucleus has gained enough energy, as a result of absorbing the neutron, to permit it to form the dumbbell shape (Fig. 4.26*C*), the restoration of the initial state *A* becomes improbable. This is because the electrostatic repulsion between the positive charges on the two ends of *C* can now overcome the relatively small portion of the nuclear binding force operating in the constricted region. Consequently, from *C* the system passes rapidly to *D* and then to *E*, representing fission into two separate nuclei which are propelled in opposite directions. The critical energy or activation energy requisite for fission to occur is thus the energy that must be added to the original nucleus in order to deform it to the state *C*, after which fission inevitably occurs, provided, of course, the mass requirements mentioned in § 4.25 are satisfied.

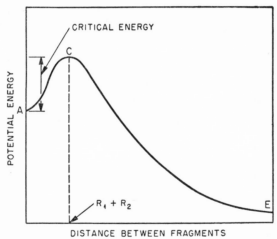

FIG. 4.29.   Potential energy as function of distance between fission fragments

4.29. The critical fission energy may be considered also with the aid of a potential energy curve, as in Fig. 4.29. At the extreme right, at *E*, two fission fragments are supposed to be far apart, so that the potential energy is virtually zero. As the fragments are brought closer together, there is an increase in potential energy due to the electrostatic repulsion of the positively charged nuclei. When the fragments reach the point C, where they are roughly in contact, the attractive forces become dominant and the potential energy decreases toward A. The latter point may be regarded as corresponding to the ground state of the compound nucleus, formed when the target nucleus captures a neutron (cf. § 2.15); that is to say, it represents the energy of the compound nucleus without the excitation energy resulting from the neutron capture. (The letters A, C, and E in Fig. 4.29 correspond to the states of the liquid drop in Fig. 4.26.) In order for fission to occur at a reasonably rapid rate the system must pass from A to E, and it can only do so, in general, if the compound nucleus gains sufficient energy to raise it to the level of C. Thus, the energy difference between the states A and C represents the critical energy for fission.

4.30. A qualitative idea of the magnitude of this critical energy may be obtained by considering the factors which determine the energies corresponding to the points A and C. The energy at A is the energy of the ground state of the compound nucleus with respect to the separated fragments at E; it is thus determined by the difference in mass of the target nucleus plus a neutron, on the one

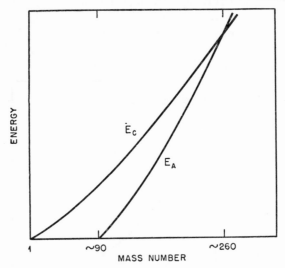

Fɪɢ. 4.30.   Dependence of critical fission energy on mass number

hand, and the sum of the masses of the two fission fragments, on the other hand. In view of the decrease of the binding energy per nucleon with mass number, for nuclides of mass number exceeding about 50 (see Fig. 1.30), this mass difference evidently increases with the mass number of the target nucleus. This conclusion is indicated by the curve E_A in Fig. 4.30. The energy at C is determined, essentially, by the electrostatic repulsion of the fission fragments, and this is proportional to $Z_1 Z_2 / (A_1^{\frac{1}{3}} + A_2^{\frac{1}{3}})$, where Z_1, Z_2 and A_1, A_2 are the atomic numbers and mass numbers, respectively. Assuming for simplicity that $Z_1 = Z_2$ and

$A_1 = A_2$, so that fission is symmetrical, the variation of E_C, i.e., the energy at C, with increasing mass number will be somewhat like that shown in Fig. 4.30.

4.31. It is evident from the vertical distance between the curves for E_C and E_A that the critical energy for fission is at first very large, but it decreases with increasing mass number (and atomic number). Thus, although fission by neutrons is theoretically possible for nuclei of mass numbers of about 90 or more, the critical energy required for the process to take place at an observable rate is greater than the largest neutron energies attainable at the present time. When the mass number is in the vicinity of 235 or so, the critical energy, as will be seen shortly, is down to about 6 Mev, so that fission by neutrons becomes an observable phenomenon. For nuclei of still higher mass number the E_A and E_C curves cross, so that E_A is above E_C. In these circumstances, that is, for mass numbers exceeding about 260, no critical energy is required for fission; in fact, such nuclei are so unstable that if they could be produced in any way they would undergo spontaneous fission within an interval of about 10^{-20} sec.

4.32. It is of interest to note that the critical energy for fission decreases with increasing mass number because the curve for E_A in Fig. 4.30 rises more rapidly than does that for E_C. This is due to the decrease in binding energy per nucleon at the higher mass numbers. The main factor contributing to this decrease is the increasing electrostatic repulsion energy of the protons. Consequently, the large magnitude of the mutual repulsion of the protons contributes to the decrease in the critical energy, thus making fission at an observable rate possible. As stated above, it also plays an important part in determining the large amount of energy liberated in fission.

4.33. Another quantitative aspect of the fission problem is provided by the liquid-drop model discussed earlier. If it is assumed that the sphere does not change its volume when it is deformed into an ellipsoid (§ 4.26), as is reasonable in view of the proportionality between the nuclear volume and mass (§ 1.34), the change in energy will be due to only two of the five factors considered in Chapter I, namely, the surface tension effect and the electrostatic repulsion energy. The former will increase in magnitude when the nucleus is deformed, because of the increased surface area, but the latter will decrease, since the charges are separated to some extent. If ϵ is a parameter representing the degree of deformation, the energy required to produce deformation is given by

$$\text{Deformation energy} = \epsilon^2 \left(5.2A^{\frac{2}{3}} - 0.117 \frac{Z^2}{A^{\frac{1}{3}}} \right), \qquad (4.33.1)$$

where the first term in the parentheses is the change in the surface tension effect and the second is that in the electrostatic repulsion energy.* When the deformation energy is zero, or negative, the spherical nucleus will deform and, conse-

---

* N. Bohr and J. A. Wheeler, *Phys. Rev.*, **56**, 426 (1939).

quently, undergo fission spontaneously. The condition for spontaneous fission is, therefore,

$$0.117 \frac{Z^2}{A^{\frac{1}{3}}} > 5.2 A^{\frac{2}{3}}$$

or

$$\frac{Z^2}{A} > 45. \tag{4.33.2}$$

In § 4.31 it was seen that a nucleus with mass number exceeding 260 would be expected to undergo instantaneous fission. If this result is combined with (4.33.2), it would appear that the maximum atomic number for stability against fission is about 110. These figures are, of course, approximate only.

4.34. The deformation energy considered above may be regarded as being equivalent to the critical energy for fission. Thus, (4.33.1) may be written as

$$\text{Critical energy} \propto A^{\frac{2}{3}} \left(5.2 - 0.117 \frac{Z^2}{A} \right).$$

For a group of elements of high mass number $A^{\frac{2}{3}}$ is almost constant, and so the critical energy will decrease as Z^2/A increases. For plutonium-239 the value of Z^2/A is 37.0, for uranium-233 it is 36.4, for uranium-235 the value is 36.0, and for uranium-238 it is 35.5. The critical energy for fission should thus increase in this order. Calculations[*] based on the liquid-drop model indicate that the critical energy is about 6.5 Mev for the compound nucleus formed as a result of neutron capture by uranium-235, and about 7.0 Mev for uranium-238.

4.35. The reference to spontaneous fission made above applies to cases in which none of the nuclei could exist for any appreciable time. It is important to point out, however, that there is always a certain probability that apparently stable or quasi-stable nuclei will undergo spontaneous fission. Even though the nucleus in its normal state does not have enough energy to permit it to pass through the critical deformation stage, the principles of wave mechanics require that there should be a definite, although small, probability for fission to take place.

Fast- and Slow-Neutron Fission

4.36. It will be recalled that the fission of uranium-235 can be brought about by slow (thermal) neutrons, with 0.025 ev energy, whereas uranium-238 requires neutrons of at least 1.1 Mev energy. The difference is partly accounted for by the smaller critical energy in the former case, but this is probably no more than about 0.5 Mev (§ 4.34), and so there is still a discrepancy that requires explanation. Similarly, although thermal neutrons cause fission of uranium-233 and plutonium-239, fast neutrons are required for thorium-232, protactinium-231,

---

[*] Bohr and Wheeler, *loc. cit.;* see also, S. Frankel and N. Metropolis, *Phys. Rev.*, **72**, 914 (1947).

and neptunium-237. The explanation of the difference, as will be shown below, lies in the fact that when fission occurs a large proportion of the critical deformation energy is provided by the binding energy of the captured neutron, and this energy varies appreciably from one nucleus to another.

4.37. The excitation energy of the compound nucleus formed by the capture of a neutron of zero kinetic energy is equal to the binding energy of a neutron (§ 2.14). It is, consequently, the energy equivalent of the mass difference between the target nucleus plus a neutron, on the one hand, and the compound nucleus on the other hand. It can be readily shown from (1.29.1) that this is the same as the total binding energy of the compound nucleus minus the total binding energy of the target nucleus. These binding energies can be determined from (1.29.1) if the respective isotopic masses are known, or from (1.44.1) if they are not. Since the two masses are generally not known, it is preferable, for consistency, to use the latter equation to calculate the binding energies of both target and compound nuclei.

4.38. To determine the excitation energy of the compound nucleus in the case of uranium-235 as target nucleus, for example, the total binding energy is first calculated for this nucleus, for which A is 235 and Z is 92. Then the corresponding quantity is determined for the compound nucleus formed by the addition of a neutron, that is, with A equal to 236 and Z to 92. The difference between these two binding energies represents the excitation energy of the compound nucleus (U^{236}) formed when a neutron of zero kinetic energy is taken up by a uranium-235 nucleus. Using (1.44.1), the result is found to be

$$\text{B.E. } (U^{236}) - \text{B.E. } (U^{235}) = 6.8 \text{ Mev.}$$

Upon repeating the calculations for uranium-238, for which A is 238 and Z is 92, and the corresponding compound nucleus with A equal to 239 and Z to 92, the excitation energy of the compound nucleus (U^{239}) is given by

$$\text{B.E. } (U^{239}) - \text{B.E. } (U^{238}) = 5.5 \text{ Mev.}$$

4.39. As mentioned in § 4.34, calculations indicate that the critical deformation energy of uranium-238 is about 7.0 Mev, but evidently only 5.5 Mev is acquired when the nucleus takes up a neutron of zero kinetic energy. It would appear, therefore, that the incident neutron would need to have at least $7.0 - 5.5 = 1.5$ Mev of kinetic energy to make fission of uranium-238 possible. Experiments show that the minimum neutron energy is about 1.1 Mev. The discrepancy between the observed (1.1 Mev) and the calculated (1.5 Mev) energies is, no doubt, due partly to the inexact nature of the calculations.

4.40. Turning now to uranium-235, it will be seen that the conditions are quite different. The critical energy for fission has been estimated to be 6.5 Mev, but, as seen above, 6.8 Mev becomes available as the result of the capture of a neutron with zero kinetic energy. It is evident, therefore, that slow neutrons should be capable of causing fission of the uranium-235 nucleus, as indeed they are.

4.41. If a detailed examination is made of the calculations which lead to the appreciably different binding energies, given in § 4.38, for the two isotopes of uranium, the cause of the discrepancy becomes apparent. It is due almost entirely to the effect of the odd-even or spin term in (1.44.1). Since the compound nucleus uranium-236 is of even-even character, this term makes a positive contribution of about 0.55 Mev to the binding energy; it is zero, however, in uranium-235, which is an odd-even nucleus. With the 238-isotope of uranium, the situation is reversed; the compound nucleus uranium-239 has an odd-even character and the spin effect is zero, but uranium-238 is even-even and the spin effect term is again about 0.55 Mev positive. This effect alone is, consequently, responsible for a difference of $2 \times 0.55 = 1.1$ Mev in the excitation energies of the compound nuclei formed by uranium-235 and uranium-238, respectively, upon the addition of a neutron.

4.42. From the foregoing considerations it may be concluded, in general, that an odd-even nucleus, i.e., one with an odd number of neutrons and an even number of protons, will produce a compound nucleus with a relatively large amount of excitation energy when it absorbs a slow neutron. Hence, provided Z^2/A for the nucleus is sufficiently high, such a neutron will be able to induce fission. Instances of this type, in addition to uranium-235, are uranium-233 and plutonium-239 ($_{94}Pu^{239}$), both of which are fissionable by slow neutrons. With even-even nuclei, like uranium-238 and thorium-232 ($_{90}Th^{232}$), the excitation energy when a neutron of zero kinetic energy is captured is relatively smaller, and hence high-energy neutrons are required to cause fission.

4.43. If a nucleus has an even number of neutrons and an odd number of protons, e.g., neptunium-237 ($_{93}Np^{237}$), the compound nucleus ($_{93}Np^{238}$), formed by the absorption of a neutron, will be of the odd-odd type, with a negative spin contribution of about 0.55 Mev. In this event, the quantity B.E. (Np^{238}) − B.E. (Np^{237}), which is the excitation energy of the compound nucleus, will be similar to that for nuclei of the even-even type. For fission to be possible it would therefore be necessary to employ neutrons of high energy.

4.44. Finally, consideration may be given to the fission of an odd-odd nucleus; the compound nucleus formed by the capture of a neutron would then be of the even-odd type, which has similar binding energy to the odd-even type. The spin term will be zero in the compound nucleus and negative in the target nucleus, so that the excitation energy will be relatively large. Thus, it is to be expected that odd-odd nuclei will undergo fission by slow neutrons. Since such species are relatively unstable in any event, the fact that they are fissionable by slow neutrons is of no practical value.

4.45. The results of the preceding paragraphs are summarized in Table 4.45; the signs of the spin terms for the compound nucleus and the target nucleus for each of the different cases are given. The relative magnitude of the excitation energy of the compound nucleus resulting from the capture of a neutron of zero kinetic energy, which is the difference between the total binding energies of the compound nucleus and the target nucleus, is indicated in the last column. In view of the natural instability of the odd-odd species, the only substances of interest for the release of nuclear energy by slow neutrons are consequently the nuclides with odd numbers of neutrons and even numbers of protons, i.e., with odd mass numbers and even atomic numbers.

TABLE 4.45. SPIN TERMS AND EXCITATION ENERGIES

Target Nucleus		Spin Terms		Excitation Energy
Neutron	Proton	Compound Nucleus	Target Nucleus	
Odd	Even	+	0	large
Even	Even	0	+	small
Even	Odd	−	0	small
Odd	Odd	0	−	large

THE FISSION CHAIN REACTION

CONDITIONS FOR A SELF-SUSTAINING CHAIN REACTION

4.46. With the information already given, it is now possible to consider the feasibility of applying the fission reaction to the practical utilization of nuclear energy. The essential condition is that a self-sustaining chain reaction should be maintained; in other words, once the fission process has been initiated in a few nuclei, it should be able to continue throughout the remainder of the material without external influence. Since at least two neutrons are released in each act of fission (§ 4.5), and these neutrons are capable of inducing the fission of other nuclei, and so on, it would appear that the requirements of a self-sustaining chain reaction can be met. However, account must be taken of the fact that the neutrons produced in the fission process can take part in other (nonfission) reactions. In addition to this competition for neutrons, there is the inevitable loss of neutrons from the system by leakage.

4.47. If a chain reaction is to be maintained, the minimum condition is that for each nucleus capturing a neutron and undergoing fission there shall be produced, on the average, at least one neutron which causes the fission of another nucleus. This condition can conveniently be expressed in terms of a *multiplication factor* or *reproduction factor*, defined as the ratio of the number of neutrons of any one generation to the number of corresponding neutrons of the immediately preceding generation. If the multiplication factor, represented by k, is exactly equal to, or slightly greater than, unity a chain reaction will be possible. But if k is less than unity, even by a very small amount, the chain cannot be maintained.

4.48. Suppose, for example, a particular generation starts with 100 neutrons; if the multiplication factor is unity, there will be 100 corresponding neutrons at the beginning of the second generation, 100 at the third, and so on. Once it has started, the fission will continue at the same rate as at the commencement. For practical purposes, however, it is necessary that k be capable of exceeding unity, if power production is to be appreciable. As seen in § 4.24, fissions must take place at the rate of 3.1×10^{10} per sec to produce 1 watt of power. The simplest way in which a required power level can be attained is for the multiplication factor to exceed unity; the number of neutrons present, and hence, the fission rate will then increase until the desired rate is reached.*

4.49. The multiplication factor k is effectively the number of neutrons present at the end of a neutron generation for each neutron present at the beginning of that generation. Since one neutron is required to maintain the chain reaction, the number of neutrons will increase by $k - 1$ in one generation. Thus, if there are n neutrons present initially, the rate of increase will be $n(k - 1)$ per generation. If l is the average time between successive neutron generations in the system under consideration, then

$$\frac{dn}{dt} = \frac{n(k - 1)}{l} = \frac{nk_{ex}}{l},$$ (4.49.1)

where k_{ex} is defined by

$$k_{ex} \equiv k - 1.$$

Upon integration of (4.49.1), it is seen that

$$n = n_0 e^{t(k_{ex}/l)},$$ (4.49.2)

where n_0 is the initial number of neutrons and n is the number after the lapse of time t. It is seen, therefore, that, if the multiplication factor is greater than unity, the number of neutrons will increase exponentially with time.

4.50. Suppose, in a particular case, k is 1.005, so that k_{ex} is 0.005. Taking the average neutron lifetime to have the reasonable value of 0.001 sec, it follows from (4.49.2) that after the lapse of a second the number of neutrons will have increased by a factor e^5, i.e., roughly 150-fold. An increase in the number of neutrons will mean an increase in the fission rate and a consequent increase in the power output. When the desired output is attained, the multiplication factor should be reduced exactly to unity, either by introducing a nonfissionable neutron absorber or by allowing some neutrons to escape. The number of neutrons present in the system, the fission rate, and the power level will then remain constant.

4.51. If the multiplication factor is less than unity, the maintenance of a self-sustaining chain reaction becomes impossible. The rate of change in the number of neutrons is again represented by (4.49.2), but k_{ex}, equal to $k - 1$, is now nega-

---

* The number of nuclei undergoing fission per sec is $\phi \Sigma_f V$, where ϕ is the thermal neutron flux per cm² per sec, Σ_f cm⁻¹ is the macroscopic cross section for fission, and Vcm³ is the volume of the reactor. Since 3.1×10^{10} fissions per sec are required to produce 1 watt, the power output will be $\phi \Sigma_f V/(3.1 \times 10^{10})$ watts.

tive, and the neutron concentration decreases continuously in an exponential manner. As long as the multiplication factor is less than unity, by no matter how small an amount, the number of neutrons must inevitably decrease with time, and the maintenance of a self-sustaining reaction is not possible.*

NEUTRON BALANCE IN A CHAIN REACTION

4.52. The value of the multiplication factor in any system consisting of fissionable material, e.g., uranium, and a moderator for slowing down the neutrons (§ 3.12) depends on the relative extents to which the neutrons take part in four main processes. These are: (*a*) complete loss or escape of neutrons from the system, generally referred to as *leakage;* (*b*) nonfission capture, by uranium-235 and uranium-238, frequently designated *resonance capture*, since it is likely to occur mainly at resonance energies (§ 2.31); (*c*) nonfission capture, sometimes called *parasitic capture*, by the moderator and by various extraneous substances ("poisons"), such as structural materials, coolant, fission products, and impurities in the uranium and in the moderator; and, finally, (*d*) fission capture of slow neutrons by uranium-235, or of fast neutrons by both uranium-235 and uranium-238. In each of these four processes neutrons are removed from the system, but in the fourth process, i.e., in the fission reaction, other neutrons are generated to replace them. Hence, if the number of neutrons produced in the latter process is just equal to (or exceeds) the total number lost by escape and by fission and nonfission capture, the multiplication factor will equal (or exceed) unity and a chain reaction should be possible.

4.53. An illustration of the type of neutron balance that might exist in a system for which the multiplication factor is exactly unity is depicted below. It is assumed that fission results only from the capture of slow neutrons, and it is supposed, for simplicity, that exactly two neutrons are produced, on the average, in each fission process. Since 100 slow neutrons are absorbed in fission processes at the beginning, and 100 are available for similar absorption at the end of the generation, the conditions for a self-sustaining chain are satisfied.

100 slow neutrons absorbed by U^{235} to cause fission
$\downarrow$
200 fission neutrons
$|\rightarrow$ 40 leak out during slowing down
$\downarrow\rightarrow$ 20 absorbed by U^{238} during slowing down
140 neutrons slowed down
$\downarrow\rightarrow$ 10 leak out as slow neutrons
130 slow neutrons available for absorption
$\downarrow\rightarrow$ 30 absorbed by moderator, U^{238}, poisons, etc.
100 slow neutrons (absorbed by U^{235} to cause fission)

---

* If an extraneous source of neutrons is present, the neutron concentration will approach a limiting value.

REACTOR TYPES

4.54. A nuclear reactor is a system usually consisting of a moderator and a fuel containing fissionable material, together with coolant and structure, in which a self-sustaining chain reaction can be maintained. In such a reactor fast neutrons are produced in the fission process; these neutrons may suffer scattering collisions, mainly elastic, as a result of which their energy is decreased; they may be absorbed by the various materials present in the system; or they may escape. Depending on the relative amounts and nature of the moderator, fuel and other substances, their geometrical arrangement, and the dimensions of the system, which largely determine the leakage, the main portion of the neutron captures leading to fission will take place in a certain energy range.

4.55. If most of the fissions result from the capture of thermal neutrons, the system is referred to as a *thermal reactor*. When most of the fission processes are due to the absorption of neutrons of higher energy, sometimes called epithermal neutrons (§ 3.13) or intermediate neutrons, the term *intermediate reactor* is used. An important type of intermediate reactor is one in which most of the fissions are induced by neutrons with energies from thermal values up to about 1000 ev. Finally, if the main source of fissions is the capture of fast neutrons by the fuel, the system is a *fast reactor*.*

4.56. Due to the relatively low cross sections for fission with neutrons of high energy, especially compared with the cross sections for nonfission reactions, it is impossible to maintain a nuclear chain reaction with fast neutrons in natural uranium, consisting of nearly 99.3 per cent of uranium-238 and 0.7 per cent of uranium-235 (Table 1.10). By using fuel material enriched in the latter isotope, or containing a sufficient proportion of plutonium-239, a chain reaction with fast neutrons can be achieved.† With natural uranium, a chain reaction is possible only if fission is mainly due to slow, i.e., thermal, neutrons; this is because the fission cross section of uranium-235 for thermal neutrons is sufficiently large to compensate for the nonfission absorption. In order to slow down the neutrons a moderator must be used, and this may be heavy water, beryllium (or beryllium oxide), carbon (graphite), or even ordinary water if an enriched fuel is used.

MULTIPLICATION FACTOR FOR THERMAL REACTORS‡

4.57. Because of their importance, and incidentally because they are most susceptible to theoretical treatment, some consideration will now be given to the conditions which determine the value of the multiplication factor for thermal

---

* For security reasons, the treatment in this book is restricted to thermal reactors.

† The atomic bomb is a reactor in which fast neutrons maintain an uncontrolled nuclear chain reaction in uranium-235 or plutonium-239.

‡ See E. Fermi, *Science*, **107**, 28 (1947).

reactors, especially those using natural uranium as fuel. In order to avoid, for the present, the problem of the loss of neutrons by leakage, it will be postulated that the multiplying system is infinite in extent. Suppose that, at a given instant representing the initiation of a generation, there are available n thermal neutrons which are captured in fuel. Let η be the average number of fast fission neutrons emitted as a result of the capture of one thermal neutron in fuel material, i.e., in both uranium-235 and uranium-238. Then, due to the absorption of the n thermal neutrons $n\eta$ fast neutrons will be produced. It should be noted that since the neutrons captured in fuel do not all necessarily lead to fission, the value of η differs, in general, from the average number (2.5 ± 0.1) of fast neutrons released per slow neutron fission (§ 4.5). If the latter number is represented by ν, then

$$\eta = \nu \frac{\Sigma_f}{\Sigma_{\text{fuel}}}, \tag{4.57.1}$$

where Σ_f is the macroscopic cross section (§ 3.42) for slow-neutron fission, and Σ_{fuel} is the total cross section for absorption of thermal neutrons, by fission and nonfission processes, in the fuel material (see Table 4.57).

TABLE 4.57.   THERMAL NEUTRON CROSS SECTIONS FOR URANIUM

	Fission		Radiative Capture	Scattering
U^{235}	549	barns	101 barns	8.2 barns
U^{238}	0		2.8	8.2
Natural	3.92		3.5	8.2

4.58. Before the $n\eta$ fast neutrons have slowed down appreciably some will be captured by, and cause fission of, uranium-235 and uranium-238 nuclei, mainly of the latter. Since more than one neutron is produced, on the average, in each fission, there will be an increase in the number of fast neutrons available. Allowance for this effect may be made by introducing the *fast fission factor*, denoted by ϵ and defined as the ratio of the total number of fast neutrons produced by fissions due to neutrons of all energies to the number resulting from thermal-neutron fissions. Consequently, as a result of the capture of n thermal neutrons in fuel, $n\eta\epsilon$ fast neutrons will be formed. For natural uranium fuel the value of ϵ has been found to be about 1.03, with either graphite or heavy water as the moderator.

4.59. As a result of collisions, mainly elastic, with the moderator, the fast neutrons will ultimately be thermalized. However, during the slowing down process some of the neutrons are captured in nonfission processes, so that not all of the $n\eta\epsilon$ fast neutrons reach thermal energies. The fraction of the fast (fission) neutrons which escape capture while being slowed down is called the *resonance escape probability*, and is represented by p. Consequently, the number of neutrons which become thermalized is $n\eta\epsilon p$.

4.60. When the energy of the neutrons has been reduced to the thermal region, they will diffuse for some time, the energy distribution remaining essentially constant, until they are ultimately absorbed by fuel, by moderator, or by such poisons as may be present. Of the thermal neutrons, therefore, a fraction f, called the *thermal utilization*, will be absorbed in fuel material; the value of f is represented by

$$f = \frac{\text{Thermal neutrons absorbed in fuel}}{\text{Total thermal neutrons absorbed}}, \qquad (4.60.1)$$

where the denominator is the total number of thermal neutrons absorbed by fuel, moderator, and other materials present in the reactor. The number of thermal neutrons captured in fuel is consequently $n\eta\epsilon pf$.

4.61. Since, for the present purpose, the multiplication factor (§ 4.47) may be defined as the ratio of the total number of thermal neutrons absorbed, on the average, in one generation to the number of thermal neutrons absorbed in the preceding generation, on the average, in an infinite medium, it follows that

$$k = \frac{n\eta\epsilon pf}{n} = \eta\epsilon pf. \qquad (4.61.1)$$

This result is sometimes referred to as the *four factor formula*. As seen above, the condition for a self-sustaining chain reaction in a system of infinite size is that the multiplication factor should be unity; the criterion for a natural uranium system is, therefore, that $\eta\epsilon pf = 1$.

4.62. In the special case of a reactor in which the fuel material contains only uranium-235 and no uranium-238, both the fast fission factor ϵ and the resonance escape probability will be virtually unity. Such a reactor can be made critical with a small proportion of fuel relative to moderator. The probability of capture while slowing down is consequently small in comparison with scattering. In these circumstances (4.61.1) would reduce to

$$k = \eta f.$$

4.63. Of the four factors involved in (4.61.1), η and ϵ are more or less fixed by the character of the fuel, but p and f can be varied to some extent. In order to insure the propagation of the nuclear fission chain, p and f should be as large as possible, although they are, of course, always less than unity. Unfortunately, such changes in the relative proportions of fuel and moderator as cause f to increase cause p to decrease. If the system contains a relatively small amount of moderator, thermal utilization will be increased [cf. equation (4.60.1)], but the larger proportion of uranium-238 means a decrease in the resonance escape probability. The reverse will be true if the proportion of moderator is large. In actual practice, therefore, it is necessary to find the composition and arrangement which gives the maximum value for the product pf, in order to maintain the chain reaction.

4.64. In a system consisting of natural uranium and graphite, an increase in the value of the product pf can be achieved by a heterogeneous lattice arrangement consisting of fairly large lumps of uranium imbedded in a mass of graphite. For reasons which will be considered in Chapter IX, the resonance escape probability is greater than for a homogeneous mixture of uranium and graphite of the same composition. However, there is some decrease in the thermal utilization, but by a proper design of the lattice and proper choice of the proportion of fuel to moderator, an overall increase in the product pf is achieved as compared with that for a uniform mixture.

4.65. One way in which the multiplication factor of a reactor can be increased is by the use of enriched fuel material, containing a larger proportion than normal of the fissionable isotope, uranium-235. If the isotopic ratio of U^{235} to U^{238} is increased, η becomes larger (cf. § 4.57) and the resulting multiplication factor is increased. Another, but smaller, effect is a decrease in f for a given ratio of U^{235} atoms to moderator atoms.

LEAKAGE OF NEUTRONS

4.66. It should be emphasized that (4.61.1) was derived for an infinite system, for which there is no leakage of neutrons; for this reason the factor k is sometimes written as k_∞, and is called the *infinite multiplication factor*. In a finite multiplying system, a factor k can be defined as above, by the right-hand side of (4.61.1). It will, however, not be the same as k_∞ for an infinite medium, for the following reasons. In calculating the resonance escape probability and the fast fission factor, the neutron energy distribution is important, since both quantities are functions of the energy. When, as in a reactor of finite size, there is neutron leakage, the energy distribution will not be the same everywhere in the system, as is true for an infinite (homogeneous) system, but will depend on the position in the reactor. Consequently, p and f, and hence the multiplication factor with no leakage, for the finite reactor, will differ from the values for the infinite system. However, for most practical purposes, k (finite size but no leakage) can be considered equal to k_∞, as defined above.

4.67. For a reactor of finite size the condition that the multiplication factor should be unity is no longer adequate for a self-sustaining chain reaction. It is required, now, that for every thermal neutron absorbed in fuel there shall be produced, on the average, one thermal neutron in addition to the loss by leakage from the reactor. If P is the total *nonleakage probability*, i.e., the probability that a neutron will not escape either during the slowing down process or while it diffuses as a thermal neutron, then the condition for a chain reaction to be maintained is

$$kP = 1, \tag{4.67.1}$$

where k is defined by (4.61.1). Only for the infinite system is the nonleakage probability unity, and then $k = 1$, satisfying the condition for the chain reaction.

For a finite reactor, P is less than unity, and hence the multiplication factor must exceed unity if the nuclear chain reaction is to be maintained.

4.68. As indicated above, the value of k is determined by the composition of the system, that is, by the nature of the fuel and the proportion of moderator, and also by the arrangement of the material. Hence, if these are specified, a chain reaction will be possible only if P is large enough to make kP equal to or greater than unity. In other words, if the chain reaction is to be self-sustaining for any given fuel-moderator system, the nonleakage probability must exceed a minimum value; thus, the permissible leakage of neutrons relative to the number being produced must be less than a certain amount.

CRITICAL SIZE OF REACTOR

4.69. The proportion of neutrons lost by escape from a finite reactor can be diminished by increasing the size of the system. The escape of neutrons occurs at the exterior, but absorption, leading to fission and neutron production, occurs throughout the whole of the interior of the reactor. The number of neutrons lost by escape thus depends on the external surface area, while the number formed is determined by the volume. To minimize the loss of neutrons, and thereby increase the nonleakage probability, it is necessary to decrease the ratio of area to volume; this can be done by increasing the size of the reactor. The *critical size* is that for which the nonleakage probability P is such that kP is just equal to unity. Since the area-to-volume ratio depends on the geometrical shape, the nonleakage probability will be determined by the shape of the reactor. For a given volume, a sphere has the smallest ratio of area to volume; hence, leakage from a spherical reactor will be less than for any other shape. The critical volume of such a reactor will consequently also be less. Leakage of neutrons can be diminished by surrounding the reactor with a suitable reflector, that is, a material, generally itself a moderator, which returns a proportion of the escaped neutrons to the reactor.

4.70. Since the value of k depends on the fuel-moderator composition and structure, it is apparent that the maximum permissible neutron leakage for a self-sustaining chain reaction will also be determined by these factors. The critical size, even for a reactor of specified geometry, will thus not be a constant, but will vary with the nature and structure of the fuel-moderator system. For example, if k is increased, by the use of enriched fuel, then it will be permissible for the nonleakage probability P to decrease, and hence the neutron leakage to increase, and still satisfy the condition that kP is equal to or greater than unity. Consequently, the critical size of the enriched reactor will be less than that of a reactor of the same geometrical shape and structure using natural uranium as fuel.

4.71. The product kP is called the *effective multiplication factor* of a reactor of finite size. It is the average number of thermal neutrons remaining in the reactor and available for absorption in one generation for each thermal neutron absorbed in that generation. The critical condition is that the effective multiplication factor shall be exactly unity [cf. equation (4.67.1)]. The chain reaction will then be maintained at a constant rate of fission and power level; this is sometimes referred to as a *steady state* of the reactor. Up to a point, a given reactor can have an indefinite number of such states corresponding to different fission rates and power levels. If the effective multiplication factor of a reactor exceeds unity, the system is said to be *supercritical*. In such a reactor the rate of fission and hence the neutron density (or flux) and the power level increase steadily. When the effective multiplication factor is less than unity, i.e., in a *subcritical reactor*, the neutron density (or flux) and power level decrease steadily.

REACTOR CONTROL

4.72. For practical operation, a reactor must be constructed so that it is actually appreciably greater than the critical size. One reason is that having an effective multiplication factor exceeding unity provides the only feasible means of increasing the number of neutrons, and hence the fission rate, up to the point where the required power level is attained (§ 4.48). Once this has been reached, it is necessary to decrease the effective multiplication factor to unity, and then the reactor will remain in a steady state, neutrons being produced just as fast as they are used up by leakage and capture.

4.73. The adjustment of the multiplication of neutrons in a thermal reactor is achieved by the insertion of *control rods* of cadmium or boron steel. Both cadmium and boron have large capture cross sections for slow neutrons (see §§ 3.69, 3.76); hence, by varying the positions of the control rods the effective multiplication factor can be made to vary over a suitable range. In order to shut down the reactor, the control rods are inserted to an extent that permits them to absorb additional neutrons. The system now loses neutrons faster than they are formed by fission; the effective multiplication factor sinks below unity, and the chain reaction dies out.

EFFECT OF DELAYED NEUTRONS

4.74. In the calculation in § 4.49 of the rate of neutron increase in a reactor with a multiplication factor exceeding unity, the mean lifetime of a neutron was taken to be 0.001 sec. This is actually the average value of the time elapsing between the birth of a neutron and its ultimate capture in a thermal reactor using natural uranium as fuel. But it gives the correct rate of neutron increase only if all the fission neutrons are released promptly, i.e., essentially at the instant of fission. It was seen in § 4.8, however, that about 0.75 per cent of the fission neutrons are delayed, and this affects the calculation of the rate of neutron increase (or decrease).

4.75. The mean lives of the five groups of delayed neutrons range from about 0.6 sec to 80 sec (Table 4.8). By weighting the values appropriately, according to the fraction in each group, the mean delay time, averaged over all the fission neutrons, is about 0.1 sec (§ 10.14). The average time between the fission capture of a neutron in two successive generations is, consequently, about $0.1 + 0.001$ sec; the first term is the average time elapsing between fission and the complete release of the neutron, whereas the second is that between release and capture in a fission process. In other words, the *effective* lifetime of a neutron is roughly 0.1 sec.

4.76. Using the value 0.1 sec for l in equation (4.49.2), and taking k to be 1.005, as before, it is found that the number of neutrons actually increases by a factor of $e^{0.05}$, i.e., about 1.05, per sec, as compared with a factor of 150 per sec if all the neutrons were prompt.* Clearly, the effect of the delayed fission neutrons, when the multiplication factor exceeds unity, is to make the rate of neutron increase much slower than it would have been had all the neutrons been released promptly.

4.77. Suppose that, in general, β is the fraction of the fission neutrons which are delayed, so that $1 - \beta$ represents the fraction of the prompt neutrons. Of the total number of fast neutrons produced for each thermal neutron absorbed in fuel $(1 - \beta)\eta$ are emitted instantaneously, whereas $\beta\eta$ are delayed and expelled gradually over a period of time. Consequently, the multiplication factor may be considered as consisting of two parts; one, equal to $k(1 - \beta)$, representing the prompt neutron multiplication factor, and the other, equal to $k\beta$, being due to the delayed neutrons. If, in the operation of a reactor, the quantity $k(1 - \beta)$ is adjusted so as to be just less than, or equal to, unity, then the rate of increase in the number of neutrons from one generation to the next will be determined essentially by the delayed neutrons. Since β is about 0.0075 for thermal fission (§ 4.8), this condition can be realized by having the effective multiplication factor between unity and 1.0075. When such is the case, the neutron flux (or density) and power level of the reactor will increase relatively slowly and adequate control is possible.

4.78. When the effective multiplication factor is equal to 1.0075, the condition of a reactor is described as *prompt critical*, since the nuclear fission chain can be maintained by means of the prompt neutrons alone. If k exceeds this value, multiplication will occur due to the prompt neutrons, irrespective of those delayed, and the neutron density will increase rapidly right from the commencement. In this condition, a reactor is difficult to control and hence it should be avoided in practice.

4.79. Just as the delayed fission neutrons affect the rate of increase of neutrons when the effective multiplication factor exceeds unity, so they influence the

---

* The calculations given here are approximate only and are intended mainly to provide a general indication of the effect of delayed neutrons. The subject will be treated more completely in Chapter X.

decay in the neutron density when the reactor is made subcritical, i.e., when it is being shut down. The delayed neutrons continue to be emitted for some time, and this maintains a fission rate that is considerably higher than would be the case if all the fission neutrons were prompt. The ultimate rate at which the neutron flux in a thermal reactor decreases after shut-down is determined essentially by the most delayed group of neutrons, i.e., by those with a mean life of 80 sec (see Table 4.8).

4.80. In reactors using heavy water or beryllium as moderator, shut-down is further delayed by the photoneutrons formed as a result of the interaction of gamma radiation from the fission products with deuterium or beryllium, respectively (§ 3.5).

Chapter V

THE DIFFUSION OF NEUTRONS*

ELEMENTARY DIFFUSION THEORY

THE TRANSPORT AND DIFFUSION EQUATIONS

5.1. The purpose of reactor theory is to determine the behavior of neutrons in scattering, absorbing, and multiplying media. In view of the complex variation, with the neutron energy, of the cross sections for various processes, a precise description of the fate of fission neutrons, as they are scattered and lose energy, are absorbed or escape from the system, would be a formidable problem without resort to simplifying assumptions.

5.2. The underlying principle for any theory of nuclear chain reactors is what may be called the *conservation* or *balance of neutrons;* thus, in a given volume, the time rate of change of neutron density is equal to the rate of production minus the rate of leakage and the rate of absorption. The general equation representing this balance may then be written as

$$\text{Production} - \text{Leakage} - \text{Absorption} = \frac{\partial n}{\partial t}, \qquad (5.2.1)$$

where $\partial n/\partial t$ is the time rate of change of the neutron density. When the system is in an equilibrium state, sometimes called a *steady state,* the time rate of change of neutron density is zero, and the steady state equation becomes

$$\text{Production} = \text{Leakage} + \text{Absorption.} \qquad (5.2.2)$$

5.3. The fundamental equation expressing the principle of conservation of neutrons is called the *Boltzmann transport equation,* because it is similar to that used by Boltzmann in his studies of gas diffusion (see Chapter XIV). In this treatment, the dependent variable is the *angular distribution of neutron velocity vectors,* $n(\mathbf{r}, v, \mathbf{\Omega})$, which is defined as the number of neutrons at $\mathbf{r}$ per unit

---

* The application of elementary diffusion theory to the diffusion of slow neutrons was first made by E. Fermi and his collaborators [cf. E. Amaldi and E. Fermi, *Phys. Rev.,* **50,** 899 (1936)]. An extensive compilation of solutions to diffusion problems will be found in P. R. Wallace and J. Le Caine, "Elementary Approximations in the Theory of Neutron Diffusion," N. R. C. 1480, National Research Council of Canada; see also, *Nucleonics,* **4,** No. 2, 30 (1949), **4,** No. 3, 48 (1949).

volume that are traveling with speed v per unit velocity in the direction Ω per unit solid angle. Thus, $n(\mathbf{r}, v, \Omega)\, d\mathbf{r}\, dv\, d\Omega$ is the number of neutrons at $\mathbf{r}$ in the volume element $d\mathbf{r}$, with speeds lying in the range between v and $v + dv$, moving in a direction lying in the element of solid angle $d\Omega$ about Ω. The usual neutron flux per unit velocity, analogous to that considered in § 3.51, is independent of angle and is related to the vector flux density by

$$\phi(\mathbf{r}, v) = \int_{\substack{\text{all} \\ \text{directions}}} n(\mathbf{r}, v, \Omega)v\, d\Omega.$$

The quantity $n(\mathbf{r}, v, \Omega)v$ is called the vector flux and is merely the number of neutrons traveling in the direction Ω which cross a unit area normal to this direction per unit time.

5.4. If the angular distribution of the neutron velocity vectors is isotropic, or nearly isotropic, or is independent of energy and position, the mathematical treatment of the problem may be simplified, since the equation expressing the conservation of neutrons no longer includes the direction of neutron velocity vectors as a variable. In this event the dependent variable may be reduced to the scalar neutron flux as defined in § 3.49, and the conservation of neutrons can then be expressed by the *diffusion equation* (§ 5.7).

5.5. Neutrons diffuse through matter as a result of being scattered by atomic nuclei. A typical neutron trajectory would be a zigzag pattern of straight line elements of varying lengths joining the points of collision. Because of neutron capture by the medium, the lengths of the trajectories of individual neutrons will be distributed from zero to infinity for an unbounded region. Some insight into neutron diffusion can be gained by considering a point source of neutrons in an infinite medium. Suppose that the problem is to calculate the mean crow-flight distance that neutrons travel from the source before being captured. Since the probability of capture is given as $\Sigma\, dx$ in the path length dx (§ 3.43), the probability that neutrons are captured at a certain distance from the source is not related to the crow-flight distance, r, in a simple way, but instead depends on the length of the actual zigzag trajectory. Further, since any particular zigzag path to a given point from the source is only one of infinitely many possible paths, the mean crow-flight distance depends on the distribution of zigzag path lengths.

5.6. Although the neutron diffusion problem is statistical in nature, it is possible, as in the kinetic theory of gases, to develop a macroscopic theory which deals with the behavior of large numbers of neutrons. In diffusion phenomena, such as the diffusion of gas molecules or of heat, it is found that the diffusing substance tends to move from regions of high density toward those of low density. Neutrons behave similarly, since there are more collisions per unit volume in regions of high density, and after colliding the neutrons move away from the collision centers.

5.7. It is found that, under certain conditions (§ 14.27), the diffusion of mono-energetic neutrons may be represented by *Fick's law of diffusion*, according to which the net number **J** of neutrons flowing in unit time through a unit area normal to the direction of flow is given by

$$\mathbf{J} = -D_0 \text{ grad } n, \tag{5.7.1}$$

where n is the number of neutrons per unit volume, and D_0 is the conventional diffusion coefficient. For present purposes, Fick's law is used in the form

$$\mathbf{J} = -D \text{ grad } \phi, \tag{5.7.2}$$

where ϕ is the ordinary neutron flux, and D is the *diffusion coefficient for flux*, having the dimensions of length. Since for monoenergetic neutrons ϕ is equal to nv, where v is the neutron velocity, it follows from (5.7.1) and (5.7.2) that D is equal to D_0/v. Fick's law is the basic assumption of elementary diffusion theory, and its consequences will be developed here from relatively simple physical considerations.

5.8. The major part of the material in this and ensuing chapters is based on the diffusion equation. The diffusion of monoenergetic neutrons, for which scattering occurs without energy loss, is considered first, since this is directly applicable, as a first approximation, to the diffusion of thermal neutrons. The slowing down of neutrons is then treated by extending the results of the one-velocity diffusion treatment.

Neutron Current Density

5.9. Consider a small area dS lying in the x, y-plane in the coordinate system represented in Fig. 5.9. In a small volume element dV at a point whose spherical coordinates are r, θ, φ, the number of scattering collisions per sec is $\Sigma_s \phi \, dV$, where ϕ is the flux in neutrons per cm² per sec, and Σ_s cm⁻¹ is the macroscopic cross section (§ 3.54). Since the neutrons are taken to be monoenergetic, the cross section will have a constant value. If the collisions are spherically symmetric, that is to say, if the scattering is isotropic in the laboratory system (§ 5.20), a neutron may leave the collision center in any direction with equal probability. Assuming, for the present, that this is the case, the probability that a neutron in dV will be scattered in the appropriate direction, so as to pass through the area dS, is given by the fractional solid angle subtended by dS at the scattering point, i.e., by $\cos \theta \, dS/4\pi r^2$.

5.10. The probability that the neutrons which have their direction of motion within this solid angle will reach the area dS without further collision is $e^{-\Sigma r}$, where Σ is the macroscopic total cross section, which includes both absorption (Σ_a) and scattering (Σ_s) contributions. Since the subsequent treatment is strictly applicable to the diffusion of neutrons *in media which are poor absorbers*, the approximation will be made here of taking Σ_a to be small, so that Σ can be re-

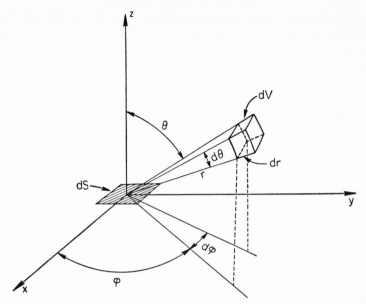

FIG. 5.9.   Calculation of neutron current density

placed by Σ_s.   The number of neutrons scattered from the volume element dV which actually reach dS per sec is thus given by

$$\Sigma_s \phi \, dV \times \frac{dS \cos \theta}{4\pi r^2} \times e^{-\Sigma_s r}.$$

Replacing dV by its equivalent $r^2 \sin \theta \, dr \, d\varphi \, d\theta$ in spherical coordinates, and rearranging, this number is found to be

$$\frac{dS}{4\pi} \phi \Sigma_s e^{-\Sigma_s r} \cos \theta \sin \theta \, dr \, d\varphi \, d\theta.$$

5.11. The total number of neutrons scattered into the area dS per sec from above, i.e., in the negative z-direction, is obtained by integrating the number coming from dV over the whole of the space lying above the x, y-plane, i.e., for all values of r between zero and infinity, for φ between zero and 2π, and for θ between zero and $\pi/2$.   If J_- is the *neutron current density*, i.e., the number of neutrons crossing unit surface per second, in the negative z-direction, the number passing through the area dS, in this direction, will be $J_- \, dS$.   This is exactly equal to the number of neutrons just calculated, so that

$$J_- \, dS = \frac{dS}{4\pi} \Sigma_s \int_0^\infty \int_0^{2\pi} \int_0^{\pi/2} \phi e^{-\Sigma_s r} \cos \theta \sin \theta \, d\theta \, d\varphi \, dr. \qquad (5.11.1)$$

5.12. In order to evaluate this integral, it is necessary to express the flux ϕ as a function of the space coordinates, and for this purpose a Taylor series expansion may be used. Thus, restricting the expansion to first order terms,

$$\phi(x, y, z) = \phi_0 + x\left(\frac{\partial\phi}{\partial x}\right)_0 + y\left(\frac{\partial\phi}{\partial y}\right)_0 + z\left(\frac{\partial\phi}{\partial z}\right)_0 + \cdots, \qquad (5.12.1)$$

where the subscript zero means that the derivatives are to be evaluated at the origin, i.e., at the element of area dS. The independent variables x, y, and z may be expressed in terms of spherical coordinates by

$$x = r \sin\theta \cos\varphi$$
$$y = r \sin\theta \sin\varphi$$
$$z = r \cos\theta.$$

But since in (5.11.1) the integration over φ is between the limits of zero and 2π, the terms containing x and y will make no contribution, and hence these terms in (5.12.1) may be eliminated. Thus, replacing z by $r \cos\theta$, and introducing (5.12.1) into (5.11.1) the result, after canceling dS from both sides, is

$$J_- = \frac{\Sigma_s}{4\pi}\left[\phi_0 \int_0^\infty \int_0^{2\pi} \int_0^{\pi/2} e^{-\Sigma_s r} \cos\theta \sin\theta \, d\theta \, d\varphi \, dr\right.$$
$$\left. + \left(\frac{\partial\phi}{\partial z}\right)_0 \int_0^\infty \int_0^{2\pi} \int_0^{\pi/2} re^{-\Sigma_s r} \cos^2\theta \sin\theta \, d\theta \, d\varphi \, dr\right] = \frac{\phi_0}{4} + \frac{1}{6\Sigma_s}\left(\frac{\partial\phi}{\partial z}\right)_0 \quad (5.12.2)$$

for the value of the total neutron current density through dS from above.

5.13. The neutron current density J_+ in the positive z-direction may be obtained in an exactly analogous manner, except that the integration over θ is from $\pi/2$ to π, so as to include only the space lying below the x, y-plane. The value of J_+ is thus found to be

$$J_+ = \frac{\phi_0}{4} - \frac{1}{6\Sigma_s}\left(\frac{\partial\phi}{\partial z}\right)_0. \qquad (5.13.1)$$

The net current density J_z in the positive z-direction is the difference between J_+ and J_-, so that

$$J_z = J_+ - J_- = -\frac{1}{3\Sigma_s}\left(\frac{\partial\phi}{\partial z}\right)_0. \qquad (5.13.2)$$

5.14. It should be pointed out that in the foregoing derivation a steady state in which the neutron flux does not vary with time has been tacitly assumed. If ϕ had been dependent on this variable, then because of the appreciable time r/v taken for the neutron to travel from the point in dV to the area dS, the neutron flux at this point would have to be known at a time r/v prior to the instant of determination of the neutron current at dS.

5.15. Although no terms were used beyond those of the first order in the Taylor series for the flux, the treatment is actually correct through the second order.

This is because the contribution to the integral made by the second order terms are either zero, or else they are identical in both J_+ and J_- so that they cancel one another in the net current density. The condition for the validity of (5.13.2) is, therefore, that the flux can be expressed with sufficient accuracy by three terms, i.e., of zero, first, and second orders, in the series expansion. Because the factor $e^{-\Sigma_s r}$ in the integral falls off rapidly with increasing r and becomes quite small beyond two or three mean free paths,* the major contribution to the neutron current density comes from scattering centers that are closer than this distance. The approximation considered above therefore will be justifiable, provided the change in $\partial\phi/\partial z$ over a distance of about two or three mean free paths is negligible.

5.16. In regions close to a fairly concentrated neutron source or to a strong absorber, or near a boundary between two media with dissimilar neutron diffusion characteristics, the rate of change of the flux with distance will be considerable. In such regions $\partial\phi/\partial z$ will not be small and the approximations leading to (5.13.2) will not be valid. However, at a distance of two or three mean free paths from a strong source or absorber or from a boundary, because of the marked decrease in the $e^{-\Sigma_s r}$ term, the flux can be expressed with quite sufficient accuracy for the present purpose by three terms of the expansion, and (5.13.2) can then be used to give the neutron current density.

5.17. If Σ_s is replaced by $1/\lambda_s$, the scattering mean free path, equations (5.12.2), (5.13.1), and (5.13.2) for the neutron current densities J_-, J_+, and the net current density J_z in the z-direction become, respectively,

$$J_- = \frac{\phi}{4} + \frac{\lambda_s}{6}\left(\frac{\partial\phi}{\partial z}\right)_0 \tag{5.17.1}$$

$$J_+ = \frac{\phi}{4} - \frac{\lambda_s}{6}\left(\frac{\partial\phi}{\partial z}\right)_0 \tag{5.17.2}$$

$$J_z = -\frac{\lambda_s}{3}\left(\frac{\partial\phi}{\partial z}\right)_0. \tag{5.17.3}$$

Similarly, for an element of area lying in the y, z-plane, the net neutron current density in the x-direction will be given by

$$J_x = -\frac{\lambda_s}{3}\left(\frac{\partial\phi}{\partial x}\right)_0, \tag{5.17.4}$$

while the corresponding expression for the neutron current density in the y-direction at an area in the x, z-plane is

$$J_y = -\frac{\lambda_s}{3}\left(\frac{\partial\phi}{\partial y}\right)_0. \tag{5.17.5}$$

---

* Since Σ_s is equal to $1/\lambda_s$, where λ_s is the scattering mean free path (§ 3.55), $e^{-\Sigma_s r}$ decreases to e^{-3}, i.e., about 0.05, of its value at a distance of three mean free paths.

5.18. If the element of area, instead of having its normal in the direction of one of the axes, is oriented so that its normal makes angles of α, β, and γ with the x, y, and z axes, respectively, the net current density J through this area will be given by the projection of three components, viz.,

$$J = -\frac{\lambda_s}{3}\left[\left(\frac{\partial\phi}{\partial x}\right)_0 \cos\alpha + \left(\frac{\partial\phi}{\partial y}\right)_0 \cos\beta + \left(\frac{\partial\phi}{\partial z}\right)_0 \cos\gamma\right]. \tag{5.18.1}$$

This expression reduces to either (5.17.3), (5.17.4), or (5.17.5) when the proper values of α, β, and γ are inserted; for example, when α and β are 90° and γ is 0°, it becomes equivalent to (5.17.3) for an element of area lying in the x, y-plane.

5.19. It will be seen from (5.18.1) that the net flow of neutrons through a unit area is dependent on its orientation, so that the neutron current is a vector quantity. Actually, as written above, it represents the scalar product of two vectors $\mathbf{N}$ and $\mathbf{J}$; the former is the unit vector normal to the element of area under consideration, i.e.,

$$\mathbf{N} = \mathbf{i}\cos\alpha + \mathbf{j}\cos\beta + \mathbf{k}\cos\gamma$$

while

$$\mathbf{J} = -\frac{\lambda_s}{3}\left[\left(\frac{\partial\phi}{\partial x}\right)_0\mathbf{i} + \left(\frac{\partial\phi}{\partial y}\right)_0\mathbf{j} + \left(\frac{\partial\phi}{\partial z}\right)_0\mathbf{k}\right], \tag{5.19.1}$$

where $\mathbf{i}$, $\mathbf{j}$, and $\mathbf{k}$ are unit vectors along the x, y, and z axes. Employing the usual vector notation, the net current density $\mathbf{J}$ can be written as

$$\mathbf{J} = -\frac{\lambda_s}{3}\operatorname{grad}\phi, \tag{5.19.2}$$

where $\operatorname{grad}\phi$ is the gradient of ϕ at the element of area where the neutron current density is determined.

TRANSPORT CORRECTIONS TO ELEMENTARY DIFFUSION THEORY

5.20. Two frames of references are used in the study of scattering collisions of neutrons with atomic nuclei. The subject is treated in some detail in Chapter VI, but for the present purpose a brief introduction will be adequate. In the *laboratory system*, or L system, the target nucleus is considered to be at rest before the collision, and it is approached by the incident neutron. In the *center of mass system*, or C system, on the other hand, the center of mass of the combination of neutron and nucleus is taken to be at rest. The *scattering angle*, i.e., the angle between the directions of motion of a neutron before and after a single collision, is represented by ψ in the L system and by θ in the C system. These angles are related to one another in a relatively simple manner, as will be shown later (§ 6.20).

5.21. It will be recalled that in § 5.9 it was postulated that the neutrons are scattered isotropically in the laboratory system, and there is no preferred direction in which a neutron will tend to travel after collision with a nucleus. It will be seen in § 6.20 that this is approximately true for collisions with heavy nuclei, but in general there will be a preferential scattering of the neutrons in the forward direction. In other words, the scattering is actually anisotropic in the L system.

5.22. Since diffusion theory deals only with the neutron density and neutron current, it cannot give the proper corrections for the anisotropic scattering in the L system. It can be shown from transport theory, however, that the diffusion approximation is satisfactory in regions which are more than two or three mean free paths away from boundaries and neutron sources, provided that the diffusion coefficient D, correct to first order terms in Σ_a/Σ, is represented by

$$D = \frac{1}{3\Sigma(1 - \bar{\mu}_0)\left(1 - \frac{4}{5} \cdot \frac{\Sigma_a}{\Sigma} + \frac{\Sigma_a}{\Sigma} \cdot \frac{\bar{\mu}_0}{1 - \bar{\mu}_0} + \cdots\right)}, \qquad (5.22.1)$$

where Σ and Σ_a are the total and absorption macroscopic cross sections, respectively, and $\bar{\mu}_0$ is the average cosine of the scattering angle per collision in the L system, i.e.,

$$\bar{\mu}_0 \equiv \overline{\cos \psi}.$$

The diffusion approximation holds in regions away from boundaries and sources, because the angular distribution of neutron velocity vectors does not then depend strongly on position.

5.23. If the scattering is isotropic in the C system,* the average cosine of the scattering angle in the L system is given by

$$\bar{\mu}_0 = \frac{\int_0^{4\pi} \cos \psi \, d\Omega}{\int_0^{4\pi} d\Omega},$$

where $d\Omega$ is an element of solid angle. Transforming the variable Ω to θ, the latter being the scattering angle in the C system, i.e., $d\Omega = 2\pi \sin \theta \, d\theta$, and substituting the expression for $\cos \psi$ in terms of $\cos \theta$, namely,

$$\cos \psi = \frac{A \cos \theta + 1}{\sqrt{A^2 + 2A \cos \theta + 1}}, \qquad (5.23.1)$$

which will be derived later (§ 6.20), the result is

$$\bar{\mu}_0 = \frac{1}{2} \int_0^{\pi} \frac{A \cos \theta + 1}{\sqrt{A^2 + 2A \cos + 1}} \sin \theta \, d\theta,$$

---

* Experimental observations indicate that scattering of neutrons with energies less than a few Mev is isotropic, i.e., spherically symmetric, in the C system. The treatment here and later (§ 6.17) is, therefore, based on the postulate of this type of scattering.

where A is the mass number of the scattering nucleus. Upon performing the integration, it is found that

$$\bar{\mu}_0 = \frac{2}{3A}, \tag{5.23.2}$$

and so $\bar{\mu}_0$ decreases with increasing mass of the scattering nucleus.

The Transport Mean Free Path

5.24. If the medium is a weak absorber, so that $\Sigma_a/\Sigma \ll 1$, equation (5.22.1) for the diffusion coefficient reduces to

$$D = \frac{1}{3\Sigma_s(1 - \bar{\mu}_0)}, \tag{5.24.1}$$

the total macroscopic cross section Σ having been replaced by the macroscopic scattering cross section Σ_s, since Σ_a is small. Further, as Σ_s may be replaced by $1/\lambda_s$, an alternative form is

$$D = \frac{\lambda_s}{3(1 - \bar{\mu}_0)}. \tag{5.24.2}$$

The quantity $1/\Sigma_s(1 - \bar{\mu}_0)$ or $\lambda_s/(1 - \bar{\mu}_0)$ is called the *transport mean free path*, and is denoted by λ_t; thus,

$$\lambda_t \equiv \frac{1}{\Sigma_s(1 - \bar{\mu}_0)} \tag{5.24.3}$$

$$\equiv \frac{\lambda_s}{1 - \bar{\mu}_0}, \tag{5.24.4}$$

so that in this case

$$D = \frac{\lambda_t}{3}. \tag{5.24.5}$$

5.25. It can be seen from (5.23.1) that for finite values of the mass number A, the scattering angle ψ in the L system is always less than θ in the C system, the difference decreasing with increasing mass number of the scattering nucleus. In other words, if scattering is isotropic in the C system, there will be preferred scattering in the forward direction in the L system for media of low and moderate mass number. Only when the mass number is large is the scattering isotropic in the L system if it is so in the C system.

5.26. According to transport theory, the scattering mean free path of the diffusion treatment should be replaced by the transport mean free path. Consequently, (5.19.2) becomes

$$\mathbf{J} = -\frac{\lambda_t}{3} \operatorname{grad} \phi \tag{5.26.1}$$

$$= -\frac{\lambda_s}{3(1 - \bar{\mu}_0)} \operatorname{grad} \phi.$$

5.27. It should be noted that if the scattering nucleus has a large mass number, then $\bar{\mu}_0$, equal to $2/3A$, is negligible in comparison with unity, and so λ_t is approximately equal to λ_s. In this case, the diffusion coefficient derived from transport theory, for a weak absorber, becomes identical with that obtained from simple diffusion theory. This is to be expected since isotropic scattering in the L system, assumed in the derivation of the latter, is approached with increasing mass of the scattering nucleus.

DIFFUSION COEFFICIENT AND NEUTRON CURRENT DENSITY

5.28. Summarizing the results of the preceding discussion, it is seen that if Fick's law is applicable, the net neutron current density can be represented by

$$\mathbf{J} = -D \text{ grad } \phi. \tag{5.28.1}$$

Then for a weak absorber

$$D = \frac{\lambda_t}{3} = \frac{1}{3\Sigma_s(1 - \bar{\mu}_0)}, \tag{5.28.2}$$

where $\bar{\mu}_0 = 2/3A$, if the scattering is isotropic in the center of mass system. The corresponding expressions for the components of the neutron current density in the z-direction are then

$$J_- = \frac{\phi}{4} + \frac{D}{2}\left(\frac{\partial \phi}{\partial z}\right)_0 = \frac{\phi}{4} + \frac{\lambda_t}{6}\left(\frac{\partial \phi}{\partial z}\right)_0 \tag{5.28.3}$$

$$J_+ = \frac{\phi}{4} - \frac{D}{2}\left(\frac{\partial \phi}{\partial z}\right)_0 = \frac{\phi}{4} - \frac{\lambda_t}{6}\left(\frac{\partial \phi}{\partial z}\right)_0 \tag{5.28.4}$$

$$J_z = -D\left(\frac{\partial \phi}{\partial z}\right)_0 = -\frac{\lambda_t}{3}\left(\frac{\partial \phi}{\partial z}\right)_0. \tag{5.28.5}$$

5.29. For carbon (graphite) the mass number A is 12, and hence $\bar{\mu}_0$ is $2/(3 \times 12)$, i.e., 0.055; consequently, by (5.28.2),

$$\lambda_t = \frac{1}{\Sigma_s \times 0.945} = \frac{\lambda_s}{0.945},$$

so that λ_t is about 5 per cent greater than λ_s. For hydrogen, on the other hand, $\bar{\mu}_0$ is $\frac{2}{3}$; so that

$$\lambda_t = 3\lambda_s,$$

and the correction for anisotropic scattering becomes important. If the medium is a moderate absorber, but Σ_a is such that $(\Sigma_a/\Sigma)^2$ may be neglected, the diffusion coefficient in (5.28.1) will then be expressed by (5.22.1).

CALCULATION OF NEUTRON LEAKAGE

5.30. The rate at which neutrons leak out of a specified volume element can be calculated from the expressions for the current density derived above provided the neutron flux, $\phi(x, y, z)$, is known as a function of the spatial coordinates.

Let a rectangular volume element dV, with dimensions dx, dy, dz be located at a point whose coordinates are x, y, z (Fig. 5.30). Consider the two faces of area

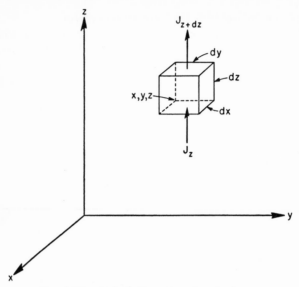

Fɪɢ. 5.30.   Calculation of neutron leakage

$dx\,dy$ which lie parallel to the x, y-plane. The number of neutrons entering the lower face per sec is $J_z\,dx\,dy$, where J_z is the net neutron current density in the z-direction; similarly, the number of neutrons leaving the upper face is $J_{z+dz}\,dx\,dy$. Using (5.28.5) to express the neutron current densities, the net rate of flow of neutrons out of the given volume element through the faces parallel to the x, y-plane is

$$(J_{z+dz} - J_z)\,dx\,dy = -D\left[\left(\frac{\partial\phi}{\partial z}\right)_{z+dz} - \left(\frac{\partial\phi}{\partial z}\right)_z\right]dx\,dy$$

$$= -D\frac{\partial^2\phi}{\partial z^2}\,dx\,dy\,dz \qquad (5.30.1)$$

$$= -D\frac{\partial^2\phi}{\partial z^2}\,dV.$$

5.31. Similarly, the net rates of loss from the faces parallel to the y, z- and x, z-planes are

$$-D\frac{\partial^2\phi}{\partial x^2}\,dV \quad \text{and} \quad -D\frac{\partial^2\phi}{\partial y^2}\,dV,$$

and the total rate at which neutrons leak out of the volume element dV is given by the sum of these three terms. The leakage rate per unit volume may then be obtained by dividing through by dV, so that

$$\begin{aligned}\text{Neutron leakage per unit volume per second} &= -D\left(\frac{\partial^2\phi}{\partial x^2} + \frac{\partial^2\phi}{\partial y^2} + \frac{\partial^2\phi}{\partial z^2}\right) \\ &= -D\,\nabla^2\phi,\end{aligned} \tag{5.31.1}$$

where ∇^2 is the symbol used for the Laplacian operator.

5.32. The leakage rate as given by (5.31.1) is quite general, within the limits of applicability of diffusion theory to neutrons, the Laplacian operator ∇^2 being expressed in the particular coordinates that are most convenient for each individual problem.   Thus, in rectangular coordinates it is defined by

$$\nabla^2 \equiv \frac{\partial^2}{\partial x^2} + \frac{\partial^2}{\partial y^2} + \frac{\partial^2}{\partial z^2}, \tag{5.32.1}$$

whereas in spherical coordinates it is

$$\nabla^2 \equiv \frac{\partial^2}{\partial r^2} + \frac{2}{r}\cdot\frac{\partial}{\partial r} + \frac{1}{r^2\sin\theta}\cdot\frac{\partial}{\partial\theta}\left(\sin\theta\frac{\partial}{\partial\theta}\right) + \frac{1}{r^2\sin^2\theta}\cdot\frac{\partial^2}{\partial\varphi^2}, \tag{5.32.2}$$

and in cylindrical coordinates

$$\nabla^2 \equiv \frac{\partial^2}{\partial r^2} + \frac{1}{r}\cdot\frac{\partial}{\partial r} + \frac{1}{r^2}\cdot\frac{\partial^2}{\partial\theta^2} + \frac{\partial^2}{\partial z^2}. \tag{5.32.3}$$

5.33. It may be mentioned that (5.31.1) could have been derived directly from (5.28.1), or the equivalent (5.19.1), by means of simple vector algebra.   The net rate of outflow of neutrons per unit volume is equal to the divergence of the vector $\mathbf{J}$, i.e., div $\mathbf{J}$, and hence from (5.28.1),

$$\begin{aligned}\text{Neutron leakage per unit volume per second} &= -\text{div } D\,\nabla\phi \\ &= -D\,\nabla^2\phi,\end{aligned} \tag{5.33.1}$$

in agreement with (5.31.1) if D is independent of position.

THE DIFFUSION EQUATION AND ITS APPLICATIONS

The Diffusion Equation

5.34. The leakage term in the general neutron balance equation (5.2.1), that is, the rate of loss expressed in neutrons per cm³ per sec, is given by (5.31.1). Because of the negative signs in both of these equations, the first term in (5.2.1) becomes $D\,\nabla^2\phi$.

5.35. The number of neutrons absorbed per cm³ per sec is equal to $\Sigma_a\phi$, where Σ_a is the macroscopic absorption cross section (§ 3.49), and hence the absorption term in (5.2.1) will be $-\Sigma_a\phi$.   Inserting this result, and the one for the leakage given above, and representing the rate of neutron production as S per cm³ per sec, the balance equation becomes

$$D\,\nabla^2\phi - \Sigma_a\phi + S = \frac{\partial n}{\partial t}. \tag{5.35.1}$$

This expression, generally referred to as the *diffusion equation*, is widely used in reactor theory.   It is applicable only to monoenergetic neutrons, and then only at distances greater than two or three mean free paths from strong sources, absorbers, or boundaries between dissimilar materials.   As will be seen throughout the course of this book, it will be used to determine the distribution of neutron flux under a variety of conditions.

BOUNDARY CONDITIONS

5.36. The diffusion equation (5.35.1) is a differential equation and such an equation does not provide a complete representation of a physical situation, since the general solution of a differential equation includes arbitrary constants of integration.   In order to determine the proper values for these constants, restrictions, in the form of *boundary conditions* obtained from the physical nature of the problem, are placed on the solutions.   The number of these boundary conditions must be sufficient to provide a unique solution, with no arbitrary constants. Some of the boundary conditions which are frequently used in the solution of neutron distribution problems by means of (5.35.1) are considered in the following paragraphs.

5.37. *The neutron flux must be finite and non-negative in the region where the diffusion equation applies.*

This condition is self-evident since the neutron flux cannot be infinite or negative.   It can, however, be zero, and it is for this reason that the particular wording given above has been employed.

5.38. *At a plane interface between two media, with different diffusion properties, the net neutron current densities in a direction normal to the interface are equal and the neutron fluxes are also equal.*

Imagine an interface between two different media, and consider two small equal areas, indicated by A and B in Fig. 5.38, one on each side of, and very close to, the interface.   All neutrons passing through the area A in the positive x-direction must enter the area B in the same direction; hence, the neutron current density at A in the positive x-direction, i.e., J_{A+}, must equal the current density at B, i.e., J_{B+}, in the same direction.   Similarly, the current densities J_{A-} and J_{B-} in the negative x-direction must be equal, so that

$$J_{A+} = J_{B+} \quad \text{and} \quad J_{A-} = J_{B-}.$$

Consequently, using the appropriate forms of (5.28.4) and (5.28.3), it follows that

$$\frac{\phi_A}{4} - \frac{\lambda_A}{6} \cdot \frac{d\phi_A}{dx} = \frac{\phi_B}{4} - \frac{\lambda_B}{6} \cdot \frac{d\phi_B}{dx}$$

and

$$\frac{\phi_A}{4} + \frac{\lambda_A}{6} \cdot \frac{d\phi_A}{dx} = \frac{\phi_B}{4} + \frac{\lambda_B}{6} \cdot \frac{d\phi_B}{dx}.$$

Subtraction of these equations gives

$$-\frac{\lambda_A}{3} \cdot \frac{d\phi_A}{dx} = -\frac{\lambda_B}{3} \cdot \frac{d\phi_B}{dx},$$

(5.38.1)

so that the net current densities in the x-direction [cf. equation (5.28.5)], i.e., normal to the interface, are equal. Further, upon addition of the equations,

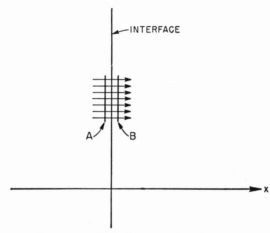

FIG. 5.38.   Diffusion at a plane interface

it is seen that

$$\phi_A = \phi_B,$$

(5.38.2)

so that the neutron fluxes also are equal at the interface.   The boundary conditions represented by (5.38.1) and (5.38.2) also apply to spherical surfaces where the flux is independent of angle, i.e., concentric homogeneous spheres and infinite cylinders.

5.39. *Near the boundary between a diffusion medium and a vacuum the neutron flux varies in such a manner that linear extrapolation would require the flux to vanish at a definite (extrapolation) distance beyond the boundary.*

Suppose the y, z-plane represents a boundary between a diffusion medium, to the left, and a vacuum, to the right.   Since there is no scattering back of neutrons from the vacuum into the diffusion medium, there is no neutron current in the negative x-direction at the boundary, i.e., where $x = 0$.   Hence, from (5.28.3),

$$J_- = \frac{\phi_0}{4} + \frac{\lambda_t}{6} \cdot \frac{d\phi_0}{dx} = 0,$$

(5.39.1)

where the zero subscript is used to indicate that the values apply at $x = 0$. The flux ϕ_0 at the boundary is positive, and so it follows from this equation that the slope $d\phi_0/dx$ of the flux distribution must be negative at the boundary, as

indicated schematically in Fig. 5.39.   If the neutron flux is extrapolated into the
vacuum, using a straight line with the same slope, $d\phi_0/dx$, as at the boundary,
the flux would vanish at a distance d given by

$$-\frac{\phi_0}{d} = \frac{d\phi_0}{dx} = -\frac{6\phi_0}{4\lambda_t},$$

(5.39.2)

using (5.39.1).   The magnitude of d, called the *linear extrapolation distance*,* is
thus given by

$$d = \tfrac{2}{3}\lambda_t,$$

(5.39.3)

for a plane boundary between a diffusion medium and a vacuum.

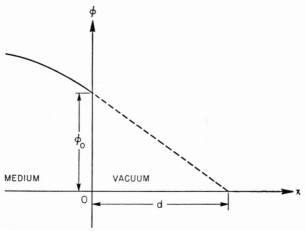

Fig. 5.39.   Extrapolation of neutron flux at a plane interface

5.40. On the basis of linear extrapolation, therefore, the neutron flux should
vanish at a distance equal to $\tfrac{2}{3}\lambda_t$ beyond a plane separating a diffusion medium
from a vacuum.   This boundary condition is sometimes stated in the following
form: *the neutron flux vanishes at the extrapolated boundary*, the latter being a distance $\tfrac{2}{3}\lambda_t$ beyond the physical boundary, in the case of a plane surface.   As
seen earlier, diffusion theory for neutrons, upon which (5.39.3) is based, breaks
down at a distance closer than two or three scattering mean free paths from a
boundary.   It is to be expected, therefore, that the linear extrapolation distance
obtained above is incorrect.   According to the more exact transport theory, the
linear extrapolation distance at a plane surface of a weakly absorbing medium
is $0.7104\lambda_t$, rather than $\tfrac{2}{3}\lambda_t$.   In order to make the results more nearly correct,
therefore, the extrapolated boundary, when using diffusion theory, is taken to
be $0.71\lambda_t$ beyond the actual plane boundary between a diffusion medium and a
vacuum.

* It is sometimes referred to as the "augmentation distance."

5.41. It is important to realize, in postulating that the neutron flux vanishes at the extrapolated boundary, there is no implication that the neutron flux is actually zero at that distance.   The concept of the hypothetical boundary where the flux vanishes, as a result of linear extrapolation, is merely a convenient mathematical device which is used to obtain a simple boundary condition.   It should be pointed out that even transport theory does not state that the neutron flux actually becomes zero at an extrapolation distance of $0.71\lambda_t$.   According to this theory, the plot of the neutron flux against the distance undergoes a marked change of direction within a mean free path or so from the interface (Fig. 5.41).

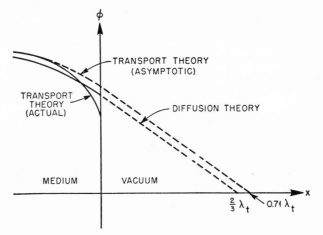

FIG. 5.41.   Transport theory and diffusion theory extrapolations

Consequently, in order that the boundary condition under consideration may be used in conjunction with diffusion theory to determine neutron flux distribution *at reasonable distances from the interface,* a so-called asymptotic linear extrapolation of the transport theory is made from the curve not too near the physical boundary.   The use of the resulting extrapolation distance of $0.71\lambda_t$, together with diffusion theory, provides a satisfactory approximation in many cases.*

5.42. A method for experimental determination of the transport mean free path of (thermal) neutrons in a given medium is based on the assumption that the neutron flux extrapolates to zero at a distance of $0.71\lambda_t$ from the physical boundary.   The neutron flux (or density) is measured at several points in the medium not too far from the boundary, but further than two or three mean free paths.   The values are then extrapolated in a linear manner to obtain the position at which the flux would apparently become zero.†

---

* The extrapolation distance is greater for curved surfaces; for a boundary of infinite curvature, i.e., zero radius, it is $\frac{4}{3}\lambda_t$.

† For experimental values of D, equal to $\lambda_t/3$, see Table 5.91.

Solution of Diffusion Equation: The Wave Equation

5.43. The diffusion equation (5.35.1) will be solved here for the special case in which the system is in a steady state and the time rate of change of the neutron density is zero; the diffusion equation then becomes

$$D\nabla^2\phi - \Sigma_a\phi + S = 0. \tag{5.43.1}$$

5.44. When the neutron source is either a point, a line, or a plane, the production term S or *source term*, as it is frequently called, is zero except at the particular source position. To solve the problem of the flux distribution in these cases, the differential equation is first solved with $S = 0$ outside the source region, and then the proper boundary conditions, to be considered below, are applied at the source. If S is set equal to zero, (5.43.1) reduces to the homogeneous form, applicable everywhere except at the source,

$$D\nabla^2\phi - \Sigma_a\phi = 0 \tag{5.44.1}$$

or

$$\nabla^2\phi - \kappa^2\phi = 0, \tag{5.44.2}$$

where

$$\kappa^2 \equiv \frac{\Sigma_a}{D}. \tag{5.44.3}$$

Since Σ_a has the dimension of reciprocal length and D of length, κ^2 is a reciprocal length squared.

5.45. Expressions of the form of (5.44.2) are often referred to as the *wave equation* because they are analogous to that which represents the propagation of waves in space. General solutions of the wave equation for various geometries can be obtained by standard methods. The particular solution of the problem of interest can then be derived by applying the appropriate boundary conditions.

Point Source in Infinite Medium

5.46. Consider a point source releasing one neutron per sec in an infinite homogeneous diffusion medium. A coordinate system is then chosen with its origin at the point source, with the result that in this system the neutron distribution will have spherical symmetry. It is now convenient to express the Laplacian operator (∇^2) in (5.44.2) in spherical coordinates, as given by (5.32.2). Since the flux distribution is spherically symmetric, it is independent of angle, and the terms involving $d\theta$ or $d\varphi$ will be zero. Consequently, the source-free equation (5.44.2) becomes

$$\frac{d^2\phi}{dr^2} + \frac{2}{r} \cdot \frac{d\phi}{dr} - \kappa^2\phi = 0, \tag{5.46.1}$$

where r is the distance from the point source; this equation does not apply, of course, at the source where r is zero.

5.47. The boundary conditions for the problem are as follows:

(i) The flux ϕ is finite everywhere except at the source, i.e., for $r > 0$.

(ii) The total number of neutrons passing through the surface of a sphere ($4\pi r^2$) must equal the source strength when the radius r approaches zero. If J is the neutron current density at the surface of the sphere, this condition, called the *source condition*, can be expressed as

$$\lim_{r \to 0} 4\pi r^2 J = 1,$$

since it has been postulated that the source emits one neutron per second.

5.48. In order to solve (5.46.1), let $\phi \equiv u/r$; the equation then reduces to

$$\frac{d^2u}{dr^2} - \kappa^2 u = 0. \tag{5.48.1}$$

Since κ^2, defined by (5.44.3), is a positive quantity, the general solution of (5.48.1) is thus

$$u = Ae^{-\kappa r} + Ce^{\kappa r},$$

and hence

$$\phi = A \frac{e^{-\kappa r}}{r} + C \frac{e^{\kappa r}}{r}, \tag{5.48.2}$$

where A and C are arbitrary constants,* which are to be evaluated by means of the boundary conditions. From condition (i) it is apparent that C must be zero, for otherwise the flux would become infinite as $r \to \infty$, so that only A remains to be determined.

5.49. The neutron current density at a point r is given by

$$J = -D \frac{d\phi}{dr} = DAe^{-\kappa r} \left(\frac{\kappa r + 1}{r^2} \right),$$

where $d\phi/dr$ has been obtained by differentiation of (5.48.2) with C equal to zero. Hence,

$$\lim_{r \to 0} 4\pi r^2 J = \lim_{r \to 0} 4\pi DAe^{-\kappa r}(\kappa r + 1).$$

By boundary condition (ii), i.e., the source condition, this must be equal to 1, so that

$$A = \frac{1}{4\pi D}.$$

Upon inserting the value for A into (5.48.2), it follows that

$$\phi = \frac{e^{-\kappa r}}{4\pi Dr}, \tag{5.49.1}$$

* Because B has a special significance in reactor theory, its use as an arbitrary constant is avoided.

since C is zero.   This expression gives the neutron flux distribution around a point source emitting 1 neutron per sec in an infinite medium in the steady state. It will be noted that the flux at any position in a given medium, i.e., D and κ constant, depends only on the distance r from the source.   Consequently if two or more point sources are present, the flux at any position can be obtained by adding the contributions from each of the individual sources.   In general, any source can be treated as being made up of a number of point sources, and the solution is given by the superposition of the point source solutions.

INFINITE PLANE SOURCE

5.50. Imagine an infinite plane source, emitting neutrons uniformly at the rate of 1 per cm² per sec, in an infinite homogeneous medium.   The coordinate system is now chosen so that the source plane coincides with the plane for which $x = 0$ at all points.   Since the source is infinite in extent, it is evident that for a given value of x, the flux will be independent of y and z.   The Laplacian operator in rectangular coordinates is now merely d^2/dx^2 so that the homogeneous diffusion equation (5.44.2) in the present case is

$$\frac{d^2\phi}{dx^2} - \kappa^2\phi = 0. \tag{5.50.1}$$

The boundary conditions are:
   (i) The flux shall be finite everywhere except at $x = 0$.
   (ii) At the source plane the current density is 0.5 neutron per cm² per sec, i.e.,

$$\lim_{x \to 0} J = 0.5. \tag{5.50.2}$$

This source condition may be clarified by considering a small area designated A in Fig. 5.50, very close to the source plane.   The net current density through

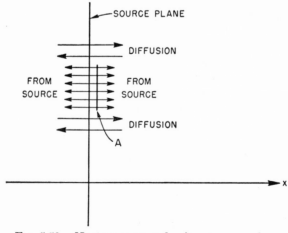

Fig. 5.50.   Neutron current density at source plane

this area is made up of the neutrons coming directly from the source which travel in the positive x-direction, plus the neutrons diffusing through the area in both positive and negative x-directions. For an area very close to the source plane, the diffusion will be virtually the same in the two opposite directions, so that this makes no contribution to the neutron current density through the area A. Consequently, the net current very near the source plane and, hence, at the source plane itself, is determined directly by the neutrons coming from the source in the positive x-direction. Since neutrons from the source plane will proceed equally in both positive and negative x-directions, as indicated in the figure, it is evident that if S is the source strength in neutrons per cm² per sec, the net current density at the source plane will be $\frac{1}{2}S$.

5.51. The general solution of (5.50.1) is

$$\phi = Ae^{-\kappa x} + Ce^{\kappa x}, \tag{5.51.1}$$

and this may be regarded as applying to absolute values of x, i.e., $|x|$, since the flux is symmetrical with respect to the $x = 0$ plane. In this event, the constant C in (5.51.1) must be zero by boundary condition (i), for otherwise the flux would become infinite as $x \to \infty$. From the source condition (ii) it follows that

$$\lim_{x \to 0} J = \lim_{x \to 0} -D\frac{d\phi}{dx} = \lim_{x \to 0} DA\kappa e^{-\kappa x}$$
$$= DA\kappa = 0.5,$$

so that

$$A = \frac{1}{2\kappa D}.$$

Introducing this value for A into (5.51.1), with C equal to zero, the result is

$$\phi = \frac{e^{-\kappa x}}{2\kappa D} \tag{5.51.2}$$

for the steady state flux distribution in the x-direction from an infinite plane source, emitting 1 neutron per cm² per sec. As indicated above, x is here the absolute value of the x-coordinate.

5.52. It was stated in § 5.49 that any neutron source may be treated as a number of point sources and the flux distribution determined by superposing the individual solutions. This may be illustrated by using the procedure to calculate the flux distribution for an infinite plane source. Since the results can be used for any function having this property of superposition, the general case will be treated first. Consider an annulus of radius a and thickness da lying in a plane, as in Fig. 5.52; the area of this annulus is $2\pi a\, da$, so that it may be regarded as being made up of $2\pi a\, da$ point sources. At a field point P on the x-axis, normal to the source plane, and at a distance r from it, let the value of a function, having the superposition property indicated above, be $G_{pt}(r)$. Then at the same point the corresponding function due to the annulus under consideration will be $G_{pt}(r)2\pi a\, da$. To obtain the value at P of the function G_{p1} due to the whole of an infinite plane source, this result is integrated over all values of a from zero to infinity; thus,

$$G_{p1} = \int_0^\infty G_{pt}(r)2\pi a\, da. \tag{5.52.1}$$

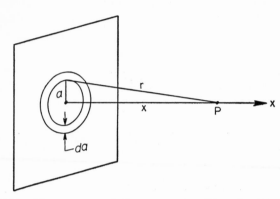

FIG. 5.52.   Plane source solution as superposition of point sources

5.53. In the case under consideration, $G_{pt}(r)$ is the flux due to a point source at a distance r, as given by (5.49.1); the flux due to infinite plane the source is then, by (5.52.1),

$$\phi = \int_0^\infty \frac{e^{-\kappa r}}{4\pi D r} 2\pi a\, da = \frac{1}{2D} \int_0^\infty \frac{e^{-\kappa r}}{r} a\, da. \tag{5.53.1}$$

If x represents the coordinate of the point P, then it can be seen from Fig. 5.52, that

$$r^2 = a^2 + x^2$$

and hence

$$r\, dr = a\, da. \tag{5.53.2}$$

Making use of this relationship to change the variable, (5.53.1) becomes

$$\phi = \frac{1}{2D} \int_x^\infty e^{-\kappa r}\, dr,$$

the limits of integration over r being now x and ∞, corresponding to 0 and ∞, respectively, for a.   The result of this integration is

$$\phi = \frac{e^{-\kappa x}}{2\kappa D},$$

in agreement with (5.51.2) for an infinite plane source.

Infinite Plane Source in Medium of Finite Thickness

5.54. If the neutrons from an infinite plane source diffuse in a slab of infinite extent but finite thickness, the flux distribution is somewhat different from the case considered above, where the thickness of the diffusion medium was taken to be infinite. In order to make the results comparable, it will be supposed that the source is at a plane of symmetry. The same arguments as were used above, in the case of the infinite plane source, lead to the source condition (ii) in § 5.50.

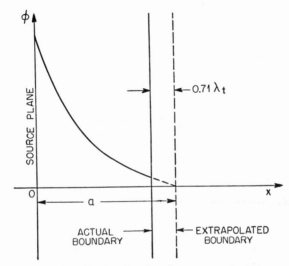

Fig. 5.54.   Flux distribution for plane source in finite medium

The general solution given by (5.51.1) then applies to the present problem. However, since the diffusion medium has a finite thickness, it is now not possible to eliminate the second term. In order to evaluate the arbitrary constants A and C it is necessary to introduce a boundary condition additional to those for the plane source in an infinite medium. The extra condition is that the flux shall vanish at the hypothetical extrapolated boundary (§ 5.39). If a is the thickness of the slab *including* the extrapolation distance $0.71\lambda_t$ (Fig. 5.54), then substitution of this value for x in (5.51.1) should give zero flux; thus,

$$\phi_a = Ae^{-\kappa a} + Ce^{\kappa a} = 0,$$
$$C = -Ae^{-2\kappa a}.$$

Inserting this value of C in (5.51.1), the general expression for the flux distribution now becomes

$$\phi = A[e^{-\kappa x} - e^{-\kappa(2a-x)}].   \tag{5.54.1}$$

5.55. To determine A, use is made, as before, of the boundary condition that at the source plane the neutron current density in the positive x-direction is 0.5;

thus,

$$\lim_{x \to 0} J = \lim_{x \to 0} - D\frac{d\phi}{dx} = \lim_{x \to 0} DA\kappa[e^{-\kappa x} + e^{-\kappa(2a-x)}]$$
$$= DA\kappa(1 + e^{-2\kappa a}) = 0.5,$$
$$A = \frac{1}{2\kappa D(1 + e^{-2\kappa a})}.$$

Hence, from (5.54.1), the flux distribution in the steady state is given by

$$\phi = \frac{e^{-\kappa x} - e^{-\kappa(2a-x)}}{2\kappa D(1 + e^{-2\kappa a})}. \tag{5.55.1}$$

When a is very large, that is, for an infinite medium, $e^{-\kappa(2a-x)}$ and $e^{-2\kappa a}$ approach zero, and (5.55.1) becomes identical, as it should, with (5.51.2).

5.56. Equation (5.55.1) may be written in an alternative form by introducing the hyperbolic functions, viz.,

$$\sinh u = \tfrac{1}{2}(e^u - e^{-u}) \quad \text{and} \quad \cosh u = \tfrac{1}{2}(e^u + e^{-u}).$$

If the numerator and denominator of (5.55.1) are multiplied by $e^{\kappa a}$, it is seen that

$$\phi = \frac{\sinh \kappa(a - x)}{2\kappa D \cosh \kappa a}. \tag{5.56.1}$$

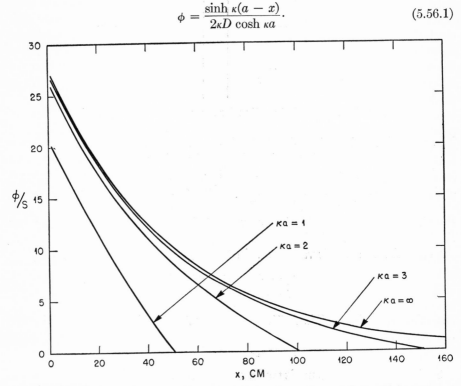

FIG. 5.57. Flux distribution for plane source in medium of finite thickness

5.57. Some idea of the effect of the finite thickness of the diffusion medium may be obtained from Fig. 5.57, in which the ratio of the flux to the source strength S, expressed in neutrons per cm^2 per sec, is plotted as a functon of the distance x from a plane source in an infinite medium, and also in media of three different thicknesses, such that κa is 1, 2, and 3 respectively.* The value of κ is taken as 0.02 cm^{-1}, which is that for graphite, and D is 0.90 cm. It is seen that when κa is 3, the flux distribution is not greatly different from that for an infinite medium, except near the boundary. This result is quite general, for κa is the important property in determining how the neutron flux falls off with distance from the infinite plane source. Thus, when the thickness of the medium, including the extrapolation distance, is about $3/\kappa$, or more, the behavior within a distance of $1/\kappa$ from the source, is essentially that of an infinite medium. It will be seen in § 5.64 that $1/\kappa$ is called the *diffusion length* of the neutrons in the given medium, and it is generally true that if the thickness is at least three times the diffusion length, it may be treated as an infinite medium at distances greater than one diffusion length from the boundary.

5.58. Attention may be called to the physical significance of the results depicted in Fig. 5.57. In the infinite medium there is no loss of neutrons, but in slabs of finite thickness neutrons will leak out. If the thickness is three or more times the diffusion length, most of the neutrons are scattered back before they reach the boundary and the leakage is very small. For slabs of lesser thickness, there is a greater loss of neutrons and this results in a more rapid falling off of the flux toward the boundary. This is very marked when the extrapolated thickness is equal to the diffusion length, i.e., $\kappa a = 1$. Only a relatively small proportion of the neutrons are scattered back before they reach the boundary and there is a marked decrease of the flux, even near the source plane.

PLANE SOURCE AND TWO SLABS OF FINITE THICKNESS

5.59. The case of an infinite plane source of neutrons diffusing into two adjacent slabs of different materials having infinite extent but finite thickness is of interest because it illustrates the use of the boundary condition in § 5.38, generally referred to as the

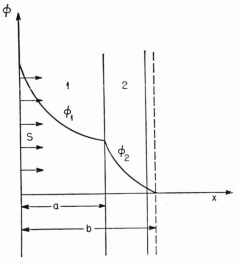

FIG. 5.59.   Flux distribution for plane source in two media of finite thickness

---

* Since (5.56.1) does not apply at the source itself, the curves are not extended to $x = 0$.

continuity of flux and current density at the interface between two media. The subscripts 1 and 2 will be used to distinguish the two materials (Fig. 5.59) so that κ_1 and D_1 refer to the slab nearest to the source, and κ_2 and D_2 to the other slab. Let a be the thickness of slab 1, and b the total thickness of the two slabs including the extrapolation distance of $0.71\lambda_{t(2)}$. As before, the flux distribution in the positive x-direction only will be considered; with an infinite plane source this is independent of y and z. The source will be taken to have such a value that the neutron current density in the positive x-direction at the source plane is S neutrons per cm^2 per sec.*

5.60. A wave equation of the form of (5.50.1) will apply to each slab, and the general solutions, of the form of (5.51.1), will then be

$$\phi_1 = A_1 e^{-\kappa_1 x} + C_1 e^{\kappa_1 x} \tag{5.60.1}$$

and

$$\phi_2 = A_2 e^{-\kappa_2 x} + C_2 e^{\kappa_2 x}. \tag{5.60.2}$$

There are, thus, four arbitrary constants, which can be evaluated by means of an equal number of boundary conditions. These are as follows:

(i) The source condition is $\lim_{x \to 0} J_+ = S$.

(ii) The flux vanishes at the extrapolated boundary of the outer slab, i.e., $\phi_2 = 0$ when $x = b$.

(iii) The neutron fluxes in the two slabs are equal at the interface, i.e., $\phi_1 = \phi_2$ when $x = a$.

(iv) The net neutron currents are equal at the interface, i.e., $J_1 = J_2$ when $x = a$.

5.61. From condition (i),

$$\lim_{x \to 0} J_+ = \lim_{x \to 0} \left(\frac{\phi_1}{4} - \frac{D_1}{2} \cdot \frac{d\phi_1}{dx} \right)$$
$$= A_1 \left(\frac{D_1 \kappa_1}{2} + \frac{1}{4} \right) - C_1 \left(\frac{D_1 \kappa_1}{2} - \frac{1}{4} \right) = S.$$

From (5.60.2) and boundary condition (ii) it follows that

$$A_2 e^{-\kappa_2 b} + C_2 e^{\kappa_2 b} = 0$$
$$A_2 = -C_2 e^{2\kappa_2 b}.$$

Since, by condition (iii), the fluxes are equal at the interface between the slabs, i.e., when $x = a$, it follows from (5.60.1) and (5.60.2) that

$$A_1 e^{-\kappa_1 a} + C_1 e^{\kappa_1 a} = A_2 e^{-\kappa_2 a} + C_2 e^{\kappa_2 a}.$$

---

* It should be noted that this is somewhat different from the case considered in § 5.52, for in the latter the source plane was assumed to be placed in the medium so that at or near the source plane there was a balance between the neutrons diffusing in both directions.

Finally, condition (iv) requires the net current densities to be equal at the boundary, i.e., $J_1 = J_2$, or

$$D_1 \frac{d\phi_1}{dx} = D_2 \frac{d\phi_2}{dx},$$

when $x = a$. Hence, from (5.60.1) and (5.60.2),

$$D_1\kappa_1(A_1 e^{-\kappa_1 a} - C_1 e^{\kappa_1 a}) = D_2\kappa_2(A_2 e^{-\kappa_2 a} - C_2 e^{\kappa_2 a}).$$

The relationships derived above from the four boundary conditions thus represent four equations in the four unknowns, A_1, A_2, C_1, and C_2, and so a complete solution of (5.60.1) and (5.60.2) is possible.

THE DIFFUSION LENGTH

SIGNIFICANCE OF DIFFUSION LENGTH

5.62. The treatment in this chapter has referred specifically to monoenergetic neutrons. In a thermal reactor there are present, of course, neutrons with energies ranging from several million down to small fractions of an electron volt. Even thermal neutrons do not all have the same energy, but, as stated in § 3.53, in weakly absorbing media they behave approximately like monoenergetic neutrons with properly averaged absorption cross section and mean free path. Since it is the behavior of thermal neutrons that is of immediate interest, the subsequent discussion will refer in particular to such neutrons, employing the results derived earlier for monoenergetic neutrons.

5.63. As the flux distribution about a point source is given by (5.49.1), it is possible to derive an expression for the mean distance traveled by a thermal neutron from the point of its formation to that at which it is absorbed. However, instead of treating the first spatial moment of the flux, as would be required in this case, it is preferable, in view of later developments, to consider the second spatial moment. This gives the mean square distance traveled by a thermal neutron from formation to capture. Consider a point source, and let ϕ be the flux in neutrons per cm² per sec at a distance r. The rate at which neutrons are absorbed is then equal to $\Sigma_a\phi$ per cm³ per sec, where Σ_a is the macroscopic absorption cross section of the medium. In a spherical shell element of radius r and thickness dr, i.e., volume $4\pi r^2\, dr$, surrounding the point source, the number of neutrons captured per second will be $4\pi r^2\, dr\, \Sigma_a\phi$. This is a measure of the probability that a neutron will be absorbed within the element dr at a distance r from the source; hence the mean square distance, $\overline{r^2}$, which a neutron travels from its source to where it is absorbed is given by

$$\overline{r^2} = \frac{\int_0^\infty r^2(4\pi r^2\Sigma_a\phi)\, dr}{\int_\rho^\infty 4\pi r^2\Sigma_a\phi\, dr}. \tag{5.63.1}$$

Since ϕ here represents the flux about a point source, it is given by (5.49.1), and hence (5.63.1) becomes

$$\overline{r^2} = \frac{\int_0^\infty r^3 e^{-\kappa r}\,dr}{\int_0^\infty r e^{-\kappa r}\,dr} = \frac{\dfrac{6}{\kappa^4}}{\dfrac{1}{\kappa^2}} = \frac{6}{\kappa^2}. \qquad (5.63.2)$$

5.64. As indicated above, the *diffusion length*, L, of the neutrons in a medium is defined as the reciprocal of κ, and so it has the dimensions of length; thus,

$$L \equiv \frac{1}{\kappa} = \sqrt{\frac{D}{\Sigma_a}}\ \text{cm}, \qquad (5.64.1)$$

since, by (5.44.3), κ^2 is defined as Σ_a/D. It follows, therefore, from (5.63.2) that

$$L^2 = \tfrac{1}{6}\overline{r^2}, \qquad (5.64.2)$$

so that the diffusion length squared is one-sixth of the mean square distance, as the crow flies, that a (thermal) neutron would travel from the point at which it just becomes thermal to capture.

5.65. If κ in (5.51.2) for diffusion from a plane source in an infinite medium is replaced by $1/L$, the result may be written in the form

$$\phi = A e^{-x/L}. \qquad (5.65.1)$$

Consequently, in this case the diffusion length is equivalent to the relaxation length (§ 3.47), i.e., the distance in which the neutron flux is decreased by a factor of e.

5.66. If (5.22.1) for the diffusion coefficient is introduced, it follows from (5.64.1) that

$$\frac{1}{L^2} = \kappa^2 = 3\Sigma\Sigma_a(1 - \bar\mu_0)\left(1 - \frac{4}{5}\cdot\frac{\Sigma_a}{\Sigma} + \frac{\Sigma_a}{\Sigma}\cdot\frac{\bar\mu_0}{1 - \bar\mu_0}\right),$$

correct to first order terms in Σ_a/Σ. For a weak absorber, this becomes

$$\frac{1}{L^2} = \kappa^2 = 3\Sigma_s\Sigma_a(1 - \bar\mu_0)$$

and for a diffusion material of high mass number, this reduces to

$$\frac{1}{L^2} = \kappa^2 \approx 3\Sigma_s\Sigma_a,$$

since, by (5.23.2), $\bar\mu_0$ is then small in comparison with unity.

MEASUREMENT OF DIFFUSION LENGTH

5.67. If it were feasible to construct an essentially infinite uniform plane source of thermal neutrons in an infinite medium, the diffusion length could be determined from measurements of the variation of the flux with distance from the source. It follows from (5.65.1) that

$$\frac{d \ln \phi}{dx} = -\frac{1}{L}, \tag{5.67.1}$$

so that a plot of experimental values of $\ln \phi$ against x, the distance from the source, should be a straight line with a slope of $-1/L$. However, actual experiments must be made with finite sources in finite media, and the results cannot be analyzed on the basis of the simple expression given above for a plane source in an infinite medium. In an infinite medium there is no net loss of neutrons due to leakage, but in a finite medium leakage occurs, and allowance must be made for this in the treatment of experimental data, as described below.

5.68. Consider a long rectangular parallelepiped of moderator material in which the diffusion length is to be measured, with a small source of fast neutrons, e.g., polonium or radium and beryllium (§ 3.2) at one end. If the material is a reasonably good moderator, then at a relatively short distance from the source a large fraction of the neutrons have been slowed down into the thermal region (see § 5.86, footnote, and § 6.154). Thus, at a not too great distance from the source the neutron flux behaves as though it came from a distributed plane source of essentially thermal neutrons. For purposes of the following analysis, therefore, it will be permissible to postulate a point source of fast neutrons giving rise to a distributed plane source of thermal neutrons.

5.69. Let this planar source of thermal neutrons be situated at $z = 0$, across the long block of material (Fig. 5.69). The x- and y-dimensions of the block, plus twice the extrapolation distance in each case, are taken to be a and b; in the positive z-direction the length of the block is c, which includes the extrapolation distance.

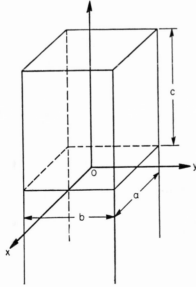

FIG. 5.69.   Rectangular parallelepiped for determination of diffusion length

5.70. The wave equation for *positive values* of z is

$$\nabla^2\phi - \kappa^2\phi = 0,$$

and the boundary conditions are:
 (i) The flux is everywhere finite and non-negative.
 (ii) The flux is zero at the extrapolated boundaries; thus,

(a) $\phi\left(\pm\dfrac{a}{2}, y, z\right) = 0$, i.e., $\phi = 0$ when $x = \pm\dfrac{a}{2}$,

(b) $\phi\left(x, \pm\dfrac{b}{2}, z\right) = 0$, i.e., $\phi = 0$ when $y = \pm\dfrac{b}{2}$,

(c) $\phi(x, y, c) = 0$, i.e., $\phi = 0$ when $z = c$.

(iii) A source condition, which will be considered later.
5.71. In rectangular coordinates, the wave equation is

$$\frac{\partial^2\phi}{\partial x^2} + \frac{\partial^2\phi}{\partial y^2} + \frac{\partial^2\phi}{\partial z^2} - \kappa^2\phi = 0. \tag{5.71.1}$$

Assume that the variables x, y, z are separable, so that it is possible to write

$$\phi = X(x)Y(y)Z(z), \tag{5.71.2}$$

where $X(x)$ is a function of x alone, $Y(y)$ of y alone, and $Z(z)$ of z alone. Making this substitution, (5.71.1) becomes

$$\frac{1}{X}\cdot\frac{d^2X}{dx^2} + \frac{1}{Y}\cdot\frac{d^2Y}{dy^2} + \frac{1}{Z}\cdot\frac{d^2Z}{dz^2} - \kappa^2 = 0. \tag{5.71.3}$$

5.72. Each of the first three terms of (5.71.3) is a function of one independent variable only, and so its value will be independent of the values of the other terms. Since κ^2 is constant, this condition can be satisfied only if each term in (5.71.3) is a constant; thus,

$$\frac{1}{X}\cdot\frac{d^2X}{dx^2} = -\alpha^2 \tag{5.72.1}$$

$$\frac{1}{Y}\cdot\frac{d^2Y}{dy^2} = -\beta^2 \tag{5.72.2}$$

$$\frac{1}{Z}\cdot\frac{d^2Z}{dz^2} = \gamma^2, \tag{5.72.3}$$

where α^2, β^2, and γ^2 are positive real quantities, and

$$-\alpha^2 - \beta^2 + \gamma^2 - \kappa^2 = 0. \tag{5.72.4}$$

5.73. The signs preceding α^2 and β^2 have been chosen for good reason, as will shortly be apparent. In the differential equation of the general form

$$\frac{d^2X}{dx^2} + k^2X = 0, \tag{5.73.1}$$

the solutions depend upon whether k^2 is a positive or a negative quantity. In the former case, i.e., k^2 is positive, the solution is the sum of imaginary exponentials which may be expressed as the sum of sine and cosine terms; thus,

$$X = A \cos kx + C \sin kx. \tag{5.73.2}$$

On the other hand, if k^2 is a negative quantity, the solution is the sum of real exponentials or hyperbolic sine and cosine terms; thus,

$$X = A \cosh kx + C \sinh kx \tag{5.73.3}$$

where the A's and C's are arbitrary constants.

5.74. The proper solution in the present problem can be derived from the boundary conditions. The flux is supposed to be everywhere finite and non-negative and to vanish at the extrapolated boundaries; in addition, the distribution must be symmetrical in the x- and y-coordinates, because the source is at the center of an x, y-plane. The flux will consequently vary somewhat in the manner shown in Fig. 5.74. The symmetry condition rules out the sin and sinh

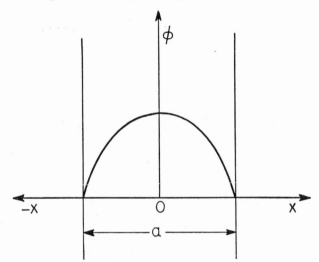

FIG. 5.74. Symmetrical flux distribution in x- (and y-) directions

terms, since they are not symmetric, and so the C's must be zero. Further, the requirement that the flux shall be zero at the extrapolated boundary eliminates the cosh term, since cosh kx increases monotonically with increasing x. The only permissible solution is, therefore,

$$X = A \cos kx,$$

and this means that k^2 must be positive to satisfy the conditions of the problem. It is evident, therefore, that if α^2 and β^2 are positive, as postulated, they must be preceded by minus signs, as written, in (5.72.1) and (5.72.2). In these circumstances, if γ^2 is positive it must appear with a positive sign in (5.72.3) because κ^2 is a real number greater than zero.

5.75. In view of the foregoing discussion, it follows that the solution of (5.72.1) must be of the form

$$X = A \cos \alpha x, \tag{5.75.1}$$

the sine term being eliminated by the boundary conditions (i) and (ii). However, in order to satisfy condition (ii$a$) more exactly, it is necessary that

$$\alpha = \frac{m\pi}{a}, \qquad m = 1, 3, 5, \cdots \tag{5.75.2}$$

with m equal to *an odd integer*. In this event, when x is equal to $a/2$, i.e., at the extrapolated boundary, then

$$X\left(\frac{a}{2}\right) = A \cos \frac{m\pi}{2} = 0,$$

as required, since the cosines of odd values of $\pi/2$ are zero.

5.76. The general solution of (5.72.1), which satisfies the boundary conditions (i) and (ii$a$), is then

$$X_m = A_m \cos \frac{m\pi x}{a}, \qquad m = 1, 3, 5, \cdots .$$

Similarly, (i) and (ii$b$) are satisfied by

$$\beta = \frac{n\pi}{b}, \tag{5.76.1}$$

so that

$$Y_n = B_n \cos \frac{n\pi y}{b}, \qquad n = 1, 3, 5, \cdots$$

is the solution of (5.72.2).

5.77. Turning to (5.72.3), it is apparent that, since γ^2 is a real positive quantity, the solutions must be of the form of (5.73.3); thus,

$$Z = C_1 \cosh \gamma z + C_2 \sinh \gamma z, \tag{5.77.1}$$

where C_1 and C_2 are constants. Since the boundary condition (ii$c$) requires Z to be zero where $z = c$, it follows that

$$0 = C_1 \cosh \gamma c + C_2 \sinh \gamma c$$

and hence,

$$C_2 = -C_1 \frac{\cosh \gamma c}{\sinh \gamma c}.$$

Upon introducing this value for C_2 into (5.77.1), the result is

$$Z = C_1 \cosh \gamma z - C_1 \frac{\cosh \gamma c}{\sinh \gamma c} \sinh \gamma z$$

$$= \frac{C_1}{\sinh \gamma c} (\sinh \gamma c \cosh \gamma z - \cosh \gamma c \sinh \gamma z)$$

$$= C_3 \sinh \gamma(c - z), \tag{5.77.2}$$

where the constant quantity $\sinh \gamma c$ has been included in C_3.

5.78. If $\sinh \gamma(c - z)$ is now expressed as the difference of two exponentials, it is seen that

$$Z = \frac{C_3}{2} [e^{\gamma(c-z)} - e^{-\gamma(c-z)}]$$
$$= Ce^{-\gamma z}[1 - e^{-2\gamma(c-z)}], \qquad (5.78.1)$$

where the constant $e^{\gamma c}$ has been included in C. If the z-dimension of the parallelepiped is very long, as postulated above, the quantity in the brackets in (5.78.1) is not very different from unity, and then this equation becomes

$$Z = Ce^{-\gamma z}. \qquad (5.78.2)$$

5.79. According to (5.72.4), γ^2 is equal to $\kappa^2 + \alpha^2 + \beta^2$, and since α and β can take on a series of values, of the form of (5.75.2) and (5.76.1), for the different m and n, it follows that for each m and n, there will be a γ given by

$$\gamma_{mn}^2 = \kappa^2 + \left(\frac{m\pi}{a}\right)^2 + \left(\frac{n\pi}{b}\right)^2, \qquad (5.79.1)$$

and the general solution of (5.72.3) will then be

$$Z_{mn} = C_{mn}e^{-\gamma_{mn}z}. \qquad (5.79.2)$$

5.80. In accordance with (5.71.2) the simplest solution of the wave equation will be a product of X, Y, and Z, but since the equation is linear, any sum of the products will be a solution. Consequently,

$$\phi = \sum_{m=1}^{\infty} \sum_{n=1}^{\infty} A_{mn} \cos \frac{m\pi x}{a} \cos \frac{n\pi y}{b} e^{-\gamma_{mn}z}, \qquad (5.80.1)$$

where the three arbitrary constants have been combined in A_{mn}. This equation satisfies the boundary conditions (i), (iia), and (iib), but in order to determine the coefficients A_{mn} for various values of m and n, it is necessary to introduce the source condition.

5.81. Consider a thermal point source, at the origin, emitting S neutrons per sec. A source of this kind may be written as $S\delta(x, y)$ at $z = 0$, where $\delta(x, y)$ is the Dirac *delta function*. This is defined to be zero everywhere except at $x = 0$ and $y = 0$, and at $x = 0$ and $y = 0$ it has such a value that

$$\int_{-\infty}^{\infty} \int_{-\infty}^{\infty} \delta(x, y) \, dx \, dy = 1, \qquad (5.81.1)$$

and then

$$\int_{-\infty}^{\infty} \int_{-\infty}^{\infty} S\delta(x, y) \, dx \, dy = S \int_{-\infty}^{\infty} \int_{-\infty}^{\infty} \delta(x, y) \, dx \, dy = S. \qquad (5.81.2)$$

As a consequence of this definition of the delta function

$$\int_{-\infty}^{\infty} f(x)\delta(x) \, dx = f(0), \qquad (5.81.3)$$

which is the value of $f(x)$ at the origin. If $f(x)$ represents the neutron source, (5.81.3) is equivalent to

$$\int_{-\infty}^{\infty} S(x)\delta(x)\, dx = S(0) = S,$$

since S is the value of the source at the origin. This result may be generalized to give (5.81.2) for the variables x and y.

5.82. In order to determine A_{mn}, the first step is to expand the source in a series of orthogonal functions that satisfy the boundary condition that it is $S\delta(x, y)$ at $z = 0$; thus,

$$S\delta(x, y) = \sum_{m=1}^{\infty} \sum_{n=1}^{\infty} S_{mn} \cos \frac{m\pi x}{a} \cos \frac{n\pi y}{b}, \qquad (5.82.1)$$

where the S_{mn}'s are coefficients related to the source strength. To determine the S_{mn}'s, each side of (5.82.1) is multiplied by $\cos (k\pi x/a) \cos (l\pi y/b)$ and integrated from $x = -a/2$ to $x = a/2$, and $y = -b/2$ to $y = b/2$. Since the functions are orthogonal in the intervals $-a/2$ to $a/2$ and $-b/2$ to $b/2$, all terms having $m \neq k$ and $n \neq l$ will be zero. Consequently,

$$S\int_{-a/2}^{a/2}\int_{-b/2}^{b/2} \delta(x, y) \cos \frac{m\pi x}{a} \cos \frac{n\pi y}{b}\, dx\, dy = S_{mn} \int_{-a/2}^{a/2} \cos^2 \frac{m\pi x}{a}\, dx \int_{-b/2}^{b/2} \cos^2 \frac{n\pi y}{b}\, dy.$$

The integrals on the right-hand side are equal to $a/2$ and $b/2$, respectively, and it follows from (5.81.1) that the integral on the left-hand side is equal to unity; hence,

$$S_{mn} = \frac{4S}{ab}. \qquad (5.82.2)$$

5.83. The source condition to be satisfied is that the number of neutrons flowing out of the plane $z = 0$ per cm^2 per sec, in each mode, i.e., for each value of m and n, must equal the number produced in that mode by the source. Since the solution of the problem has formally been restricted to positive values of z, then, by the arguments presented in § 5.50, the current density at $z = 0$, in any mode, is equal to half the number of neutrons produced in that mode.* The net current density in the mn-mode in the z-direction at $z = 0$ is given by (5.28.5), using (5.80.1) for ϕ_{mn} in the present case; the result is

$$J_{mn} = -D \left(\frac{\partial \phi_{mn}}{\partial z}\right)_0 = D\gamma_{mn} A_{mn} \cos \frac{m\pi x}{a} \cos \frac{n\pi y}{b}.$$

This is equal to half the number of neutrons emitted by the source in the mn-mode; equation (5.82.1) gives this as

$$\frac{1}{2}\left(\frac{4S}{ab}\right) \cos \frac{m\pi x}{a} \cos \frac{n\pi y}{b},$$

making use of (5.82.2) for the value of S_{mn}. Comparison of the two results shows that

$$A_{mn} = \frac{2S}{abD\gamma_{mn}}.$$

* The general results are unchanged if, for lack of symmetry, the fraction is not one half.

The complete equation for the flux is consequently

$$\phi(x, y, z) = \frac{2S}{abD} \sum_{m=1}^{\infty} \sum_{n=1}^{\infty} \frac{1}{\gamma_{mn}} \cos \frac{m\pi x}{a} \cos \frac{n\pi y}{b} \, e^{-\gamma_{mn} z}. \qquad (5.83.1)$$

5.84. This expression consists of a fundamental term, with $m = 1$ and $n = 1$, and a series of harmonic terms, with other odd values of m and n.   Each term falls off exponentially from the source with a different relaxation length, equal to $1/\gamma_{mn}$.   It is evident from (5.79.1) that γ_{mn} increases with increasing m and n, and so the harmonics fall off more rapidly than does the fundamental term, and at an appreciable distance from the source the latter makes virtually the sole contribution to the neutron flux.

5.85. To illustrate the manner in which the contributions from the various modes behave as a function of z, calculations have been made for graphite with

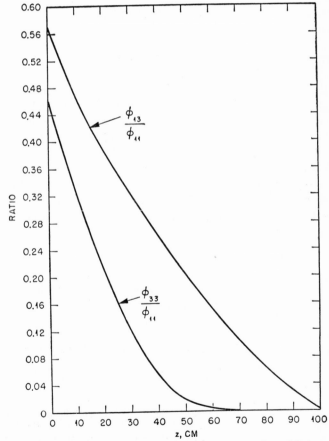

FIG. 5.85.   Relative contributions of higher harmonics as function of distance from source

$m = 1, n = 1; m = 1, n = 3$ (same as $m = 3, n = 1$); and $m = 3, n = 3$. The diffusion length is taken as 50 cm, so that κ^2, equal to $1/L^2$, is 4×10^{-4} cm^2, and it is supposed that $a = b = 222$ cm, which is a reasonable value for an actual experiment. Using these data γ_{11}, γ_{13}, and γ_{33} are calculated, by the aid of (5.79.1). The variation of the flux along the z-axis is then obtained by setting $x = 0$ and $y = 0$ in (5.83.1). The ratios ϕ_{13}/ϕ_{11} and ϕ_{33}/ϕ_{11} are plotted as functions of z in Fig. 5.85. It is seen that beyond two diffusion lengths (about 100 cm) from the source the contributions of the harmonics become very small. The same will be found to be true for calculations made along any line parallel to the z-axis. In view of the foregoing arguments, it follows that for measurements made beyond about two diffusion lengths from the thermal source, the flux consists essentially of the fundamental ($m = 1$, $n = 1$) term. Hence, the flux variation along any line parallel to the z-axis, i.e., for any constant x and y, is given by (5.83.1) in the simplified form

$$\phi(z) = \text{const.} \times e^{-\gamma_{11} z}, \tag{5.85.1}$$

so that

$$\frac{d \ln \phi(z)}{dz} = -\gamma_{11}. \tag{5.85.2}$$

5.86. In the experimental study of diffusion lengths, therefore, the neutron flux at various distances z from the source, along a line parallel to the z-axis, is determined by irradiating indium foils and measuring their induced beta activities.* The logarithms of the saturation activities (§ 3.62), which are proportional to $\ln \phi(z)$, are then plotted against z, and the slope of the linear portion, for values of z that are neither too near the source nor too near the end of the block, gives $-\gamma_{11}$, according to (5.85.2). Some actual experimental results obtained with graphite are plotted in Fig. 5.86; the value of γ_{11} is 0.0325 cm^{-1}. Knowing γ_{11} it is possible to calculate κ from (5.79.1) in the form

$$\kappa^2 = \gamma_{11}^2 - \left(\frac{\pi}{a}\right)^2 - \left(\frac{\pi}{b}\right)^2, \tag{5.86.1}$$

since m and n are both unity. In the experiment from which the results in Fig. 5.86 were derived, $a = b = 175.7$ cm, including the extrapolation distance; hence κ^2 is found to be 4.108×10^{-4} cm^{-2}, and the diffusion length L, equal to $1/\kappa$, is 49.3 cm.

5.87. It is of interest to note that the terms $(\pi/a)^2$ and $(\pi/b)^2$ allow for leakage of neutrons from the sides of the parallelepiped with finite dimensions a and b in the x- and y-directions. If these had been infinite, the correction terms would be

---

* A measurement of the *cadmium ratio*, i.e., the ratio of the activity of the foil without and with a covering of cadmium (§ 3.89), should be made at each point. If this is constant, the fast source neutrons have become completely thermalized in the region of the moderator in which the diffusion length is being determined (cf. § 5.68).

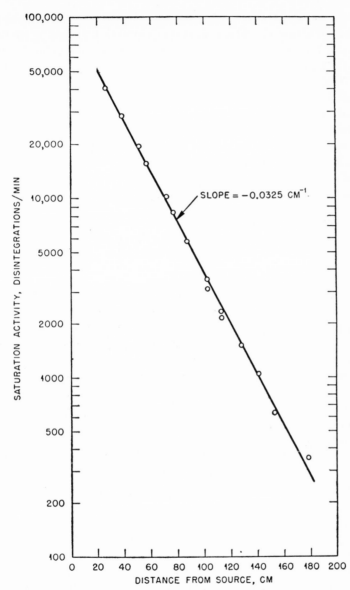

FIG. 5.86. Experimental data for determination of diffusion length in graphite

zero; there would then be no leakage and the solution would reduce to $\kappa = 1/L = \gamma_{11}$. The thermal neutron flux in the z-direction, as given by (5.85.1), would then fall off according to the relationship $\phi(z) = \text{constant} \times e^{-z/L}$, which is identical in form with (5.65.1) for diffusion from a plane source of thermal neutrons in an infinite medium.

Harmonic and End Corrections

5.88. If the ϕ_{13} and ϕ_{33} harmonics make a significant contribution to the thermal flux, it is necessary to apply a correction to the measured activities of the indium foils along the z-axis. The values will be proportional to the flux which, by (5.83.1), will now be represented approximately by

$$\phi(z) = \text{const.} \times e^{-\gamma_{11}z} \left[1 + \gamma_{11}e^{\gamma_{11}z}\left(\frac{1}{\gamma_{13}} e^{-\gamma_{13}z} + \frac{1}{\gamma_{31}} e^{-\gamma_{31}z} + \frac{1}{\gamma_{33}} e^{-\gamma_{33}z}\right)\right],$$

where the quantity in the square brackets is the "harmonic correction factor." A preliminary value of the diffusion length is obtained by neglecting the higher harmonics, and γ_{13}, γ_{31}, and γ_{33} can be calculated from (5.79.1). The experimental activities of the indium foil are then divided by the correction factor and the results are plotted, as in § 5.86, to give a new value of γ_{11} and hence of the diffusion length. If necessary, the process may be repeated until the values of the diffusion length converge to the required accuracy.

5.89. The exponential decrease of the (corrected) flux in the z-direction, which enters through (5.78.2), will not be applicable near the end of the finite block, i.e., when z approaches c in magnitude. The plot of $\ln \phi(z)$ against z will deviate from a straight line, for points near the top of the block, because the term in the brackets in (5.78.1) was neglected. This is called the "end correction term," and if the measured fluxes are divided by $1 - e^{-2\gamma(c-z)}$, the logarithms of the corrected values will fall on a straight line for all values of z, except the very lowest. In order to apply the correction, it is necessary to know γ and c; a provisional value of the former is obtainable from the linear slope of the $\ln \phi(z)$ against z curve for points not too near the top or bottom. The method of least squares can then be applied to the logarithms of the corrected fluxes to yield a better value for γ. By successive approximations the γ used in the end correction becomes identical with that derived by the method of least squares from the slope of $\ln \phi(z)$ against z.

5.90. The extrapolated height c of the block can be obtained in several ways. One is to find the value of c, slightly greater than the measured (geometrical) height, which provides the best fit of the data to a straight line. Another is to make flux measurements near the top of the experimental structure and from the results to find where the flux extrapolates to zero. A third method is to measure the flux at three equally spaced points along a vertical axis; if the coordinates are z, $z + \epsilon$, and $z + 2\epsilon$, and the observed neutron fluxes are ϕ_1, ϕ_2, and ϕ_3, respectively, then it can be shown by means of (5.78.2) that

$$\cosh \gamma\epsilon = \frac{\phi_1 + \phi_3}{2\phi_2} \tag{5.90.1}$$

and

$$\tanh \gamma(c - z - \epsilon) = \frac{\phi_1 + \phi_3}{\phi_1 - \phi_3} \tanh \gamma\epsilon. \tag{5.90.2}$$

As ϕ_1, ϕ_2, and ϕ_3 are known, the value of cosh $\gamma\epsilon$ can be determined from (5.90.1), and then tanh $\gamma\epsilon$ will be known. Hence tanh $\gamma(c - z - \epsilon)$ can be calculated from (5.90.2). Since z and ϵ are known, the use of a provisional value for γ permits c to be estimated. The result can be improved using increasingly more accurate values for γ obtained as described above. It is now possible to apply the end correction term and, from the best linear plot of the corrected values of ln $\phi(z)$ against the vertical distance z, the slope, equal to $-\gamma_{11}$, is obtained. Finally, κ^2 is determined, as described above.

EXPERIMENTAL RESULTS

5.91. In Table 5.91 are collected values for the diffusion length (L), the macroscopic absorption cross section (Σ_a), and the diffusion constant (D) for thermal neutrons in four important moderating materials. It will be recalled from (5.64.1) that $L^2 = D/\Sigma_a$. Since the values depend on the densities, these are also recorded.

TABLE 5.91.   THERMAL DIFFUSION PROPERTIES OF MODERATORS

Moderator	Density	L	Σ_a	D
Water (H_2O)	1.00 g/cm³	2.88 cm	0.017 cm⁻¹	0.142 cm
Heavy Water (D_2O)	1.1	100	0.000080	0.80
Beryllium	1.84	23.6	0.0013	0.70
Carbon (Graphite)	1.62	50.2	0.00036	0.903

DIFFUSION KERNELS

INTEGRAL FORM OF THE DIFFUSION EQUATION: DIFFUSION KERNELS IN INFINITE MEDIA

5.92. The neutron flux at a distance r from a point source emitting one neutron per sec in an infinite medium is given by (5.49.1) as

$$\phi = \frac{e^{-\kappa r}}{4\pi D r}.$$

This result can be put in a more general form so as to express the flux at a field point denoted by the vector $\mathbf{r}$ due to a point source at the vector $\mathbf{r}_0$; thus,

$$\phi = \frac{e^{-\kappa |\mathbf{r}-\mathbf{r}_0|}}{4\pi D |\mathbf{r} - \mathbf{r}_0|}. \tag{5.92.1}$$

5.93. In order to derive the flux distribution from a distributed source of neutrons at $\mathbf{r}_0$, represented by $S(\mathbf{r}_0)$ neutrons per cm³ per sec, the following procedure can be used. In the volume element $d\mathbf{r}_0$ about the point $\mathbf{r}_0$, there are $S(\mathbf{r}_0) d\mathbf{r}_0$ neutrons emitted per second. These source neutrons contribute $d\phi$ neutrons per cm² per sec to the flux at $\mathbf{r}$, and hence, from (5.92.1),

$$d\phi = \frac{e^{-\kappa |\mathbf{r}-\mathbf{r}_0|}}{4\pi D |\mathbf{r} - \mathbf{r}_0|} S(\mathbf{r}_0) d\mathbf{r}_0.$$

Since the diffusion equation is linear, the flux at $\mathbf{r}$ due to the distributed source is a superposition of the fluxes due to point sources. The total flux at $\mathbf{r}$ resulting from the distributed sources $S(\mathbf{r}_0)$ is obtained by integrating the expression for $d\phi$ over all space; thus,

$$\phi(\mathbf{r}) = \int_{\text{all space}} S(\mathbf{r}_0) \frac{e^{-\kappa|\mathbf{r}-\mathbf{r}_0|}}{4\pi D |\mathbf{r} - \mathbf{r}_0|} \, d\mathbf{r}_0. \tag{5.93.1}$$

In this volume integral the *kernel*, represented by

$$G_{\text{pt}} = \frac{e^{-\kappa|\mathbf{r}-\mathbf{r}_0|}}{4\pi D |\mathbf{r} - \mathbf{r}_0|}, \tag{5.93.2}$$

is called the *point diffusion kernel*. Comparison with (5.92.1) shows that, physically, it is the flux at $\mathbf{r}$ from a point source of one neutron per sec at $\mathbf{r}_0$.

5.94. The form of the diffusion kernel will depend on the geometry of the source. In the case of plane sources in an infinite medium, the diffusion kernel can be obtained directly from the solution of the diffusion equation for a plane source in an infinite medium [equation (5.51.2)]. The *plane diffusion kernel* for a source of one neutron per cm² per sec from a plane at x_0 is

$$G_{\text{pl}} = \frac{e^{-\kappa|x-x_0|}}{2\kappa D} \tag{5.94.1}$$

and the flux at x due to the plane source distribution $S(x_0)$ at x_0 is given by

$$\phi(x) = \int_{\text{all space}} S(x_0) \frac{e^{-\kappa|x-x_0|}}{2\kappa D} \, dx_0. \tag{5.94.2}$$

It should be noted that since κ has the dimensions of reciprocal length and D has the dimensions of length, the plane diffusion kernel is dimensionless. Hence, it is seen from (5.94.2) that $S(x_0)$ must here be expressed as the number of neutrons per cm² of source plane per cm of distance perpendicular to this plane per second. Then $S(x_0) \, dx_0$ is given, as required, in the same units as the flux, namely, neutrons per cm² per second.

5.95. Just as the flux distribution for a plane source can be derived from that of a point source by integration, as shown in § 5.52, so the plane diffusion kernel can be obtained, in an exactly analogous manner, from the point diffusion kernel. In fact, this is the general method used to determine diffusion kernels for sources of different geometries, e.g., spherical shell, cylindrical shell, etc. The results for a number of cases are summarized in Table 5.95.* Some applications of diffusion kernels to problems concerned with nuclear reactors will be given later.

---

* The symbols I_0 and K_0, in the line and cylindrical shell kernels, refer to modified Bessel functions of the first and second kinds of zero order (see Fig. 7.55).

TABLE 5.95. DIFFUSION KERNELS IN INFINITE MEDIA

Source Geometry	Notation	Source Normalization (per second)	Kernel
Point	$G_{pt}(\mathbf{r}, \mathbf{r}')$	1 neutron	$\dfrac{e^{-\kappa \mid \mathbf{r} - \mathbf{r}' \mid}}{4\pi D \mid \mathbf{r} - \mathbf{r}' \mid}$
Plane	$G_{pl}(x, x')$	1 neutron per cm²	$\dfrac{e^{-\kappa \mid x - x' \mid}}{2\kappa D}$
Line	$G_1(r, \varphi, r', \varphi')$	1 neutron per unit length	$\dfrac{1}{2\pi D} K_0(\kappa\rho)$ $\rho^2 = r^2 + r'^2 - 2rr' \cos (\varphi' - \varphi)$
Spherical shell	$G_s(r, r')$	1 neutron per shell of radius r'	$\dfrac{1}{8\pi rr'\kappa D} \left(e^{-\kappa \mid r - r' \mid} - e^{-\kappa \mid r + r' \mid}\right)$
Cylindrical shell	$G_c(r, r')$	1 neutron per shell of radius r' and unit length	$\dfrac{1}{2\pi D} \times \begin{cases} K_0(\kappa r)I_0(\kappa r') & r > r' \\ K_0(\kappa r')I_0(\kappa r) & r < r' \end{cases}$

5.96. Attention may be called to the fact that the diffusion kernels derived above apply to infinite media. They are consequently displacement kernels, that is to say, they depend only on the distance from the source to the field point. In a medium of finite dimensions, the kernels are no longer displacement kernels but are more complicated since they include the effect of the boundaries of the medium on the neutron flux.

THE ALBEDO CONCEPT*

THE ALBEDO IN DIFFUSION THEORY

5.97. In the study of nuclear reactors with reflectors, the situation arises in which two different media, indicated by A and B, are in contact. Neutrons are produced in the former, e.g., the reactor core, but not in the latter, e.g., the reflector; however, not all the neutrons diffusing from the source medium A into the medium B stay there, for some of the neutrons are scattered back from B into A. Within the approximations of the simple diffusion theory treated above, it is possible to define the *reflection coefficient* or *albedo* of the medium B as a quantity dependent only on the properties of the latter and independent of the source medium A with which it is in contact.

5.98. The albedo β of the medium B will be defined as

$$\beta \equiv \frac{J_{\text{out}}}{J_{\text{in}}}, \tag{5.98.1}$$

* See E. Amaldi and E. Fermi, *Phys. Rev.*, **50**, 899 (1936); G. Placzek, in "The Science and Engineering of Nuclear Power" (edited by C. Goodman), Vol. II, Chapter 7, Addison-Wesley Press, 1949.

where J_{out} is the neutron current density out of the medium B and J_{in} is that into this medium, at the interface with the source medium A. Thus, the albedo is the fraction of the neutrons entering the medium B which are reflected (or scattered) back to the source medium. The current out of the medium B across the surface of separation from a source to the left (Fig. 5.98), i.e., J_{out}, is equiva-

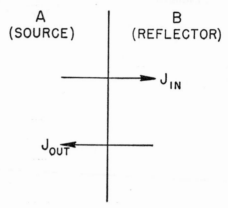

FIG. 5.98.   Albedo at plane source-reflector interface

lent to J_- as given by (5.28.3); similarly, J_{in} will be expressed by J_+, with appropriate modification. The albedo, according to simple diffusion theory, is thus

$$\beta = \frac{J_-}{J_+} = \frac{\dfrac{\phi}{4} + \dfrac{D}{2} \cdot \dfrac{d\phi}{dx}}{\dfrac{\phi}{4} - \dfrac{D}{2} \cdot \dfrac{d\phi}{dx}} = \frac{1 + \dfrac{2D}{\phi} \cdot \dfrac{d\phi}{dx}}{1 - \dfrac{2D}{\phi} \cdot \dfrac{d\phi}{dx}}, \tag{5.98.2}$$

where ϕ and $d\phi/dx$ are measured at the interface between the source and the reflecting medium. If the albedo is to be expressed in terms of the properties of the medium B, then D and ϕ and $d\phi/dx$ at the interface may be regarded as referring to that medium. However, it can be readily shown that because of the continuity of neutron flux and neutron current density at the interface (§ 5.38), ϕ and $D(d\phi/dx)$ may refer to either A or B.

CALCULATION OF ALBEDO

Case I. *Infinite Slab Medium*

5.99. Since both ϕ and $d\phi/dx$ depend on the geometry of the system, the albedo will also vary with the geometry. A few simple cases will be solved here for purposes of illustration. If the reflecting medium is an infinitely thick slab, the neutron flux falls off as $e^{-\kappa x}$ [cf. (5.51.2)]; hence $d\phi/dx$ varies as $-\kappa e^{-\kappa x}$, and (5.98.2) becomes

$$\beta = \frac{1 - 2\kappa D}{1 + 2\kappa D}. \tag{5.99.1}$$

If κD is small in comparison with unity, as is frequently the case, this reduces to

$$\beta \approx 1 - 4\kappa D.$$

The albedo for the infinite slab may thus be calculated from the diffusion coefficient and κ, the latter being the reciprocal of the diffusion length. Some of the results for thermal neutrons will be found in Table 5.102.

Case II. *Slab of Finite Thickness*

5.100. If a is the thickness of the slab, including the extrapolation distance, then the falling off of the flux with distance from the interface is given by (5.56.1). This may be written as

$$\phi = C \sinh \kappa(a - x),$$

where C is equal to the constant denominator of (5.56.1), so that

$$\frac{d\phi}{dx} = -\kappa C \cosh \kappa(a - x).$$

Hence, using (5.98.2), the albedo is given by

$$\beta = \frac{1 - 2\kappa D \coth \kappa a}{1 + 2\kappa D \coth \kappa a}. \qquad (5.100.1)$$

As $a \to \infty$, then $\kappa a \to \infty$ and $\coth \kappa a \to 1$; consequently, for a slab of infinite thickness (5.100.1) reduces, as it should, to (5.99.1).

5.101. Since $\coth \kappa a$ is a positive quantity, varying from ∞ (for $\kappa a = 0$) to 1 (for $\kappa a = \infty$), the albedo for a finite slab, as given by (5.100.1), is smaller than that for a slab of infinite thickness, the difference becoming less with increasing thickness a of the former. The physical significance of this result is that neutrons leak out of the finite slab and so there are fewer available to be scattered back. The leakage decreases with increasing thickness of the finite slab. However, when κa is only 1.5, the value of $\coth \kappa a$ is already down to 1.105, and for κa equal to 2.0, $\coth \kappa a$ is 1.037, so that the albedo for the finite slab will differ from the infinite slab value by no more than a few per cent. Thus, when the thickness of the slab is about twice the diffusion length, i.e., when $a/L = \kappa a \geqq 2$, the reflective properties are essentially those of an infinite slab.

5.102. Some values of the albedo for an infinite slab and for a slab of 40 cm thickness, calculated by means of (5.99.1) and (5.100.1), respectively, using the data in Table 5.91, are recorded in Table 5.102. From the values of a/L in the

TABLE 5.102. ALBEDO FOR INFINITE AND FINITE SLABS

Material	Infinite Slab	Finite Slab (40 cm)	a/L
Water	0.821	0.821	14
Heavy water	0.968	0.919	0.40
Beryllium	0.889	0.881	1.7
Graphite	0.930	0.892	0.80

last column, it is seen that the albedo in the finite slab does in fact approach that for an infinite medium when the thickness of the former is about twice the diffusion length.   Incidentally, the high values of the albedo for these moderators are of interest; nearly 90 per cent of the thermal neutrons impinging on a graphite slab of 40 cm thickness will be reflected back.

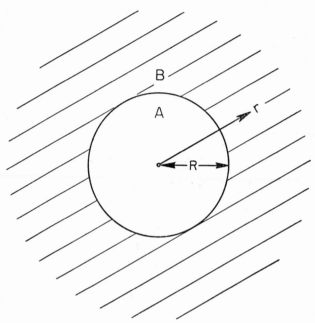

FIG. 5.103.   Albedo at surface between spherical source and infinite medium

Case III.   *Infinite Medium Surrounding a Sphere*

5.103. If region A, a sphere of radius R, containing a symmetric source of neutrons at its center, is surrounded by an infinitely thick reflector B (Fig. 5.103), the flux in region B, taking the origin at the center of the sphere, is

$$\phi = \frac{Ce^{-\kappa r}}{r},$$

provided r is greater than R, i.e., for points in the medium B.   At the interface, i.e., when $r = R$,

$$\frac{1}{\phi} \cdot \frac{d\phi}{dr} = -\left(\kappa + \frac{1}{R}\right),$$

so that from (5.98.2),

$$\beta = \frac{1 - 2D\left(\kappa + \frac{1}{R}\right)}{1 + 2D\left(\kappa + \frac{1}{R}\right)}. \tag{5.103.1}$$

As is to be expected, (5.103.1) becomes identical with (5.99.1) for an infinite slab when the radius R of the sphere becomes infinite.

5.104. A comparison of (5.103.1) and (5.99.1) shows that the albedo at an interior spherical surface is less than for an infinite flat surface. The physical reason for this is that the probability of a neutron being scattered back, after it has gone an appreciable distance into the diffusion medium, depends on the solid angle subtended by the source region. In the case of an infinite flat surface this angle approaches 2π, but it will obviously be much less for a sphere, to an extent dependent on the radius of the latter.

Albedo and Diffusion Properties

5.105. It will be apparent from an examination of (5.99.1) (5.100.1), and (5.103.1) that, in general, the albedo will be large when κD is small. Since κ is equal to $1/L$, this condition is that D/L should be small or, in other words, that the diffusion coefficient (or the transport mean free path) should be small in comparison with the diffusion length. For a medium in which this situation occurs, the albedo will approach unity, and most of the neutrons reaching the surface will be reflected back to the source. As will be seen in Chapter X, this fact is important in connection with the choice of a reflector for a nuclear reactor.

Albedo as a Boundary Condition

5.106. One application of the albedo is to replace the boundary condition at an interface between a source medium A and a finite diffusion medium B not containing a source, as in Case II above. According to (5.98.2)

$$1 + \frac{2D}{\phi} \cdot \frac{d\phi}{dx} = \beta \left(1 - \frac{2D}{\phi} \cdot \frac{d\phi}{dx} \right),$$

where β is the albedo, and upon rearrangement this gives

$$\frac{1}{\phi} \cdot \frac{d\phi}{dx} = -\frac{1}{2D} \left(\frac{1-\beta}{1+\beta} \right), \tag{5.106.1}$$

where ϕ and $d\phi/dx$ are taken at the interface between the media.

5.107. If B is in the form of a finite slab, as shown in Fig. 5.107, then, from (5.100.1)

$$\beta = \frac{1 - 2\kappa D \coth \kappa T}{1 + 2\kappa D \coth \kappa T},$$

where T is the thickness of the slab B, including the extrapolation distance. Upon introducing this value for β into (5.106.1), it is found that

$$\frac{1}{\phi} \cdot \frac{d\phi}{dx} = -\kappa \coth \kappa T$$

or

$$\frac{D}{\phi} \cdot \frac{d\phi}{dx} = -\kappa D \coth \kappa T, \tag{5.107.1}$$

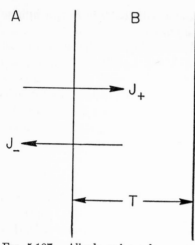

FIG. 5.107.   Albedo as boundary condition

which may be used as a boundary condition. However, by combining (5.38.1) and (5.38.2) it is seen that, at the boundary,

$$\frac{D_A}{\phi_A} \cdot \frac{d\phi_A}{dx} = \frac{D_B}{\phi_B} \cdot \frac{d\phi_B}{dx},$$

and hence (5.107.1) may be written in the form

$$\frac{D_A}{\phi_A} \cdot \frac{d\phi_A}{dx} = -\kappa_B D_B \coth \kappa_B T, \quad (5.107.2)$$

where the subscripts refer to the media A and B, respectively.   By using this boundary condition in the problem in § 5.59, with T equal to $b - a$, it can be shown to be equivalent to the boundary condition (iv), together with (iii).

5.108. The linear extrapolation distance at an interface is given by [cf. (5.39.2)]

$$d = -\frac{\phi}{d\phi/dx},$$

where d is the distance from the interface at which the neutron flux would extrapolate (linearly) to zero.   Hence, using (5.106.1),

$$d = 2D\left(\frac{1+\beta}{1-\beta}\right) = \frac{2\lambda_t}{3}\left(\frac{1+\beta}{1-\beta}\right), \quad (5.108.1)$$

where the diffusion coefficient D has been replaced by $\lambda_t/3$ [cf. (5.24.5)].   In terms of the more accurate transport theory (cf. § 5.40), this would become

$$d = 0.71\lambda_t\left(\frac{1+\beta}{1-\beta}\right). \quad (5.108.2)$$

This boundary condition is useful when the finite medium B is so thin that diffusion theory cannot be used (§ 5.16).   In this case, the diffusion coefficient and the transport mean free path refer to the medium A.   In the event that B is a vacuum, the albedo β is zero, and then (5.108.1) reduces to (5.39.3), while (5.98.2) gives the result in § 5.40.

ALBEDO AND NUMBER OF BOUNDARY CROSSINGS

5.109. In the passage of neutrons from a medium A to a medium B, the albedo of medium B is the probability that neutrons incident on B from A will be reflected.   Similarly the albedo of A is then the probability that neutrons incident on A from B will be reflected.   The albedo of each medium is related to the average number of times that a neutron crosses the boundary between the two media. Let α be the albedo of A for neutrons incident on A from B, and β be the albedo of B for neutrons incident from A. The average number of crossings made by neutrons in going from medium A to medium B will now be calculated.

5.110. The probability that a neutron from A will be reflected from B is β and the probability that it will make only one crossing is $1 - \beta$. The probability that the fraction β of neutrons reflected back to A will be reflected back to B is $\alpha\beta$; and, correspondingly, the probability that neutrons will make two and only two crossings is $\beta(1 - \alpha)$. In general, the probability that a neutron will make just n crossings in going from A to B is

$$p(n) = (\alpha\beta)^{\frac{n-1}{2}}(1 - \beta),$$

where n is an odd integer. The average number $\bar{n}$ of crossings that a neutron makes in going from A to B is

$$
\bar{n} = \frac{\sum\limits_{n=1,3,5,\cdots}^{\infty} np(n)}{\sum\limits_{n=1,3,5,\cdots}^{\infty} p(n)}
$$

$$
= \frac{1 + 3(\alpha\beta) + 5(\alpha\beta)^2 + 7(\alpha\beta)^3 + \cdots}{1 + (\alpha\beta) + (\alpha\beta)^2 + (\alpha\beta)^3 + \cdots}
$$

$$
= \frac{1 + \alpha\beta}{1 - \alpha\beta}. \tag{5.110.1}
$$

5.111. If an imaginary plane is considered in a region of infinite extent, α becomes equal to β, and (5.110.1) gives the average number of crossings that a neutron makes in going from one side of an imaginary plane in the medium to the other side; thus, in this particular case

$$
\bar{n} = \frac{1 + \beta^2}{1 - \beta^2}.
$$

For example, if the medium is graphite of infinite size, $\beta = 0.93$ and $\bar{n} = 14$.

Experimental Determination of Albedo

5.112. A method for the experimental determination of the albedo of a medium is to place in it a source of slow neutrons; then at a convenient position, away from the boundaries, to insert a thin foil of metal which becomes radioactive when it absorbs slow neutrons but, at the same time, does not have too high an absorption cross section. If ν slow neutrons per sec strike each side of the foil and none pass through, 2ν neutrons will strike per second. Actually, some of these will pass through the foil and then will return and strike it again from the original direction; the probability of this occurring is equal to β, the albedo of the medium. A portion of these will pass through once more, return and strike again, the probability being now β^2. The total number of impacts on the foil per second will be given by

$$2\nu(1 + \beta + \beta^2 + \cdots) = \frac{2\nu}{1 - \beta}.$$

5.113. Suppose now that a sheet of cadmium is placed on one side of the foil so that it absorbs virtually all the neutrons which strike the foil from that side. Slow neutrons will now strike the foil from one side only, and those passing through will not return. The number of impacts is now ν per second and, since the activation of the foil will be proportional to the number of neutrons which strike it, it follows that

$$\frac{\text{Activity of foil without cadmium}}{\text{Activity of foil with cadmium}} = \frac{2\nu}{1 - \beta} \cdot \frac{1}{\nu} = \frac{2}{1 - \beta}.$$

From measurements of the activity of the thin foil in the two cases, the albedo of the medium can be determined.

PROBLEMS

1. An isotropic point source of thermal neutrons is placed at the center of a uniform spherical medium of radius R, scattering cross section Σ_s, and absorption cross section Σ_a. The sphere is in a vacuum.

(a) If Σ_s is zero, what is the probability that source neutrons will escape from the sphere?

(b) Since Σ_s is not zero in practical cases, what is the probability that neutrons will escape from the sphere if $\Sigma_s \neq 0$? Physically, why is the leakage probability different in the two cases? Calculate the leakage probability for graphite for the two cases.

2. Find the neutron flux in an infinite medium from an infinitely long line source emitting one neutron per cm per sec by (a) using the point diffusion kernel, and (b) solving the boundary value problem directly.

3. Q thermal neutrons are produced per cm³ per sec uniformly in an infinite medium.

(a) What is the thermal neutron flux?

(b) A plane indium foil that may be considered infinite in extent in two dimensions and 0.0025 cm thick is placed in the medium. Calculate the depression of the neutron flux and the rate of activation of the foil per cm² if the medium is (i) H_2O and (ii) graphite.

4. I_0 neutrons per cm² are incident upon the plane face of a large block of graphite. What is the neutron flux in the block, assuming that it extends over all space where $x \geq 0$ and that neutrons are incident from $x < 0$? What fraction of the neutrons is reflected?

5. Derive a harmonic correction factor for data taken along the z-axis in the diffusion length measurement if the single source on the axis is replaced by two identical sources placed at $x = \pm \frac{1}{4}a$, $y = 0$, $z = 0$. Assume that the cross section of the assembly is square, i.e., $a = b$. What is the advantage of this arrangement?

Chapter VI

THE SLOWING DOWN OF NEUTRONS*

THE SCATTERING OF NEUTRONS

INTRODUCTION

6.1. In the preceding discussion of the diffusion of neutrons, it has been assumed that the latter all have the same energy, e.g., thermal energy. As stated in Chapter IV, however, neutrons produced in fission are fast, and they are subsequently slowed down by collisions with the nuclei of a moderator. This matter is of importance in connection with the theory of thermal reactors because the average crow-flight distance a neutron travels, between its birth as a fast neutron and its attainment of thermal energy, determines the neutron leakage while slowing down. It consequently has a direct bearing on the critical size of the reactor (§ 4.69).

6.2. After a general outline of the mechanics of elastic collisions, the treatment of the problem of slowing down in a medium in which fast neutrons are being produced continuously will be divided into two parts. First, consideration will be given to the distribution of neutrons as a function of energy, irrespective of their position. Subsequently, the spatial distribution of the neutrons, as a result of diffusion during slowing down, will be investigated. It is this latter aspect of the subject which is closely related to neutron leakage and the critical size of a nuclear reactor.

THE MECHANICS OF ELASTIC SCATTERING

6.3. As seen in Chapter III, the slowing down of fast neutrons is due almost entirely to elastic scattering suffered by the neutrons upon collision with nuclei of the moderator. Such collisions can be treated by the methods of classical mechanics, assuming the neutron and the scattering nucleus to behave as perfectly elastic spheres. By applying the principles of conservation of momentum

---

* A large part of the theory presented in this chapter was originally developed by E. Fermi; the theory of resonance capture was first worked out by E. P. Wigner. Solutions to many slowing down problems are given by P. R. Wallace and J. Le Caine in the references cited at the beginning of Chapter V.

and of energy, it is possible to derive a relationship between the scattering angle and the energy of the neutron before and after a collision with a nucleus. Upon introduction of an empirical scattering law, various useful results can be obtained.

6.4. It was indicated briefly in § 5.20 that, when considering elastic collisions of neutrons with atomic nuclei, two convenient frames of reference are used. These are the laboratory (L) system and the center of mass (C) system. In the former, the target nucleus is assumed to be at rest, whereas in the latter it is the center of mass of the neutron-nucleus system which is taken to be stationary. In the L system, the viewpoint is essentially that of an external observer, but in the C system it is that of an observer who travels with the center of mass of the neutron and nucleus taken together. For purposes of theoretical treatment the latter frame of reference is simpler, although actual measurements are made in the former.

6.5. The conditions before and after a collision in the two systems are shown in Fig. 6.5. Suppose that in the L system the neutron, having a mass of unity*

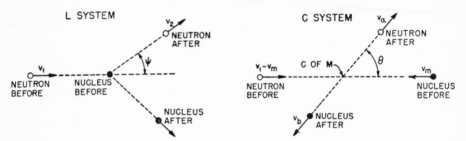

Fig. 6.5. Neutron scattering in laboratory (L) and center of mass (C) systems

on the conventional atomic mass scale (§ 1.4), moves with a speed v_1 toward a stationary nucleus with a mass number A. The speed of the neutron is thus v_1, with respect to the target nucleus, and, since its mass is unity, the momentum is also v_1. As the target nucleus is stationary, this represents the total momentum in the L system. The total mass of the colliding particles is $A + 1$, and consequently the speed v_m of the center of mass in the L system, i.e., with respect to the stationary nucleus, is given by

$$v_m = \frac{v_1}{A + 1}.$$ (6.5.1)

6.6. In the C system the center of mass is assumed to be at rest; hence, in this system, the nucleus must approach the center of mass with the speed v_m, defined by (6.5.1). Since the speed of the neutron relative to the nucleus before colli-

---

* The actual mass of the neutron is 1.00897 amu (§ 1.5), but the discrepancy between this value and unity, as postulated here, is negligible.

sion is v_1, the neutron must approach the center of mass with a speed of $v_1 - v_m$. The speed of the neutron before collision in the C system is thus

$$v_1 - v_m = \frac{Av_1}{A + 1},$$ (6.6.1)

using (6.5.1) for v_m.

6.7. It is seen, therefore, that in the C system the neutron and the scattering nucleus are apparently moving toward one another with velocities of $Av_1/(A + 1)$ and $v_1/(A + 1)$, respectively. The momentum of the neutron (mass unity) is consequently $Av_1/(A + 1)$, in its initial direction of motion, while that of the nucleus (mass A) is $Av_1/(A + 1)$ in the opposite direction. The total momentum before collision, with respect to the center of mass, is then zero, and by the principle of the conservation of momentum it must also be zero after the collision.

6.8. Following the collision, a neutron in the C system leaves in a direction making an angle θ with its original direction; this is the scattering angle in the C system. The recoil nucleus must then move in the opposite direction, since the center of mass is always on the line joining the two particles. If v_a is the speed of the neutron and v_b that of the nucleus after collision, in the C system, then the requirement that the total momentum shall be zero is expressed by

$$v_a = Av_b.$$ (6.8.1)

6.9. The speeds of the neutron and nucleus before collision, in the C system, are given by (6.6.1) and (6.5.1), respectively, as seen above. Consequently, the conservation of energy condition may be written as

$$\frac{1}{2}\left(\frac{Av_1}{A + 1}\right)^2 + \frac{1}{2} A \left(\frac{v_1}{A + 1}\right)^2 = \frac{1}{2} v_a{}^2 + \frac{1}{2} Av_b{}^2,$$ (6.9.1)

where the left-hand side gives the total kinetic energy before collision and the right-hand side is that after collision. Upon solving (6.8.1) and (6.9.1) for v_a and v_b, it is found that

$$v_a = \frac{Av_1}{A + 1} \quad \text{and} \quad v_b = \frac{v_1}{A + 1}.$$

Comparison of these results with (6.6.1) and (6.5.1) shows that the speeds of the neutron and the nucleus, in the C system, after the collision are the same as the respective values before the collision. Therefore an observer situated at the center of mass of the colliding particles would, before impact, see the neutron and nucleus moving toward him from opposite directions with velocities inversely proportional to their masses. After the collision the particles would appear to move away from him in opposite directions, usually different from the initial directions, with their speeds unchanged.

6.10. In order to determine the loss of kinetic energy of the neutron upon collision, it is necessary to transform the results obtained in the C system back to the L system. To carry out this transformation, use is made of the fact that the two systems must always move relative to one another with the velocity of the center of mass in the L system, i.e., $v_m = v_1/(A + 1)$, as derived in § 6.5.   Hence, the final velocity of the neutron, after collision, in the L system is obtained by adding the vector (v_m) representing the motion of the center of mass in the L system to the vector v_a indicating the velocity of the neutron after collision in the C system, as shown in Fig. 6.10.   The angle between the vectors, as may be seen from Fig. 6.5, is θ, the scattering angle in the C system.

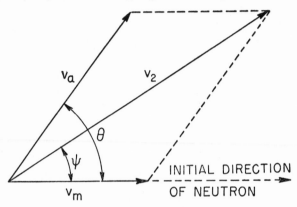

FIG. 6.10.   Transformation from C system to L system

6.11. If v_2 is the velocity of the neutron after collision in the L system, then by the law of cosines

$$v_2{}^2 = v_m{}^2 + v_a{}^2 + 2v_m v_a \cos \theta.$$

Introducing the values for v_m and v_a given by (6.5.1) and (6.6.1), respectively, the result is

$$v_2{}^2 = \left(\frac{v_1}{A + 1}\right)^2 + \left(\frac{Av_1}{A + 1}\right)^2 + \frac{2Av_1{}^2}{(A + 1)^2} \cos \theta$$
$$= \frac{v_1{}^2(A^2 + 2A \cos \theta + 1)}{(A + 1)^2}. \tag{6.11.1}$$

ENERGY CHANGE IN SCATTERING

6.12. The kinetic energy E_1 of the neutron before scattering is $\frac{1}{2}mv_1{}^2$, and the energy E_2 after the collision is $\frac{1}{2}mv_2{}^2$; hence, the ratio of the neutron energy after collision to that before collision is given by (6.11.1) as

$$\frac{E_2}{E_1} = \frac{v_2{}^2}{v_1{}^2} = \frac{A^2 + 2A \cos \theta + 1}{(A + 1)^2}. \tag{6.12.1}$$

This result may be expressed in an alternative form which is useful for certain purposes; thus, if α is defined by

$$\alpha \equiv \left(\frac{A - 1}{A + 1}\right)^2, \tag{6.12.2}$$

(6.12.1) becomes

$$\frac{E_2}{E_1} = \tfrac{1}{2}[(1 + \alpha) + (1 - \alpha)\cos\theta]. \tag{6.12.3}$$

6.13. The maximum value of the ratio E_2/E_1, i.e., the minimum loss of energy, occurs when $\theta = 0$, i.e., for a glancing collision; then $\cos\theta$ is unity, and (6.12.3) becomes

$$\frac{E_{\max}}{E_1} = 1 \quad\text{or}\quad E_{\max} = E_1. \tag{6.13.1}$$

In this event, the energies of the neutron before and after scattering are equal, and the neutron suffers no energy loss in the collision.

6.14. The minimum value of E_2/E_1, or the maximum possible energy transfer, occurs when θ is π, i.e, for a head-on collision; the value of $\cos\theta$ is now -1, and from (6.12.3)

$$\frac{E_{\min}}{E_1} = \alpha \quad\text{or}\quad E_{\min} = \alpha E_1. \tag{6.14.1}$$

It is seen, therefore, that the minimum value of the energy to which a neutron can be reduced in an elastic scattering collision is αE_1, where E_1 is the energy before the collision. The maximum fractional loss of energy in a collision is given by

$$\frac{E_1 - E_{\min}}{E_1} = 1 - \alpha, \tag{6.14.2}$$

where the actual maximum possible energy loss in a collision is $E_1(1 - \alpha)$.

6.15. Since, by (6.12.2), the quantity α is related to the mass number A of the target nucleus, it is evident that the loss of energy suffered by a neutron in a collision will also depend on this mass number. It is of interest to see, therefore, how α varies with the mass number of the target nucleus. For hydrogen, $A = 1$, and so $\alpha = 0$; it is consequently possible for a neutron to lose all of its kinetic energy in one collision with a hydrogen nucleus. This arises, of course, because the masses of the neutron and the hydrogen nucleus (proton) are essentially equal. For carbon, $A = 12$ and $\alpha = 0.716$; hence, the maximum possible fractional loss of energy of a neutron in a collision with a carbon nucleus is $1 - 0.716 = 0.284$.

6.16. Upon expansion, (6.12.2) for α can be written as

$$\alpha = 1 - \frac{4}{A} + \frac{8}{A^2} - \frac{12}{A^3} + \cdots \tag{6.16.1}$$

and for values of A in excess of about 50, there is no serious error in writing

$$\alpha \approx 1 - \frac{4}{A}. \tag{6.16.2}$$

The maximum fractional loss of energy per collision is then

$$1 - \alpha \approx \frac{4}{A}. \tag{6.16.3}$$

Consequently, for a target nucleus of mass number 100, the maximum fractional loss of energy a neutron can suffer in a collision is about 4 per cent; for a mass number of 200 it is 2 per cent.

SCATTERING LAW

6.17. The ratio of the neutron energy after collision to that before collision has been obtained, in the form of (6.12.3), as a function of the mass A of the scattering nucleus and of the angle of scattering θ in the center of mass system, on the basis of perfectly elastic collisions. If an empirical scattering law is specified in terms of a probability distribution for scattering as a function of the scattering angle, a corresponding distribution of neutron energy can be obtained by means of this equation.

6.18. Experiments indicate that the scattering of neutrons with energies less than a few Mev is spherically symmetric, i.e., isotropic, in the center of mass system. This is the empirical scattering law which will be postulated in the whole of the subsequent discussion.

6.19. Assuming spherically symmetric scattering, the probability that a neutron will be scattered into an element of solid angle $d\Omega$, corresponding to a conical element lying between the scattering angles θ and $\theta + d\theta$ in the C system, is

$$p(\theta) \, d\theta = \frac{d\Omega}{4\pi} = \frac{2\pi \sin \theta \, d\theta}{4\pi}$$
$$= \tfrac{1}{2} \sin \theta \, d\theta. \tag{6.19.1}$$

The probability that after scattering a neutron with initial energy E_1 will have an energy in the interval E_2 to $E_2 + dE_2$ is

$$p(E_2) \, dE_2 = p(\theta) \frac{d\theta}{dE_2} \, dE_2. \tag{6.19.2}$$

From (6.12.3), which relates E_2 to θ,

$$\frac{d\theta}{dE_2} = - \frac{2}{E_1(1 - \alpha) \sin \theta}$$

and hence

$$p(E_2) \, dE_2 = - \frac{dE_2}{E_1(1 - \alpha)}. \tag{6.19.3}$$

Thus, the probability that after scattering the energy of a neutron will lie in a specified interval ΔE is independent of the final energy and is, in fact, equal to ΔE divided by $E_1(1 - \alpha)$, the latter quantity being the maximum possible energy decrement per collision (§ 6.14). Since dE (or ΔE) is negative, because the neutron loses energy in a collision, the probability $p(E_2)\, dE_2$ is actually positive, as expected. The integral of $p(E_2)\, dE_2$ over the complete range from E_1 to αE_1 must, of course, be equal to unity; thus,

$$\int_{E_1}^{\alpha E_1} p(E_2)\, dE_2 = -\frac{1}{E_1(1-\alpha)} \int_{E_1}^{\alpha E_1} dE_2 = 1. \tag{6.19.4}$$

6.20. Although scattering is spherically symmetric in the C system, it is not so in the L system unless the mass of the scattering nucleus is large compared to the mass of the neutron. In the latter case, the center of mass of the system is located virtually at the nucleus and the L system becomes identical with the C system. The same conclusion may be reached in another manner. It is seen from Fig. 6.10 that

$$v_2 \cos \psi = v_a \cos \theta + v_m$$
$$= \frac{Av_1}{A+1} \cos \theta + \frac{v_1}{A+1}, \tag{6.20.1}$$

where ψ is the scattering angle in the L system. Further, from (6.11.1)

$$v_2 = \frac{v_1}{A+1} \sqrt{A^2 + 2A \cos \theta + 1}, \tag{6.20.2}$$

so that

$$\cos \psi = \frac{A \cos \theta + 1}{\sqrt{A^2 + 2A \cos \theta + 1}}. \tag{6.20.3}$$

For a heavy scattering nucleus, $A \gg 1$ and hence, from (6.20.3), $\cos \psi \to \cos \theta$; in other words, the scattering angle in the L system then approaches that in the C system. Consequently, if scattering for relatively heavy nuclei is spherically symmetric in the latter system, it will also be so in the former.

AVERAGE LOGARITHMIC ENERGY DECREMENT

6.21. A useful quantity in the study of the slowing down of neutrons is the average value of the decrease in the natural logarithm of the neutron energy in a single collision, or the *average logarithmic energy decrement per collision*. It is the average for all collisions of $\ln E_1 - \ln E_2$, i.e., of $\ln(E_1/E_2)$, where E_1 is the energy of the neutron before and E_2 that after a collision. If this quantity is represented by the symbol ξ, then

$$\xi \equiv \overline{\ln \frac{E_1}{E_2}} = \frac{\displaystyle\int_{E_1}^{\alpha E_1} \ln \frac{E_1}{E_2}\, p(E_2)\, dE_2}{\displaystyle\int_{E_1}^{\alpha E_1} p(E_2)\, dE_2}, \tag{6.21.1}$$

where $p(E_2)\, dE_2$ is the probability defined in § 6.19. The integration is over all possible values of the energy after collision, from the minimum, equal to αE_1, to the maximum, E_1.

6.22. The denominator of (6.21.1) is equal to unity, as may be seen from (6.19.4), and if the expression for $p(E_2) \, dE_2$ as given by (6.19.3) is introduced, it follows that

$$\xi = - \int_{E_1}^{\alpha E_1} \ln \frac{E_1}{E_2} \cdot \frac{dE_2}{E_1(1 - \alpha)}. \tag{6.22.1}$$

The integration may be readily performed by changing the variable to x, where

$$x \equiv \frac{E_2}{E_1},$$

so that

$$\xi = \frac{1}{1 - \alpha} \int_{1}^{\alpha} \ln x \, dx$$

$$= 1 + \frac{\alpha}{1 - \alpha} \ln \alpha. \tag{6.22.2}$$

Recalling the definition of α from (6.12.2), it follows that

$$\xi = 1 + \frac{(A - 1)^2}{2A} \ln \frac{A - 1}{A + 1}. \tag{6.22.3}$$

For values of A in excess of about 10, a good approximation is

$$\xi \approx \frac{2}{A + \frac{2}{3}}. \tag{6.22.4}$$

Even for $A = 2$, the error of (6.22.4) is only 3.3 per cent.

6.23. It will be noted that the value of ξ is independent of the initial energy of the neutron, provided scattering is symmetrical in the center of mass system.* It is this fact which makes ξ a useful quantity.   Incidentally, since ξ, which is the average value of $\ln (E_1/E_2)$, depends only on the mass number of the scattering nucleus, and is independent of the initial energy, so also must be the average value of the fraction E_1/E_2.   In other words, in collisions with specified scattering nuclei, a neutron always loses, on the average, the same fraction of the energy it had before collision.   This fraction decreases with increasing mass of the nucleus.

6.24. The values of ξ for a number of elements, especially those of low mass number, are given in Table 6.24.   The average number of collisions with nuclei of a particular moderator (§ 3.12) required to decrease the energy of a fission neutron, with initial energy of, say, 2 Mev, to the thermal value of 0.025 ev is

---

* Strictly speaking, this is true, provided the vibrational or thermal energy of the scattering nucleus is small compared with the energy of the neutrons, so that the nucleus may be regarded as being at rest before a collision.

TABLE 6.24. SCATTERING PROPERTIES OF NUCLEI

Element	Mass No.	ξ	Collisions to Thermalize
Hydrogen...............	1	1.000	18
Deuterium..............	2	0.725	25
Helium.................	4	0.425	43
Lithium................	7	0.268	67
Beryllium..............	9	0.209	86
Carbon.................	12	0.158	114
Oxygen.................	16	0.120	150
Uranium...............	238	0.00838	2172

obtained upon dividing $\ln (2 \times 10^6/0.025)$ by ξ for the given nuclear species; thus,

$$\text{Average number of collisions to thermalize (2 Mev to 0.025 ev)} = \frac{\ln \dfrac{2 \times 10^6}{0.025}}{\xi} = \frac{18.2}{\xi}. \tag{6.24.1}$$

Some values obtained from this equation are included in Table 6.24.*

SLOWING DOWN POWER AND MODERATING RATIO

6.25. According to (6.24.1), ξ is inversely proportional to the number of scattering collisions required to slow down a neutron from fission energy to thermal energy. Consequently, it is a partial measure of the moderating capacity of the scattering material. A good moderator is one in which there is a considerable decrease in energy per collision on the average, and hence it is desirable that ξ should be as large as possible. However, a large ξ is of little value unless the probability of scattering, as indicated by the scattering cross section, is also large. The product $\xi\Sigma_s$, where Σ_s is the macroscopic cross section for scattering, is called the macroscopic *slowing down power;* it is a better measure of the efficiency of a moderator, for it represents the slowing down capacity of all the nuclei in 1 cm³ of material. Since Σ_s is equal to $N_0\rho\sigma_s/A$, where N_0 is the Avogadro number, ρ is the density of the moderator, σ_s its microscopic cross section and A the atomic (or molecular) weight, the slowing down power is expressed by $N_0\rho\sigma_s\xi/A$. The values for a number of materials consisting of, or containing, elements of low atomic weight are recorded in Table 6.25; the scattering cross sections (Table 3.79) are assumed to be constant in the energy range from 1 to 10^5 ev.

---

* The use of ξ in (6.24.1) implies that the proper average value of E_1/E_2 to be employed in the calculation is the geometric average. This view is generally accepted, although it has been the subject of some controversy [cf., H. A. Bethe, *Rev. Mod. Phys.*, **9**, 120 (1937), footnote 27]. If the arithmetic average of E_1/E_2 is used, the results are somewhat different, especially for elements of low mass number. The average number of collisions required to reduce the neutron energy from 2 Mev to 0.025 ev is then 26 for H, 31 for D, and 119 for C.

TABLE 6.25. SLOWING DOWN PROPERTIES OF MODERATORS

TABLE 6.25. SLOWING DOWN PROPERTIES OF MODERATORS

Moderator	Slowing Down Power	Moderating Ratio
Water	1.53 cm^{-1}	72
Heavy water	0.170	12,000
Helium	1.6×10^{-5} *	83
Beryllium	0.176	159
Carbon	0.064	170

* At atmospheric pressure and temperature.

6.26. Although the slowing down power gives a satisfactory indication of the ability of a material to slow down neutrons, it does not take into account the possibility that the material may be a strong absorber of neutrons.   The slowing down power of boron, for example, is better than that of carbon, but boron would be useless as a moderating material because of its high cross section for neutron absorption (§ 3.76).   It is for this reason that boron is omitted from the tables given above; its slowing down power for neutrons is of no practical interest. In fact, any substance with appreciable absorption would be useless as a moderator.   The ratio of the slowing down power, as defined in § 6.25, to the macroscopic absorption cross section Σ_a, that is, $\Sigma_s \xi / \Sigma_a$, called the *moderating ratio*, is the more important quantity, from the theoretical standpoint, in expressing the effectiveness of a moderator.   Some approximate values of this ratio, using thermal absorption cross sections, are given in Table 6.25 above.   It is seen that heavy water (deuterium oxide) should be an excellent moderator.   Where the employment of a liquid moderator is not convenient, beryllium and carbon are evidently possible, but less efficient, alternatives to heavy water.   Ordinary water could be used in certain circumstances, but lithium, like boron, would not be satisfactory, because of its high absorption cross section.

LETHARGY

6.27. For many purposes, it is convenient to express the energy E of a neutron in a logarithmic, dimensionless form by defining a quantity u, called the *lethargy* or logarithmic energy decrement; thus,

$$u \equiv \ln \frac{E_0}{E}, \tag{6.27.1}$$

where E_0 is the initial energy of the source neutrons produced by fission.   For the source neutrons themselves the lethargy is obviously zero, and the value increases as the neutrons are slowed down.

6.28. If u_1 is the lethargy corresponding to E_1, the energy of a neutron before a scattering collision, and u_2 is the lethargy equivalent to E_2, the energy after a collision, then the lethargy change $u_2 - u_1$ is given by

$$u_2 - u_1 = \ln \frac{E_1}{E_2}.$$

Since the quantity ξ defined in § 6.21 is the average value of ln (E_1/E_2), it is evident that ξ may also be regarded as the average change in lethargy of a neutron per collision.   For spherically symmetric scattering, this is independent of the neutron energy (§ 6.23).   Thus, regardless of its energy, a neutron must, on the average, suffer the same number of collisions to increase its lethargy by a given amount.   This fact represents one of the advantages of the use of the lethargy variable.

6.29. According to equation (6.27.1),

$$E = E_0 e^{-u},$$

so that the plot of E against u, as in Fig. 6.29, is exponential in nature.   If a series of vertical lines are drawn at distances ξ apart, then, in view of the result derived in the preceding paragraph, the heights will represent the average values of the neutron energy for successive collisions.   It is seen, therefore, that a neu-

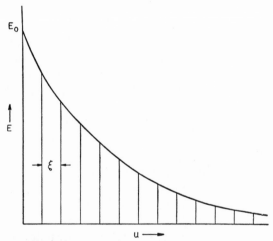

FIG. 6.29.   Relationship between energy and lethargy

tron loses, on the average, considerably more energy in earlier scattering collisions than it does in the later ones.

SLOWING DOWN IN INFINITE NONABSORBING MEDIA

INTRODUCTION

6.30. Suppose that fast neutrons are being produced at a definite rate, by fission, for example, uniformly throughout the volume of a particular moderator. As the neutrons collide with the nuclei of the moderator they steadily lose energy, but since fast neutrons are continuously being generated, a steady state distribution of neutron energies will soon be attained.   This energy distribution will, of course, depend on the extent to which neutrons are absorbed in the system, and on their escape from it while being slowed down.   For the present it will be postulated that *the moderator system is infinite in extent*, so that there is no loss of neutrons by leakage.   Further, consideration will first be given to the case in which there is no absorption of neutrons during the slowing down process. Subsequently, it will be shown what modification must be made to allow for neutron capture.

6.31. In the following treatment the steady state energy distribution will be developed for spherically symmetric scattering in the center of mass system, as postulated earlier (§ 6.18).   The results are not applicable to low neutron energies comparable to the vibration quanta of atoms forming part of a crystalline structure, e.g., about 0.3 ev for a hydrogen-containing compound and 0.2 ev for carbon (graphite).*   At these low energies the scattering nuclei cannot be regarded as stationary with respect to the neutrons in the laboratory system.

Slowing Down in Hydrogen

6.32. Because the solution of the equations is relatively simple, it is convenient to consider first the slowing down of neutrons in a hydrogen moderator.   The energy distribution of neutrons in the steady state will then approximate that in water, where most of the slowing down results from scattering by hydrogen nuclei.   The special point about slowing down in hydrogen, as compared with that in moderators consisting of heavier nuclei, is that a neutron may lose the whole of its energy in a single collision with a hydrogen nucleus, but this is not possible with heavier nuclei (§ 6.15).

6.33. Let $\phi(E')$ be the neutron flux per unit energy at energy E', and $\Sigma_s(E')$ be the corresponding macroscopic scattering cross section.   Then the number of scattering collisions per cm^3 per sec experienced by those neutrons within an energy element dE' is $\Sigma_s(E')\phi(E')\,dE'$.   This may be written in the form $F(E')\,dE'$, where $F(E')$, called the *collision density* per unit energy, is defined by

$$F(E') \equiv \Sigma_s(E')\phi(E'). \qquad (6.33.1)$$

6.34. After collision with hydrogen nuclei, the energy of the neutrons, initially E', will lie between E' and zero.   The fraction of the neutrons scattered into an energy element dE is thus dE/E'.   Hence, the number of neutrons scattered into the energy element dE, per cm^3 per sec, from scattering collisions in dE', is equal to $F(E')\,dE' \times dE/E'$.   The total number of neutrons scattered into dE, as a result of all collisions *of this type*, i.e., after previous scattering, from E_0 down to E, where E_0 is the energy of the source neutrons, is thus given by

$$\text{Number of neutrons scattered into } dE \atop \text{after previous scattering} = \int_E^{E_0} \frac{F(E')\,dE'}{E'}\,dE. \qquad (6.34.1)$$

* For monatomic metals and gases, e.g., helium, the vibrational quanta are much smaller.

6.35. In the foregoing calculation it is assumed that neutrons have already been scattered into the energy element dE' and then into dE. However, since a single collision with a hydrogen nucleus may decrease the energy of a neutron from its initial value E_0 to zero, some neutrons will be scattered into the element dE as a result of their first collision. If Q is the number of source neutrons entering the system, per cm³ per sec, at energy E_0, the number of first collisions is Q. Of these, the fraction dE/E_0 is scattered into the element dE, and hence,

$$\text{Number of neutrons scattered into } dE \text{ in first collisions} = \frac{Q}{E_0}\, dE. \tag{6.35.1}$$

The total number of neutrons scattered, per cm³ per sec, into the energy element dE, as a result of first or subsequent collisions, is then given by the sum of the quantities in (6.34.1) and (6.35.1).

6.36. Since it has been postulated that there is no absorption of neutrons, the condition for a steady state of neutron energy distribution is that the number of neutrons scattered out of each energy element is equal to the total number scattered into it per cm³ per sec. By the definition in § 6.33, the number of neutrons scattered, per cm³ per sec, out of the element dE is $F(E)\, dE$. Consequently, the steady state condition is

$$F(E) = \frac{Q}{E_0} + \int_E^{E_0} \frac{F(E')}{E'}\, dE', \tag{6.36.1}$$

the dE, which is common to each term, being cancelled out.

6.37. As the integral equation (6.36.1) is a function only of the lower limit, it can be differentiated, and the resulting differential equation can then be solved with the appropriate boundary condition. Thus, differentiation of (6.36.1) with respect to E gives the differential equation,

$$\frac{dF(E)}{dE} = -\frac{F(E)}{E}, \tag{6.37.1}$$

of which the general solution, obtained on integration, is

$$F(E) = \frac{\text{const.}}{E}.$$

The boundary condition, derived from (6.36.1), is

$$F(E_0) = \frac{Q}{E_0},$$

and, hence, the solution of (6.37.1) is

$$F(E) = \frac{Q}{E}, \tag{6.37.2}$$

as given by E. Amaldi and E. Fermi.* From the definition of $F(F)$, according to (6.33.1), the neutron flux per unit energy is then

$$\phi(E) = \frac{Q}{E\Sigma_s},$$ (6.37.3)

where Σ_s is a function of the neutron energy, although the argument has been omitted for simplicity. The results obtained above may be expressed in terms of lethargy as the variable in place of energy.

6.38. The neutron flux per unit lethargy, i.e., $\phi(u)$, is related to the neutron flux per unit energy, i.e., $\phi(E)$, by

$$\phi(u)\,du = -\phi(E)\,dE,$$ (6.38.1)

the negative sign being introduced since an increase in energy is equivalent to a decrease in lethargy. Upon differentiation of (6.27.1), it is seen that

$$du = -\frac{dE}{E},$$ (6.38.2)

and consequently (6.38.1) becomes

$$\phi(u) = E\phi(E).$$ (6.38.3)

Similarly, it can be readily shown that the collision density per unit lethargy, i.e., $F(u)$, can be expressed as

$$F(u) = \phi(u)\Sigma_s(u) = EF(E).$$ (6.38.4)

6.39. The foregoing relationships involving lethargy are completely general, irrespective of the nature of the moderator. When applied to scattering in hydrogen, the neutron flux per unit lethargy is obtained from (6.37.3) and (6.38.3) as

$$\phi(u) = \frac{Q}{\Sigma_s},$$ (6.39.1)

where Σ_s is a function of the energy (or lethargy). The collision density per unit lethargy is, then,

$$F(u) = Q.$$ (6.39.2)

Thus, the collision density per unit lethargy in hydrogen is constant at all values of the lethargy (or energy) and is equal to the source strength.

SLOWING DOWN DENSITY IN HYDROGEN

6.40. An important quantity in the study of neutron scattering is the *slowing down density*. This is represented by the symbol q and is defined as the number of neutrons, per cm^3 per sec, that slow down past a given energy E. The fraction of collisions in hydrogen taking place in the energy element dE' which scatter

* E. Amaldi and E. Fermi, *Phys. Rev.*, **50**, 899 (1936).

neutrons past energy E is E/E'.* Hence, the number of neutrons, per cm³ per sec, slowed down past energy E after scattering in the element dE' is $F(E')\, dE' \times E/E'$. The total number slowed down past E, after previous scattering in the energy range from E_0 to E, is obtained, as before, by integration between these limits; thus,

$$\text{Number of neutrons slowed down past energy } E \text{ after previous scattering} = E \int_E^{E_0} \frac{F(E')}{E'}\, dE'. \quad (6.40.1)$$

6.41. To obtain the slowing down density, there must be added the number of neutrons, per cm³ per sec, slowed down past E as a result of first collisions of source neutrons. The fraction of such collisions which lead to scattering past energy E is E/E_0, and since the number of first collisions is equal to Q, the number of source neutrons (§ 6.35), it follows that

$$\text{Number of neutrons slowed down past energy } E \text{ in first collisions} = \frac{QE}{E_0}. \quad (6.41.1)$$

Consequently, the slowing down density q, in the case of hydrogen moderator with no absorption of neutrons, is given by

$$q = \frac{QE}{E_0} + E \int_E^{E_0} \frac{F(E')}{E'}\, dE'. \quad (6.41.2)$$

6.42. In the steady state condition, $F(E')$ is equal to Q/E', according to (6.37.2), and hence (6.41.2) becomes

$$q = \frac{QE}{E_0} + QE \int_E^{E_0} \frac{dE'}{E'^2}$$
$$= Q. \quad (6.42.1)$$

6.43. Thus, in an infinite hydrogen medium in which there is no absorption of neutrons, the slowing down density is constant, independent of the energy, and is equal to the source strength. This is, of course, to be expected physically. If there are no losses, by leakage or absorption, during the slowing down process, the same number of neutrons will slow down past all energies in the steady state. Further, this number must be equal to the number of source neutrons entering the system.

SLOWING DOWN IN MEDIA OF MASS NUMBER GREATER THAN UNITY

6.44. In the general case of neutron moderation in media containing a single type of nucleus of mass number greater than unity, it is not possible to express the collision density, or the slowing down density, over the whole range of en-

---

* This is derived from the result obtained in § 6.19. Neutrons scattered past E must have energies in the range from E to zero, while the maximum possible energy decrement of neutrons scattered in the element dE' is from E' to zero.

ergies in terms of a single integral, as was done for scattering in hydrogen [cf., equations (6.36.1) and (6.41.2)]. For heavier nuclei the minimum possible energy of neutrons after first collisions is αE_0 (§ 6.14), where, as before, E_0 is the energy of the source neutrons. In evaluating the collision (or slowing down) density, neutrons in the energy interval from E_0 to αE_0 must therefore be treated separately from those of energies less than αE_0.

6.45. Slowing down of neutrons into the interval from E_0 to αE_0 will result from both first-collision scattering of source neutrons as well as from multiple scattering of neutrons with energies between E_0 and E. At neutron energies less than αE_0, however, the first-collision scattering of source neutrons can no longer contribute to the collision (or slowing down) density. The steady state energy distribution will thus be expressed differently in the intervals from E_0 to αE_0 and from αE_0 to zero, respectively. The cases will thus be considered separately.

· Case I.   *Neutron Energies in the Interval from E_0 to αE_0 ($\alpha E_0 < E < E_0$)*

6.46. As for scattering in hydrogen, the number of scattering collisions, per cm³ per sec, of neutrons in the energy element dE' is $F(E') \, dE'$. The fraction of the neutrons scattered into the element dE is $dE/(E' - \alpha E')$, since $E' - \alpha E'$ is the energy interval into which scattering is possible. The number of neutrons scattered into dE, from collisions in dE', is thus $F(E') \, dE' \times dE/E'(1 - \alpha)$. The total number of neutrons scattered into dE, after previous scattering in the range from E_0 to E, is then obtained by integration between E and E_0, as in § 6.34.

6.47. Of the source neutrons having energy E_0, the fraction $dE/(E_0 - \alpha E_0)$ is scattered into the energy element dE. Hence, if Q is the number of source neutrons entering the system, per cm³ per sec, the number of neutrons scattered into dE in first collisions is $Q \, dE/E_0(1 - \alpha)$.

6.48. The number of neutrons, per cm³ per sec, scattered out of the energy element dE is $F(E) \, dE$; hence in the steady state, when the number of neutrons scattered into the element is equal to the number scattered out, it follows that

$$F(E) = \frac{Q}{E_0(1 - \alpha)} + \int_E^{E_0} \frac{F(E')}{E'(1 - \alpha)} \, dE'. \qquad (6.48.1)$$

6.49. The integral equation can be solved, as before, by differentiating with respect to E, giving

$$\frac{dF(E)}{dE} = - \frac{F(E)}{E(1 - \alpha)}, \qquad (6.49.1)$$

the general solution of which, obtained by integration, is

$$F(E) = \frac{\text{const.}}{E^{\frac{1}{1-\alpha}}}. \qquad (6.49.2)$$

6.50. The boundary condition of the problem, from (6.48.1), is

$$F(E_0) = \frac{Q}{E_0(1-\alpha)},$$
(6.50.1)

and hence the solution for the present case is

$$F(E) = \frac{QE_0^{\frac{\alpha}{1-\alpha}}}{1-\alpha} \cdot \frac{1}{E^{\frac{1}{1-\alpha}}}.$$
(6.50.2)

This expression gives the collision density per unit energy, in the steady state, for neutrons with energy E, when $\alpha E_0 < E < E_0$, i.e., in the energy interval from E_0 to αE_0.

6.51. The corresponding value of $F(u)$, the collision density per unit lethargy, can be obtained by using (6.38.4); thus,

$$F(u) = \frac{QE_0^{\frac{\alpha}{1-\alpha}}}{1-\alpha} \cdot \frac{1}{E^{\frac{\alpha}{1-\alpha}}}.$$
(6.51.1)

It will be noted that, since α is zero for hydrogen moderator, (6.50.2) and (6.51.1) reduce to (6.37.2) and (6.39.2), respectively, when α is set equal to zero.

6.52. Some actual plots of $F(u)$ will be given below, after the behavior in the lower energy interval has been considered. In the meantime, it can be seen from (6.51.1) that $F(u)$ increases monotonically as E decreases within the interval E_0 to αE_0. The minimum value of $F(u)$, for neutron energy E_0, is

$$F(u)_{\min} = \frac{Q}{1-\alpha},$$

while the maximum value, for neutron energy αE_0, is

$$F(u)_{\max} = \frac{Q}{1-\alpha} \cdot \frac{1}{\alpha^{\frac{\alpha}{1-\alpha}}}.$$

Case II. *Neutron Energies Less than αE_0 ($E < \alpha E_0$)*

6.53. As in § 6.34, the number of neutrons scattered into the energy element dE, from collisions in dE', is $F(E') \, dE' \times dE/E'(1-\alpha)$. The maximum energy of a neutron, which could have energy E after such scattering, is E/α. Hence the total number of neutrons scattered into dE is obtained by integrating the foregoing expression over the limits from E to E/α. Since there are now no first collisions to be included,

$$\text{Number of neutrons scattered into } dE = \int_E^{E/\alpha} \frac{F(E') \, dE'}{E'(1-\alpha)} \, dE.$$

6.54. If $F(E)$ is the collision density per unit energy, the number of neutrons scattered out of the element dE is $F(E)\,dE$. Hence, in the steady state, when the number of neutrons scattered into dE must equal the number scattered out,

$$F(E) = \int_E^{E/\alpha} \frac{F(E')}{E'(1-\alpha)}\,dE'. \tag{6.54.1}$$

A complete solution of this equation, for all values of E less than αE_0 has been obtained,* but it will not be given here. The general nature of the results will be described, and then a simple solution will be derived for the so-called asymptotic case, when E is much less than αE_0.

6.55. The collision density per unit lethargy, i.e., $F(u)$, as derived from the complete solution of (6.54.1), is plotted in Figs. 6.55a and 6.55b as a function of the neutron energy for scattering in hydrogen, deuterium, and carbon. The source neutrons are assumed to have an energy of 2 Mev, and the results are normalized to 1 source neutron per cm³ per sec. It will be shown below (§ 6.66) that the asymptotic value of $F(u)$, approached when the neutron energy is appreciably less than E_0, is Q/ξ in the general case. Since Q is here assumed to be unity, the asymptotic value of $F(u)$ in Figs. 6.55a and 6.55b is $1/\xi$. For hydrogen as moderator, this result, with $\xi = 1$, applies at all values of the neutron energy.

6.56. An examination of the curves shows that in the energy interval from E_0 to αE_0 the collision density $F(u)$, for nuclei of mass number greater than unity, increases monotonically with decreasing energy, as expected (§ 6.52). In this interval, the first collisions of the source neutrons contribute equally to $F(u)$ for all values of the energy, and the multiple scattering tends to increase $F(u)$ with decreasing neutron energy.

6.57. At $E = \alpha E_0$, the value of $F(u)$ exhibits a sharp discontinuity, decreasing by an amount equal to $\alpha Q/(1-\alpha)$. That this is so may be seen by setting E equal to αE_0 in the integration limits of (6.48.1) and (6.54.1), which hold in the energy intervals from E_0 to αE_0 and from αE_0 down to zero, respectively. If the respective values of $F(\alpha E_0)$ are distinguished by the subscripts 1 and 2, it is seen that

$$F_1(\alpha E_0) = \frac{Q}{E_0(1-\alpha)} + \int_{\alpha E_0}^{E_0} \frac{F(E')}{E'(1-\alpha)}\,dE'$$

and

$$F_2(\alpha E_0) = \int_{\alpha E_0}^{E_0} \frac{F(E')}{E'(1-\alpha)}\,dE'.$$

Upon subtraction, it follows that

$$F_1(\alpha E_0) - F_2(\alpha E_0) = \frac{Q}{E_0(1-\alpha)},$$

* G. Placzek, *Phys. Rev.*, **69**, 423 (1946).

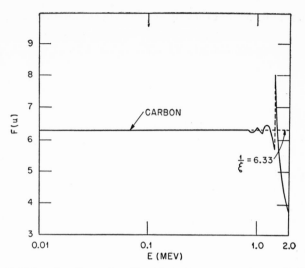

FIG. 6.55a.   Collision density as function of neutron energy for scattering in carbon

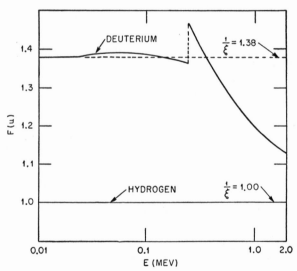

FIG. 6.55b.   Collision density as function of neutron energy for scattering in hydrogen and deuterium

and this represents the discontinuity in $F(E)$ at $E = \alpha E_0$. The corresponding discontinuity in $F(u)$ is obtained, according to (6.38.4), upon multiplying by the energy value at αE_0. Its value is thus $\alpha Q/(1 - \alpha)$, as stated above.

6.58. Physically, the discontinuity arises from the fact that in the energy interval αE_0 to $\alpha E_0 + dE$ the source neutrons contribute to the flux after a single scattering collision, but they do not do so in the interval from αE_0 to $\alpha E_0 -$ dE. The collision density at an energy just larger than αE_0 will thus be considerably greater than at an energy just smaller than αE_0.

6.59. As the energy falls below αE_0, the collision density per unit lethargy at first increases with decreasing energy; it then oscillates about the asymptotic value $1/\xi$ (or Q/ξ, in general) and finally dampens out to the latter. The maxima and minima are a consequence of the discontinuous behavior of $F(u)$ when the neutron energy is αE_0. The effect of collisions with neutrons of energy $\alpha E_0'$ will appear down to an energy of $\alpha^2 E_0$, and collisions at the latter energy will have an effect down to $\alpha^3 E_0$, and so on. However, because multiple collisions tend to produce a more uniform energy distribution, the maxima and minima in $F(u)$ become less and less marked with decreasing neutron energy, and have virtually disappeared completely at energies less than about $\alpha^3 E_0$.

6.60. At lower energies the contributions to $F(u)$ come entirely from neutrons that have been scattered several times. The number of scattering collisions per unit lethargy is then expected to be constant, since ξ, the average logarithmic energy decrement per collision, is independent of energy (§ 6.23). Consequently, when the energy is below $\alpha^3 E_0$, approximately, $F(u)$ attains its asymptotic value of $1/\xi$ (or Q/ξ, in general).

6.61. Since α increases with increasing mass number, $\alpha^3 E_0$ will also increase correspondingly. Hence, the larger the mass of the scattering nucleus, the higher the neutron energy at which $F(u)$ approaches its asymptotic value. This is seen to be the case in Figs. 6.55a and 6.55b; for carbon the collision density is equal to $1/\xi$ for neutron energies of less than about 0.7 Mev, but for deuterium this is not so until the neutron energy is down to about 0.02 Mev. The maximum deviation from asymptotic behavior, which is determined by the magnitude of the discontinuity at energy αE_0, also increases with α and hence with the mass number. However, as just shown, the oscillations do not extend as far down the energy scale.

6.62. It will be seen below that the foregoing results have a particular significance in the case of slowing down in an absorbing medium, through a series of resonance lines. Each line acts as a negative source and introduces oscillations in the collision density which persist down to an energy interval of about $\alpha^3 E_r$ below the resonance line at energy E_r. Consequently, it is only when the spacing between resonance lines is at least $\alpha^3 E_r$ that the resonance lines can be treated as independent.

Case III.   *Asymptotic Case* $(E \ll \alpha E_0)$

6.63. As stated earlier, (6.54.1) can be solved fairly simply in the asymptotic case. A solution is then of the form

$$F(E) = \frac{\text{const.}}{E},$$ (6.63.1)

as may be verified by substituting const./E' for $F(E')$ in equation (6.54.1) and performing the integration.   Since $F(u)$ is equal to $EF(E)$, by (6.38.4), it is independent of the neutron energy.   The problem now is to determine the value of the constant in (6.63.1).

6.64. The first step is to derive an expression for the slowing down density for neutrons of energy less than αE_0.   The fraction of collisions taking place in the energy element dE' which scatter neutrons past energy E is $(E - \alpha E')/E'(1 - \alpha)$. The numerator is the interval below E into which scattering from dE' (or energy E') is possible, and the denominator $E'(1 - \alpha)$ is the maximum energy range of neutrons scattered in the element dE'.   Since $F(E')\ dE'$ is the total number of scattering collisions, per cm³ per sec, in the energy element dE', the number of these collisions which lead to scattering past energy E is $F(E')\ dE' \times (E - \alpha E')/E'(1 - \alpha)$.   The total number of neutrons scattered past energy E, which is the slowing down density q, as defined in § 6.40, is then obtained by integration between E and E/α as in § 6.53; thus,

$$q = \int_{E}^{E/\alpha} F(E') \frac{E - \alpha E'}{E'(1 - \alpha)}\ dE', \tag{6.64.1}$$

provided E is less than αE_0.

6.65. By (6.63.1), $F(E')$ may be replaced by const./E', so that the expression for q becomes

$$q = \frac{\text{const.}}{1 - \alpha} \int_{E}^{E/\alpha} \frac{E - \alpha E'}{E'^2}\ dE'$$

$$= \text{const.} \times \left(1 + \frac{\alpha}{1 - \alpha} \ln \alpha\right). \tag{6.65.1}$$

Upon introducing (6.22.2) into (6.65.1), it follows that

$$q = \text{const.} \times \xi. \tag{6.65.2}$$

6.66. If there is no leakage or absorption, as postulated in § 6.30, the same number of neutrons must slow down past each energy; hence, for all energies, the slowing down density must be a constant equal to Q, the source strength. It follows, therefore, that in these circumstances

$$q = Q,$$

and, hence, it can be seen from (6.65.2) that the constant is Q/ξ.   If this value is substituted into (6.63.1), the result is

$$F(E) = \frac{Q}{E\xi}. \tag{6.66.1}$$

Using (6.38.4) to relate $F(E)$ to $F(u)$, then

$$F(u) = \frac{Q}{\xi}. \tag{6.66.2}$$

6.67. From the expressions for $F(E)$ and $F(u)$ and the general definitions of these quantities given by (6.33.1) and (6.38.4), respectively, it follows that

$$\phi(E) = \frac{Q}{E\Sigma_s\xi} = \frac{q}{E\Sigma_s\xi} \qquad (6.67.1)$$

and

$$\phi(u) = \frac{Q}{\Sigma_s\xi} = \frac{q}{\Sigma_s\xi}, \qquad (6.67.2)$$

since q is equal to Q. An alternative form of (6.67.2) is

$$q = \xi\Sigma_s\phi(u), \qquad (6.67.3)$$

thus giving an expression for the asymptotic slowing down density which will be used later.

6.68. It is of interest to note that, when ξ is set equal to unity, the results obtained in the two foregoing paragraphs become identical with the corresponding expressions applicable to hydrogen moderator at all energies. The various equations may thus be regarded as quite general, although for moderators having mass numbers greater than unity they should be restricted to neutrons with energies appreciably less than the source energy.

SLOWING DOWN IN SYSTEM OF SEVERAL NUCLIDES

6.69. In an infinite, nonabsorbing system containing two or more nuclides of different mass, an expression for the collision (and slowing down) density can be readily obtained for the asymptotic case, i.e., when $E \ll \alpha E_0$. Let $F_i(E')$ be the collision density per unit energy, at neutron energy E', for scattering from nuclei of the ith kind; then $F_i(E')\, dE'$ is the total number of neutrons scattered per cm^3 per sec by the ith nuclei in the energy interval dE'. Of these, a fraction $dE/E'(1 - \alpha_i)$ will be scattered into the interval dE, as shown in § 6.19; hence,

$$\begin{array}{l}\text{Number of neutrons scattered into } dE \\ \text{from } dE' \text{ by the } i\text{th nuclei}\end{array} = \frac{F_i(E')\, dE'}{E'(1 - \alpha_i)}\, dE.$$

6.70. If the energy E is less than $\alpha_i E_0$, integration of this expression between the limits of E and E/α_i will give the total number of neutrons scattered into the energy element dE; thus,

$$\begin{array}{l}\text{Number of neutrons scattered into } dE \\ \text{by the } i\text{th nuclei}\end{array} = \int_E^{E/\alpha_i} \frac{F_i(E')\, dE'}{E'(1 - \alpha_i)}\, dE. \qquad (6.70.1)$$

6.71. If there are N different nuclides present in the moderator, and $F(E)$ is the total collision density for scattering from all the different nuclei, then the steady state condition is

$$F(E) = \sum_{i=1}^{N} \int_E^{E/\alpha_i} \frac{F_i(E')}{E'(1 - \alpha_i)}\, dE'. \qquad (6.71.1)$$

6.72. The collision density per unit energy is proportional to the scattering cross section (§ 6.33), and hence

$$F_i(E') = \frac{\Sigma_{si}}{\Sigma_s} F(E'), \qquad (6.72.1)$$

where $F(E')$ is the total collision density per unit energy at E' for all the N kinds of scattering nuclei; Σ_{si} is the macroscopic scattering cross section of the ith nuclear species, and Σ_s is the total macroscopic scattering cross section, equal to the sum of the Σ_{si}'s for all the nuclear species present. It is to be understood that the cross sections refer to neutrons of energy E', although the argument has been omitted for simplicity. Upon making the appropriate substitution for $F_i(E')$, (6.71.1) becomes

$$F(E) = \sum_{i=1}^{N} \int_{E}^{E/\alpha_i} \frac{\Sigma_{si}}{\Sigma_s} \cdot \frac{F(E')}{E'(1 - \alpha_i)} \, dE'. \qquad (6.72.2)$$

6.73. If the scattering cross sections are constant, or vary with energy in the same way, so that Σ_{si}/Σ_s is constant, a solution is possible for the asymptotic case, when $E \ll \alpha_i E_0$ for all the moderator nuclei. The procedure is similar to that used above (§ 6.63, *et seq.*). The total slowing down density is given by

$$q = \sum_{i=1}^{N} \int_{E}^{E/\alpha_i} \frac{\Sigma_{si}}{\Sigma_s} F(E') \frac{E - \alpha_i E'}{E'(1 - \alpha_i)} \, dE',$$

and using the solution

$$F(E) = \frac{\text{const.}}{E}$$

for (6.72.2), it is found that

$$q = \text{const.} \times \sum_{i=1}^{N} \frac{\Sigma_{si}}{\Sigma_s} \xi_i = \frac{\text{const.}}{\Sigma_s} \times \sum_{i=1}^{N} \Sigma_{si} \xi_i. \qquad (6.73.1)$$

In the asymptotic region the total slowing down density is equal to the source strength Q, and so it follows that

$$F(E) = \frac{Q}{\dfrac{E}{\Sigma_s} \displaystyle\sum_{i=1}^{N} \Sigma_{si} \xi_i}. \qquad (6.73.2)$$

6.74. The mean value of the average logarithmic energy decrement per collision $\bar{\xi}$ for neutrons slowing down in a system of several nuclear species is defined by

$$\bar{\xi} \equiv \frac{\displaystyle\sum_{i=1}^{N} \Sigma_{si} \xi_i}{\displaystyle\sum_{i=1}^{N} \Sigma_{si}} = \frac{\displaystyle\sum_{i=1}^{N} \Sigma_{si} \xi_i}{\Sigma_s},$$

since Σ_s is the sum of the separate Σ_{si}'s. Upon substituting this result into (6.73.2), it is found that

$$F(E) = \frac{Q}{\bar{\xi}E},$$ (6.74.1)

and by (6.38.4)

$$F(u) = \frac{Q}{\bar{\xi}}.$$ (6.74.2)

These results are seen to be analogous to (6.66.1) and (6.66.2) for the asymptotic case of a single nuclear species as moderator, with ξ replaced by the mean value $\bar{\xi}$. The corresponding expressions for the neutron flux, per unit energy and per unit lethargy, respectively, are

$$\phi(E) = \frac{Q}{\bar{\xi}\Sigma_s E} \quad \text{and} \quad \phi(u) = \frac{Q}{\Sigma_s \bar{\xi}},$$ (6.74.3)

and since $Q = q$, the slowing down density may be written as

$$q = \bar{\xi}\Sigma_s \phi(u),$$ (6.74.4)

as in § 6.67. It may be repeated, for emphasis, that these equations apply to the asymptotic case, when the neutron energies are less than $\alpha_i E_0$ for all the nuclear species present in the moderator, and when their scattering cross sections are either independent of, or vary in the same way with, the energy.

6.75. In a system containing hydrogen and a heavier nuclear species, the collision density at energies near the source energy is determined essentially by the heavier nuclei. At lower energies, however, the scattering by hydrogen nuclei becomes important. This occurs because first collisions with hydrogen result in a uniform distribution of neutron energies essentially down to zero, neglecting the thermal energy of the scattering atoms. First collisions with heavier nuclei, on the other hand, are accompanied by relatively small changes in the neutron energies and thus they influence the collision density at energies near the source energy.

DETERMINATION OF SLOWING DOWN DENSITY

6.76. In principle, the slowing down density for any energy could be determined if there were available a material with a sharp resonance peak at this energy, with negligible cross sections at other energies. Such an ideal substance is, of course, unknown, but a fair approximation can be realized by means of an indium foil completely surrounded by cadmium foil, as described in § 3.89. From the saturation activity of the indium foil placed in the scattering medium, i.e., in the moderator, the flux in the resonance region can be derived by means of (3.62.3). The corresponding slowing down density can then be obtained from (6.74.4), provided the absorption in the medium is small.

6.77. In order to allow for the variation of the absorption cross section of indium with neutron energy in the resonance region, the following procedure is employed. First, (3.62.3) is written in the form

$$A_\infty = V \int \Sigma_{\mathrm{In}}(E)\phi(E) \, dE, \qquad (6.77.1)$$

where $\Sigma_{\mathrm{In}}(E)$ is the macroscopic absorption cross section of indium for neutrons of energy E, and $\phi(E)$ is the neutron flux per unit energy interval at this energy. The integration is carried over all energies down to the cadmium cut off; as indicated in § 3.89, this is effectively the range from 0.5 to 2 ev, with the main contribution around 1.44 ev.

6.78. If the measurement is made in a moderator in which the absorption is small compared with the scattering, $\phi(E)$ is related to the slowing down density by (6.74.3), and hence (6.77.1) becomes

$$A_\infty = \frac{Vq}{\bar\xi} \int \frac{\Sigma_{\mathrm{In}}(E)}{\Sigma_s(E)} \cdot \frac{dE}{E}, \qquad (6.78.1)$$

where $\Sigma_s(E)$ is the macroscopic scattering cross section of the moderator for neutrons of energy E. In the asymptotic region, the slowing down density in a nonabsorbing, or weakly absorbing, material is independent of the energy and so it is taken out of the integral. In the resonance region of indium, Σ_s for the moderator is essentially constant, and hence (6.78.1) may be written as

$$A_\infty = q \frac{V}{\bar\xi \Sigma_s} \int \Sigma_{\mathrm{In}}(E) \frac{dE}{E}, \qquad (6.78.2)$$

so that the slowing down density is proportional to the experimentally determined saturation activity of the indium foil. The integral in (6.78.2) can be evaluated by graphical integration of the known cross sections in the resonance region (Fig. 3.69). Since the volume V of the foil is known, and the properties $\bar\xi$ and Σ_s of the moderator may be assumed to be available, the slowing down density of neutrons in the indium resonance energy region can be calculated.

6.79. For certain practical purposes it is not necessary to know the actual slowing down density, and a quantity which is proportional to this density is adequate. In cases of this kind, the saturation activity of the cadmium-covered indium foil, of constant volume, as determined in a given moderator, provides a direct measure of the slowing down density of neutrons in the indium resonance region. Some examples of the application of this procedure will be given later.

SLOWING DOWN IN INFINITE MEDIA WITH CAPTURE

SLOWING DOWN WITH CAPTURE IN HYDROGEN MODERATOR

6.80. The treatment of the slowing down of neutrons in media in which neutron absorption, i.e., capture, occurs is more difficult than that given above for nonabsorbing media. The only case which can be exactly solved at all easily is that of moderation in a homogeneous mixture of hydrogen and a heavy absorber, such as uranium. As stated earlier, uranium-238 has fairly sharp resonance peaks for slow neutrons. Neutrons slowed down into the resonance region, as a result of scattering by the moderator, are likely to be captured by the uranium, and are thus removed from the system. The presence of a neutron absorber, especially one with one or more resonances, will thus affect the steady state energy distribution of neutrons in slowing down.

6.81. In the analysis of the behavior of neutrons in a mixture of hydrogen and uranium given here, it will be postulated, as before, that the system is infinite in extent, so that there is no loss of neutrons by leakage. Scattering will also be supposed to be spherically symmetric in the center of mass system. In addition, it will be assumed that scattering by uranium nuclei does not change the energy of the neutrons. In other words, the mass of the uranium nucleus will be taken to be infinite, i.e., $\xi = 0$, so that the moderator is effectively a single nuclear species, namely, hydrogen, rather than a mixture.

6.82. The collision density, that is, the *total* number of scattering and absorption collisions suffered by neutrons per cm^3 per sec per unit energy, for neutrons of energy E, is now

$$F(E) \equiv (\Sigma_a + \Sigma_s)\phi(E), \tag{6.82.1}$$

where Σ_a is the macroscopic cross section for absorption of neutrons of energy E, and Σ_s is that for scattering. The collision density per unit energy for absorption is $\Sigma_a\phi(E)$, while that for scattering is $\Sigma_s\phi(E)$; the sum of these two quantities for neutrons of energy E is equal to $F(E)$, the total collision density.

6.83. In the steady state, the number of neutrons scattered into an energy element dE, as a result of collisions with hydrogen nuclei, is equal to the number of neutrons scattered out from this element, *plus* the number absorbed (or captured). Let Q be the number of source neutrons of energy E_0, produced uniformly throughout the system, per cm^3 per sec. Then, if there is no appreciable absorption of source neutrons, it can be shown, by a method similar to that in §§ 6.34, 6.35, that for scattering in hydrogen mixed with a heavy absorber, the steady state condition is

$$F(E) = \frac{Q}{E_0} + \int_E^{E_0} \frac{\Sigma_s}{\Sigma_a + \Sigma_s} \cdot \frac{F(E')}{E'} \, dE'. \tag{6.83.1}$$

6.84. If the absorption of source neutrons is not negligible, the first term on the right-hand side of (6.83.1) should be multiplied by $\Sigma_s/(\Sigma_a + \Sigma_s)$, where the cross sections apply to neutrons having the source energy E_0. For the present treatment this factor will be regarded as essentially equal to unity since, usually, absorption is appreciable only for energies much less than source energies in nuclear reactors.

6.85. To solve the integral equation (6.83.1) it is first differentiated with respect to E, to give

$$\frac{dF(E)}{dE} = -\frac{\Sigma_s}{\Sigma_a + \Sigma_s} \cdot \frac{F(E)}{E}. \tag{6.85.1}$$

The quantity $\Sigma_s/(\Sigma_a + \Sigma_s)$ is, of course, a function of the energy, but the argument (E) is omitted here in order to simplify the notation. Upon rearrangement and integration, (6.85.1) becomes

$$-\int_{F(E)}^{F(E_0)} \frac{dF(E')}{F(E')} = \int_E^{E_0} \frac{\Sigma_s}{\Sigma_a + \Sigma_s} \cdot \frac{dE'}{E'}$$

or

$$\ln \frac{F(E)}{F(E_0)} = \int_E^{E_0} \frac{\Sigma_s}{\Sigma_a + \Sigma_s} \cdot \frac{dE'}{E'}. \qquad (6.85.2)$$

6.86. The boundary condition derived from (6.83.1) is

$$F(E_0) = \frac{Q}{E_0},$$

and this combined with (6.85.2) gives

$$F(E) = \frac{Q}{E_0} \exp\left(\int_E^{E_0} \frac{\Sigma_s}{\Sigma_a + \Sigma_s} \cdot \frac{dE'}{E'}\right) \qquad (6.86.1)$$

as the solution of (6.83.1). Since

$$\frac{\Sigma_s}{\Sigma_a + \Sigma_s} = 1 - \frac{\Sigma_a}{\Sigma_a + \Sigma_s},$$

equation (6.86.1) can be rewritten in the form

$$F(E) = \frac{Q}{E} \exp\left(-\int_E^{E_0} \frac{\Sigma_a}{\Sigma_a + \Sigma_s} \cdot \frac{dE'}{E'}\right). \qquad (6.86.2)$$

The exponential term in this equation is the *resonance escape probability*, $p(E)$, referred to in § 4.59, as can be shown in the following manner.

6.87. For slowing down in hydrogen, the slowing down density $q(E)^*$ at energy E in the steady state is given by

$$q(E) = \frac{QE}{E_0} + E\int_E^{E_0} \frac{\Sigma_s}{\Sigma_a + \Sigma_s} \cdot \frac{F(E')}{E'} dE', \qquad (6.87.1)$$

as may be shown by the procedure in § 6.40, *et seg.* [cf. equation (6.41.2)]. It will be noted from (6.83.1) that the integral in (6.87.1) is equal to $F(E) - Q/E_0$, and so equation (6.87.1) becomes

$$q(E) = \frac{QE}{E_0} + E\left[F(E) - \frac{Q}{E_0}\right]$$

or

$$q(E) = EF(E). \qquad (6.87.2)$$

Using the expression for $F(E)$ given by (6.86.2), the result is

$$q(E) = Q \exp\left(-\int_E^{E_0} \frac{\Sigma_a}{\Sigma_a + \Sigma_s} \cdot \frac{dE'}{E'}\right). \qquad (6.87.3)$$

---

* The argument (E) is used here, although it was omitted earlier, because the slowing down density in the resonance region is a function of the neutron energy.

6.88. The probability that a neutron will escape capture in slowing down from E_0 to E, i.e., the resonance escape probability $p(E)$ for neutrons of energy E, is equal to the ratio of the slowing down density at E with absorption to that without absorption. The slowing down density $q(E)$ with absorption is given by (6.87.3) whereas, according to § 6.42, if there is no capture of neutrons the slowing down density in hydrogen is equal merely to Q. Hence, it follows that

$$p(E) = \frac{q(E)}{Q} = \exp\left(-\int_E^{E_0} \frac{\Sigma_a}{\Sigma_a + \Sigma_s} \cdot \frac{dE'}{E'}\right), \qquad (6.88.1)$$

so that the exponential term represents the resonance escape probability in a mixture of hydrogen with a heavy absorber. This is seen to be identical with the exponential in (6.86.2).

SLOWING DOWN WITH CAPTURE IN MEDIA OF MASS NUMBER GREATER THAN UNITY

6.89. In absorbing media consisting of nuclei of mass number greater than unity, the calculation of the collision density and of the resonance escape probability cannot be performed analytically for the general case in which no restriction is placed on the variation of the absorption cross section with energy. As seen above, in a moderator of mass number exceeding unity, a neutron of any energy E can be scattered only to αE, and two different energy regions should be distinguished.

6.90. In considering the resonance capture of neutrons in a reactor as they slow down, in a mixture of uranium with beryllium or carbon, for example, the energy of the source (fission) neutrons is large compared to that of the region in which resonance capture becomes important. Hence, it is necessary only to determine the steady state condition for the neutron energy $E \ll \alpha E_0$, where E_0 is the energy above which effectively all fission neutrons are emitted.

6.91. For the general case of a system containing N types of scattering nuclei, some or all of which may also be absorbers, the steady state equation is then

$$F(E) = \sum_{i=1}^{N} \int_E^{E/\alpha_i} \frac{\Sigma_{si}}{\Sigma_a + \Sigma_s} \cdot \frac{F(E')}{1 - \alpha_i} \cdot \frac{dE'}{E'}. \qquad (6.91.1)$$

This is equivalent to (6.72.2), modified by the introduction of the absorption cross section. Since (6.91.1) is a function both of E and of E/α_i, it is not possible to differentiate it and obtain a simple differential equation, which can then be solved with the aid of the boundary condition at E_0, as in the preceding instances.

6.92. An exact solution of (6.91.1) for $E \ll \alpha E_0$ can be obtained for the trivial case of constant cross sections; this would imply no resonance absorption and hence is of little practical value. Asymptotic solutions can be obtained for other special cases, such as, slowly varying capture, $1/v$ capture,* and widely spaced resonances; in addition, various numerical methods can be used to solve particular problems.

6.93. Instead of evaluating the collision density, it is of greater practical interest to derive expressions for the resonance escape probability. Three cases of importance will be considered here: these are (a) a series of widely spaced resonances, (b) slowly varying capture, and (c) very weak capture.

RESONANCE ESCAPE PROBABILITY FOR WIDELY SPACED RESONANCES

6.94. It was seen in § 6.59, in the treatment of slowing down without absorption in a moderator with mass number greater than unity, that in the energy region from E_0, i.e., the source energy, down to about $\alpha^3 E_0$ the neutron collision density $F(u)$ oscillates, damping out to a constant value for neutron energies less than $\alpha^3 E_0$. As indicated in § 6.62, a narrow absorption resonance acts very much like a negative source; it produces fluctuations in the collision density in an energy region from E_r, the resonance energy, down to about $\alpha^3 E_r$.

6.95. The same conclusion may be expressed in terms of lethargy units. If u_r is the lethargy corresponding to the resonance energy E_r, and u is that equivalent to $\alpha^3 E_r$, where the oscillations have damped out, then,

$$u_r = \ln \frac{E_0}{E_r} \quad \text{and} \quad u = \ln \frac{E_0}{\alpha^3 E_r}.$$

Consequently, the lethargy range over which the oscillations in $F(u)$ occur is given by

$$u - u_r = 3 \ln \frac{1}{\alpha}.$$

Damping out of the fluctuations in the collision density due to resonance absorption will thus have occurred when the neutron lethargy is $3 \ln \frac{1}{\alpha}$ units greater than that of the resonance.

6.96. If a second resonance occurs at a lower energy, the number of neutrons captured in this resonance region depends on the spacing between the two resonances. If they are separated by about $4 \ln \frac{1}{\alpha}$ lethargy units, or more, the capture in the second resonance will be independent of the spacing, since $F(u)$ will then have reached a constant value over a lethargy range of $\ln \frac{1}{\alpha}$ preceding the second resonance. The number of neutrons scattered into this resonance region will be constant, independent of the energy of the second resonance. In general, it may be stated that the number of neutrons scattered into a lethargy element Δu depends entirely on the behavior of $F(u)$ in the interval $u - \ln \frac{1}{\alpha}$

---

* G. Placzek, *Phys. Rev.*, **69**, 430 (1946).

to u. The foregoing conclusions are applicable only for a narrow (line) resonance, so that resonance absorption occurs essentially at a definite energy and not over a range of energies.

6.97. Provided the resonances are sufficiently spaced, so that the collision density per unit lethargy is constant over a lethargy interval of at least $\ln \dfrac{1}{\alpha}$ preceding each resonance, an expression for the resonance escape probability may be developed in a simplified, nonrigorous manner, as follows.* The treatment is restricted to the case where the widths of the resonances, in terms of lethargy, are small compared to ξ, the average change in lethargy per collision (§ 6.28). Further, it is assumed that the resonances are in the asymptotic region of the energy, i.e., $E_r \ll \alpha E_0$, so that the fluctuations in the collision density due to the source have damped out.

6.98. In the case postulated above, the collision density $F(u)$ is constant for energies greater than E_1, up to E_1/α at least, where E_1 is the energy of the first resonance.† If ΔE_1 is the width of the resonance, the number of neutrons captured in the element ΔE_1 is $\Sigma_a \phi(E_1) \Delta E_1$, where $\phi(E_1)$ is the depleted neutron flux, of energy E_1, per unit energy. If there were no absorption of neutrons, the number scattered into an energy interval ΔE_1 would be equal to the number scattered out, i.e., to $\Sigma_s \phi_n(E_1) \Delta E_1$, where $\phi_n(E_1)$ is the neutron flux per unit energy without capture. When absorption occurs, the number of neutrons scattered into ΔE_1 must be equal to the total number lost from that energy element, that is, to the number scattered out, $\Sigma_s \phi(E_1) \Delta E_1$, plus the number absorbed, $\Sigma_a \phi(E_1) \Delta E_1$. Since the number of neutrons scattered into the interval ΔE_1 is the same with capture and without capture, it follows that

$$\Sigma_s \phi_n(E_1) \Delta E_1 = (\Sigma_s + \Sigma_a)\phi(E_1) \Delta E_1. \qquad (6.98.1)$$

6.99. From (6.74.3)

$$\phi_n(E_1) = \frac{Q}{\bar{\xi}\Sigma_s E_1}, \qquad (6.99.1)$$

where $\bar{\xi}$ is the mean value of the average logarithmic energy decrement per collision for neutrons slowing down in the mixture. Substitution for ϕ_n in (6.98.1) then gives

$$\phi(E_1) \Delta E_1 = \frac{Q}{\bar{\xi}(\Sigma_s + \Sigma_a)} \cdot \frac{\Delta E_1}{E_1}.$$

The probability that neutrons will be captured in ΔE_1 is

$$\frac{\Sigma_a \phi(E_1) \Delta E_1}{Q} = \frac{\Sigma_a}{\bar{\xi}(\Sigma_s + \Sigma_a)} \cdot \frac{\Delta E_1}{E_1}.$$

---

* The derivation was originally given by E. P. Wigner, unpublished.

† This is, of course, the same as saying that $F(u)$ is constant in the lethargy interval for u_1 to $u_1 - \ln (1/\alpha)$.

Hence, the probability p_1 that neutrons will escape capture in the first resonance is

$$p_1 = 1 - \frac{\Sigma_a}{\bar{\xi}(\Sigma_s + \Sigma_a)} \cdot \frac{\Delta E_1}{E_1}. \tag{6.99.2}$$

6.100. Consider next the second resonance, which occurs for neutrons of energy E_2; the width of the resonance is ΔE_2. As postulated above, the spacing between the resonances is such that the collision density $F(u)$ has become constant some distance above the second resonance. The neutron flux per unit energy without capture at the second resonance, i.e., $\phi_n(E_2)$, is equal to the asymptotic form without capture multiplied by p_1; thus,

$$\phi_n(E_2) = \frac{p_1 Q}{\bar{\xi}\Sigma_s E_2}.$$

Using (6.99.2), the probability p_2 that source neutrons will escape capture in the first two resonances is consequently found to be

$$p_2 = \left[1 - \frac{\Sigma_a}{\bar{\xi}(\Sigma_s + \Sigma_a)} \cdot \frac{\Delta E_1}{E_1}\right]\left[1 - \frac{\Sigma_a}{\bar{\xi}(\Sigma_s + \Sigma_a)} \cdot \frac{\Delta E_2}{E_2}\right].$$

6.101. In general, for n resonances, the resonance escape probability is

$$p_n = \prod_{i=1}^{n}\left[1 - \frac{\Sigma_a}{\bar{\xi}(\Sigma_s + \Sigma_a)} \cdot \frac{\Delta E_i}{E_i}\right].$$

Upon taking logarithms of each side, the result is

$$\ln p_n = \sum_{i=1}^{n} \ln\left[1 - \frac{\Sigma_a}{\bar{\xi}(\Sigma_s + \Sigma_a)} \cdot \frac{\Delta E_i}{E_i}\right]. \tag{6.101.1}$$

If the second term in the brackets is very small in comparison with unity, which is the case if

$$\Delta E_i \ll \bar{\xi}E_i,$$

i.e., for narrow resonances, the logarithmic expression of (6.101.1) can be expanded in a series and higher order terms omitted. Consequently,

$$\ln p_n \approx -\sum_{i=1}^{n} \frac{\Sigma_a}{\bar{\xi}(\Sigma_s + \Sigma_a)} \cdot \frac{\Delta E_i}{E_i}. \tag{6.101.2}$$

6.102. The resonance escape probability can be written in the usual integral form (§ 6.88) if the entire resonance region is imagined to be divided into m contiguous energy bands of width ΔE_j. In the regions between the resonances Σ_a is understood to be zero; then,

$$-\sum_{i=1}^{n} \frac{\Sigma_a}{\bar{\xi}(\Sigma_s + \Sigma_a)} \cdot \frac{\Delta E_i}{E_i} = -\sum_{j=1}^{m} \frac{\Sigma_a}{\bar{\xi}(\Sigma_s + \Sigma_a)} \cdot \frac{\Delta E_j}{E_j},$$

so that, from (6.101.2)

$$p(E) = \lim_{m \to \infty} \exp\left[-\sum_{j=1}^{m} \frac{\Sigma_a}{\bar{\xi}(\Sigma_s + \Sigma_a)} \cdot \frac{\Delta E_j}{E_j} \right]$$

or

$$p(E) = \exp\left[-\int_{E}^{E_0} \frac{\Sigma_a}{\bar{\xi}(\Sigma_s + \Sigma_a)} \cdot \frac{dE'}{E'} \right]. \tag{6.102.1}$$

This is the form in which the resonance escape probability is frequently expressed; except for hydrogen moderator and a heavy absorber, it is strictly applicable only to widely spaced, narrow resonances. For a mixture of hydrogen and a heavy absorber, $\bar{\xi}$ is equal to unity, and (6.102.1) then reduces to the exact (6.88.1). The resonance escape probability as defined by (6.102.1) will be used in the discussion of heterogeneous reactors consisting of natural uranium in a graphite moderator (Chapter IX).

6.103. It may be noted that, even if the absorption cross section becomes infinitely large over a finite energy interval, the integral in (6.102.1) and the resonance escape probability remain finite. Consider, for example, the case where $\Sigma_a \to \infty$ in an energy region from E_1 to E_2, where $E_0 > E_1 > E_2$, and is zero elsewhere. Since $\Sigma_a/(\Sigma_s + \Sigma_a)$ may now be set equal to unity, (6.102.1) becomes

$$p(E) = \exp\left(-\int_{E_2}^{E_1} \frac{1}{\bar{\xi}} \cdot \frac{dE'}{E'} \right)$$
$$= \left(\frac{E_2}{E_1} \right)^{\frac{1}{\bar{\xi}}}.$$

6.104. The resonance escape probability is thus finite, in spite of the absorption cross section being infinite. For hydrogen as moderator, this result is a direct consequence of the fact that a certain proportion of the scattered neutrons will jump across the resonance. It can be seen on general grounds that, with heavier moderators, scattered neutrons will be able to cross the resonance region only if the latter is narrow, and if the resonances are widely separated. These are, of course, the postulates upon which (6.102.1) is based. If the width of the "infinite" resonance is equal to or greater than the maximum energy decrease in a scattering collision, no neutrons will slow down past the resonance. The resonance escape probability will then be zero for all energies less than or equal to E_2, the lower limit of the resonance region.

RESONANCE ESCAPE PROBABILITY FOR SLOWLY VARYING CAPTURE

6.105. If the absorption cross section in the resonance region does not vary rapidly with the neutron energy, it is possible to derive an approximate expression for the resonance escape probability.* In the case of a nonabsorbing moderator. $F(u)$, i.e., $\Sigma_s \phi(u)$, is constant in the asymptotic region. If, however, an absorber

---

* The derivation given here is essentially that of G. Goertzel and E. Greuling, unpublished.

is present, $\Sigma_s\phi(u)$ will decrease depending on the absorption cross section. If Σ_a does not vary much over a lethargy interval $\ln (1/\alpha)$, the scattering collision density $\Sigma_s\phi(u)$, which may be represented by $F_s(u)$, will not vary rapidly in that interval.

6.106. Assuming, as before, that neutrons are produced uniformly in an infinite medium, and the source energy is E_0, then the slowing down density for energies less than αE_0 is given by

$$q(E) = \int_E^{E/\alpha} F_s(E') \frac{E - \alpha E'}{E'(1 - \alpha)} \, dE' \qquad (6.106.1)$$

for a single moderator, with an absorber of infinite mass. This equation is identical in form with (6.64.1), for a nonabsorbing medium, except that $F(E)$ is given here more explicitly as the scattering collision density and not the total collision density defined by (6.82.1). Upon transforming the variable from energy to lethargy, it can be readily shown that, for lethargies greater than $\ln (1/\alpha)$, (6.106.1) becomes

$$q(u) = \int_{u-\epsilon}^u \frac{F_s(u')}{1 - \alpha} (e^{u'-u} - \alpha) \, du', \qquad (6.106.2)$$

where

$$\epsilon \equiv \ln (1/\alpha).$$

6.107. If $F_s(u)$ varies slowly in a lethargy interval ϵ, i.e., $\ln (1/\alpha)$, then $F_s(u')$ is given adequately by the first two terms of a Taylor series expansion about u, and (6.106.2) can be written as

$$q(u) = \frac{1}{1 - \alpha} \int_{u-\epsilon}^u \left[F_s(u) + (u' - u) \frac{dF_s(u)}{du} \right] (e^{u'-u} - \alpha) \, du'. \quad (6.107.1)$$

Upon integrating with respect to u', the result is

$$q(u) = \xi F_s(u) + a \frac{dF_s(u)}{du}, \qquad (6.107.2)$$

where

$$a \equiv \frac{\alpha + \alpha\epsilon + \frac{1}{2}\alpha\epsilon^2 - 1}{1 - \alpha}$$

and ξ has the same significance as before.

6.108. Returning to (6.106.2) and differentiating with respect to u, it is found that

$$\frac{dq}{du} = F_s(u) - \frac{1}{1 - \alpha} \int_{u-\epsilon}^u F_s(u')e^{u'-u} \, du'. \qquad (6.108.1)$$

Again, representing $F_s(u')$ by the first two terms of a Taylor series, this becomes

$$\frac{dq}{du} = F_s(u) - \frac{1}{1 - \alpha} \int_{u-\epsilon}^u \left[F_s(u) + (u' - u) \frac{dF_s(u)}{du} \right] e^{u'-u} \, du', \quad (6.108.2)$$

and upon integration the result is

$$\frac{dq}{du} = \xi \frac{dF_s(u)}{du}.$$ (6.108.3)

If (6.107.2) is now multiplied by ξ and (6.108.3) by a, and the expressions subtracted, it follows that

$$-a\frac{dq}{du} + \xi q = \xi^2 F_s(u)$$

$$= \xi^2 \Sigma_s \phi(u),$$ (6.108.4)

where $F_s(u)$ is replaced by its equivalent $\Sigma_s \phi(u)$.

6.109. In the lethargy interval from u to $u + du$ the slowing down density will decrease from q to $q - dq$, because of the absorption of neutrons of lethargy u in the interval du. If Σ_a is the macroscopic absorption cross section for neutrons of lethargy u, and $\phi(u)$ is the flux per unit lethargy, then

$$-dq = \Sigma_a \phi(u)\, du,$$

since the decrease in the slowing down density must be equal to the number of neutrons absorbed per cm³ per sec in the lethargy interval du. This result may be expressed as

$$\frac{dq}{du} = -\Sigma_a \phi(u).$$ (6.109.1)

6.110. Upon substituting (6.109.1) into (6.108.4), the flux per unit lethargy is given in terms of the slowing down density by

$$\phi(u) = \frac{q}{\xi \Sigma_s + \gamma \Sigma_a},$$ (6.110.1)

where

$$\gamma \equiv -\frac{a}{\xi} = \frac{1 - \alpha - \alpha\epsilon - \frac{1}{2}\alpha\epsilon^2}{1 - \alpha - \alpha\epsilon}.$$ (6.110.2)

Some values of γ for a few moderators are given in Table 6.110; the corresponding values for ξ, from Table 6.24, are also included.

TABLE 6.110.   FUNCTIONS USED IN CALCULATION OF RESONANCE ESCAPE PROBABILITY

Element	γ	ξ
Hydrogen	1.000	1.000
Deuterium	0.583	0.725
Beryllium	0.149	0.209
Carbon	0.116	0.158

6.111. The resonance escape probability can be obtained by substituting the value of $\phi(u)$ given by (6.110.1) into the differential equation (6.109.1); thus,

$$\frac{dq}{du} = -\frac{\Sigma_a}{\xi \Sigma_s + \gamma \Sigma_a} q$$

or

$$\frac{dq}{q} = -\frac{\Sigma_a}{\xi\Sigma_s + \gamma\Sigma_a}\, du.$$

Upon integration between the lethargy limits of u and zero, where the latter is the lethargy of the source neutrons, the result is

$$\frac{q}{q_0} = \exp\left(-\int_0^u \frac{\Sigma_a}{\xi\Sigma_s + \gamma\Sigma_a}\, du\right). \tag{6.111.1}$$

The left-hand side of this equation is the ratio of the slowing down density (q) at lethargy u to that (q_0) at the source. If there had been no capture of neutrons, the slowing down density would, in the asymptotic region, have been equal to q_0, which is identical with the source strength. Hence q/q_0, as given by (6.111.1), must be equal to the resonance escape probability at the lethargy u. Transforming this equation back to E as the variable, it is found that

$$p(E) = \exp\left(-\int_E^{E_0} \frac{\Sigma_a}{\xi\Sigma_s + \gamma\Sigma_a}\cdot\frac{dE'}{E'}\right), \tag{6.111.2}$$

where $\Sigma_a/(\xi\Sigma_s + \gamma\Sigma_a)$ is a function of the energy.

6.112. It is of interest to point out that, for hydrogen, γ and ξ are both unity, and then the approximate (6.111.2) becomes identical with the rigorous (6.88.1) for the resonance escape probability in a hydrogen moderator with an absorber of infinite mass.

RESONANCE ESCAPE PROBABILITY FOR WEAK RESONANCE CAPTURE

6.113. If the macroscopic absorption cross section is much less than the macroscopic scattering cross section in a given absorbing system, i.e., $\Sigma_a \ll \Sigma_s$, the neutron flux in the asymptotic region will not be very different from the value to be expected if there were no absorption. An expression for the resonance escape probability, similar in form to (6.88.1), can then be derived in a simple manner.

6.114. The decrease $-dq$ in the slowing down density in an energy interval dE is equal to the number of neutrons absorbed per cm³ per sec in dE (cf. § 6.109); hence,

$$-dq = \Sigma_a\phi(E)\, dE, \tag{6.114.1}$$

where $\phi(E)$ is the neutron flux per unit energy at energy E. In the case under consideration, $\phi(E)$ may be regarded as essentially the same as for the nonabsorbing case, so that by (6.74.3)

$$\phi(E) = \frac{q}{\xi\Sigma_s E}. \tag{6.114.2}$$

Hence, combining (6.114.1) and (6.114.2),

$$\frac{dq}{q} = \frac{\Sigma_a}{\xi\Sigma_s} \cdot \frac{dE}{E},$$

and upon integration it follows that

$$q(E) = Q \exp\left(-\int_E^{E_0} \frac{\Sigma_a}{\xi\Sigma_s} \cdot \frac{dE'}{E'}\right).$$

The resonance escape probability $p(E)$ is thus given by

$$p(E) = \frac{q(E)}{Q} = \exp\left(-\int_E^{E_0} \frac{\Sigma_a}{\xi\Sigma_s} \cdot \frac{dE'}{E'}\right). \tag{6.114.3}$$

6.115. The same result can be obtained from (6.102.1) by postulating that $\Sigma_s \gg \Sigma_a$. It is evident that (6.102.1) should reduce to (6.114.3) for this condition since, if Σ_a is very small compared to Σ_s, the collision density does not oscillate appreciably due to resonance absorption and the restriction of wide spacing as applied to strong resonance lines may be removed.

6.116. Similarly, if $\xi\Sigma_s \gg \gamma\Sigma_a$, equation (6.111.2) also reduces to the same form as (6.114.3). In this case absorption is small, in any event, so that the condition of slowly varying absorption cross section is no longer significant.

THE FERMI AGE TREATMENT

The Continuous Slowing Down Model

6.117. A general discussion of energy relations in scattering has been given in the preceding parts of this chapter; now the spatial distribution of the neutrons of various energies, resulting from diffusion during the slowing down process, will be considered. As stated earlier (§ 6.1), the average crow-flight distance a fission neutron travels while slowing down has a direct bearing on the critical size of a reactor. If this average distance is large, then the reactor will have to be large, so as to reduce the probability of escape of the neutrons before they have been slowed down to thermal energies. Thus, the distribution of neutrons in space as a result of diffusion during the slowing down process determines the probability of loss by leakage from the thermal reactor during the course of this process.

6.118. A relatively simple approach to the problem, which is applicable to slowing down in media other than those containing very light nuclei, e.g., hydrogen and deuterium, is based on the following model. Consider a neutron produced at the fission energy E_0; it will travel for a certain time with this energy before it collides with a nucleus. After the collision its energy will be decreased, and it will then travel with this constant lower energy until it meets another nucleus. Since the neutron is now moving with a smaller speed, the time between collisions is, on the average, increased. This process of movement at constant energy followed by a collision in which the energy is lowered will continue until the neutron is thermalized.

6.119. Since the average change in the logarithm of the neutron energy per collision, i.e., ξ, is independent of the energy (§ 6.22), it follows that a time plot of $\ln E$ of a neutron, from fission energy (E_0) down to thermal energy (E_{th}) will be of the form of Fig. 6.119. This is seen to consist of a series of steps of approxi-

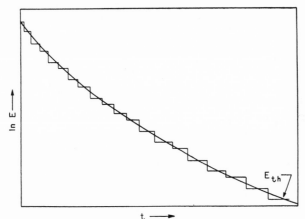

FIG. 6.119.　Continuous slowing down approximation

mately equal height ξ, but of gradually increasing length. The horizontal lines represent the constant energy of the neutron while it is diffusing between collisions, and the lengths of these lines give the time elapsing between successive collisions. It should be noted that the plot is for a single neutron, and so there will be some fluctuations from the average behavior to which the discussion refers, as is indicated below.

6.120. Because individual neutrons behave differently, even if originating with the same energy, they will not all have the same energy after the lapse of a certain time from birth. In other words, the plot of $\ln E$ against t, as in Fig. 6.119, will vary from one neutron to another, although they all start with the same fission energy E_0 and diffuse in the same medium. If the latter consists of nuclei of moderate or high mass, the spread of energies among the neutrons is relatively small, and it is possible to represent the behavior of a large number of individual neutrons by means of an average behavior. With carbon, for example, the maximum fractional energy change suffered by a neutron in a collision is 0.27, compared with an average value of about 0.17. It is evident, therefore, that even in a carbon (graphite) medium the neutron energy spread at any specified time after leaving the source will not be large. The spread is still less for media containing heavier nuclei.

6.121. Further, under such conditions that the behavior of the neutrons can be reasonably represented by an average, the logarithmic change of energy per collision is small. That is to say, the height of the steps in Fig. 6.119 will be small. As a result, the series of steps may be replaced, without serious error, by a continuous curve, such as that shown in the diagram. In other words, it is assumed, as an approximation, that during slowing down the neutrons lose energy continuously, rather than discontinuously as is actually the case. Thus, the subsequent treatment is based on the postulate that the over-all, discontinuous, slowing down behavior of a large number of neutrons can be represented, to a satisfactory approximation, by a single continuous curve.

6.122. It is important to point out that the foregoing approximation is valid only for moderators consisting of elements of fairly high mass number; it does not apply to media containing hydrogen, deuterium, or other light nuclei. It is possible, for example, for a neutron to lose all its energy, from E_0 to thermal, in a single collision with hydrogen. When neutrons are slowed down by light nuclei there is, consequently, a considerable spread of energies and it is not justifiable to represent the slowing down characteristics of a large number of neutrons by an average behavior. Further, because of the large changes in neutron energy per collision, and hence the small number of collisions required to reduce the energy to thermal values, the representation of the slowing down by a continuous curve, as described above, is completely invalid.

The Age Equation Without Capture

6.123. The subsequent treatment will be restricted to the diffusion of neutrons in media other than those containing elements of the lowest atomic weight. The first problem is to develop a differential equation which will represent the continuous slowing down behavior in a nonabsorbing medium. It will be assumed that all neutrons that have diffused for a time t, after leaving their source, have the same lethargy u, and the relationship between dt and du will be used to derive an expression for the spatial distribution of the slowing down density.

6.124. Suppose that, after diffusing for a time t, all the neutrons have velocity v, and let λ_s be the scattering mean free path, i.e., the average distance the neutron travels between collisions with nuclei. The number of collisions a neutron suffers in the subsequent time interval dt is then $v\,dt/\lambda_s$. Since ξ is the average logarithmic energy change per collision, it follows that the decrease in $\ln E$ is equal to ξ times the number of collisions in the time dt; hence,

$$-d \ln E = \frac{\xi v}{\lambda_s}\, dt, \qquad (6.124.1)$$

where the left-hand side represents the logarithmic energy loss during the time interval dt. Upon replacing $-d \ln E$ by du, the corresponding lethargy increase (cf. § 6.27), it follows that

$$du = \frac{\xi v}{\lambda_s} dt. \tag{6.124.2}$$

This is the differential equation, referred to above, which relates u to t, on the basis of the continuous slowing down model. In this treatment it is assumed, of course, that there is no loss of neutrons by absorption.

6.125. Consider now, at a field point represented by the vector $\mathbf{r}$, the neutrons which have diffused for a time t. During the subsequent interval dt they will leak away from a volume element at $\mathbf{r}$ at a rate given by $-D \nabla^2 \phi(\mathbf{r}, t)$, in accordance with (5.33.1), where $\phi(\mathbf{r}, t)$ is the flux of the specified neutrons at the given point. Since ϕ may be replaced by vn, where n is the corresponding neutron density, the rate of leakage is expressed by $-Dv \nabla^2 n(\mathbf{r}, t)$. If there is no absorption of neutrons, this will give the rate of decrease of neutron density with time; hence, eliminating the negative signs,

$$Dv \nabla^2 n(\mathbf{r}, t) = \frac{\partial n(\mathbf{r}, t)}{\partial t}, \tag{6.125.1}$$

where D, which depends on the velocity v, and v itself are functions of the energy. For the present purpose it is convenient to define $n(\mathbf{r}, t)$ on both sides of (6.125.1) as the neutron density per *unit time interval*, so that $n(\mathbf{r}, t) \, dt$ is the number of neutrons per cm³ which have diffused for a time between t and $t + dt$ after leaving the source.

6.126. The next step in the treatment is to transform the independent variable from t to u, as defined above. If $n(\mathbf{r}, u)$ is the number of neutrons per cm³ per unit lethargy, the number of neutrons per cm³ with lethargy between u and $u + du$ is $n(\mathbf{r}, u) \, du$. If this lethargy interval du corresponds to the time interval dt considered above, then

$$n(\mathbf{r}, u) \, du = n(\mathbf{r}, t) \, dt,$$

and hence,

$$n(\mathbf{r}, t) = n(\mathbf{r}, u) \frac{\partial u}{\partial t} = \frac{\xi v}{\lambda_s} n(\mathbf{r}, u), \tag{6.126.1}$$

making use of (6.124.2) to give $\partial u/\partial t$.

6.127. By combining the general relationship

$$\frac{\partial n(\mathbf{r}, t)}{\partial t} = \frac{\partial u}{\partial t} \cdot \frac{\partial n(\mathbf{r}, t)}{\partial u}$$

with (6.124.2) for $\partial u/\partial t$, the result is

$$\frac{\partial n(\mathbf{r}, t)}{\partial t} = \frac{\xi v}{\lambda_s} \cdot \frac{\partial n(\mathbf{r}, t)}{\partial u},$$

and then, from (6.126.1), it follows that

$$\frac{\partial n(\mathbf{r}, t)}{\partial t} = \frac{\xi v}{\lambda_s} \cdot \frac{\partial}{\partial u} \left[\frac{\xi v}{\lambda_s} n(\mathbf{r}, u) \right]. \tag{6.127.1}$$

Upon inserting (6.126.1) into the left-hand side and (6.127.1) into the right-hand side, (6.125.1) becomes

$$Dv \, \nabla^2 \left[\frac{\xi v}{\lambda_s} n(\mathbf{r}, u) \right] = \frac{\xi v}{\lambda_s} \cdot \frac{\partial}{\partial u} \left[\frac{\xi v}{\lambda_s} n(\mathbf{r}, u) \right]. \tag{6.127.2}$$

In view of the definition of $n(\mathbf{r}, u)$ given above, $vn(\mathbf{r}, u)$ will be equivalent to $\phi(\mathbf{r}, u)$, the neutron flux per unit lethargy interval; further, since λ_s is equal to $1/\Sigma_s$, the macroscopic scattering cross section for the material, (6.127.2) may be written as

$$D \, \nabla^2 [\xi \Sigma_s \phi(\mathbf{r}, u)] = \xi \Sigma_s \frac{\partial}{\partial u} [\xi \Sigma_s \phi(\mathbf{r}, u)]. \tag{6.127.3}$$

The quantity in the brackets on each side of (6.127.3) is the slowing down density, as may be seen from (6.67.3); representing this by q, equation (6.127.3), after slight rearrangement, becomes

$$\nabla^2 q = \frac{\xi \Sigma_s}{D} \cdot \frac{\partial q}{\partial u}. \tag{6.127.4}$$

6.128. A new variable $\tau(u)$ is now introduced, defined by

$$\tau(u) \equiv \int_0^u \frac{D}{\xi \Sigma_s} \, du. \tag{6.128.1}$$

Upon making the transformation which replaces u by $\tau(u)$, equation (6.127.4) reduces to

$$\nabla^2 q = \frac{\partial q}{\partial \tau}, \tag{6.128.2}$$

and this is known as the *Fermi age equation*. The quantity $\tau(u)$ is called the *Fermi age* or the *symbolic age*, frequently abbreviated to *age*, of the neutrons. It must be emphasized, however, that it is not a unit of time, but rather of length squared. This can be readily understood from (6.128.2) when it is realized that the Laplacian operator implies differentiation twice with respect to a distance. It is of interest to note that the age equation is identical in form with the standard heat diffusion equation.

6.129. The quantity τ in (6.128.2) is related to the chronological age of the neutrons, as can be shown in the following manner. The chronological age t may be defined as the time required by the neutron to slow down, on the average, from its original (fission) energy E_0 to the energy E, i.e., the time between its leaving the source and its attainment of the lethargy u. Hence, by using (6.124.2) to change the variable in (6.128.1), which defines τ, the result is

$$\tau = \int_0^t Dv \, dt$$
$$= \int_0^t D_0 \, dt, \tag{6.129.1}$$

where Dv has been replaced by D_0, the conventional diffusion coefficient (§ 5.7). If an average diffusion coefficient $\bar{D}_0$ during the slowing down time t is defined by

$$\bar{D}_0 = \frac{1}{t} \int_0^t D_0 \, dt,$$

then (6.129.1) becomes

$$\tau = \bar{D}_0 t. \tag{6.129.2}$$

Consequently, the Fermi age τ is equal to the slowing down time (or chronological age) of the neutrons multiplied by the average diffusion coefficient over the time t. Thus, immediately after leaving the source the value of τ is zero, but it increases as the slowing down time of the neutrons increases and their energy decreases.

6.130. In the foregoing treatment, the slowing down has been stated in terms of the lethargy u, so that q and τ in (6.128.1) and (6.128.2) are functions of u. However, they may equally well be expressed as functions of the energy, by transforming the variables. According to § 6.27, $du = - dE/E$, and so the definition of the neutron age, as given by (6.128.1), now becomes

$$\tau(E) \equiv \int_E^{E_0} \frac{D}{\xi \Sigma_s} \cdot \frac{dE}{E}, \tag{6.130.1}$$

and the age equation (6.128.2) is applicable, with the slowing down density $q(E)$ evaluated at energy E.

SOLUTION OF THE FERMI AGE EQUATION

Case I.   *Plane Source of Fast (Monoenergetic) Neutrons in Region of Infinite Extent*

6.131. Consider a source of fast neutrons, consisting of an infinite plane emitting S neutrons per cm² per sec with energy E_0. Supposing the source to lie in the y, z-plane passing through the origin, then the Fermi age equation is

$$\nabla^2 q(x, \tau) = \frac{\partial q(x, \tau)}{\partial \tau} \quad \text{for } x \neq 0. \tag{6.131.1}$$

At the source, the age of the neutrons is zero, and the source condition may be written as

$$q(x, 0) = S \, \delta(x), \tag{6.131.2}$$

$\delta(x)$ being the Dirac delta function (§ 5.81).

6.132. To solve (6.131.1) the variables are separated by letting

$$q(x, \tau) = X(x)T(\tau), \tag{6.132.1}$$

so that the age equation becomes

$$\frac{1}{X} \cdot \frac{d^2 X}{dx^2} = \frac{dT}{d\tau} \cdot \frac{1}{T}.$$

Since the left-hand side of this equation is a function of x only, and the right-hand a function of τ only, each may be set equal to a constant $-\alpha^2$, where α^2 is a real positive quantity;* thus,

$$\frac{1}{X} \cdot \frac{d^2X}{dx^2} = -\alpha^2 \quad \text{and} \quad \frac{dT}{d\tau} = -\alpha^2 T.$$

The general solutions of these differential equations are

$$X = A \cos \alpha x + C \sin \alpha x$$

and

$$T = Fe^{-\alpha^2\tau}.$$

Therefore, by (6.132.1),

$$q = e^{-\alpha^2\tau}(A \cos \alpha x + C \sin \alpha x), \tag{6.132.2}$$

where the constant F has been incorporated into the arbitrary constants A and C.

6.133. It is now convenient to write these solutions in an alternative form making use of the Fourier integral.† For a function $f(x)$ the appropriate expression is

$$f(x) = \frac{1}{\pi} \int_0^\infty d\alpha \int_{-\infty}^\infty f(x') \cos [\alpha(x' - x)] \, dx'. \tag{6.133.1}$$

By (6.131.2), when $\tau = 0$, then $q(x, 0)$ is equal to $S \delta(x)$; hence, it is required to write the solutions for q in such a form that, when $\tau = 0$, $q(x, \tau)$ reduces to the Fourier integral of $S \delta(x)$. These are given by

$$q = \frac{1}{\pi} S \delta(x')e^{-\alpha^2\tau} \cos [\alpha(x' - x)], \tag{6.133.2}$$

where x' and α are independent of x and τ, so that they represent constants of integration.

6.134. Since the age equation is linear, (6.133.2) may be multiplied by $d\alpha \, dx'$ and integrated over all values of α and x' to obtain a complete solution. Thus, the formal solution is

$$q(x, \tau) = \frac{1}{\pi} \int_0^\infty d\alpha \int_{-\infty}^\infty S \delta(x')e^{-\alpha^2\tau} \cos [\alpha(x' - x)] \, dx', \tag{6.134.1}$$

since

$$q(x, 0) =: S \delta(x) = \frac{1}{\pi} \int_0^\infty d\alpha \int_{-\infty}^\infty S \delta(x') \cos [\alpha(x' - x)] \, dx'.$$

* This is necessary from physical considerations, since the slowing down density cannot increase with increasing age of the neutrons.

† For a discussion of Fourier integrals, see R. V. Churchill, "Fourier Series and Boundary Value Problems," McGraw-Hill Book Company, Inc., New York, 1949.

The integral with respect to α is

$$\int_0^\infty e^{-\alpha^2\tau} \cos[\alpha(x' - x)]\, d\alpha = \sqrt{\frac{\pi}{4\tau}}\, e^{-(x'-x)^2/4\tau},$$

and so (6.134.1) becomes

$$q(x, \tau) = \frac{1}{\sqrt{4\pi\tau}} \int_{-\infty}^\infty S\, \delta(x') e^{-(x'-x)^2/4\tau}\, dx'.$$

Further, since

$$\int_{-\infty}^\infty f(x')\, \delta(x')\, dx' = f(0),$$

the final solution of the Fermi age equation for the slowing down density becomes

$$q(x, \tau) = \frac{S}{\sqrt{4\pi\tau}}\, e^{-x^2/4\tau}. \tag{6.134.2}$$

6.135. This result can be generalized to give the slowing down density at x due to a plane source of neutrons at x_0 by noting that x in the solution given above is the distance between the source plane and the position or field plane; hence, for a unit plane source

$$q(x, \tau) = \frac{e^{-|x-x_0|^2/4\tau}}{\sqrt{4\pi\tau}}. \tag{6.135.1}$$

Case II. *Point Source of Fast (Monoenergetic) Neutrons in Region of Infinite Extent*

6.136. The solution of the Fermi age equation for the case of a point source in an infinite medium can be obtained directly from the solution of the plane source, derived above, by means of a procedure which is analogous to that used in § 5.52. Since the medium is supposed to be infinite, and no boundaries are present, the slowing down density at any field point will depend only on the distance to that point from the source. In the case of a plane source the result will then be the sum of the slowing down densities due to an appropriate number of point sources. If $q_{pt}(r)$ is the slowing down density for neutrons of a specific age from a point source, as determined at a field point r, and $q_{pl}(x)$ is the value for a plane source, as observed at x, then by the arguments in § 5.52, it is readily seen that

$$q_{pl}(x, \tau) = \int_0^\infty q_{pt}(r, \tau) 2\pi a\, da. \tag{6.136.1}$$

The problem is now the inverse of that considered previously, since q_{pl} is known, while q_{pt} is to be determined.

6.137. The value of q_{pt} in terms of q_{pl} can be obtained by first replacing the variable a by r. From geometry, $x^2 + a^2 = r^2$ and $r\, dr = a\, da$ (§ 5.53); then q_{pl} is given by

$$q_{pl}(x, \tau) = 2\pi \int_x^\infty q_{pt}(r, \tau) r\, dr. \tag{6.137.1}$$

Upon differentiating with respect to x, it follows that

$$\frac{dq_{\mathrm{pl}}(x, \tau)}{dx} = -2\pi q_{\mathrm{pt}}(x, \tau)x \tag{6.137.2}$$

or

$$q_{\mathrm{pt}}(x, \tau) = -\frac{1}{2\pi x}\frac{dq_{\mathrm{pl}}(x, \tau)}{dx}. \tag{6.137.3}$$

Finally, differentiation of (6.134.2), which expresses $q_{\mathrm{pl}}(x, \tau)$, gives

$$\frac{dq_{\mathrm{pl}}(x, \tau)}{dx} = -\frac{2xS}{4\tau\sqrt{4\pi\tau}}e^{-x^2/4\tau}. \tag{6.137.4}$$

6.138. Since the distance x in $q_{\mathrm{pt}}(x, \tau)$ now represents the distance between the source and a field point, it can be replaced by the general symbol r, as usual. Hence, by combining (6.137.3) and (6.137.4) the slowing down density at a distance r, from a point source of one neutron per sec, is

$$q(r, \tau) = \frac{e^{-r^2/4\tau}}{(4\pi\tau)^{\frac{3}{2}}}. \tag{6.138.1}$$

In the general case of a unit point source at $\mathbf{r}_0$, with a field point at $\mathbf{r}$, the result is

$$q(\mathbf{r}, \tau) = \frac{e^{-|\mathbf{r}-\mathbf{r}_0|^2/4\tau}}{(4\pi\tau)^{\frac{3}{2}}}. \tag{6.138.2}$$

DISTRIBUTION OF SLOWING DOWN DENSITY ABOUT A POINT SOURCE

6.139. Assuming a point source to be at the origin of the coordinate system, the slowing down density is given by (6.138.1); from this it is possible to calculate $q(r, \tau)$ as a function of r, i.e., the distance from the source, for any specified value

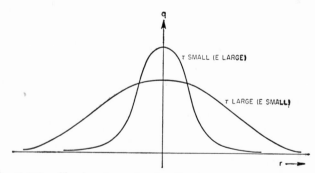

FIG. 6.139.   Slowing down density distribution about a point source

of the age, τ.   For each age, the results fall on a Gauss error curve, as shown in Fig. 6.139, the shape of which depends on whether τ is small, i.e., the energy is near the fission energy, or large, i.e., the energy is in the vicinity of the thermal value.

If τ is small, the curve is high and narrow, but for τ large, it is lower and more spread out. That this must be so may be seen from a qualitative examination of (6.138.1). The magnitude of $q(r, \tau)$ for r equal to zero, which gives the height of the curve, is $1/(4\pi\tau)^{\frac{3}{2}}$, and this is seen to be large for small values of τ. Further, the "width" of the curve, i.e., the distance in which $q(r, \tau)$ falls to $1/e$ of its maximum value, is readily found to be equal to $2\sqrt{\tau}$, and this increases with increasing τ.

6.140. The fact that the Fermi age τ is a measure of the width of the curve means that it determines the distribution of the slowing down density about the source. This is to be expected on physical grounds. A very small τ means that the neutrons have suffered little slowing down, and so they have not diffused far from the source. Consequently, most of the neutrons will have high energies and be in the neighborhood of the source; this corresponds to a high and narrow distribution curve. On the other hand, when τ is large, the neutrons will have undergone considerable slowing down and a large proportion will have diffused an appreciable distance from the source. The distribution curve of the slowing down density will thus be low and broad.

Physical Significance of Age

6.141. A more precise physical significance can be associated with the Fermi age by calculating the second spatial moment of the slowing down density, denoted by $\overline{r^2}(\tau)$, in a manner similar to that used in connection with diffusion. Thus,

$$\overline{r^2}(\tau) = \frac{\int_0^\infty r^2 \left[4\pi r^2 q(r, \tau)\right] dr}{\int_0^\infty 4\pi r^2 q(r, \tau)\, dr},$$

where $q(r, \tau)$ is the number of neutrons per cm³ per sec slowed down past a given energy, corresponding to the age τ, at the field point r. Using (6.138.1) to express $q(r, \tau)$ for a point source,

$$\overline{r^2}(\tau) = \frac{\int_0^\infty r^4 e^{-r^2/4\tau}\, dr}{\int_0^\infty r^2 e^{-r^2/4\tau}\, dr} = 6\tau. \qquad (6.141.1)$$

Consequently, the age τ is one-sixth of the mean square (crow-flight) distance traveled by a neutron from the time of its emission, i.e., age zero, to the time at which its age is τ.

6.142. Although the result of (6.141.1) is quite general, that is to say, it applies to neutrons of any energy and, hence, of any age, it is of special interest in connection with thermal neutrons. Thus $\sqrt{\tau_{\text{th}}}$ is referred to as the *slowing down length* of the thermal neutron. It is an important quantity in determining the extent to which neutrons leak out of a finite thermal reactor while being slowed down.

Experimental Determination of Age

6.143. In the experimental determination of the age of neutrons, the slowing down density for neutrons of a specific energy is measured at various distances from a source of fast neutrons placed in the given medium.   For example, the

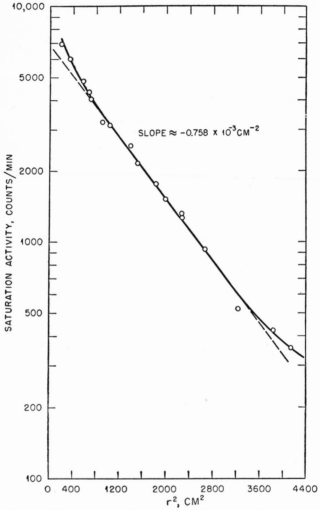

Fig. 6.144.   Experimental data for determination of age in graphite

source may be a mixture of polonium or radium and beryllium located at the center of a large graphite structure, which is treated as an infinite medium.   A quantity proportional to the slowing down density for indium resonance energy, i.e., about 1.4 ev, for various locations is then given by the saturation activity of cadmium-covered indium foils, as described in § 6.76, *et seq.* The distribution of the slowing down density about the point source will be represented by (6.138.1), and upon taking logarithms, it is seen that for neutrons of a given energy, i.e., τ is constant,

$$\ln q(r) = \text{const.} - \frac{r^2}{4\tau}.$$

The plot of the logarithm of the indium activity against the square of the distance from the source should thus be a straight line of slope equal to $-1/4\tau$.

6.144. The results of an actual experiment for the determination of the age of neutrons from a polonium-beryllium source in graphite are given in the semi-logarithmic plot in Fig. 6.144. The slope of the central (linear) portion is -0.758×10^{-3} cm^{-2}, and hence the age of the neutrons at indium resonance is 330 cm^2. It will be seen that the plot deviates from linear both close to and far from the source. The observed slowing down density near the source is higher than expected because a considerable portion of neutrons of energy greater than 1.4 ev, the indium resonance peak, is still present. Since indium has a reasonably large cross section for absorption of such neutrons (Fig. 3.69), they are included in the measurements made at short distances from the source; the results are consequently too high. On the other hand, at considerable distances from the source the slowing down is essentially complete and subsequently the virtually monoenergetic (thermal) neutrons merely undergo diffusion. The flux distribution then falls off with distance as $e^{-k'r}$ rather than as e^{-kr^2}.

6.145. The method described above gives the age of neutrons having the indium resonance energy as derived from a polonium-beryllium source; alternatively a uranium fission source could be used. In any case, since the source neutrons are not monoenergetic, the observed age will be a mean value. Further, the indium resonance energy of 1.4 ev is appreciably greater than the mean thermal energy of 0.025 ev; in fact, nearly one-third of the collisions made by a fission neutron in graphite take place in this range. A correction must, therefore, be applied to the age measured at indium resonance. In Table 6.145 are recorded

TABLE 6.145.   AGE OF THERMAL NEUTRONS FROM FISSION SOURCE

Moderator	Age (cm^2)	Slowing Down Length (cm)
Water	33	5.7
Heavy Water	120	11.0
Beryllium	98	9.9
Graphite	350	18.7

the ages of thermal neutrons from fission for ordinary and heavy water, beryllium, and graphite at 20°C. The data for the first two substances are not really the Fermi ages, since the continuous slowing down theory does not apply to them; they are experimentally determined values of $\overline{r^2}/6$ for thermal neutrons, to which the age is physically equivalent [cf. (6.141.1)].

Diffusion and Slowing Down Times

6.146. It is of interest to determine the average time spent by a neutron in slowing down from fission to thermal energies, i.e., the average chronological age as defined in § 6.129. Equation (6.124.1) may be written in the form

$$-\frac{dE}{E} = \frac{\xi v}{\lambda_s} dt,$$ (6.146.1)

where dE is the energy loss suffered by a neutron in time dt, according to the continuous slowing down model. The total time t required for the energy to be decreased from the fission energy E_0 to the thermal energy E_{th}, i.e., the average chronological age of fast neutrons when they become thermal neutrons, is obtained by rearrangement and integration of (6.146.1); thus,

$$t = \int_0^t dt = \int_{E_{th}}^{E_0} \frac{\lambda_s}{\xi v} \cdot \frac{dE}{E}.$$ (6.146.2)

6.147. Replacing v by $\sqrt{2E/m}$, where m is the actual mass of a neutron, and assuming an average value of λ_s, represented by $\bar{\lambda}_s$, (6.146.2) becomes

$$t = \frac{\bar{\lambda}_s}{\xi} \sqrt{2m} \left(\frac{1}{\sqrt{E_{th}}} - \frac{1}{\sqrt{E_0}} \right).$$ (6.147.1)

In order to evaluate t in sec, $\bar{\lambda}_s$ must be in cm, as usual, m in grams (1.66×10^{-24} gram), and E_0 and E_{th} in ergs (1 Mev $= 1.60 \times 10^{-6}$ erg). The data and results for the four common moderators are given in Table 6.147; the slowing down times are from $E_0 = 2$ Mev to $E_{th} = 0.025$ ev.

TABLE 6.147. SLOWING DOWN AND DIFFUSION TIMES FOR THERMAL NEUTRONS

Moderator	$\bar{\lambda}_s$ (cm)	Slowing Down Time (sec)	Diffusion Time (sec)
Water	1.1	10^{-5}	2.1×10^{-4}
Heavy water	2.6	4.6×10^{-5}	0.15
Beryllium	1.6	6.7×10^{-5}	4.3×10^{-3}
Graphite	2.6	1.5×10^{-4}	1.2×10^{-2}

6.148. For purposes of comparison the average *diffusion time* or *lifetime* of a thermal neutron, as it is often called, i.e., the average time spent diffusing as a thermal neutron before capture by the moderator at ordinary temperatures, is given in the last column of Table 6.147. The average lifetime l_0 of a thermal neutron, in an infinite medium, is equal to the average distance traveled before absorption, i.e., the absorption mean free path $\lambda_a (= 1/\Sigma_a)$, divided by the mean velocity v of the neutrons, i.e.,

$$l_0 = \frac{\lambda_a}{v} = \frac{1}{\Sigma_a v}.$$ (6.148.1)

The mean velocity of thermal neutrons at ordinary temperatures is taken as 2.2×10^5 cm per sec (§ 3.19). It is seen from the results in Table 6.147 that the average slowing down time in a moderator is usually much less than the so-called lifetime or diffusion time of the thermal neutrons. It should be noted that the calculations made above are for infinite media, in which there is no leakage of neutrons from the system, and there is no absorption other than that due to the moderator itself.

SLOWING DOWN AND DIFFUSION OF FAST NEUTRONS FROM INFINITE PLANE SOURCE IN AN INFINITE MEDIUM

6.149. In § 5.50, *et seq.*, the flux distribution about an infinite plane source of thermal neutrons was calculated from diffusion theory. In the present section it will be shown, by a separate consideration of slowing down and diffusion, how the results for the distribution of thermal neutrons are modified when the source is one of fast neutrons which suffer slowing down. The procedure involves, first, the solution of the age equation, as in § 6.131, *et seq.*, to satisfy the source condition; then the slowing down density, evaluated from the thermal age, is used as the source term in the thermal neutron diffusion equation.

6.150. The thermal neutron slowing down density for an infinite plane source emitting one neutron per cm^2 per sec is given by (6.134.2) as

$$q(x) = \frac{e^{-x^2/4\tau}}{\sqrt{4\pi\tau}}, \tag{6.150.1}$$

where the x-axis is normal to the plane of the fast neutron source; in this expression τ is the age of the thermal neutrons from the given source. Consequently, in an element of volume, at the position x_0, having a cross section of 1 cm^2 and a thickness dx_0 cm, the source of thermal neutrons is

$$S(x_0) \, dx_0 = \frac{e^{-x_0^2/4\tau}}{\sqrt{4\pi\tau}} \, dx_0. \tag{6.150.2}$$

Now, upon introducing the infinite plane diffusion kernel, as recorded in Table 5.95, it follows that the thermal flux at x is given by

$$\phi(x) = \int_{-\infty}^{\infty} \frac{e^{-\kappa |x - x_0|}}{2\kappa D} \cdot \frac{e^{-x_0^2/4\tau}}{\sqrt{4\pi\tau}} \, dx_0$$

$$= \frac{1}{4\kappa D \sqrt{\pi\tau}} \int_{-\infty}^{\infty} \exp\left(-\kappa |x - x_0| - \frac{x_0^2}{4\tau}\right) dx_0. \tag{6.150.3}$$

6.151. In order to evaluate the integral in (6.150.3), it is split into two parts, one from $x_0 = -\infty$ to $x_0 = x$, and the other from $x_0 = x$ to $x_0 = \infty$; in the former $x > x_0$, so that $|x - x_0|$ in the exponent may be replaced by $x - x_0$, while in the latter, $x_0 > x$ and then $|x - x_0|$ is equal to $x_0 - x$. Consequently, (6.150.3) may be written as

$$\phi(x) = \frac{1}{4\kappa D\sqrt{\pi\tau}}\left[\int_{-\infty}^{x}\exp\left(-\kappa x + \kappa x_0 - \frac{x_0^2}{4\tau}\right)dx_0 + \int_{x}^{\infty}\exp\left(\kappa x - \kappa x_0 - \frac{x_0^2}{4\tau}\right)dx_0\right]$$

$$= \frac{1}{4\kappa D\sqrt{\pi\tau}}\left[e^{-\kappa x}\int_{-\infty}^{x}\exp\left(\kappa x_0 - \frac{x_0^2}{4\tau}\right)dx_0 + e^{\kappa x}\int_{x}^{\infty}\exp\left(-\kappa x_0 - \frac{x_0^2}{4\tau}\right)dx_0\right].$$

$$(6.151.1)$$

These integrals are of the form $\int e^{-u^2}\,du$, leading to the error functions, the values of which are tabulated.

6.152. Consider the first integral represented by

$$I_1 = \int_{-\infty}^{x}\exp\left(\kappa x_0 - \frac{x_0^2}{4\tau}\right)dx_0 = e^{\kappa^2\tau}\int_{-\infty}^{x}\exp-\left(\frac{x_0}{2\sqrt{\tau}} - \kappa\sqrt{\tau}\right)^2 dx_0,$$

and let

$$u \equiv \left(\frac{x_0}{2\sqrt{\tau}} - \kappa\sqrt{\tau}\right),$$

so that

$$du = \frac{dx_0}{2\sqrt{\tau}}.$$

Then the expression for the integral I_1 becomes

$$I_1 = 2\sqrt{\tau}\,e^{\kappa^2\tau}\int_{-\infty}^{\frac{x}{2\sqrt{\tau}}-\kappa\sqrt{\tau}}e^{-u^2}\,du$$

$$= \sqrt{\tau}\,e^{\kappa^2\tau}\left[2\int_{-\infty}^{0}e^{-u^2}\,du + \sqrt{\pi}\,\frac{2}{\sqrt{\pi}}\int_{0}^{\frac{x}{2\sqrt{\tau}}-\kappa\sqrt{\tau}}e^{-u^2}\,du\right]$$

$$= \sqrt{\pi\tau}\,e^{\kappa^2\tau}\left[1 + \mathrm{erf}\left(\frac{x}{2\sqrt{\tau}} - \kappa\sqrt{\tau}\right)\right], \qquad (6.152.1)$$

where the error function (erf) is defined by

$$\mathrm{erf}\,(x) \equiv \frac{2}{\sqrt{\pi}}\int_{0}^{x}e^{-u^2}\,du.$$

In a similar manner it can be shown that the second integral in (6.151.1) is

$$I_2 = \int_{x}^{\infty}\exp\left(-\kappa x_0 - \frac{x_0^2}{4\tau}\right)dx_0$$

$$= \sqrt{\pi\tau}\,e^{\kappa^2\tau}\left[1 - \mathrm{erf}\left(\frac{x}{2\sqrt{\tau}} + \kappa\sqrt{\tau}\right)\right]. \qquad (6.152.2)$$

Using (6.152.1) and (6.152.2) for the solutions of the integrals, (6.151.1) becomes

$$\phi(x) = \frac{e^{\kappa^2\tau}}{4\kappa D}\left\{e^{-\kappa x}\left[1 + \mathrm{erf}\left(\frac{x}{2\sqrt{\tau}} - \kappa\sqrt{\tau}\right)\right] + e^{\kappa x}\left[1 - \mathrm{erf}\left(\frac{x}{2\sqrt{\tau}} + \kappa\sqrt{\tau}\right)\right]\right\},$$

$$(6.152.3)$$

which is the expression for the thermal flux distribution in the case of a plane source of fast neutrons at the origin.

6.153. If the source had consisted of thermal neutrons, the age τ would be zero. The same will be true, in general, if the flux distribution applies to neutrons of the same energy as the source. In other words, for the case of diffusion of monoenergetic neutrons, τ would be zero and (6.152.3) should reduce to (5.51.2) for the distribution of monoenergetic neutrons about an infinite plane source. Setting $\tau = 0$, the error functions are both unity and $e^{\kappa^2\tau}$ is also unity; hence

$$\phi(x) = \frac{1}{4\kappa D}(2e^{-\kappa x} + 0) = \frac{e^{-\kappa x}}{2\kappa D}, \tag{6.153.1}$$

which is identical with (5.51.2), as expected.

6.154. A comparison of the thermal flux distribution from a plane source of fast neutrons, as given by (6.152.3), with that for a similar source of slow neu-

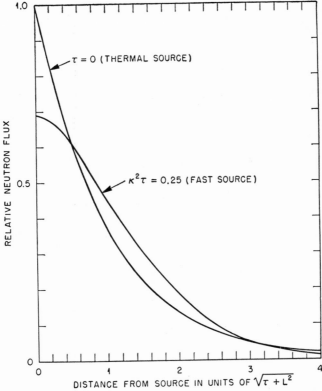

Fɪɢ. 6.154. Thermal flux distribution for infinite plane source in infinite medium

trons, as obtained from (6.153.1), is made in Fig. 6.154. The relative flux is plotted against the distance from the source in units of $\sqrt{\tau + L^2}$, where L is the diffusion length.   One curve is for a thermal source ($\tau = 0$), and the other is for a fast neutron source with $\kappa^2\tau$ (or τ/L^2) equal to 0.25.   In this case, $\sqrt{\tau + L^2}$, called the *migration length* (§ 7.64), is not very different from the diffusion length of the slow neutrons.   It is seen that the flux distribution for a plane source of fast neutrons in an infinite slowing down medium becomes virtually identical with that for a similar source of thermal neutrons beyond about three migration lengths.

Fermi Age Equation with Weak Capture

6.155. In the derivation of the Fermi age equation given above, it was postulated that there was no absorption of neutrons during the slowing down process. If the capture is not great and the cross section does not vary rapidly with energy, the Fermi age treatment may be modified to give results which are satisfactory to a fair degree of approximation.

6.156. Consider an interval of lethargy du lying between u and $u + du$.   The number of neutrons entering this interval per cm³ per sec, because they are slowed down from higher energies, is the slowing down density at u, i.e., $q(u)$; on the other hand, the number leaving this interval, because they are degraded to lower energies, is $q(u + du)$.*   The excess neutrons entering over those leaving the lethargy interval is thus $q(u) - q(u + du)$ which may be represented by $-(\partial q/\partial u)\, du$, assuming that the slowing down density can be treated as a continuous function of the energy (or lethargy).   This excess number of neutrons is balanced, in the steady state, by the leakage of neutrons, which is $D(u)\, \nabla^2\phi(u)\, du$, where $\phi(u)$ is the flux per unit lethargy interval, and by the absorption $\Sigma_a\phi(u)\, du$, in the specified interval du.   The steady-state equation is

$$D \nabla^2\phi(u) - \Sigma_a\phi(u) - \frac{\partial q(u)}{\partial u} = 0, \qquad (6.156.1)$$

the factor du having been cancelled out from each term.   It should be noted that the absorption cross section Σ_a refers only to absorption of neutrons during slowing down, and does not apply to capture that may take place subsequently, e.g., after the neutrons have become thermalized in a reactor.

6.157. According to (6.110.1), the relationship between the flux per unit lethargy interval and the slowing down density $q'(u)$ with absorption, in the case of slowly varying capture cross section, is given by

$$\phi(u) = \frac{q'(u)}{\xi\Sigma_s + \gamma\Sigma_a},$$

where Σ_s and Σ_a are the macroscopic cross sections for scattering and absorption, respectively, of the neutrons of lethargy u.   Hence, (6.156.1) may be written as

---

* It should be recalled that, in accordance with its definition, u increases as the energy decreases.

$$\frac{D}{\xi\Sigma_s + \gamma\Sigma_a} \nabla^2 q'(u) - \frac{\Sigma_a}{\xi\Sigma_s + \gamma\Sigma_a} q'(u) = \frac{\partial q'(u)}{\partial u} \qquad (6.157.1)$$

where the q's have been primed throughout to indicate that they refer to the slowing down density with absorption. The assumption is made that ξ, Σ_s, and Σ_a are independent of position, which is approximately true for a bare reactor.

6.158. As seen in § 6.111, the slowing down density q' with absorption may be related to that without absorption, i.e., q, in a system of infinite extent, by the approximate relationship

$$q'(u) = q(u) \exp\left(-\int_0^u \frac{\Sigma_a}{\xi\Sigma_s + \gamma\Sigma_a} du\right). \qquad (6.158.1)$$

By making this substitution in (6.157.1) and noting that differentiation of $q'(u)$ with respect to u gives two terms, one of which cancels the second term on the left-hand side, the result is

$$\frac{D}{\xi\Sigma_s + \gamma\Sigma_a} \nabla^2 q(u) = \frac{\partial q}{\partial u}. \qquad (6.158.2)$$

If now the age τ', for slowing down with absorption, is defined by

$$\tau'(u) = \int_0^u \frac{D}{\xi\Sigma_s + \gamma\Sigma_a} du, \qquad (6.158.3)$$

(6.158.2) reduces to

$$\nabla^2 q = \frac{\partial q}{\partial \tau'}. \qquad (6.158.4)$$

If the absorption during slowing down is fairly small, so that $\xi\Sigma_s + \gamma\Sigma_a$ is not very different from $\xi\Sigma_s$, equation (6.158.3) for the age with absorption approaches (6.128.1) which defines the age without absorption, and (6.158.4) becomes essentially the same as the Fermi equation (6.128.2).

6.159. It will be observed that the exponential term in (6.158.1) is the resonance escape probability $p(u)$, as given in § 6.111, so that it is possible to write, for the case of weak capture,

$$q'(u) = q(u)p(u),$$

where $q(u)$ is the slowing down density without capture. It follows, therefore, from the result of the preceding paragraph, that the slowing down density with weak capture is approximately equal to the slowing down density without capture that is a solution of the Fermi equation, for the same energy, multiplied by the resonance escape probability at that energy.

PROBLEMS

1. S fast neutrons per cm³ with energy E_0 are being uniformly produced in an infinite homogeneous scattering medium per sec and are slowing down without absorption to a lower energy E_1, such that $E_1 \ll \alpha E_0$, where a very high absorption resonance exists. Assuming that all neutrons having energies in the interval $E_1 - E_2$ are absorbed, calculate the fraction of source neutrons that slow down past E_2 if $E_2 < E_1$ and $E_2 > \alpha E_1$, where α is defined by (6.12.2).

2. In some experiments it is necessary to increase the neutron source strength above that available from a thermal column of a reactor or from a Po-Be source. This may be done by means of a fission plate which contains U–235. To illustrate, consider an infinite plane source of thermal neutrons emitting S neutrons per cm² per sec in an infinite graphite medium. A very thin sheet containing U–235 is placed at a distance a from this thermal neutron source. Neglect the scattering effects of the fission plate, depression of the flux, and the absorption of fast neutrons.

(a) What is the slowing density at τ_{th} as a function of position?
(b) What is the thermal neutron flux?
(c) What is the power of the fission plate per cm²?

3. Develop a rigorous formula for the resonance escape probability in an infinite homogeneous non-hydrogeneous medium that has constant scattering and absorption cross sections.

Chapter VII

THE BARE HOMOGENEOUS THERMAL REACTOR*

(Sources Determined by Fermi Age Theory)

THE CRITICAL EQUATION

INTRODUCTION

7.1. In the preceding chapters the diffusion and slowing down of neutrons from various sources were considered without specific reference to the nature of these sources or the detailed properties of the medium. The results will now be applied specifically to a multiplying system — in particular to the bare, homogeneous, thermal reactor — consisting of fuel material and moderator, as described in Chapter IV. It will be recalled that in such a system slow neutrons are absorbed by the fuel material and nuclear fission occurs. The fast neutrons produced in this process are then slowed down, as a result of elastic collisions with the moderator nuclei. During the slowing down process some neutrons are lost by capture and by leakage from the system, while the remainder reach thermal energies. Some of these thermal neutrons leak from the reactor, whereas others are absorbed by the fuel and cause fission, and so on.

7.2. If a multiplying system of fuel and moderator is in a steady state, i.e., the time rate of change of the neutron density is zero, and there is no extraneous neutron source present, then a self-sustaining chain reaction must be proceeding. Just as many neutrons are being produced by fission as are lost by absorption and leakage. The system is then in the *critical state*, and the effective multiplication factor is unity. A steady state is possible in a subcritical system if an extraneous source is present because the deficit between the neutron absorption and leakage, on the one hand, and the production by fission, on the other hand, would be made up by the extraneous source of neutrons. However, such a system is not critical in the strict sense, since the chain reaction is not self-sustaining. Upon removal of the extraneous source, the neutron density would steadily decrease.

---

* The subject matter of this chapter is due almost entirely to the work of E. Fermi and his associates.

7.3. The purpose of the present chapter is to find the conditions under which a reactor will become critical and maintain a self-sustaining nuclear chain reaction. Suppose that an extraneous source of neutrons is placed in a subcritical assembly of uranium and moderator. Owing to the presence of fissionable material, the source neutrons will be multiplied; that is to say, some of the source neutrons captured by the fuel will cause fission which in turn will produce more neutrons, and so on. Eventually a steady state will occur if the system is subcritical; otherwise the neutron density would increase without limit. The first problem is to calculate the neutron distribution in a simple assembly with an extraneous source of neutrons. As a result of this calculation, the conditions under which a chain reaction becomes self-sustaining will be found.

7.4. In this book, the thermal neutron chain reaction only will be discussed. Physically, this means that the ratio of moderator atoms to uranium atoms is sufficiently large so that relatively few neutrons are captured during slowing down. Further, it will be assumed that the slowing down density and hence the source of thermal neutrons in the system will be given by the Fermi age equation, as derived in the preceding chapter. To simplify the details of the treatment, without loss of generality, it will be supposed that both fission neutrons and extraneous source neutrons are emitted at a single energy.

SOURCE NEUTRONS AND FERMI AGE THEORY

7.5. The diffusion equation (5.35.1) for thermal neutrons may be written in the form

$$D \, \nabla^2\phi(\mathbf{r}, t) - \Sigma_a\phi(\mathbf{r}, t) + pq(\mathbf{r}, \tau_{\text{th}}, t) = \frac{1}{v} \cdot \frac{\partial\phi(\mathbf{r}, t)}{\partial t}, \qquad (7.5.1)$$

where the thermal neutron flux at any point $\mathbf{r}$ and time t is represented by $\phi(\mathbf{r}, t)$ and Σ_a is the macroscopic cross section for thermal neutrons. The first term in (7.5.1) gives the algebraic gain per cm³ per sec in a volume element at $\mathbf{r}$, due to diffusion of thermal neutrons;* the second term is the loss by absorption; and the third term is the source term, which will be derived in the next paragraph. Since $\phi(\mathbf{r}, t)$ is equal to $n(\mathbf{r}, t)v$, where v is the mean velocity of thermal neutrons, the right-hand side is equivalent to $\partial n(\mathbf{r}, t)/dt$, and is, of course, the net rate of increase of neutrons per cm³ per sec.

7.6. The number of fission and extraneous source neutrons reaching thermal energies per cm³ per sec is equal to the slowing down density at these energies. If there were no absorption during slowing down, this would be equal to $q(\mathbf{r}, \tau_{\text{th}}, t)$, which is the appropriate solution of the age equation, where τ_{th} is the age of thermal neutrons. As seen in § 6.159, an approximate allowance for weak capture during slowing down can be made by multiplying $q(\mathbf{r}, \tau_{\text{th}}, t)$ by the resonance escape probability, so that the required slowing down density, which is equal to

---

* Since $\nabla^2\phi(\mathbf{r})$ is always negative for a reactor, the algebraic gain is actually a numerical loss of neutrons, representing the leakage (cf. § 5.34).

the thermal neutron source term in (7.5.1), is given by $pq(\mathbf{r}, \tau_{\text{th}}, t)$, where p is the resonance escape probability in slowing down from fission energies to thermal energies.

7.7. The slowing down density $q(\mathbf{r}, \tau_{\text{th}}, t)$ can be obtained by solving the age equation

$$\nabla^2 q(\mathbf{r}, \tau, t) = \frac{\partial q(\mathbf{r}, \tau, t)}{\partial \tau} \tag{7.7.1}$$

with the proper conditions. One of these is given by a consideration of the slowing down density of the neutrons having the source energy; this is represented by $q(\mathbf{r}, 0, t)$, since the age of these neutrons is zero.* It can be readily shown (see Fig. 7.33), from the definitions in § 4.57, *et seq.*, that for each thermal neutron absorbed, there are produced $f\eta\epsilon$ fast (fission) neutrons, where f is the thermal utilization, η is the average number of fission neutrons for each neutron captured by fuel, and ϵ is the fast fission factor. Since, by definition, the infinite multiplication factor k is equal to $f\eta\epsilon p$ [cf. (4.61.1)], it follows that k/p represents the number of fast neutrons, which are available for slowing down, for each thermal neutron absorbed. The total number of thermal neutrons absorbed per cm³ per sec is $\Sigma_a\phi(\mathbf{r}, t)$, as given by the second term in (7.5.1); hence the total number of fast (fission) neutrons produced per cm³ per sec is $(k/p)\Sigma_a\phi(\mathbf{r}, t)$. This quantity, plus the extraneous source $S(\mathbf{r})$, must be equal to the slowing down density at the energy of the fission (and extraneous source) neutrons; thus,

$$q(\mathbf{r}, 0, t) = \frac{k}{p} \Sigma_a\phi(\mathbf{r}, t) + S(\mathbf{r}), \tag{7.7.2}$$

which is a coupling condition between the thermal diffusion equation and the age equation.

7.8. The slowing down density depends on time also. However, slowing down times are usually small compared to thermal diffusion times (see Table 6.147), and hence the variation of $q(\mathbf{r}, \tau, t)$ with time, for all values of τ, may be considered to arise entirely from the variation of the thermal flux, as expressed by (7.5.1).

7.9. Further conditions on (7.7.1) arise from a consideration of the flux and slowing down density at the boundary. If the system has no re-entrant surface, the boundary condition on the thermal flux is that it shall vanish 0.71 λ_t beyond the physical boundary (§ 5.40). If λ_t does not vary with energy, the slowing down density will also vanish at the same surface. To simplify the treatment, it will be assumed that the extrapolation distance is independent of energy, so that

$$\left.\begin{array}{l} \phi = 0 \\ q = 0 \end{array}\right\} \text{ at the extrapolated boundary.} \tag{7.9.1}$$

---

* Actually, as stated in § 4.7, there is an energy spectrum for fission neutrons, but it will be assumed here that these neutrons are all produced with the same average energy, from which they are slowed down continuously to an average thermal energy.

It may be noted that, for large thermal reactors, the extrapolation distance $0.71\lambda_t$ is small in comparison with the dimensions of the system. The results, obtained by assuming an extrapolation distance independent of energy, consequently do not differ appreciably from those which would be derived from a more rigorous treatment.

7.10. Since $q(\mathbf{r}, \tau, t)$ is, in general, a function of the space coordinates $\mathbf{r}$, of the age τ, and of the time t, a solution of (7.7.1) may be sought by separating these variables, by writing

$$q(\mathbf{r}, \tau, t) = R(\mathbf{r})\Theta(\tau)T(t), \tag{7.10.1}$$

where $R(\mathbf{r})$ is a function of the space coordinates only, $\Theta(\tau)$ of the age only, and $T(t)$ of time only. Making the substitution of (7.10.1) into (7.7.1) then gives

$$\frac{\nabla^2 R(\mathbf{r})}{R(\mathbf{r})} = \frac{1}{\Theta(\tau)} \cdot \frac{d\Theta(\tau)}{d\tau}. \tag{7.10.2}$$

Since the left-hand side depends only on $R(\mathbf{r})$ and the right-hand side only on $\Theta(\tau)$, it is possible to set each side equal to a constant; thus,

$$\frac{\nabla^2 R(\mathbf{r})}{R(\mathbf{r})} = -B^2$$

or

$$\nabla^2 R(\mathbf{r}) + B^2 R(\mathbf{r}) = 0, \tag{7.10.3}$$

and

$$\frac{1}{\Theta(\tau)} \cdot \frac{d\Theta(\tau)}{d\tau} = -B^2. \tag{7.10.4}$$

The solution of (7.10.4) is

$$\Theta(\tau) = Ae^{-B^2\tau}, \tag{7.10.5}$$

where B^2 must be a real positive number in order to satisfy the physical requirement that the slowing down density $q(\mathbf{r}, \tau, t)$ cannot increase with the neutron age.

THE APPROACH TO CRITICAL

7.11. Consideration will now be given to (7.10.3). Suppose, for simplicity, a fuel-moderator assembly has the shape of a parallel-sided, infinite slab, having a finite thickness a, including the extrapolation distance. An extraneous source of neutrons is placed at the plane of symmetry of the slab (Fig. 7.11).* If the origin of the coordinates is taken at the source plane, the spatial distribution of the slowing down density (and the flux) then depends on only one variable. Thus $R(\mathbf{r})$ in (7.10.3) may be replaced by $X(x)$, and (7.10.3) becomes

$$\frac{d^2 X(x)}{dx^2} + B^2 X(x) = 0, \tag{7.11.1}$$

where B^2 is a positive, real number, as stated above.

* A more general treatment, based on a finite parallelepiped assembly, with an extraneous source at the center, is given in Chapter XII.

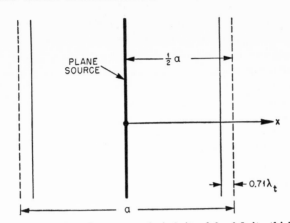

FIG. 7.11.   Infinite plane source in infinite slab of finite thickness

7.12. By the method used in § 5.72, *et seq.* (see also, § 7.38), it can be readily shown that a solution of this equation which satisfies both the requirements of symmetry and the boundary condition on the slowing down density, namely, $q = 0$ when $x = \frac{1}{2}a$, is

$$X_n = A_n \cos \frac{n\pi x}{a}, \tag{7.12.1}$$

where n can be any odd integer.   The values of B^2 are then given by

$$B_n{}^2 = \left(\frac{n\pi}{a}\right)^2, \tag{7.12.2}$$

these being the *eigenvalues* of the problem, each corresponding to an *eigenfunction* X_n defined by (7.12.1).   It can be seen from (7.12.2) that the lowest (or fundamental) eigenvalue is the one for which n is unity, i.e., $B_1{}^2$; all the other possible eigenvalues, namely, $B_3{}^2$, $B_5{}^2$, etc., must be larger.

7.13. The complete solution of (7.10.3) is given by summing the expressions in (7.12.1) for all odd integers n from unity to infinity; if the result, which represents $R(\mathbf{r})$, together with (7.10.5) is inserted into (7.10.1), the equation for the slowing down density becomes

$$q(\mathbf{r}, \tau, t) = \sum_{n=1}^{\infty} A_n \cos \frac{n\pi x}{a} e^{-B_n{}^2\tau} T_n(t). \tag{7.13.1}$$

7.14. The extraneous source at the plane of symmetry of the slab may be expanded in terms of a Fourier series (cf. § 5.82); thus,

$$S(\mathbf{r}) = S\delta(x) = \sum_{n=1}^{\infty} S_n \cos \frac{n\pi x}{a}, \tag{7.14.1}$$

where, as above, n has odd integral values. Then, from (7.13.1), (7.14.1), and the coupling condition (7.7.2), it follows that

$$\phi(\mathbf{r}, t) = \frac{p}{k\Sigma_a} \sum_{n=1}^{\infty} [A_n T_n(t) - S_n] \cos \frac{n\pi x}{a}. \tag{7.14.2}$$

7.15. Equations (7.13.1) and (7.14.2) may now be substituted into the thermal diffusion equation (7.5.1), and from the orthogonality of the Fourier cosine series, each term corresponding to a value of n is linearly independent; hence, it is found that

$$-\frac{p}{k}\left[\frac{DB_n^2}{\Sigma_a} + 1\right][A_n T_n(t) - S_n] + pA_n e^{-B_n^2\tau_{\text{th}}}T_n(t) = \frac{1}{v} \cdot \frac{p}{k\Sigma_a} A_n \frac{dT_n}{dt}. \tag{7.15.1}$$

7.16. The diffusion length L of the thermal neutrons is defined by $L^2 = D/\Sigma_a$ (§ 5.64), and $1/v\Sigma_a$ is equal to the mean lifetime l_0 of thermal neutrons in an infinite medium (§ 6.148). Thus, (7.15.1) can be reduced to

$$\frac{dT_n(t)}{dt} = \left[\frac{ke^{-B_n^2\tau_{\text{th}}} - (1 + L^2B_n^2)}{l_0}\right]T_n(t) + \frac{(1 + L^2B_n^2)S_n}{l_0 A_n}. \tag{7.16.1}$$

Defining the quantities k_n and l_n by

$$k_n \equiv \frac{ke^{-B_n^2\tau_{\text{th}}}}{1 + L^2B_n^2} \tag{7.16.2}$$

and

$$l_n \equiv \frac{l_0}{1 + L^2B_n^2},$$

(7.16.1) becomes

$$\frac{dT_n(t)}{dt} = \left(\frac{k_n - 1}{l_n}\right)T_n(t) + \frac{S_n}{A_n l_n}. \tag{7.16.3}$$

7.17. The solution of (7.16.3) is

$$T_n(t) = e^{(k_n-1)\frac{t}{l_n}} + \frac{S_n}{A_n(1 - k_n)},$$

and the thermal flux, from (7.14.2), is then

$$\phi(\mathbf{r}, t) = \frac{p}{k\Sigma_a} \sum_{n=1}^{\infty}\left[A_n e^{(k_n-1)\frac{t}{l_n}} + \frac{ke^{-B_n^2\tau_{\text{th}}}S_n}{(1 + L^2B_n^2)(1 - k_n)}\right]\cos\frac{n\pi x}{a}. \tag{7.17.1}$$

Since the second term in the brackets contains S_n, this evidently represents the contribution to the thermal neutron flux due to the extraneous source. The first term is then the contribution of the fuel-moderator system.

7.18. The importance of (7.17.1) lies in the fact that it permits a derivation of the condition for a given multiplying system to become critical. It may be seen from (7.12.2) that, as the thickness a of a slab increases, the value of B_n^2, for a given n, decreases, and this means that k_n, as defined by (7.16.2), increases correspondingly.   As long as the dimensions are such that k_n is less than unity for all possible B_n's, that is, for all odd integral values of n, then $k_n - 1$ will be negative.   The first term in the brackets in (7.17.1) will then decrease exponentially with time.   The only way to maintain a steady state, in which the thermal neutron flux remains constant, would be to include an extraneous source.   After a short time, the exponential term would decay almost to zero, and the flux would be determined by the constant second term in (7.17.1).   A fuel-moderator system of this kind is subcritical and is not strictly self-sustaining.

7.19. If the assembly of fuel and moderator is increased in size, the B_n's will decrease, and a point will be reached when the lowest B_n, namely B_1, will be such that k_1 is exactly unity.   Since B_1 is the lowest eigenvalue, k_1 will be larger than all other possible values of k_n.   With $k_n = 1$, the first term in (7.17.1) becomes constant, while the second term becomes infinite if an extraneous source is present.   Hence, if a steady state is to be realized, this source must be removed. When this is done, the moderator-fuel system will obviously be self-sustaining; the thermal neutron flux will remain constant in the absence of an extraneous source.

THE CRITICAL CONDITION

7.20. The *critical equation* which represents the condition for a self-sustaining chain reaction is thus, from (7.16.2),

$$k_1 = \frac{ke^{-B_1^2 \tau_{\text{th}}}}{1 + L^2 B_1^2} = 1. \tag{7.20.1}$$

This means that a given arrangement of fuel and moderator will become critical, i.e., it will be capable of maintaining a self-sustaining chain reaction, when its dimensions are just large enough for the corresponding value of the lowest eigenvalue B_1 to satisfy the critical equation (7.20.1).

7.21. As stated above, k_1, for $n = 1$, is the largest k_n; all others must consequently be less than unity.   The corresponding values of the first term in the brackets in (7.17.1) must then decay exponentially in time, since $k_n - 1$ is negative, and for a true steady state all must be zero.   Therefore, when a chain-reacting system is critical, the series expansions for the flux, in (7.14.2) and (7.17.1), and for the slowing down density, given by (7.13.1), both reduce to a single term, in which $n = 1$.

7.22. It is, then, possible to write, for the steady (critical) state in the infinite slab arrangement under consideration,

$$\phi(\mathbf{r}) = \frac{p}{k\Sigma_a} A \cos \frac{\pi x}{a} \tag{7.22.1}$$

and

$$q(\mathbf{r}, \tau_{\text{th}}) = A \cos \frac{\pi x}{a} e^{-B^2 \tau_{\text{th}}}, \tag{7.22.2}$$

where B^2 has been written for B_1^2, the lowest, and only significant, eigenvalue. The t variable has been omitted, since, in the steady state, the flux and slowing down density are independent of time. Hence, from (7.22.1) and (7.22.2),

$$q(\mathbf{r}, \tau_{th}) = \frac{k}{p} \Sigma_a \phi(\mathbf{r}) \, e^{-B^2 \tau_{th}}, \tag{7.22.3}$$

so that the slowing down density for thermal neutrons is everywhere proportional to the thermal neutron flux, since k, p, Σ_a, and $e^{-B^2 \tau_{th}}$ are constants for neutrons of a specified energy.* Although this result has been derived here for an infinite slab, it is independent of the shape of the assembly; it applies to any self-sustaining, chain-reacting, critical system in which the thermal neutron source is determined by Fermi age theory.†

MATERIAL AND GEOMETRIC BUCKLINGS

7.23. Since the thermal neutron flux and the slowing down density are everywhere proportional, the thermal flux in the critical system also satisfies the wave equation (7.10.3), i.e.,

$$\nabla^2 \phi(\mathbf{r}) + B^2 \phi(\mathbf{r}) = 0, \tag{7.23.1}$$

where B^2 is equal to B_1^2 of (7.20.1). Thus, B^2, called the *buckling*,‡ is the lowest eigenvalue of the wave equation for the critical reactor, subject to the condition that the flux shall go to zero at the extrapolated boundary. The critical equation for a bare, homogeneous reactor may thus be written as

$$\frac{ke^{-B^2 \tau}}{1 + L^2 B^2} = 1, \tag{7.23.2}$$

provided the continuous slowing down (Fermi age) model is applicable. It may be noted that, since k is dimensionless, and the dimensions of both τ and L^2 are (length)^2, the buckling has the dimensions of a reciprocal area.

7.24. It has been found convenient to distinguish between two kinds of buckling. The *material buckling*, B_m^2, is the value of B^2 that satisfies the critical, transcendental equation (7.23.2), so that in the critical reactor the spatial flux distribution is given by

$$\nabla^2 \phi(\mathbf{r}) + B_m^2 \phi(\mathbf{r}) = 0. \tag{7.24.1}$$

---

* It is assumed that k and p are the same at all points in the system.

† The proportionality of $q(\mathbf{r}, \tau)$ and $\phi(\mathbf{r})$ is an important result, since then the steady state equation, in conjunction with the zero flux boundary condition, becomes self-adjoint, i.e., the eigenfunctions of the problem then form a complete orthogonal set over the reactor volume, including the extrapolation distance. This simplifies considerably the perturbation theory for bare, homogeneous reactors (Chapter XIII).

‡ The name "buckling," suggested by J. A. Wheeler, originated from the fact that $-\nabla^2 \phi(\mathbf{r})/\phi(\mathbf{r}) = B^2$ is a measure of the curvature (or buckling) of the neutron flux at any point $\mathbf{r}$ in the critical reactor.

It is seen from (7.23.2) that the material buckling is a specific property of the multiplying medium; its value is dependent only on k, τ, and L^2, which are determined by the material and composition of the medium. The *geometric buckling*, $B_g{}^2$, on the other hand, is defined as the lowest eigenvalue that results from solving the wave equation

$$\nabla^2\phi(\mathbf{r}) + B_g{}^2\phi(\mathbf{r}) = 0, \qquad (7.24.2)$$

with the boundary condition that $\phi(\mathbf{r})$ shall be zero at the extrapolated boundary of the system. As will be evident from §§ 7.11, 7.12, and as will be shown in more detail later, the lowest eigenvalue $B_g{}^2$ is a property only of the geometry, i.e., the shape and size, of the system under consideration.

7.25. The distinction between the material and geometric bucklings will be apparent from an examination of (7.24.1) and (7.24.2). The solution of (7.24.1), with a single value of $B_m{}^2$ determined by (7.23.2), will give the thermal neutron flux $\phi(\mathbf{r})$ at any point in a critical reactor. However, (7.24.2) does not, in general, represent the flux distribution with a single value of $B_g{}^2$. If the system is not critical, the thermal flux is obtained as a sum of terms, as in (7.14.2) or (7.17.1), involving all the eigenvalues of (7.24.2). For a critical (or near critical) system, the terms beyond the first drop out, and then the flux distribution can be expressed by means of the lowest eigenvalue of (7.24.2) only. In these circumstances (7.24.1) and (7.24.2) become identical, so that the critical condition can be written as

$$B_g{}^2 = B_m{}^2. \qquad (7.25.1)$$

In other words, the geometric buckling, $B_g{}^2$, of the critical system of a specified shape is equal to the material buckling, $B_m{}^2$, for the given multiplying medium. It will be seen below that the geometric buckling is inversely related to the dimensions of the system [cf. (7.12.2)]. Hence, if $B_g{}^2$ is less than $B_m{}^2$, the reactor will be larger than the critical size and the system will be supercritical; but if $B_g{}^2$ is greater than $B_m{}^2$, the system will be subcritical.

7.26. If the geometry of a reactor is prescribed, the value of the geometric buckling is fixed (§ 7.36, *et seq.*). If this is set equal to B^2 in (7.23.2), it is possible to determine the composition of fuel and moderator which will make the reactor critical, since k, τ, and L^2 are properties of the materials and their proportions (§ 7.65, *et seq.*). Alternatively, if the composition of the multiplying medium is specified, so that k, τ, and L^2 are known, the material buckling can be obtained from (7.23.2). If this is then identified with the geometric buckling, the size of the critical reactor, for a required shape, can be calculated.

7.27. It was seen in § 4.71 that the criticality condition is that the effective multiplication factor shall be unity. In view of the critical equation (7.20.1), where $B_1{}^2$ is the lowest eigenvalue and hence is equivalent to the geometric buckling, the effective multiplication factor may be defined by

$$k_{\text{eff}} \equiv \frac{ke^{-B_g{}^2\tau}}{1 + L^2B_g{}^2}. \qquad (7.27.1)$$

When the reactor is critical, B_g^2 is equal to B_m^2, and the right-hand side of (7.27.1) becomes identical with the left-hand side of (7.23.2); k_{eff} is then equal to unity. as required. In a subcritical system, k_{eff} is less than unity; this arises because the reactor is smaller than the critical size, i.e., B_g^2 is larger than the critical value B_m^2 for the given multiplying medium. Similarly, as stated above, a reac- tor will be supercritical when the geometry is such that B_g^2 is smaller than B_m^2; it follows from (7.27.1) that k_{eff} is then greater than unity.

Neutron Balance in a Thermal Reactor

7.28. Before proceeding to derive the connection between the geometric buckling and the size and shape of a thermal reactor, it is of interest to consider the significance of the quantities in the critical equation (7.23.2). If the reactor were infinite in size, so that there were no leakage, the critical condition would be that the infinite multiplication factor k should be unity (§ 4.47). The use of the continuous slowing down (Fermi) model evidently introduces two factors namely, $e^{-B^2\tau}$ and $(1 + L^2B^2)^{-1}$, which take into account the fact that the reactor has finite dimensions, so that leakage of neutrons from the system occurs.

7.29. As seen above, the number of thermal neutrons absorbed per cm³ per sec is equal to $\Sigma_a\phi(\mathbf{r})$. By definition, k is the number of thermal neutrons pro- duced, on the average, in one generation for each thermal neutron absorbed, in an infinite medium. Hence, if the reactor were infinite, and there were no leak- age of neutrons during slowing down, the density of source neutrons would be $(k/p)\Sigma_a\phi(\mathbf{r})$. The actual number of neutrons becoming thermalized per cm³ per sec is equal to $pq(\mathbf{r}, \tau)$ as shown in § 7.6, and, from (7.22.3), this is seen to be equal to $k\Sigma_a\phi(\mathbf{r})e^{-B^2\tau}$. Thus the factor $e^{-B^2\tau}$ represents the probability that the fast neutrons do not leak out of the finite reactor while being slowed down; in other words, $e^{-B^2\tau}$ is the nonleakage probability of the neutrons during the slowing down process.*

7.30. The algebraic gain of thermal neutrons per cm³ per sec by diffusion in a volume element at a point $\mathbf{r}$ in a reactor is given in (7.5.1) as $D\,\nabla^2\phi(\mathbf{r})$; hence, the rate of loss, i.e., the number of neutrons leaking out per cm³ per sec, is $-D\,\nabla^2\phi(\mathbf{r})$, in agreement with (5.31.2). Since $-D\,\nabla^2\phi(\mathbf{r})$ is equal to $DB^2\phi(\mathbf{r})$, by (7.23.1), where D, B^2, and $\phi(\mathbf{r})$ are all positive quantities, it follows that the actual number of thermal neutrons leaking out of a volume element of the reactor is $DB^2\phi(\mathbf{r})$ per cm³ per sec. The number of thermal neutrons absorbed per cm³ per sec is $\Sigma_a\phi(\mathbf{r})$; hence, the ratio of thermal leakage to thermal absorption at any point, and consequently for the reactor as a whole, is given by

$$\frac{\text{Thermal Leakage}}{\text{Thermal Absorption}} = \frac{DB^2}{\Sigma_a} = L^2B^2, \qquad (7.30.1)$$

* This expression for the nonleakage probability was obtained by Fermi even before the dis- covery of fission [cf. E. Fermi and F. Rasetti, *Ricerca Scient.*, **9**, 472 (1938)].

since D/Σ_a is equal to L^2, as seen above. The fraction of the neutrons slowed to thermal energies which are absorbed is now obtained by adding unity to each side of (7.30.1) and inverting; the result is

$$\frac{\text{Thermal Absorption}}{\text{Thermal Absorption} + \text{Thermal Leakage}} = \frac{1}{1 + L^2B^2}. \qquad (7.30.2)$$

Thus, $1/(1 + L^2B^2)$ is the fraction of the neutrons thermalized in the reactor which are absorbed as thermal neutrons. In other words, $1/(1 + L^2B^2)$ is the nonleakage probability of the thermal neutrons.

7.31. It is of interest to examine the physical significance of the various quantities which appear in the nonleakage probability factors. It was seen earlier that when the reactor system is small B^2 is large, and vice versa. A large value of B^2 will mean that both $e^{-B^2\tau}$ and $1/(1 + L^2B^2)$ will be relatively small. Consequently, as is to be expected, the neutron leakage, both during slowing down and while thermal, will be large for a small reactor. Next consider the age, τ; as shown in § 6.141, this is related to the average (crow-flight) distance traveled by a neutron while slowing down. It is to be anticipated, therefore, that a large τ will mean a small nonleakage probability, as is in fact the case, since $e^{-B^2\tau}$ is then small. Similar considerations apply to the diffusion length, L, which is a measure of the average distance traveled by the thermal neutrons before capture. A large value of L should mean a large probability of leakage from the reactor, and this is in agreement with the thermal nonleakage probability represented by $1/(1 + L^2B^2)$.

7.32. The product of the two terms $e^{-B^2\tau}$ and $1/(1 + L^2B^2)$ is thus the total nonleakage probability of the neutrons in the finite reactor from their source as fission neutrons to their capture as thermal neutrons. This is the quantity which was represented by the symbol P in § 4.67, and so $ke^{-B^2\tau}/(1 + L^2B^2)$ must be equal to the effective multiplication factor. Comparison with (7.27.1) shows that B^2 in the nonleakage probability terms is actually the geometric buckling of the system. If, for a given multiplying medium, the reactor is too small, so that B_g^2 is larger than the critical value, the nonleakage probabilities will be smaller, i.e., the total neutron leakage will be larger, than is permissible if a chain reaction is to be maintained.

7.33. By combining the results obtained above, on the basis of the theory of continuous slowing down of neutrons, with the discussion in § 4.57, et seq., of the significance of the quantities which make up the multiplication factor, it is possible to draw up the accompanying scheme (Fig. 7.33) for a single cycle or generation of a thermal neutron chain in a finite reactor of critical size. The chain is started with one thermal neutron, on the right-hand side of the box at the top of the page, and it then follows the path indicated by the arrows, down the right-hand side and up the left-hand side. The zigzag lines imply fission processes, and the arrows to right and left of the main path represent neutron losses due to various causes. The number of neutrons produced in a thermal fission is

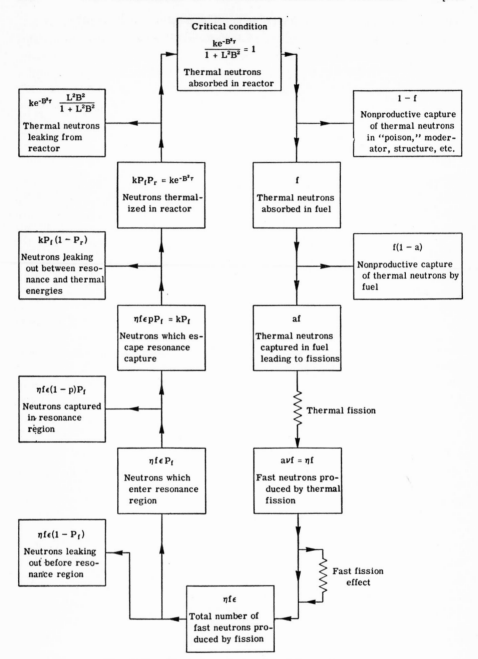

Fig. 7.33. Neutron cycle in critical thermal reactor

represented by ν, while a is the ratio of the fission cross section to the total cross section for absorption in fuel of thermal neutrons. The nonleakage probability during slowing down has been divided into two parts: P_f is that from fission energies to the resonance region, and P_r is from resonance to thermal energies. The product $P_f P_r$ is the total nonleakage probability during slowing down and hence is equal to $e^{-B^2\tau}$. For the reactor to be just critical, the quantities on the two sides of the equation in the box at the top must be equal, and this is seen to be in accord with (7.23.2).

GENERATION TIME

7.34. The average time between successive generations of thermal fissions, called the *generation time*, is equal to the sum of the slowing down time of the fast fission neutrons and of the diffusion time, or lifetime, of the thermal neutrons. The slowing down time in the reactor will be approximately the same as for the moderator, as calculated in § 6.146, *et seq.*, but the lifetime of the thermal neutrons will be decreased because of the larger absorption cross section [cf. (6.148.1)]. Further, allowance must be made for leakage from the reactor. The mean (or average) lifetime l_0 of a thermal neutron in an infinite medium is defined by

$$l_0 = \frac{\lambda_a}{v} = \frac{1}{\Sigma_a v}, \tag{7.34.1}$$

based on the supposition that all the neutrons remain in the system and none escape. However, in a system of finite size only the fraction $1/(1 + L^2B^2)$ of the thermal neutrons do not escape, as seen above. The average lifetime l of a thermal neutron in a finite reactor is thus diminished by this fraction, so that

$$l = \frac{l_0}{1 + L^2B^2}. \tag{7.34.2}$$

7.35. For a graphite-uranium reactor, the mean value of Σ_a may be about .005 cm^{-1}, and v is 2×10^5 cm per sec, so that l_0 is about 10^{-3} sec. For a large reactor $1 + L^2B^2$ is not much greater than unity, so that l may be taken to be about 10^{-3} sec. The slowing down time, as seen in Table 6.147, is 1.5×10^{-4} sec, in graphite, so that in the uranium-graphite system the generation time is essentially equal to the lifetime of thermal neutrons. For a reactor in which a considerable proportion of the fissions are caused by neutrons with energies above thermal, the generation time is defined as the average time between successive fissions *of all types*. This is determined largely by the appropriately weighted slowing down times to the various energies at which the fissions occur.

THE GEOMETRIC BUCKLING

REACTORS OF VARIOUS SHAPES

7.36. As stated earlier, the geometric buckling is the lowest eigenvalue of B_g^2 obtained from the solution of the wave equation (7.24.2) for a system of particular size and shape, subject to the condition that $\phi(\mathbf{r})$ shall vanish at the extrapolated boundary. Expressions for the geometric buckling will now be derived for reactors of various shapes. The treatment here will be restricted to the following geometries: an infinite slab of finite thickness, a rectangular parallelepiped, a sphere, and a finite cylinder. The method can, however, be extended to many other geometrical shapes.

Case I. *Infinite Slab Reactor of Finite Thickness*

7.37. Consider an infinite slab reactor of finite thickness H; this thickness includes the extrapolation distance (§ 5.40) at each face, so that it is the actual geometrical thickness plus twice the extrapolation distance of $0.71\lambda_t$. The origin O of the coordinates is taken at the center of the slab (Fig. 7.37), and the problem

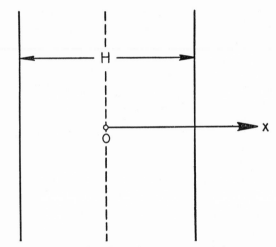

Fig. 7.37. Infinite plane slab reactor of finite thickness

involves only one variable, namely, x. To relate the geometric buckling to the thickness of the slab, it is required to solve the wave equation (7.24.2) with the condition that $\phi(x)$ shall become zero at the extrapolated boundary. The boundary condition is, therefore, that

$$\phi(x) = 0, \quad \text{when} \quad x = \pm \tfrac{1}{2}H,$$

since $+\tfrac{1}{2}H$ and $-\tfrac{1}{2}H$ are the coordinates of the extrapolated boundaries, to the right and left of the origin, respectively.

7.38. In the present case, the Laplacian operator is merely d^2/dx^2, and consequently the wave equation (7.24.2) becomes

$$\frac{d^2\phi(x)}{dx^2} + B_g^2\phi(x) = 0. \tag{7.38.1}$$

The requirements that $\phi(x)$ shall be finite within the slab and become zero at the extrapolated boundaries lead (cf. § 5.74) to the permissible solution

$$\phi(x) = A \cos B_g x, \qquad (7.38.2)$$

since $B_g{}^2$ is real and positive.

7.39. Upon applying to (7.38.2) the boundary condition that $\phi(x)$ shall be zero when $x = \frac{1}{2}H$, the result is

$$A \cos \frac{B_g H}{2} = 0.$$

Since A cannot be zero, for then $\phi(x)$ would be zero everywhere, it follows that

$$\cos \frac{B_g H}{2} = 0,$$

and hence

$$\frac{B_g H}{2} = \frac{n}{2}\pi,$$

where n is an odd integer. In other words, $B_g H/2$ must be equal to an odd number of half integral values of π if $\cos B_g H/2$ is to be zero. By definition, the geometric buckling is the lowest eigenvalue of the wave equation, so that n must be unity, and hence

$$\frac{B_g H}{2} = \frac{\pi}{2}$$

or

$$B_g{}^2 = \left(\frac{\pi}{H}\right)^2. \qquad (7.39.1)$$

This equation gives the geometric buckling $B_g{}^2$ of the infinite slab in terms of H, its thickness. The value of H which would make the geometric buckling equal to the critical (or material) buckling, i.e., the value which would satisfy (7.23.2) when B^2 is replaced by $(\pi/H)^2$, is the *critical thickness* of the infinite slab reactor for the given materials and composition.

7.40. Upon inserting the value for B_g given by (7.39.1) into (7.38.2), the spatial distribution of the neutron flux, in the x-direction, in a bare, infinite slab (thermal) reactor in the critical state is found to be

$$\phi(x) = A \cos \frac{\pi x}{H}, \qquad (7.40.1)$$

where H is the critical thickness. The proportionality constant A is determined by the power level of the reactor, since the power output is, in principle, independent of the size of the system, provided it is critical.

Case II. *Rectangular Parallelepiped Reactor*

7.41. Consider a bare nuclear reactor in the form of a parallelepiped with edges of length a, b, c, which include the extrapolation distances; let the origin of the coordinates be at the center of the reactor (Fig. 7.41). Since three rec-

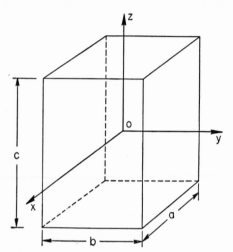

FIG. 7.41.   Rectangular parallelepiped reactor

tangular coordinates must be taken into consideration, the Laplacian operator is given by (5.32.1), and hence the form of the wave equation (7.24.2) to be solved is

$$\frac{\partial^2\phi}{\partial x^2} + \frac{\partial^2\phi}{\partial y^2} + \frac{\partial^2\phi}{\partial z^2} + B_g{}^2\phi = 0, \qquad (7.41.1)$$

where ϕ represents $\phi(x, y, z)$. The boundary condition is that

$$\phi(x, y, z) = 0, \quad \text{when} \quad x = \pm \tfrac{1}{2}a, \quad \text{or} \quad y = \pm \tfrac{1}{2}b, \quad \text{or} \quad z = \pm \tfrac{1}{2}c,$$

so that $\phi(x, y, z)$ shall go to zero at the extrapolated boundaries in the three directions.

7.42. If the variables are separable, so that

$$\phi(x, y, z) = X(x)\,Y(y)Z(z), \qquad (7.42.1)$$

then (7.41.1) becomes

$$\frac{1}{X} \cdot \frac{d^2X}{dx^2} + \frac{1}{Y} \cdot \frac{d^2Y}{dy^2} + \frac{1}{Z} \cdot \frac{d^2Z}{dz^2} + B_g{}^2 = 0, \qquad (7.42.2)$$

where each of the first three terms is a function of one variable only. It is thus possible to set each term equal to a constant quantity; thus,

$$\frac{1}{X} \cdot \frac{d^2X}{dx^2} = -\alpha^2 \qquad (7.42.3)$$

$$\frac{1}{Y} \cdot \frac{d^2Y}{dy^2} = -\beta^2 \tag{7.42.4}$$

$$\frac{1}{Z} \cdot \frac{d^2Z}{dz^2} = -\gamma^2. \tag{7.42.5}$$

Consequently, from (7.42.2)

$$\alpha^2 + \beta^2 + \gamma^2 = B_g{}^2, \tag{7.42.6}$$

where, as will be seen shortly, α^2, β^2, and γ^2, are all positive quantities.

7.43. It will be noted that the problem here is similar in many respects to that in § 5.72, *et seq.*, equations (7.42.3) and (7.42.4) being identical in form with (5.72.1) and (5.72.2), respectively, with similar boundary conditions. The only solution which satisfies the requirement of symmetry and that $\phi(x, y, z)$ shall be zero at the extrapolated boundary [cf. (5.75.1)] is

$$X = A \cos \alpha x, \tag{7.43.1}$$

which means that α^2 must be a real, positive quantity. This result is seen to be identical in form with (7.38.2) for the infinite slab. Hence, by introducing the boundary condition that the thermal neutron flux shall become zero at the extrapolated boundary where $x = \frac{1}{2}a$, it can be readily shown that the smallest value of α is

$$\alpha = \frac{\pi}{a} \quad \text{and} \quad \alpha^2 = \left(\frac{\pi}{a}\right)^2, \tag{7.43.2}$$

and so

$$X = A \cos \frac{\pi x}{a}. \tag{7.43.3}$$

7.44. Since there is no essential difference between the x, y, and z dimensions, it can be found, by a procedure exactly equivalent to that given above, that β^2 and γ^2 must be real, positive quantities, and

$$\beta^2 = \left(\frac{\pi}{b}\right)^2 \quad \text{and} \quad \gamma^2 = \left(\frac{\pi}{c}\right)^2.$$

Hence, the lowest eigenvalue of $B_g{}^2$, which must also be positive, is given by

$$B_g{}^2 = \left(\frac{\pi}{a}\right)^2 + \left(\frac{\pi}{b}\right)^2 + \left(\frac{\pi}{c}\right)^2. \tag{7.44.1}$$

The geometric buckling is thus simply related to the dimensions a, b, c of the reactor.

7.45. The neutron flux distribution $\phi(x, y, z)$ in the critical reactor is obtained by inserting the solutions for X, Y, and Z, all of which are of the form of (7.43.3), into (7.42.1); the result is

$$\phi(x, y, z) = A \cos \frac{\pi x}{a} \cos \frac{\pi y}{b} \cos \frac{\pi z}{c}, \tag{7.45.1}$$

where, as before, A is dependent on the power output of the reactor.

7.46. By using the method of Lagrange multipliers for constrained extremums, it is readily found that for a specified value of $B_g{}^2$, subject to the conditions of (7.44.1), which is the constraint, a rectangular parallelepiped reactor will have a minimum volume when its three dimensions are equal. The reactor is then a cube of side a, and from (7.44.1)

$$B_g{}^2 = 3\left(\frac{\pi}{a}\right)^2,$$

so that

$$a = \sqrt{3}\,\frac{\pi}{B_g}.$$

The minimum volume, V, for a given value of $B_g{}^2$, is equal to a^3; hence,

$$V = \left(\sqrt{3}\,\frac{\pi}{B_g}\right)^3 = \frac{161}{B_g{}^3}. \tag{7.46.1}$$

If a reactor is to be constructed in the form of a parallelepiped, it will have a minimum volume, and hence use the minimum amount of material, when it is cubic in shape. The actual critical volume can then be obtained by substituting the value of $B_m{}^2$ which satisfies (7.23.2), for the prescribed composition of the medium, for $B_g{}^2$ in (7.46.1).

Case III. *Spherical Reactor*

7.47. In the treatment of a spherical reactor spherical coordinates are used. If the origin is chosen at the center of the sphere (Fig. 7.47), symmetry considerations rule out any dependence of the flux on the angles θ and φ; hence, the La-

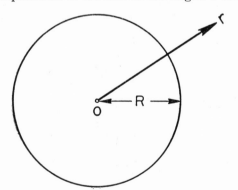

FIG. 7.47.   Spherical reactor

placian operator is obtained from (5.32.2) by eliminating the terms in θ and φ. The wave equation (7.24.2) thus reduces to

$$\frac{d^2\phi}{dr^2} + \frac{2}{r}\cdot\frac{d\phi}{dr} + B_g{}^2\phi = 0, \tag{7.47.1}$$

with the usual boundary conditions that ϕ is everywhere finite and that it becomes zero at the extrapolated boundary of the spherical reactor. A solution of (7.47.1), with B_g^2 positive, is

$$\phi(r) = A \frac{\sin B_g r}{r} + C \frac{\cos B_g r}{r},$$

but the fact that the $\phi(r)$ is finite at the origin eliminates the cosine term. Hence, a permissible solution of (7.47.1) is

$$\phi(r) = A \frac{\sin B_g r}{r}. \tag{7.47.2}$$

7.48. If R is the radius of the spherical reactor, including the extrapolation distance for thermal neutrons, then the boundary condition requires that $\phi(r)$ shall be zero when $r = R$; hence, from (7.47.2)

$$A \frac{\sin B_g R}{R} = 0.$$

Since A and R are not zero, this means that $\sin B_g R = 0$, and consequently,

$$B_g R = n\pi,$$

where n is zero or an integer. In this case, the solution with n equal to zero is trivial, and hence the lowest eigenvalue is that for $n = 1$, which leads to the result

$$B_g^2 = \left(\frac{\pi}{R}\right)^2. \tag{7.48.1}$$

The geometric buckling can be related to the volume, V, of the sphere by writing

$$V = \frac{4}{3}\pi R^3 = \frac{4\pi^4}{3B_g^3} = \frac{130}{B_g^3}.$$

If B_g^2 is set equal to B_m^2 for the specified medium, this equation will give the volume of the critical reactor.

7.49. The flux distribution in the critical spherical reactor is obtained by combining (7.47.2) and (7.48.1); the result is

$$\phi(r) = \frac{A}{r} \sin \frac{\pi r}{R}, \tag{7.49.1}$$

where, as in other cases, A is proportional to the power level at which the reactor is operating, and R is the critical radius.

Case IV. *Finite Cylindrical Reactor*

7.50. In the treatment of a cylindrical reactor of finite height, the Laplacian operator is expressed in cylindrical coordinates by (5.32.3). If the z-axis is made to coincide with the vertical axis of the cylinder, only the z- and r-coordinates need be considered (Fig. 7.50) and the wave equation becomes

$$\frac{\partial^2 \phi}{\partial r^2} + \frac{1}{r} \cdot \frac{\partial \phi}{\partial r} + \frac{\partial^2 \phi}{\partial z^2} + B_g^2 \phi = 0. \tag{7.50.1}$$

The boundary conditions of the problem are that $\phi(r, z)$ shall be finite and that it shall go to zero at the extrapolated boundaries, i.e., when $r = R$ or $z = \frac{1}{2}H$, the origin being taken at midway up the cylinder of height H.

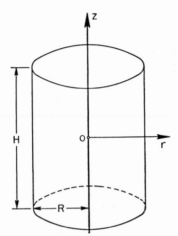

FIG. 7.50.   Finite cylindrical reactor

7.51. The solution of (7.50.1) is performed by first separating the variables r and z by writing

$$\phi(r, z) = \Theta(r)Z(z), \tag{7.51.1}$$

so that (7.50.1) becomes, after dividing by ΘZ,

$$\frac{1}{\Theta} \left(\frac{d^2\Theta}{dr^2} + \frac{1}{r} \cdot \frac{d\Theta}{dr} \right) + \frac{1}{Z} \cdot \frac{d^2Z}{dz^2} + B_g^2 = 0, \tag{7.51.2}$$

in which the first term depends on Θ only, and the second term on Z only; each of the terms can consequently be set equal to a constant.   Let

$$\frac{1}{\Theta} \left(\frac{d^2\Theta}{dr^2} + \frac{1}{r} \cdot \frac{d\Theta}{dr} \right) = -\alpha^2, \tag{7.51.3}$$

where α^2 is a constant, which may be a positive or a negative quantity, although it will be shown later that it is positive.   Similarly, let

$$\frac{1}{Z} \cdot \frac{d^2Z}{dz^2} = -\beta^2, \tag{7.51.4}$$

where β^2 may be positive or negative, although it is actually positive. Consequently, by (7.51.2)

$$-\alpha^2 - \beta^2 + B_g{}^2 = 0$$

and

$$B_g{}^2 = \alpha^2 + \beta^2. \tag{7.51.5}$$

7.52. By rearranging (7.51.3), and multiplying through by Θr^2, the result is

$$r^2 \frac{d^2\Theta}{dr^2} + r \frac{d\Theta}{dr} + \alpha^2 r^2 \Theta = 0, \tag{7.52.1}$$

which can be transformed into Bessel's equation in the following manner. Let u be a new dependent variable defined by

$$u \equiv \alpha r, \tag{7.52.2}$$

so that

$$\frac{du}{dr} = \alpha$$

since α is a constant. Then it is possible to write

$$\frac{d\Theta}{dr} = \frac{d\Theta}{du} \cdot \frac{du}{dr} = \alpha \frac{d\Theta}{du} \tag{7.52.3}$$

and hence,

$$\frac{d^2\Theta}{dr^2} = \frac{d}{dr}\left(\alpha \frac{d\Theta}{du}\right) = \frac{d}{du}\left(\alpha \frac{d\Theta}{du}\right)\frac{du}{dr} = \alpha^2 \frac{d^2\Theta}{du^2}. \tag{7.52.4}$$

Making the substitution in (7.52.1) for r, $d\Theta/dr$, and $d^2\Theta/dr^2$, as given by (7.52.2), (7.52.3), and (7.52.4), respectively, the former becomes

$$u^2 \frac{d^2\Theta}{du^2} + u \frac{d\Theta}{du} + u^2 \Theta = 0. \tag{7.52.5}$$

7.53. The general Bessel equation of order n is

$$x^2 \frac{d^2y}{dx^2} + x \frac{dy}{dx} + (x^2 - n^2)y = 0,$$

and hence (7.52.5) is a Bessel equation of zero order, provided u^2, and hence α^2, is a positive quantity. The general solution of (7.52.5) is

$$\Theta = AJ_0(u) + CY_0(u) \tag{7.53.1}$$

where J_0 and Y_0 are Bessel functions of the first and second kinds, respectively, of zero order.*

---

* See N. W. McLachlan, "Bessel Functions for Engineers," Clarendon Press, Oxford, 1934.

7.54. If α^2 is a negative quantity, then (7.52.1) is a form of the modified Bessel equation

$$x^2 \frac{d^2y}{dx^2} + x \frac{dy}{dx} - (x^2 - n^2)y = 0,$$

of order zero.   The solution will then be of the form

$$\Theta = A'I_0(u) + C'K_0(u), \tag{7.54.1}$$

where I_0 and K_0 are modified Bessel functions of the first and second kinds, of zero order.

7.55. A choice between the two possible solutions, depending on whether α^2 is positive or negative, is made by using the boundary conditions.   The values of the functions J_0, Y_0, I_0, and K_0 for various values of u are plotted against u in Fig. 7.55, and an examination of the curves shows that Y_0, I_0, and K_0 can be

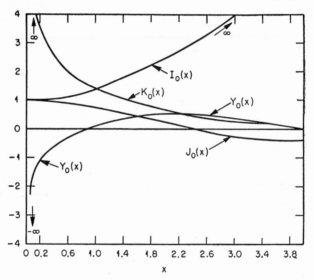

FIG. 7.55.   Zero-order Bessel functions

eliminated, since Y_0 becomes $-\infty$ and K_0 becomes ∞ when u is zero, whereas I_0 increases to infinity as u increases.   The only permissible solution of (7.52.1) is therefore derived from (7.53.1), namely,

$$\Theta(r) = AJ_0(u) = AJ_0(\alpha r), \tag{7.55.1}$$

and consequently α^2 is positive.

7.56. In order to evaluate α, use is made of the boundary condition that $\phi(r, z)$ shall go to zero at the extrapolated boundary, i.e., when $r = R$.   Since $\Theta(r)$ represents the part of $\phi(r, z)$ which is dependent on r, it follows from (7.55.1) that

$$\Theta(r) = AJ_0(\alpha R) = 0,$$

and since the constant A cannot be zero, for this would make $\Theta(r)$ zero everywhere, it is apparent that

$$J_0(\alpha R) = 0.$$

This means that αR is equal to the value of u for which $J_0(u)$ is zero. It appears from Fig. 7.55 that there is more than one value of u which will satisfy this condition; however, the lowest eigenvalue of α^2 corresponds to the solution for which u has the smallest value. This is the first zero of the Bessel function J_0, namely, 2.405. Hence, αR is equal to 2.405, so that

$$\alpha = \frac{2.405}{R} \quad \text{and} \quad \alpha^2 = \left(\frac{2.405}{R}\right)^2 \tag{7.56.1}$$

and (7.55.1) gives

$$\Theta(r) = A J_0\left(\frac{2.405r}{R}\right). \tag{7.56.2}$$

7.57. The foregoing treatment has provided a solution for (7.51.3); it now remains to solve the z-dependent equation (7.51.4). Taking into account the symmetrical distribution of the flux about the origin in the z-direction and utilizing the usual boundary condition, it can be readily shown by a procedure similar to that used for the infinite slab (§ 7.38) that the solution of (7.51.4) is

$$Z(z) = C \cos\frac{\pi z}{H}, \tag{7.57.1}$$

and the lowest eigenvalue of β^2 is

$$\beta^2 = \left(\frac{\pi}{H}\right)^2. \tag{7.57.2}$$

7.58. By combining (7.51.5), (7.56.1), and (7.57.2), the geometric buckling for the finite, cylindrical reactor, in terms of its radius and height, is given by

$$B_g{}^2 = \left(\frac{2.405}{R}\right)^2 + \left(\frac{\pi}{H}\right)^2. \tag{7.58.1}$$

From (7.51.1), (7.56.2), and (7.57.1), the thermal neutron flux distribution in the critical reactor is seen to be

$$\phi(r, z) = A J_0\left(\frac{2.405r}{R}\right) \cos\frac{\pi z}{H}, \tag{7.58.2}$$

where R and H are the critical radius and height, respectively.

Minimum Volume for Finite Cylinder

7.59. The smallest volume for which a cylindrical reactor will have a specified buckling can be determined directly by the Lagrange multiplier method for a minimum value of $\pi R^2 H$, subject to the constraint given by (7.58.1). Alternatively, (7.58.1) may be rearranged to yield

$$R^2 = \frac{(2.405)^2 H^2}{B_g{}^2 H^2 - \pi^2}, \tag{7.59.1}$$

and then the volume V of the cylinder, equal to $\pi R^2 H$, is

$$V = \frac{\pi (2.405)^2 H^3}{B_g^2 H^2 - \pi^2}.$$

Upon differentiation with respect to H and setting the result equal to zero, the condition for the minimum volume is found to be

$$B_g^2 H^2 = 3\pi^2,$$

so that

$$H = \sqrt{3}\, \frac{\pi}{B_g} = \frac{5.441}{B_g}. \tag{7.59.2}$$

If this value for H is inserted into (7.59.1), it is seen that

$$R = \sqrt{\frac{3}{2}} \left(\frac{2.405}{B_g} \right) = \frac{2.945}{B_g}. \tag{7.59.3}$$

The minimum volume of the cylindrical reactor for a given value of B_g is thus

$$V_{\min} = \pi R^2 H = \frac{148.2}{B_g^3}. \tag{7.59.4}$$

SUMMARY AND REVIEW

7.60. The results obtained in the cases considered above are summarized in Table 7.60. If it is required that a particular reactor shall be just critical, the

TABLE 7.60.   BUCKLING FOR VARIOUS GEOMETRIES

Geometry	Buckling	Minimum Critical Volume
Infinite Slab	$\left(\dfrac{\pi}{H}\right)^2$	—
Rectangular Parallelepiped	$\left(\dfrac{\pi}{a}\right)^2 + \left(\dfrac{\pi}{b}\right)^2 + \left(\dfrac{\pi}{c}\right)^2$	$\dfrac{161}{B^3}$
Sphere	$\left(\dfrac{\pi}{R}\right)^2$	$\dfrac{130}{B^3}$
Finite Cylinder	$\left(\dfrac{2.405}{R}\right)^2 + \left(\dfrac{\pi}{H}\right)^2$	$\dfrac{148}{B^3}$

geometric buckling, for a specified shape, must be equal to the material buckling, determined by the composition (§ 7.25). For any given composition and shape, the minimum critical volume is indicated by the results in the last column, where B^2 is the critical (or material) buckling. It is seen that for a specified composition the critical volume (and mass) of a spherical reactor is less than for any of the other shapes. The reason is that, for any particular quantity of material, the sphere has the smallest surface area. As stated in the qualitative discussion in Chapter IV, neutron production takes place throughout the volume of the system, but leakage occurs only at the surface. Hence, for a given composition, the reactor with the smallest ratio of surface to volume will have the smallest critical mass.

7.61. An examination of equations (7.40.1), (7.43.3), (7.49.1), and (7.57.3) shows that the thermal flux distributions in critical reactors, for the cases considered, can all be represented in terms of functions of u, namely, $\cos\dfrac{\pi u}{2}$, $\dfrac{\sin \pi u}{\pi u}$, and J_0 (2.405u), where u has the respective values given in Table 7.61. These

TABLE 7.61.   THERMAL FLUX DISTRIBUTION IN CRITICAL BARE REACTORS

Geometry	Coordinate	Function	u
Infinite Slab	x	$\cos\dfrac{\pi u}{2}$	$x/\tfrac{1}{2}H$
Rectangular Parallelepiped	x	$\cos\dfrac{\pi u}{2}$	$x/\tfrac{1}{2}a$
	y	$\cos\dfrac{\pi u}{2}$	$y/\tfrac{1}{2}b$
	z	$\cos\dfrac{\pi u}{2}$	$z/\tfrac{1}{2}c$
Sphere	r	$\dfrac{\sin \pi u}{\pi u}$	r/R
Finite Cylinder	r	$J_0(2.405u)$	r/R
	z	$\cos\dfrac{\pi u}{2}$	$z/\tfrac{1}{2}H$

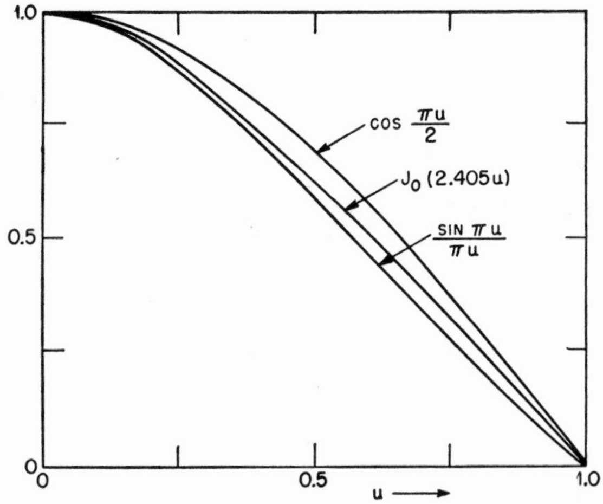

FIG. 7.61.   Functions for determination of flux distribution

functions, for values of u from zero to unity, are shown in Fig. 7.61; it will be noted from the last column of the table that $u = 1$ corresponds to the extrapolated boundary in each case, so that the flux is then zero. From the closeness of the three curves it is apparent that the cosine function can be used in all cases, as a first approximation, without incurring serious error.

PROPERTIES OF CRITICAL REACTORS

LARGE REACTORS

7.62. In view of the inverse relationships between the geometric buckling and the dimensions of a reactor, it follows that B^2 is small for a large reactor.* Consequently, for such a reactor or, in general, when k is only slightly larger than unity, $e^{-B^2\tau}$ may be expanded in series form and all terms beyond the second neglected; thus,

$$e^{-B^2\tau} \approx 1 - B^2\tau \approx (1 + B^2\tau)^{-1}.$$

In these circumstances, the critical equation (7.23.2) becomes

$$\frac{k}{(1 + L^2B^2)(1 + B^2\tau)} \approx 1 \qquad (7.62.1)$$

or

$$\frac{k}{1 + B^2(L^2 + \tau)} \approx 1. \qquad (7.62.2)$$

7.63. According to the arguments in § 6.141, the Fermi age of thermal neutrons is equal, numerically, to one-sixth of the mean square distance traveled by a neutron from the time of its emission from the source to its attainment of thermal energy, i.e., during the slowing down process. If this distance is represented by r_s^2, then $\tau = \frac{1}{6}\overline{r_s^2}$, and (7.62.2) may be written as

$$\frac{k}{1 + B^2(L^2 + \frac{1}{6}\overline{r_s^2})} \approx 1.$$

The quantity $L^2 + \frac{1}{6}\overline{r_s^2}$ is referred to as the *migration area* and is indicated by M^2; i.e.,

$$M^2 \equiv L^2 + \frac{1}{6}\overline{r_s^2}, \qquad (7.63.1)$$

so that when B^2 is small or, in general, when k does not greatly exceed unity,

$$\frac{k}{1 + M^2B^2} = 1 \qquad (7.63.2)$$

or

$$B^2 = \frac{k - 1}{M^2}. \qquad (7.63.3)$$

This expression may be regarded as defining the material buckling for a medium having a multiplication factor not much greater than unity, so that the critical system will be large. Although (7.63.3) has been derived here from the continuous slowing down model, it will be shown in Chapter XII that it is quite general and independent of any model. The definition of M^2 in (7.63.1) is also general, although in continuous slowing down theory it is frequently represented as $L^2 + \tau$.

* In the remainder of this chapter, the treatment refers to critical reactors, and so the distinction between B_g^2 and B_m^2 is not necessary.

7.64. Since L^2 is one-sixth of the mean square distance a thermal neutron travels — as a thermal neutron — before capture (§ 5.64), it is seen from (7.63.1) that the migration area M^2 is one-sixth of the mean square distance a neutron travels from its formation as a fast (fission) neutron to its capture as a thermal neutron. The square root of M^2, called the *migration length*, is thus a measure of the distance traveled by a neutron from its source to its capture.

CALCULATION OF CRITICAL SIZE AND COMPOSITION

7.65. In the design of nuclear reactors, it is necessary to know something, in advance, of the dimensions and fuel-to-moderator ratio required to make the reactor critical. In this connection two types of problems are of interest: first, given a particular size of reactor, it is required to determine the ratio of fuel to moderator, which will make it just critical and, second, given a specified fuel-to-moderator ratio, it is desired to find the critical size. Both kinds of problem may be illustrated by considering a relatively simple, but fairly practical, case in which the fuel is assumed to be pure uranium-235 and the moderator is beryllium. It should be pointed out, however, that because of the many simplifying assumptions made in the preceding chapters, the results of the calculations given below are approximate only. Their chief use, in actual practice, would be to serve as a guide in the design of critical experiments.

7.66. Suppose it is required to make a homogeneous, bare, spherical reactor of 50-cm radius; what is the ratio of uranium-235 to beryllium that would make this just critical? The infinite multiplication factor k is equal to $\eta f p \epsilon$ (§ 4.61) and it is sufficiently accurate to assume here that p and ϵ are unity, so that $k = \eta f$ (§ 4.62). If the absorption cross sections of the extraneous materials present in the system are small, or negligible,

$$k = \eta f = \eta \frac{\Sigma_\mathrm{U}}{\Sigma_\mathrm{U} + \Sigma_\mathrm{Be}} = \eta \frac{z}{z + 1}, \qquad (7.66.1)$$

since the thermal neutron flux may be taken as being the same in both fuel and moderator in the homogeneous system. In this expression, z is the ratio of the macroscopic absorption cross sections of uranium to beryllium, i.e.,

$$z \equiv \frac{\Sigma_\mathrm{U}}{\Sigma_\mathrm{Be}} = \frac{\sigma_\mathrm{U}}{\sigma_\mathrm{Be}} \cdot \frac{N_\mathrm{U}}{N_\mathrm{Be}}, \qquad (7.66.2)$$

where σ_U and σ_Be are the nuclear absorption cross sections, and N_U and N_Be are the respective numbers of atoms of uranium and of beryllium in the system. The problem is, therefore, to determine the value of the ratio $N_\mathrm{U}/N_\mathrm{Be}$ for which a spherical reactor of 50-cm radius will be just critical.

7.67. It will be seen that the proportion of uranium-235 to beryllium in the critical system is quite small, so that the slowing down properties of the homogeneous mixture are essentially those of pure beryllium. This fact permits the derivation of a relatively simple expression for the diffusion length. By definition, $L^2 = D/\Sigma_a$ and in the mixture the diffusion coefficient D of thermal neutrons is essentially that of beryllium, i.e., it may be taken as D_{Be}. The absorption cross section Σ_a is approximately $\Sigma_U + \Sigma_{Be}$, so that

$$L^2 = \frac{D_{Be}}{\Sigma_U + \Sigma_{Be}} = \frac{D_{Be}/\Sigma_{Be}}{z+1}.$$

The numerator D_{Be}/Σ_{Be} is equal to the square of the diffusion length for pure beryllium; representing this by L_0^2, it follows that

$$L^2 = \frac{L_0^2}{z+1}. \tag{7.67.1}$$

7.68. Upon introducing the values for k and L^2, as given by (7.66.1) and (7.67.1), respectively, into the critical equation (7.23.2), it is seen that

$$\frac{ke^{-B^2\tau}}{1 + L^2B^2} = \frac{\eta z e^{-B^2\tau}}{z + 1 + L_0^2B^2} = 1.$$

If this equation is solved for z, the result is

$$z = \frac{1 + L_0^2B^2}{\eta e^{-B^2\tau} - 1}. \tag{7.68.1}$$

The B^2 in this equation, which was derived from (7.23.2), is the material buckling of the uranium-beryllium system. Its value may be determined in the present case by setting it equal to the geometric buckling of a spherical (critical) reactor of 50-cm radius, as postulated in § 7.66. For a sphere,

$$B^2 = \left(\frac{\pi}{R}\right)^2$$

by (7.48.1), where R is the extrapolated radius, which is approximately the geometric radius plus $0.71\lambda_t$, and λ_t is the transport mean free path (§ 5.40), or $0.71 \times 3D$, since D is $\lambda_t/3$. In the present case, D is virtually that of beryllium, i.e., 0.70 cm, so that R is $50 + 1.5 = 51.5$ cm. Hence,

$$B^2 = \left(\frac{\pi}{51.5}\right)^2 = 37.2 \times 10^{-4} \text{ cm}^{-2}.$$

7.69. The value of η is obtained from (4.57.1) which, in the present case, i.e., pure uranium-235 as fuel, takes the form

$$\eta = \nu \frac{\sigma_f}{\sigma_f + \sigma_c},$$

where σ_f is the fission cross section of uranium-235 and σ_c is its capture (non-fission) cross section. These are 549 and 101 barns, respectively (Table 4.57);

since ν is 2.5, it follows that η is 2.1. For beryllium, L_0^2 is 560 cm^2 and τ is 98 cm^2; hence, (7.68.1) gives

$$z = 6.6.$$

The total absorption cross sections σ_{Be} and σ_U are 0.0084 and 650 barns, respectively, the latter being the sum of the fission and capture cross sections, and so, by (7.66.2),

$$\frac{N_U}{N_{Be}} = \frac{\sigma_{Be}}{\sigma_U} z = \frac{0.0084}{650} \times 6.6 = 8.5 \times 10^{-5}.$$

This is the atomic ratio of uranium to beryllium required to make the 50 cm-radius spherical reactor critical. From the densities of the fuel and moderator the critical mass of uranium-235 can then be calculated.

7.70. It is of interest to note that in the system under consideration k, as given by (7.66.1), i.e., $\eta z/(z + 1)$, is about 1.84; this means that, since $k_{eff} = 1$ for a critical reactor, about 45 per cent of the neutrons are lost due to leakage. The fraction of source neutrons leaking from the reactor during slowing down is $1 - e^{-B^2\tau}$, which is about 30 per cent in the present case, while the proportion of those which have been slowed down and leak out as thermal neutrons is $L^2B^2/(1 + L^2B^2)$, i.e., 22 per cent, or 15 per cent of the total source neutrons, for the critical reactor of 50 cm radius. It is evident that, in such a relatively small bare reactor, there would be a very large leakage of neutrons, most of the leakage taking place during the moderation of the fission neutrons. It should be remembered that in the foregoing calculations the resonance escape probability has been taken as unity.

7.71. The second type of problem, which is the inverse of the one just considered, is to determine the critical size corresponding to a given composition of core material; in other words, given η, L_0^2, τ, and z, it is required to find the value of B^2 for the critical system. The answer is to be found again in (7.68.1), but the calculation is now more involved since it necessitates the solving of a transcendental equation. The method of solution is to write the critical equation (7.68.1) in the form

$$e^{-B^2\tau} = \frac{1}{\eta z} (z + 1 + L_0^2 B^2), \tag{7.71.1}$$

and let

$$x \equiv B^2\tau, \qquad A \equiv \frac{z+1}{\eta z} \quad \text{and} \quad C \equiv \frac{L_0^2}{\eta z \tau},$$

where A and C are constants, and x is a variable. The critical equation (7.71.1) then becomes

$$e^{-x} = A + Cx, \tag{7.71.2}$$

and this can be solved by iteration without difficulty. Since x is not large, e^{-x} may be taken as approximately equal to $1 - x$; then, A and C being known, a preliminary value of $x = (1 - A)/(C + 1)$ is obtained from (7.71.2). With this x, the two sides of the latter equation are evaluated.   In general the results will not be equal, but if the left-hand side is the larger, then it is known that the chosen x is too small, and vice versa.   Hence, another value of x is guessed, and the procedure repeated; after three or four trials, the value of $x = B^2\tau$, correct to three significant figures, which will satisfy (7.71.1) can be found.   Since τ is known, the buckling B^2 can be determined, and the dimensions of the critical reactor can be calculated.*

EXPERIMENTAL DETERMINATION OF CRITICAL SIZE:
THE CRITICAL ASSEMBLY

7.72. Two experimental methods have been used for the determination of the critical size of a reactor.   The "exponential pile" method, which is applicable only to large reactors, such as those using natural uranium as fuel, will be described in Chapter IX.   The other procedure, to be considered here, is that of the *critical assembly*.   This requires the construction of a system consisting of the fuel material and moderator, in the desired proportions, which can gradually be built up until it approaches the critical dimensions.   At the center of the assembly is placed a neutron source, emitting about 10^7 neutrons per sec; this is called the primary source.   As a result of the fissions induced in the fuel there is an apparent multiplication of the primary source neutrons.   This multiplication may be defined as the ratio of the total thermal neutron flux, due to both the primary source and fissions, to the flux due to the primary source only.

7.73. It was seen in § 7.17 that the second term in (7.17.1) represents the contribution to the thermal flux of a point source at the center of a subcritical assembly of fuel and moderator.   The presence of k_n in this term indicates that the fast extraneous (primary source) neutrons are multiplied by fissions.   If no fissionable material were present, so that k_n would be zero, the thermal flux would be determined solely by the sum of the source terms, like the second in the brackets in (7.17.1), with $1 - k_n$ replaced by unity.   The effect of fissions, when fuel is present, is therefore to multiply each of these source terms, for the different values of n, by $1/(1 - k_n)$.   It is assumed that scattering and slowing down are the same in both cases, i.e., with and without fissionable material.

7.74. As the critical state is approached, the only value of k_n that is significant is the highest, previously called k_1, which, as seen from (7.20.1), is identical with effective multiplication factor, k_{eff}, defined by (7.27.1).   It follows, therefore, that in the system containing fissionable material the multiplication of the primary source neutrons is then determined only by $1/(1 - k_{eff})$.   At the critical state k_{eff} is exactly unity, and hence the multiplication becomes infinite.   When the assembly is subcritical all the values of k_n are less than unity (§ 7.18) and the multiplication is finite.   But, as the size of the assembly is increased, the multiplication of primary source neutrons increases and it becomes infinite when the critical state is attained.

* Graphical methods of solution based on the use of nomographs have been devised.

7.75. Results similar to those just described would be expected if, instead of a point source, the source were distributed throughout the assembly in such a way that the source strength $S(\mathbf{r})$ were proportional to the lowest eigenfunction of the equation $\nabla^2 S(\mathbf{r}) + B^2 S(\mathbf{r}) = 0$, where $S(\mathbf{r})$ is zero on the extrapolated boundary of the assembly. As before, the system is assumed to be homogeneous and to have no re-entrant surface. The source neutrons will now have the same spatial distribution as the thermal neutron flux, and hence as the fission source, in a bare reactor. The nonleakage probability for the extraneous source neutrons will then be the same as for fission neutrons, and the multiplication factor of neutrons in the finite system in each generation will be k_{eff}. Thus, if S fast neutrons are emitted by the source, there will be $k_{\text{eff}}S$ at the end of one generation, $k^2_{\text{eff}}S$ at the end of two generations, and so on. The multiplication of the neutrons in the moderator-fuel system can then be represented by

$$\frac{S + k_{\text{eff}}S + k_{\text{eff}}^2 S + k_{\text{eff}}^3 S + \cdots}{S} = \frac{1}{1 - k_{\text{eff}}},$$

which is the same as for a central point source. As the size of the assembly approaches the critical, k_{eff} tends to unity, and the multiplication becomes infinite.

7.76. The multiplication can be determined experimentally by measuring the thermal neutron flux within the assembly, at a specified distance from the source. The measurement is first made in the absence of fuel and then repeated at the same point with fuel. The ratio of the two values gives the required multiplication, at a certain fixed field point, for the particular size of the assembly. The observations are repeated for assemblies of various sizes approaching the critical.

7.77. For practical purposes, it is convenient to use the reciprocal of the multiplication of source neutrons; this will decrease in value as the assembly grows in size, and will become zero at the critical dimensions. The reciprocal multiplication, at two or more field points, is plotted as a function of the size of the assembly or, better, as a function of the mass of fuel material, e.g., uranium-235. It is then not necessary for the system to become critical, for the critical mass or size can be determined by extrapolating the curves to zero value of the reciprocal multiplication, as shown in Fig. 7.77.

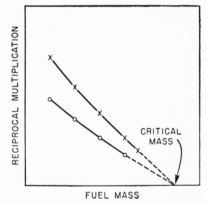

FIG. 7.77. Determination of critical mass

7.78. If desired, an actual critical assembly may be gradually built up until the critical condition is attained. If the system is actually critical, the neutron flux will remain constant with time in the absence of an extraneous source, since a system that is just critical is in a self-sustaining steady state.   If the assembly is still subcritical the flux will decrease steadily when the source is removed.   In the event that the system is supercritical the flux would increase exponentially with time.

CRITICAL MASS AND RADIUS AND REACTOR COMPOSITION

7.79. The variation of the critical mass and critical radius of a thermal reactor, as the ratio of fuel to moderator is changed, presents some interesting features. The curves in Fig. 7.79 give the critical radius of a bare (unreflected) sphere con-

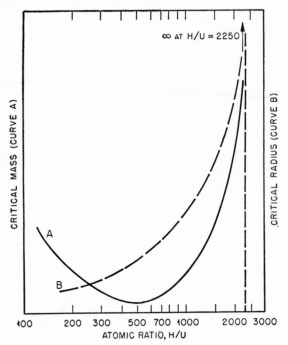

FIG. 7.79.   Critical mass and critical radius as functions of atomic ratio H/U

taining a solution of a salt of pure uranium-235 in ordinary water, and the corresponding mass of uranium, for various atomic ratios of hydrogen to uranium in the system.   It is seen that, while the critical radius increases steadily as the proportion of uranium decreases, the critical mass passes through a minimum. There is thus a particular composition of the solution for which the critical system involves a minimum mass of fuel.

7.80. The type of behavior illustrated in Fig. 7.79 is quite general for thermal reactors and is due to the following circumstances.   At the low ratio of moderator to fuel, e.g., low H/U in Fig. 7.79, the critical size of the assembly is small and the nonleakage probability is also small.   This is compensated for by the high proportion of fuel which makes k large.   As the ratio H/U is increased, k decreases relatively slowly, but the nonleakage probability at first increases rapidly (Fig. 7.80).   Consequently, the critical radius (and volume) increases

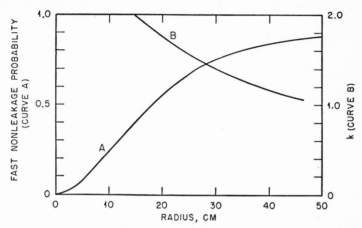

FIG. 7.80.   Fast nonleakage probability and multiplication factor as functions of radius

relatively slowly.   The critical mass of fuel is determined, very roughly, by the critical volume divided by the H/U ratio; hence, if the volume increases less rapidly than does the value of the critical H/U, the critical mass will actually decrease to a minimum.   At this point, further increase in the critical size, due to the decreased proportion of fuel, results in relatively little further change in the nonleakage probability, but k continues to decrease steadily because of increasing absorption by the moderator.   The critical mass then increases rapidly, becoming infinite when k is unity.

7.81. As the ratio of moderator to fuel, i.e., H/U in the present case, increases, the radius of the critical reactor becomes so large, that the total nonleakage probability approaches unity.   In this case, k must equal unity for the critical reactor, and so, by (7.66.1),

$$\eta \frac{z}{z+1} = 1,$$

or by using the appropriate form of (7.66.2), which defines z,

$$\frac{N_H}{N_U} = \frac{\sigma_U}{\sigma_H}(\eta - 1).$$

The values of σ_U and σ_H are 650 and 0.32 barns, respectively, and since η is 2.1 for uranium-235 (§7.69),

$$\frac{N_H}{N_U} \approx 2250.$$

This represents the largest ratio of H/U for which a self-sustaining chain reaction is possible, since this is the composition which makes k just equal to unity. Any increase in the proportion of hydrogen will result in a multiplication factor less than unity, due to parasitic capture in moderator, and a critical system will be impossible. Consequently, the curve in Fig. 7.79 for the critical mass becomes asymptotic with a vertical line drawn at H/U = 2250; at this composition, a (bare) homogeneous thermal reactor would have to be infinitely large to be critical.

PROBLEMS

1. Find the minimum atomic ratio of U^{235} to moderator atoms that will support a thermal neutron chain reaction in an infinitely large system for H_2O, D_2O, Be, and graphite at 20°C.

2. Calculate and plot the critical mass of bare, spherical, homogeneous thermal assemblies containing U^{235} fuel, as a function of the atomic ratio of moderator atoms to U^{235} atoms for the following moderators: D_2O, Be, and graphite at 20°C.

3. Derive an expression for the geometric buckling of a system having the shape of a hemisphere.

4. A bare, spherical reactor of 75-cm radius containing a uniform mixture of U^{235} and Be is operated at 20°C. Find the critical mass, the fraction of fission neutrons leaking out as epithermal neutrons, and as thermal neutrons. If 100 grams of Cd is uniformly dispersed in the assembly, what is the increase in fuel required to maintain criticality?

5. Find the spatial distribution of fuel in a bare, spherical, thermal reactor that leads to a uniform power distribution. Treat all neutrons as being produced, scattered, and absorbed at a single energy.

Chapter VIII

HOMOGENEOUS REACTOR WITH REFLECTOR: THE GROUP–DIFFUSION METHOD

GENERAL CONSIDERATIONS

PROPERTIES OF A REFLECTOR

8.1. The critical mass of a reactor can be decreased by surrounding the core with a scattering material, e.g., graphite, beryllium, etc. This acts as a reflector since it scatters back into the chain-reacting system neutrons which would otherwise have been lost as a result of leakage. A reflector thus reduces neutron leakage from the reactor core and permits a given fuel-moderator system to become critical when the dimensions of the core are appreciably less than are required for a bare reactor. In this way, the use of a reflector makes possible appreciable savings in the quantity of fissionable material required.

8.2. In addition to decreasing the critical volume (and mass) of the core, the reflector increases the average power output of the reactor for a given weight of fuel. As seen in Chapter IV, the power level is proportional to the average thermal neutron density or flux in the core. In a reactor with reflector, the neutron flux in the center of the core is not essentially different from that in a bare reactor, but near the boundary the thermal flux is appreciably higher in the former case. This is represented in an approximate manner in Fig. 8.2, where the thermal neutron flux is indicated for a bare reactor and for one surrounded by a reflector.* The vertical lines represent the extrapolated boundaries of the core

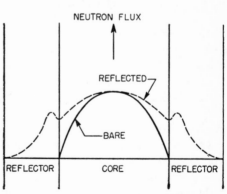

FIG. 8.2. Thermal flux distribution in bare and reflected reactors

---

* The small "humps" in the flux in the reflector are explained later (§ 8.58).

and reflector. The average thermal neutron flux over the whole core and, hence, the power output under given conditions are thus increased by the reflector. The outermost regions of the core are used more effectively when a reflector is present than is the case for a bare reactor (see also, § 8.36, *et seq.*).

8.3. A general idea of the properties required for a reflector can be obtained from the following considerations. The chance of a neutron returning from the reflector to the core is greater, the smaller the mean distance the neutron penetrates into the reflector from the core. In other words, it is related to the scattering mean free path and hence to the diffusion coefficient. The smaller the scattering mean free path, the closer to the core will a neutron suffer its first collision, on the average. This increases in two ways the chance that the neutron will return to the core.

8.4. First, assuming approximately isotropic scattering (§ 6.18, *et seq.*), the probability that a neutron after its first collision will be scattered in such a direction that it is headed for the core is proportional to the solid angle subtended by the core at the point of the scattering collision. The smaller the scattering mean free path, the larger will be this solid angle, and hence the greater the chance for the neutron to return to the core. Second, the probability that a neutron will be absorbed in any medium in the interval from x to $x + dx$ is $\Sigma_a \, dx$ (§ 3.45), where Σ_a is the absorption cross section. Hence, the probability that a neutron will be absorbed in the reflector before it can return to the core is Σ_a per unit path length. It is seen, therefore, that the shorter the path back to the core, the smaller the proportion of neutrons absorbed in the reflector.

8.5. In addition to the requirement that the scattering mean free path, and hence the transport mean free path and the diffusion coefficient, of neutrons in the reflector shall be small, it is evident, especially from the remarks at the end of the preceding paragraph, that the absorption cross section of the reflector should also be small. The conclusions are in harmony with those reached in Chapter V in connection with the consideration of the albedo. It was seen that a material will have a large albedo, and hence be a good reflector, when the quantity κD is small. Since κ is equal to $\sqrt{\Sigma_a/D}$, this is equivalent to the requirement that the product $\Sigma_a D$ shall be small, and so is identical with the conclusion reached above from general qualitative considerations.

8.6. It may be noted that an appreciable proportion of the neutrons leaking from a reactor core do so during the slowing down process. These will be neutrons with energies in excess of the thermal value. It would be advantageous if they were returned to the core with their energies reduced, and this can be achieved by using a good thermalizing material, i.e., a light element with high scattering cross section, as reflector. Actually, such materials, provided they have small absorption cross sections, best meet the other conditions referred to above.

THE GROUP–DIFFUSION METHOD*

Introduction

8.7. The theoretical treatment of a reflected reactor presents a difficult problem. For a critical bare reactor, the slowing down density — and hence the thermal neutron source term — is everywhere proportional to the neutron flux. The thermal diffusion equation is then linear and homogeneous, and definite solutions can be readily obtained. Because the multiplying and slowing down properties of the reflector are, in general, different from those of the reactor core, the neutron energy spectrum, which is fairly uniform throughout the bare reactor, changes markedly in the vicinity of the core-reflector interface. As a result, solution of the Fermi age equation to obtain the thermal neutron source term for the diffusion equation, as in § 7.10, *et seq.*, becomes difficult.

8.8. One way of simplifying the analysis of the slowing down of neutrons in composite media is by means of the *group-diffusion method*. In this treatment, it is postulated that the energy of the neutrons, from the source energy to thermal energy, can be divided into a finite set of energy intervals or energy groups. Within each group, the neutrons are assumed to diffuse, without energy loss, until they have suffered the average number of collisions which would be required to decrease their energy to that of the next (lower) group. At this point it is supposed that the neutrons are suddenly transferred to the latter group. This process is supposed to continue while the neutron energy is degraded from the group of highest (fission) energy to that of lowest (thermal) energy.

Group Constants

8.9. Since the energy spectrum of the neutrons in a reactor covers a continuous range from thermal energies to about 10 Mev, the group-diffusion concept is evidently an approximation. This is partially overcome by assigning appropriate average values for each group to the various properties such as the cross sections and the diffusion coefficient of the core and the reflector. The procedure for evaluating these *group constants*, as they are frequently called, will be illustrated by reference to the case of two energy groups.

8.10. In the two-group treatment, neutrons of thermal energy constitute one group while all of those of higher energy are in the other group. Assuming all neutrons to originate from a monoenergetic (fission) source with energy E_0, it will be supposed that they retain this energy until they have undergone the average number of scattering collisions to reduce their energies to the thermal value E_{th}; the neutrons will then be degraded to the lower energy group. The grouping together of all neutrons with energies higher than thermal is, of course, a gross over-simplification, and the average properties of the neutrons in the "fast" group are derived in the following manner.

---

* This method, as applied to reactor calculations, was developed by F. L. Friedman, A. M. Weinberg, and J. A. Wheeler.

8.11. The number of scattering collisions suffered by the fast group of neutrons is

$$\begin{matrix} \text{No. of collisions per cm}^3 \text{ per sec} \\ \text{in fast group} \end{matrix} = \int_{E_{\text{th}}}^{E_0} \Sigma_s(E) n(E) v \, dE, \qquad (8.11.1)$$

where $\Sigma_s(E)$ is the macroscopic scattering cross section of neutrons of energy E, $n(E)$ is the corresponding neutron density per unit energy interval, and v is the velocity of these neutrons. The total flux ϕ_1 of the fast neutron group is

$$\phi_1 = \int_{E_{\text{th}}}^{E_0} n(E) v \, dE, \qquad (8.11.2)$$

and so it is possible to define an average cross section $\overline{\Sigma}_s$ for the group by

$$\overline{\Sigma}_s = \frac{\int_{E_{\text{th}}}^{E_0} \Sigma_s(E) n(E) v \, dE}{\int_{E_{\text{th}}}^{E_0} n(E) v \, dE}. \qquad (8.11.3)$$

Consequently, it follows that (8.11.1) may be written as

No. of collisions per cm³ per sec in fast group $= \overline{\Sigma}_s \phi_1$.

8.12. The average loss in the logarithm of the energy per collision is ξ, and the average number of collisions required to degrade a source neutron from E_0 to E_{th} is

$$\text{Average number of collisions from } E_0 \text{ to } E_{\text{th}} = \frac{1}{\xi} \ln \frac{E_0}{E_{\text{th}}}. \qquad (8.12.1)$$

The rate at which neutrons are transferred from the fast to the slow group is equal to the number of scattering collisions per cm³ per sec, $\overline{\Sigma}_s \phi_1$, divided by the number of collisions required to decrease the energy from E_0 to E_{th}, given by (8.12.1). Hence,

$$\begin{matrix} \text{No. of neutrons transferred from the fast to} \\ \text{the slow group per cm}^3 \text{ per sec} \end{matrix} = \frac{\overline{\Sigma}_s \phi_1}{\dfrac{1}{\xi} \ln \dfrac{E_0}{E_{\text{th}}}}. \qquad (8.12.2)$$

It is now possible to postulate a "slowing down" cross section Σ_1 for fast neutrons, such that $\Sigma_1 \phi_1$ gives the number of neutrons per cm³ per sec which are degraded from the fast to the slow group. This quantity is, of course, that given by (8.12.2), so that the slowing down cross section is defined by

$$\Sigma_1 = \frac{\overline{\Sigma}_s}{\dfrac{1}{\xi} \ln \dfrac{E_0}{E_{\text{th}}}}. \qquad (8.12.3)$$

8.13. The diffusion coefficient of the fast neutron group is derived from a consideration of the fast neutron current density; this can be represented [cf. (5.28.1)] by

$$\text{Fast neutron current density} = -\int_{E_{th}}^{E_0} D(E) \text{ grad } \phi(\mathbf{r}, E) \, dE$$

and also by $-D_1 \text{ grad } \phi_1$, where D_1 is the fast diffusion coefficient and ϕ_1 is the fast neutron flux. Hence, it follows that

$$D_1 \text{ grad } \phi_1 = D_1 \int_{E_{th}}^{E_0} \text{grad } \phi(\mathbf{r}, E) \, dE = \int_{E_{th}}^{E_0} D(E) \text{ grad } \phi(\mathbf{r}, E) \, dE$$

or

$$D_1 = \frac{\int_{E_{th}}^{E_0} D(E) \text{ grad } \phi(\mathbf{r}, E) \, dE}{\int_{E_{th}}^{E_0} \text{grad } \phi(\mathbf{r}, E) \, dE}. \tag{8.13.1}$$

It can be seen from this equation that D_1 is constant only if $\phi(\mathbf{r}, E)$ is separable into a function of $\mathbf{r}$ multiplied by a function of E, i.e., if the variation in the neutron flux spectrum from point to point in the medium can be neglected. This assumption is usually made for simplicity and, hence, replacing $D(E)$ by $\frac{1}{3}\lambda_t$, (8.13.1) becomes

$$D_1 = \frac{\int_{E_{th}}^{E_0} \frac{1}{3}\lambda_t(E)\phi(E) \, dE}{\int_{E_{th}}^{E_0} \phi(E) \, dE} \tag{8.13.2}$$

where $\phi(E)$ is the neutron flux spectrum. If the latter can be represented by the asymptotic $1/E$ distribution (cf. § 6.63, et seq.), then (8.13.2) reduces to

$$D_1 = \frac{\int_{E_{th}}^{E_0} \frac{1}{3}\lambda_t(E) \frac{dE}{E}}{\ln (E_0/E_{th})}. \tag{8.13.3}$$

8.14. The group-diffusion method will be applied here to the study of thermal reactors with reflectors. It will be illustrated first by a detailed consideration of the cases in which the energies are treated as being in one group and two groups, respectively. The generalized or multi-group treatment, involving a large number of groups, will then be outlined briefly.

ONE GROUP OF NEUTRONS

8.15. In the simplest case, sometimes referred to as *one-group theory*, it is supposed that all production, diffusion, and absorption of neutrons occurs at a single energy, namely, the thermal energy. Although this represents a considerable approximation for an actual thermal reactor with reflector, it can, at least, be used to give preliminary results which can be refined later. Since it is postulated that fission neutrons have thermal energies, the problem of slowing down does not arise; the resonance escape probability and the fast fission factor (§§ 4.58, 4.59) are then both unity.   The over-all multiplication factor is thus equivalent to ηf.

8.16.   Using the subscripts c and r to indicate the core and reflector, respectively, the steady state diffusion equation (5.43.1) for the core neutrons is

$$D_c \nabla^2 \phi_c - \Sigma_{ac} \phi_c + k \Sigma_{ac} \phi_c = 0, \tag{8.16.1}$$

where D_c is the diffusion coefficient and Σ_{ac} is the macroscopic absorption cross section for the core neutrons.   The form of the third term in the equation, i.e., the source term, arises from the fact that, by definition of the multiplication factor (§ 4.47), k neutrons are produced for every one absorbed.   If no extraneous source is present, as is assumed to be the case, the steady state, to which (8.16.1) applies, is also the critical state of the reactor.   Upon dividing through this equation by D_c and rearranging, it is seen that

$$\nabla^2 \phi_c + (k - 1) \frac{\Sigma_{ac}}{D_c} \phi_c = 0,$$

and this may be written in the form of the wave equation, i.e.,

$$\nabla^2 \phi_c + B_c{}^2 \phi_c = 0. \tag{8.16.2}$$

Hence, the critical buckling $B_c{}^2$ is given by

$$B_c{}^2 = (k - 1) \frac{\Sigma_{ac}}{D_c} = \frac{k - 1}{L_c{}^2}, \tag{8.16.3}$$

where L_c is the diffusion length of neutrons in the core, $L_c{}^2$ being equal to D_c/Σ_{ac}. This expression may be used to derive an approximate value for the buckling of the critical system.   However, for actual calculation purposes, it is preferable to use [cf. (7.63.3)] the form

$$B_c{}^2 = \frac{k - 1}{M_c{}^2}, \tag{8.16.4}$$

where $M_c{}^2$ is the core migration area, which may be taken as equal to $L_c{}^2 + \tau$, where τ is the Fermi age of thermal neutrons in the given core system.

8.17.   The reflector is assumed to be nonmultiplying, that is to say, it is supposed to contain no fuel material.   There is consequently no source term in the neutron diffusion equation for the reflector; it is thus

$$D_r \nabla^2 \phi_r - \Sigma_{ar} \phi_r = 0, \tag{8.17.1}$$

where D_r and Σ_{ar} are the diffusion coefficient and macroscopic absorption cross section for the neutrons in the reflector.   This expression may also be written as

$$\nabla^2 \phi_r - \kappa_r{}^2 \phi_r = 0, \tag{8.17.2}$$

where κ_r, equal to $1/L_r$, is the reciprocal of the diffusion length in the reflector, and $\kappa_r{}^2$ is Σ_{ar}/D_r (§ 5.44).

8.18. To solve the differential equations (8.16.2) and (8.17.2) with appropriate boundary conditions set by the geometry of the reactor, in order to obtain the critical buckling, it is convenient to consider cases which can be reduced to one-dimensional symmetrical problems. Such cases are an infinite plane slab reactor, a sphere, and an infinite cylinder, a point in the plane or at the center of symmetry being chosen as the origin of the one-coordinate system.

Case I. *Infinite Plane Slab*

8.19. The first case to be considered is that of an infinite plane slab of half-thickness $\frac{1}{2}H$, with a reflector on each side of thickness T, which includes the extrapolation distance (Fig. 8.19). The origin of the coordinate is taken at the

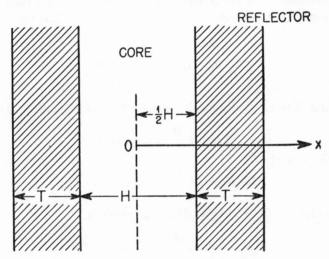

Fig. 8.19.   Infinite slab reactor with reflector

plane of symmetry of the system. For convenience, positive values only of x will be considered; the results are the same for negative values, and so x may be regarded as the absolute value $|x|$ of this coordinate. Without going into details, it can be readily shown that the solution of (8.16.2), for the neutron flux in the core, subject to the conditions that the flux shall be symmetrical and that it shall everywhere be finite and non-negative, is

$$\phi_c(x) = A \cos B_c x, \tag{8.19.1}$$

where A is an arbitrary constant.

8.20. The general solution of the reflector equation (8.17.2) involves hyperbolic sines and cosines, since κ^2 is a positive quantity; thus, the neutron flux in the reflector is given by

$$\phi_r(x) = A' \cosh \kappa_r x + C' \sinh \kappa_r x, \tag{8.20.1}$$

subject to the boundary condition that the flux is zero at the extrapolated boundary of the reflector, i.e., when $x = \frac{1}{2}H + T$.   This leads to the result

$$\phi_r(\tfrac{1}{2}H + T) = A' \cosh \kappa_r(\tfrac{1}{2}H + T) + C' \sinh \kappa_r(\tfrac{1}{2}H + T) = 0,$$

so that

$$A' = -C' \tanh \kappa_r(\tfrac{1}{2}H + T). \qquad (8.20.2)$$

If this value for A' is now inserted into (8.20.1), it is found that the solution of (8.17.2) is

$$\phi_r(x) = C \sinh \kappa_r(\tfrac{1}{2}H + T - x), \qquad (8.20.3)$$

where C is a new arbitrary constant.

8.21. The arbitrary constants A and C may be related by introducing the boundary conditions that the neutron flux and current density shall be continuous at the core-reflector interface (§ 5.38), i.e., when $x = \frac{1}{2}H$; these lead to

$$\phi_c(\tfrac{1}{2}H) = \phi_r(\tfrac{1}{2}H)$$

and

$$D_c \frac{d\phi_c(\tfrac{1}{2}H)}{dx} = D_r \frac{d\phi_r(\tfrac{1}{2}H)}{dx}.$$

Using the first of these conditions, it follows from (8.19.1) and (8.20.3) that

$$A \cos B_c \frac{H}{2} = C \sinh \kappa_r T \qquad (8.21.1)$$

and, from the second,

$$A D_c B_c \sin B_c \frac{H}{2} = C D_r \kappa_r \cosh \kappa_r T. \qquad (8.21.2)$$

Then, upon dividing (8.21.2) by (8.21.1), the result is

$$D_c B_c \tan B_c \frac{H}{2} = D_r \kappa_r \coth \kappa_r T. \qquad (8.21.3)^*$$

This transcendental equation is the critical equation for the reflected infinite slab reactor according to the one-group treatment.   Since D_c, B_c, D_r, and κ_r can be estimated from the known properties of the fuel, moderator, and reflector materials, as indicated below, (8.21.3) gives the critical half-thicknesses $\frac{1}{2}H$ corresponding to a specified reflector thickness T; thus, the reflector thickness required for an infinite slab reactor of given thickness to become critical can be obtained.

8.22. As seen in § 8.16, B_c^2 is equal to $(k-1)/L_c^2$ or, better, to $(k-1)/(L_c^2+\tau)$, and its value can be calculated if the composition of the core is specified.   If the ratio of fuel to moderator is fairly low, it is possible to write, by means of (7.67.1),

$$L_c^2 = \frac{L_{0c}^2}{z + 1},$$

---

* This equation can be derived directly from (5.107.2) for the boundary condition based on the albedo of the reflector.

where L_{0c} is the diffusion length of neutrons in pure moderator, and z is the ratio of the macroscopic cross sections of the fuel and the moderator in the core [cf. (7.66.2)]. In the one-group treatment, k may be taken as equal to ηf (§ 8.15), so that

$$k = \eta f = \eta \frac{z}{z+1},$$

as in (7.66.1). Upon substituting these values into the expression for B_c^2, it is found that

$$B_c^2 = \frac{\eta z - (z+1)}{L_{0c}^2 + \tau(z+1)}, \tag{8.22.1}$$

where τ may be taken as the age of the neutrons in the pure (core) moderator. The buckling, and hence the critical dimensions, of the core can thus be calculated for specific materials. Alternatively, if the dimensions of the critical core are given, the buckling can be obtained directly in the usual manner (see Table 7.60).

8.23. The values of D_c and D_r are essentially those for pure moderator and for reflector material, respectively, and so they can be obtained from the respective transport mean free paths; finally, κ_r is equal to $1/L_r$ for the reflector material. All the information is thus available for the one-group calculation of the relationship between the thickness T of the reflector and the critical half-thickness $\frac{1}{2}H$ of the infinite slab core. The results of a typical case are shown in Fig. 8.23.

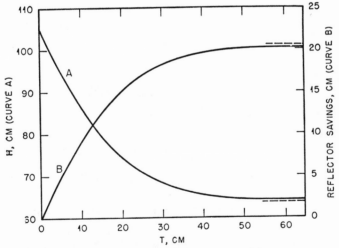

FIG. 8.23. Reflector savings for infinite slab reactor

It is seen that, as the reflector thickness increases, the critical core thickness decreases at first, but beyond a certain thickness of reflector, the core size does not decrease appreciably. As will be explained below, a reflector having a thickness of about two diffusion lengths behaves virtually as a reflector of infinite thickness.

8.24. As T approaches zero, coth $\kappa_r T$ tends to infinity; hence, it will be seen from (8.21.3) that tan $B_c H/2$ becomes infinite and $B_c H/2$ approaches $\pi/2$. Thus for an infinite slab reactor with no reflector ($T = 0$), the one-group treatment leads to the critical equation $B_c H_0/2 = \pi/2$, or $B_c = \pi/H_0$, which has the same form as for a bare, infinite slab reactor (§ 7.39). However, B_c is not identical with B_g of (7.39.1), because it is assumed in the one-group treatment that neutrons are produced and absorbed at the same energy. A closer approximation is obtained if B_c is defined by (8.16.4), rather than by (8.16.3).

REFLECTOR SAVINGS

8.25. The decrease in the critical size of a reactor, due to a reflector, is expressed by means of the *reflector savings*, δ, defined by

$$\delta = \tfrac{1}{2}H_0 - \tfrac{1}{2}H, \tag{8.25.1}$$

where H_0 is the critical thickness of the bare slab reactor and H is the thickness with a reflector. Since H_0 is equal to π/B_c, as seen above, it follows that

$$\delta = \frac{\pi}{2B_c} - \frac{H}{2}$$

or

$$\frac{H}{2} = \frac{\pi}{2B_c} - \delta.$$

Substituting this value for $H/2$ in the critical equation (8.21.3), the result is

$$D_c B_c \tan\left(\frac{\pi}{2} - B_c\delta\right) = D_r \kappa_r \coth \kappa_r T$$

or

$$D_c B_c \cot B_c\delta = D_r \kappa_r \coth \kappa_r T.$$

Upon inverting and rearranging, this becomes

$$\tan B_c\delta = \frac{D_c B_c}{D_r \kappa_r} \tanh \kappa_r T \tag{8.25.2}$$

or

$$\delta = \frac{1}{B_c}\left[\tan^{-1}\left(\frac{D_c B_c}{D_r \kappa_r} \tanh \kappa_r T\right)\right] \tag{8.25.3}$$

for a given slab reactor. From this equation the reflector savings can be calculated for various specified thicknesses T of the reflector. The general nature of the variation of the reflector savings with the thickness of the reflector is depicted in Fig. 8.23.

8.26. If either the reflector thickness T is relatively small, so that δ is small, or the reactor core, i.e., H, is large, so that B_c is small, the quantity $B_c\delta$ will be small, and tan $B_c\delta$ in (8.25.2) may be replaced by $B_c\delta$; this equation then gives

$$\delta \approx \frac{D_c}{D_r \kappa_r} \tanh \kappa_r T,$$

or, since κ_r is equal to $1/L_r$,

$$\delta \approx \frac{D_c}{D_r} L_r \tanh \frac{T}{L_r}. \qquad (8.26.1)$$

If $D_c = D_r$, as for example if the moderator and reflector are of the same material and the proportion of fuel in the core is not large, then (8.26.1) reduces to

$$\delta \approx L_r \tanh \frac{T}{L_r}. \qquad (8.26.2)$$

8.27. If the diffusion length in the reflector is appreciably larger than the thickness, so that T/L_r is small, $\tanh T/L_r$ may be replaced by T/L_r; equation (8.26.1) then becomes

$$\delta \approx \frac{D_c}{D_r} T.$$

In the special case in which $D_c = D_r$, the reflector savings for a large reactor with a thin reflector is equal to the thickness of the reflector.

8.28. For a very thick reflector, on the other hand, T/L_r is large and $\tanh T/L_r$ approaches unity. The reflector savings for a large reactor is then given by (8.26.1) as

$$\delta \approx \frac{D_c}{D_r} L_r, \qquad (8.28.1)$$

so that δ attains a constant limiting value which is independent of the reflector thickness (Fig. 8.23). If the diffusion coefficients in the core and reflector are equal, it is seen that, for a large reactor with thick reflector, the reflector savings is approximately equal to the diffusion length of the neutrons in the reflector. For thermal neutrons, with graphite as reflector, this would be about 50 cm (Table 5.91).

8.29. A number of interesting qualitative conclusions can be drawn from the foregoing equations. In the first place, it is seen that in (8.26.1), (8.27.1), and (8.28.1), at least, the reflector savings is inversely related to the diffusion coefficient D_r of the reflector. This is in agreement with the results derived in § 8.3, et seq. Further, for a thick reflector, the reflector savings is seen from (8.28.1) to be determined by the ratio L_r/D_r. Since $L_r{}^2$ is defined by D_r/Σ_{ar}, where Σ_{ar} is the absorption cross section of the reflector, it is seen that $L_r{}^2/D_r$ is equal to $1/\Sigma_{ar}$. It would appear, therefore, that the reflector savings will be relatively large when the absorption cross section of the reflector is small. This conclusion is again in harmony with the earlier discussion.

8.30. It will be noted from the equations given above that for a specified large reactor and reflector material, so that D_c/D_r is fixed, the reflector savings is influenced primarily by the thickness of the reflector if the latter is thin [equation (8.27.1)] and by the neutron diffusion length if the reflector is thick [equation (8.28.1)]. It is apparent, therefore, that, according to the results of the one-group treatment, little is to be gained by using a reflector of thickness exceeding the thermal diffusion length. More exact calculations show that a reflector thickness of about 1.5 times the migration length is virtually equivalent to an infinite reflector, as far as the effect on the critical mass is concerned. It is of interest in this connection to recall the result obtained in § 5.57 and § 5.101, that, as far as diffusion of monoenergetic neutrons is concerned, a medium having a thickness of two or three diffusion lengths behaves virtually as an infinite medium.

Case II. *Symmetrical Reflected Reactor with Spherical Core*

8.31. It is unnecessary to discuss the one-group treatment of a spherical reflected reactor in detail; but the results will be outlined briefly. Taking the origin of the r-coordinate at the center of the core, it is found that

$$\phi_c(r) = \frac{A \sin B_c r}{r}$$

and

$$\phi_r(r) = \frac{A' \sinh \kappa_r (R + T - r)}{\kappa_r r},$$

where R is the radius of the core, and T is the thickness of the symmetrical reflector which surrounds it. Introducing the continuity conditions for neutron flux and current density at the boundary, and dividing the results, as in § 8.21, it is found that

$$\cot B_c R = \frac{1}{B_c R}\left(1 - \frac{D_r}{D_c}\right) - \frac{D_r}{D_c B_c L_r} \coth \frac{T}{L_r}, \tag{8.31.1}$$

where L_r has been written for $1/\kappa_r$. This is the critical equation for the spherical reflected reactor according to the one-group method. From (8.31.1) it is possible to calculate the thickness T of reflector required to cause a spherical reactor of radius R to become critical. The reflector savings in this case is defined by

$$\delta = R_0 - R,$$

where R_0, equal to π/B_c (cf. § 7.48), is the critical radius of the bare reactor.

8.32. In the case of a large reactor, i.e., R is large, so that B_c is small, or a small reflector thickness, when δ is small, the value of $B_c \delta$ will be small. It is then possible to obtain an explicit expression for δ in terms of the properties of the system. Replacing R by $R_0 - \delta$ and R_0 by π/B_c,

$$\cot B_c R = \cot (B_c R_0 - B_c \delta)$$
$$= \cot (\pi - B_c \delta) = -\cot B_c \delta.$$

Since $B_c \delta$ is small, $\cot B_c \delta$ is approximately equal to $1/B_c \delta$, so that

$$\cot B_c R \approx -\frac{1}{B_c \delta}.$$

If this result is substituted into (8.31.1), a quadratic in δ^2 is obtained, of which the solution is

$$\delta \approx \tfrac{1}{2}\left[\frac{D_r}{D_c}\delta_0 + R_0 - \sqrt{\left(\frac{D_r}{D_c}\delta_0 + R_0\right)^2 - 4R_0\delta_0}\right], \qquad (8.32.1)$$

where

$$\delta_0 \equiv \frac{D_c}{D_r}L_r \tanh \frac{T}{L_r}.$$

The solution with the plus sign preceding the square root term is neglected as giving an unreasonably large value for the reflector savings.

8.33. In the special case where D_c/D_r is unity, as well as $B_c\delta$ small, (8.32.1) becomes

$$\delta \approx L_r \tanh \frac{T}{L_r}, \qquad (8.33.1)$$

which is identical with the corresponding equation (8.26.2) for an infinite slab reactor. The same result can be obtained directly from (8.31.1) if $B_c\delta$ is small and D_c is equal to D_r. If the radius R_0 of the critical reactor without reflector is large, the reflector savings, with $B_c\delta$ small, is given by (8.32.1) as

$$\delta \approx \frac{D_c}{D_r}L_r \tanh \frac{T}{L_r}.$$

8.34. Further simplification of the foregoing equations may be made, as for the slab reactor, by considering the cases where $T \ll L_r$ or $T \gg L_r$. The general conclusions reached for the spherical reactor are the same as for the infinite slab, namely, that, especially for a large reactor, little is to be gained by increasing the thickness of the reflector to values much greater than about twice the diffusion length L_r of thermal neutrons in the reflector material.

8.35. A similar treatment to that given above can be applied to an infinite cylindrical reactor surrounded by a symmetrical reflector shell. The details will not be given, as the conclusions are essentially similar to those described above. In any event, it should be emphasized that, irrespective of the shape of the reactor, although the qualitative behavior derived from the one-group treatment is correct, the quantitative results must not be taken too seriously. If they are used at all, they must be treated as being in the nature of a first approximation.

RATIO OF MAXIMUM TO AVERAGE NEUTRON FLUX IN SLAB REACTOR

8.36. The core flux distribution, in the x-direction, of an infinite, homogeneous slab, reflected reactor is given by (8.19.1) as $\phi_c(x) = A \cos B_c x$, where B_c is defined by (8.21.3). The maximum flux, which is that along the plane of symmetry, i.e., when x is zero, is then

$$\phi_{\max} = A,$$

where A is determined by the power level of the reactor. The average flux is obtained by integrating over the thickness of the slab and dividing by the thickness; thus,

$$\phi_{av} = \frac{1}{H} \int_{-H/2}^{H/2} A \cos B_c x \, dx$$

$$= \frac{2A}{B_c H} \sin \frac{B_c H}{2}.$$

Hence, the ratio of maximum to average flux is

$$\frac{\phi_{max}}{\phi_{av}} = \frac{\frac{1}{2} B_c H}{\sin \frac{1}{2} B_c H}. \qquad (8.36.1)$$

This result, combined with (8.21.3) in the form

$$\tfrac{1}{2} B_c H = \tan^{-1} \left(\frac{D_r \kappa_r}{D_c B_c} \coth \kappa_r T \right),$$

may be used to calculate the ratio of maximum to average flux for various thicknesses of core and reflector. Particular values for H and T are chosen and then, with D_c, D_r, and κ_r known, the transcendental equation is solved for B_c by a process of iteration. With B_c and H known for a given value of T, the ratio expressed by (8.36.1) can be readily calculated. For zero thickness of reflector, i.e., for the bare reactor, B_c is π/H (§ 8.24) and, hence, the ratio ϕ_{max}/ϕ_{av} is $\pi/2$, i.e., 1.57. On the other hand, for large reflector thicknesses, i.e., as $T \rightarrow \infty$, $\coth \kappa_r T \rightarrow 1$, and then $\tfrac{1}{2} B_c H = \tan^{-1} (D_r \kappa_r / D_c B_c)$. From this the limiting value of ϕ_{max}/ϕ_{av} can be calculated for any core thickness.

8.37. The results for a reactor core, consisting mainly of beryllium, with a beryllium reflector, so that D_r/D_c is unity, and $\kappa_r = 1/L_r = 0.0423$ cm^{-1}, are shown in Fig. 8.37 for infinite slabs of 25, 50, and 75 cm thickness, respectively, for reflector thicknesses up to 50 cm. The initial sharp decrease in the ratio of maximum to average flux with increase in reflector thickness indicates a flattening of the flux distribution in the reactor core resulting from the presence of the reflector (§ 8.2). With increasing thickness of the latter, however, a limiting value is approached asymptotically when the reflector thickness is about twice the diffusion length of the thermal neutrons, i.e., about 48 cm in this case; further increase in thickness has little effect on the neutron flux distribution. This is in general agreement with the results given in § 8.30.

Two Groups of Neutrons

8.38. The one-group calculations given above are approximate because the properties of the material in the core are very different for fast and slow neutrons. Actually, the reflector savings based on the one-group treatment are found to be too low for the following reasons. In the first place, since the one-group method assumes all the neutrons to be thermal, no allowance is made for the

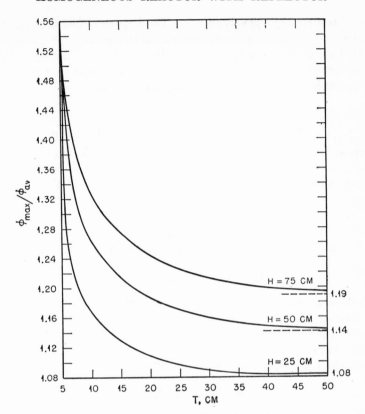

FIG. 8.37. Ratio of maximum to average flux as function of reflector thickness

fact that fast neutrons entering the reflector have a higher probability than do thermal neutrons of being scattered back into the core due to the extra collisions they make while being slowed down. Further, neutrons which enter the reflector with energies above the resonance level are moderated in the reflector; they then return to the core as thermal neutrons, having completely avoided the resonance capture to which they would have been liable if they had reached thermal energies in the core before entering the reflector. Both these factors tend to increase the effectiveness of the reflector, as compared with that to be expected if all the neutrons had thermal energies. Consequently, taking into account the range of neutron energies, from the maximum fission energy to thermal values, gives reflector savings greater than those calculated above by the one-group method.

8.39. A second approximation is to suppose that the neutrons may be divided into two groups, namely, slow (thermal) and fast, as described in § 8.10. Consider, first, the core of a reactor in which there is no resonance capture. In the following treatment the fast neutrons will be represented by the subscript 1 and the thermal neutrons by the subscript 2.   The number of fast neutrons produced by fission is $k\Sigma_{2c}\phi_{2c}$ per cm^3 per sec, where Σ_{2c} is the macroscopic absorption cross section for thermal neutrons in the core of the reactor, and this may be taken as the source term for *fast neutrons* in the diffusion equation for the *core*.   Thus, for the reactor in the steady state, this equation becomes

$$D_{1c}\, \nabla^2\phi_{1c} - \Sigma_{1c}\phi_{1c} + k\Sigma_{2c}\phi_{2c} = 0, \tag{8.39.1}$$

where Σ_{1c} is a fictitious absorption cross section, which is actually a slowing down cross section, having exactly the significance described in § 8.12.   Thus, $\Sigma_{1c}\phi_{1c}$ gives the number of thermal neutrons produced per cm^3 per sec.   If there is a small amount of resonance capture, (8.39.1) will apply if allowance is made by including the resonance escape probability in the calculation of k.   In this case, ϕ_{1c} will be p times the flux without capture, and $\Sigma_{1c}\phi_{1c}$ will, as before, give the number of thermal neutrons produced.

8.40. For the *thermal neutrons* in the *core*, the steady state diffusion equation is

$$D_{2c}\, \nabla^2\phi_{2c} - \Sigma_{2c}\phi_{2c} + \Sigma_{1c}\phi_{1c} = 0, \tag{8.40.1}$$

where the slow-neutron source term $\Sigma_{1c}\phi_{1c}$ is the number of fast neutrons, per cm^3 per sec, slowed down into the thermal group, the resonance capture during slowing down being neglected.   The absorption cross section Σ_{2c} has the same significance as in (8.39.1).

8.41. In the *reflector*, the steady-state diffusion equation for *fast neutrons* is

$$D_{1r}\, \nabla^2\phi_{1r} - \Sigma_{1r}\phi_{1r} = 0, \tag{8.41.1}$$

there being no source term, since there is assumed to be no multiplication in the reflector.   The cross section Σ_{1r} is here a slowing down cross section, defined in a manner exactly similar to Σ_{1c} in (8.39.1), except that the former applies to the reflector.   For *slow neutrons* in the *reflector*, the diffusion equation is

$$D_{2r}\, \nabla^2\phi_{2r} - \Sigma_{2r}\phi_{2r} + \Sigma_{1r}\phi_{1r} = 0, \tag{8.41.2}$$

where Σ_{2r} is the true absorption cross section.

8.42. In attempting to solve the four differential diffusion equations, it will be recalled that all neutron fluxes must be finite and non-negative.   In addition, in dealing with symmetrical reactors, there is the requirement that both fast- and slow-neutron flux distributions shall be symmetrical about the plane, axis, or center of symmetry (cf. § 5.74).   Further, there will be a continuity of both fast- and slow-neutron fluxes and current densities at the core-reflector interface.   Also, both fast- and slow-neutron fluxes will become zero at the extrapolated boundary of the finite reflector.   For simplicity, it will be supposed that the linear extrapolation distances are the same for thermal and fast neutrons; the error introduced in this manner is negligible in comparison with other approximations of the two-group treatment.

8.43. Of the four differential equations to be solved, namely, (8.39.1), (8.40.1), (8.41.1), and (8.41.2), all except (8.41.1) are inhomogeneous. However, the homogeneous parts of the other three equations, and also (8.41.1), are wave equations. Consequently, for the core equations (8.39.1) and (8.40.1), solutions of the type

$$\nabla^2\phi_{1c} + B^2\phi_{1c} = 0 \tag{8.43.1}$$

and

$$\nabla^2\phi_{2c} + B^2\phi_{2c} = 0 \tag{8.43.2}$$

may be tried, and the conditions necessary for these solutions to apply can be found. It will be noted that the constants B^2 are taken to be the same for both fast- and slow-neutron groups. This may be justified by deriving an expression for ϕ_{1c} in terms of ϕ_{2c}, from (8.40.1), and then inserting this value for ϕ_{1c} in (8.39.1). A relationship is thus obtained involving ϕ_{2c} only. Next, an expression for ϕ_{2c} is obtained in terms of ϕ_{1c}, from (8.39.1), and this is substituted in (8.40.1), thus yielding an equation containing ϕ_{1c} only. The result is found to be identical with that for ϕ_{2c}, so that when the homogeneous parts are expressed in the form of the wave equation, B^2 must be the same in both cases.

8.44. Upon substituting $-B^2\phi_{1c}$ for $\nabla^2\phi_{1c}$ in (8.39.1) and $-B^2\phi_{2c}$ for $\nabla^2\phi_{2c}$ in (8.40.1), it is seen that

$$-(D_{1c}B^2 + \Sigma_{1c})\phi_{1c} + k\Sigma_{2c}\phi_{2c} = 0$$

and

$$\Sigma_{1c}\phi_{1c} - (D_{2c}B^2 + \Sigma_{2c})\phi_{2c} = 0.$$

The condition that these simultaneous equations should have a nontrivial solution is that the determinant of the coefficients shall vanish (Cramer's rule); i.e.,

$$(D_{1c}B^2 + \Sigma_{1c})(D_{2c}B^2 + \Sigma_{2c}) - k\Sigma_{1c}\Sigma_{2c} = 0, \tag{8.44.1}$$

which is the characteristic or critical equation for the core of a reflected reactor on the basis of two energy groups of neutrons. Upon dividing through by $\Sigma_{1c}\Sigma_{2c}$, the result is

$$\left(\frac{D_{1c}}{\Sigma_{1c}}B^2 + 1\right)\left(\frac{D_{2c}}{\Sigma_{2c}}B^2 + 1\right) = k \tag{8.44.2}$$

or

$$(1 + L_{1c}^2B^2)(1 + L_{2c}^2B^2) = k, \tag{8.44.3}$$

where D_{2c}/Σ_{2c} is the square of the diffusion length, L_{2c}, of thermal neutrons in the core (§ 5.64), and D_{1c}/Σ_{1c} has been replaced by the square of a fictitious diffusion length, L_{1c}. However, since Σ_{1c} is really a slowing down cross section, it can be shown by the method of § 5.63, *et seq.*, that L_{1c}^2 is equal to $\frac{1}{6}\overline{r_s^2}$, where $\overline{r_s^2}$ is the mean square distance traveled by a neutron in the fast group before it becomes thermal. Consequently, by (6.141.1), L_{1c}^2 is equivalent to τ_c, the Fermi age of the thermal neutrons in the core material. If L_{1c}^2 is replaced by τ_c, the critical equation (8.44.3) becomes

$$(1 + \tau_c B^2)(1 + L_{2c}^2 B^2) = k$$

or

$$\frac{k}{(1 + \tau_c B^2)(1 + L_{2c}^2 B^2)} = 1. \tag{8.44.4}$$

This is also the two-group critical equation for a bare reactor; it is similar in form to (7.62.1) for a large reactor, assuming continuous slowing down.

8.45. Since τ_c, L_{2c}, and k are properties of the materials constituting the reactor core, (8.44.4) gives the permissible values of B^2 if the solutions of the core differential equations (8.39.1) and (8.40.1) are to be of the wave-equation form postulated above. The critical equation (8.44.4) is actually a quadratic in B^2, and so there are two possible solutions which will now be considered. Upon multiplying out and rearranging, the equation takes the form

$$B^4 + \left(\frac{1}{\tau_c} + \frac{1}{L_{2c}^2}\right) B^2 - \frac{k-1}{\tau_c L_{2c}^2} = 0. \tag{8.45.1}$$

Of the two solutions for B^2 one is positive and the other is negative; they will be represented by μ^2 and $-\nu^2$, respectively, so that both μ^2 and ν^2 are positive quantities. The solutions are then

$$\mu^2 = \frac{1}{2}\left[-\left(\frac{1}{\tau_c} + \frac{1}{L_{2c}^2}\right) + \sqrt{\left(\frac{1}{\tau_c} + \frac{1}{L_{2c}^2}\right)^2 + \frac{4(k-1)}{\tau_c L_{2c}^2}}\right] \tag{8.45.2}$$

and

$$-\nu^2 = \frac{1}{2}\left[-\left(\frac{1}{\tau_c} + \frac{1}{L_{2c}^2}\right) - \sqrt{\left(\frac{1}{\tau_c} + \frac{1}{L_{2c}^2}\right)^2 + \frac{4(k-1)}{\tau_c L_{2c}^2}}\right]. \tag{8.45.3}$$

The general solutions of the core equations (8.39.1) and (8.40.1) involve linear combinations of μ^2 and $-\nu^2$. It will be noted that these are both properties of the reactor core materials.

8.46. Consider now the core wave equations (8.43.1) and (8.43.2); let the solutions for the flux corresponding to the two values μ^2 and $-\nu^2$ for B^2 be X and Y, respectively; then these equations may be written as

$$\nabla^2 X + \mu^2 X = 0 \tag{8.46.1}$$

and

$$\nabla^2 Y - \nu^2 Y = 0, \tag{8.46.2}$$

where, as seen above, μ^2 and ν^2 are both positive quantities. The solution of these equations depends on the geometry of the reactor, and the cases to be considered here will, as before, be restricted to those which can be treated as symmetrical, one-dimensional problems. The permissible solutions for X and Y for an infinite slab, a sphere, and a cylinder of infinite length are given in Table 8.46, taking into consideration the fact that the flux is finite and non-negative and that it is symmetrical.

TABLE 8.46. SOLUTIONS OF WAVE EQUATIONS FOR NEUTRON FLUX IN CORE

Geometry	X	Y
Infinite slab.................	$\cos \mu x$	$\cosh \nu x$
Sphere.......................	$\dfrac{\sin \mu r}{r}$	$\dfrac{\sinh \nu r}{r}$
Infinite cylinder..............	$J_0(\mu r)$	$I_0(\nu r)$

8.47. The general solutions of (8.39.1) and (8.40.1) are linear combinations of X and Y, namely,

$$\phi_{1c} = AX + CY \tag{8.47.1}$$

and

$$\phi_{2c} = A'X + C'Y. \tag{8.47.2}$$

These solutions appear to involve four arbitrary constants, but it will now be shown that only two are independent. Although (8.47.1) and (8.47.2) give the most general solutions of (8.39.1) and (8.40.1), permissible solutions are $\phi_{1c} = AX$ and $\phi_{2c} = A'X$, so that, by (8.46.1), $\nabla^2 \phi_{2c} = -\mu^2 A'X$. Upon substituting these in (8.40.1),* the result is

$$-D_{2c}\mu^2 A'X - \Sigma_{2c}A'X + \Sigma_{1c}AX = 0. \tag{8.47.3}$$

The ratio A'/A is represented by S_1 and called the *coupling coefficient*, i.e.,

$$S_1 \equiv \frac{A'}{A},$$

and, hence, by (8.47.3)

$$S_1 = \frac{\Sigma_{1c}}{D_{2c}\mu^2 + \Sigma_{2c}}. \tag{8.47.4}$$

Since D_{2c}/Σ_{2c} is equal to $L_{2c}{}^2$, and D_{1c}/Σ_{1c} is equivalent to the age τ_c (§ 8.44), this may be arranged to give

$$S_1 = \frac{D_{1c}}{\tau_c D_{2c}} \cdot \frac{1}{\dfrac{1}{L_{2c}{}^2} + \mu^2}. \tag{8.47.5}$$

8.48. Similarly by substituting CY for ϕ_{1c}, $C'Y$ for ϕ_{2c}, and $\nu^2 C'Y$ for $\nabla^2 \phi_{2c}$, equation (8.40.1) becomes

$$D_{2c}\nu^2 C'Y - \Sigma_{2c}C'Y + \Sigma_{1c}CY = 0. \tag{8.48.1}$$

Again, defining the coupling coefficient S_2 as C'/C, it is found that

$$S_2 \equiv \frac{C'}{C} = \frac{D_{1c}}{\tau_c D_{2c}} \cdot \frac{1}{\dfrac{1}{L_{2c}{}^2} - \nu^2}. \tag{8.48.2}$$

---

* Instead of equation (8.40.1), the fast-neutron flux equation (8.39.1) may equally well be used, but the subsequent treatment is more involved.

8.49. It is seen from (8.47.5) and (8.48.2) that S_1 and S_2 depend on D_{1c}, D_{2c}, τ_c, L_{2c}, μ, and ν, all of which are properties of the core material and so are not arbitrary. Thus, the four constants A, A', C, and C' are really equivalent to only two arbitrary constants, which may be represented by A and C. The general solutions of the core diffusion equations may thus be written as

$$\phi_{1c} = AX + CY \tag{8.49.1}$$
$$\phi_{2c} = S_1 AX + S_2 CY. \tag{8.49.2}$$

8.50. Attention may now be turned to the *reflector*. If (8.41.1) is divided through by D_{1r} and (8.41.2) by D_{2r}, the results are

$$\nabla^2 \phi_{1r} - \kappa_{1r}{}^2 \phi_{1r} = 0 \tag{8.50.1}$$

and

$$\nabla^2 \phi_{2r} - \kappa_{2r}{}^2 \phi_{2r} + \frac{\Sigma_{1r}}{D_{2r}} \phi_{1r} = 0, \tag{8.50.2}$$

respectively, where $\kappa_{1r}{}^2$ is equal to Σ_{1r}/D_{1r} and $\kappa_{2r}{}^2$ to Σ_{2r}/D_{2r}. The equation (8.50.1) may be solved directly since it is already in the homogeneous wave-equation form, noting that $\kappa_{1r}{}^2$ is a positive quantity. Further, results of the same form, with $\kappa_{2r}{}^2$ replacing $\kappa_{1r}{}^2$, will be solutions of the homogeneous part, i.e., the first two terms, of (8.50.2).

8.51. Taking into consideration the boundary condition that the fast- and slow-neutron fluxes go to zero at the same extrapolated boundary of the reflector, the permissible solutions of (8.50.1), for three different geometries, are given in Table 8.51. They are represented by the symbol Z, it being understood that

TABLE 8.51.   SOLUTIONS OF WAVE EQUATIONS FOR NEUTRON FLUX IN REFLECTOR

Geometry	Z	Z (T infinite)
Infinite slab	$\sinh \kappa_r(\tfrac{1}{2}H + T - x)$	$e^{-\kappa_r x}$
Sphere	$\dfrac{\sinh \kappa_r(R + T - r)}{r}$	$\dfrac{e^{-\kappa_r r}}{r}$
Infinite cylinder	$I_0(\kappa_r r) - \dfrac{I_0}{K_0}[\kappa_r(R + T)]\,K_0(\kappa_r r)$	$K_0(\kappa_r r)$

Z_1, the solution of (8.50.1), contains κ_{1r}, while Z_2, the solution of the homogeneous part of (8.50.2), contains κ_{2r}. As before, $\tfrac{1}{2}H$ is the half-thickness of the infinite slab, R is the radius of the sphere or of the infinite cylinder, and T is the reflector thickness in each case. For thick reflectors, which may be treated as having infinite thickness, the solutions of the wave equations are given in the column headed Z (T infinite).

8.52. The general solution of the fast-neutron flux equation (8.41.1) is then simply

$$\phi_{1r} = FZ_1, \tag{8.52.1}$$

where F is an arbitrary constant; no other terms are necessary since the equation is homogeneous. For the slow-neutron flux equation (8.41.2) or (8.50.2), however, the general solution is

$$\phi_{2r} = GZ_2 + S_3\phi_{1r} = GZ_2 + S_3FZ_1, \qquad (8.52.2)$$

where G is an arbitrary constant, and the factor S_3 is the reflector coupling coefficient.

8.53. In order to evaluate S_3, the ϕ_{2r}'s in (8.50.2) may be replaced by $S_3\phi_{1r}$; it is unnecessary to include the GZ_2 term as it appears in (8.52.2), since it is a solution of the homogeneous equation and would make a contribution of zero in any event. The resulting expression is

$$S_3 \nabla^2\phi_{1r} - S_3\kappa_{2r}^2\phi_{1r} + \frac{\Sigma_{1r}}{D_{2r}} \phi_{1r} = 0.$$

Since $\nabla^2\phi_{1r}$ is equal to $\kappa_{1r}^2\phi_{1r}$, by (8.50.1), it follows that

$$S_3\kappa_{1r}^2\phi_{1r} - S_3\kappa_{2r}^2\phi_{1r} + \frac{\Sigma_{1r}}{D_{2r}} \phi_{1r} = 0,$$

and hence

$$S_3 = \frac{\Sigma_{1r}}{D_{2r}} \left(\frac{1}{\kappa_{2r}^2 - \kappa_{1r}^2}\right). \qquad (8.53.1)$$

The factor Σ_{1r} may be eliminated by introducing the Fermi age, τ_r, for the reflector, equal to D_{1r}/Σ_{1r} (cf. § 8.44). It is evident from this result that S_3 is determined by the nature of the reflector material.

8.54. The equations (8.52.1) and (8.52.2) for the reflector, and the corresponding equations (8.49.1) and (8.49.2) for the core, contain four unknowns, i.e., A, C, F, and G, and there are four continuity conditions, namely, that the fast- and slow-neutron fluxes and current densities are continuous at the core-reflector interface. These conditions lead to the following equations:

$$AX + CY = FZ_1$$
$$S_1AX + S_2CY = S_3FZ_1 + GZ_2$$
$$D_{1c}(AX' + CY') = D_{1r}FZ_1',$$
$$D_{2c}(S_1AX' + S_2CY') = D_{2r}(S_3FZ_1' + GZ_2'),$$

where X', Y', Z_1', and Z_2' are the first derivatives of X, Y, Z_1, and Z_2, respectively, with respect to x or r, as the case may be, *all evaluated at the core-reflector interface.*

8.55. The foregoing equations may be rearranged so as to give a homogeneous set of equations in A, C, F, and G; thus,

$$\begin{aligned}
XA &+ YC &- Z_1F & &= 0\\
(S_1X)A &+ (S_2Y)C &- (S_3Z_1)F &- Z_2G &= 0\\
(D_{1c}X')A &+ (D_{1c}Y')C &- (D_{1r}Z_1')F & &= 0\\
(S_1D_{2c}X')A &+ (S_2D_{2c}Y')C &- (S_3D_{2r}Z_1')F &- (D_{2r}Z_2')G &= 0.
\end{aligned}$$

For a consistent set of solutions, the determinant of the coefficients must be zero; that is,

$$
\begin{vmatrix}
X & Y & -Z_1 & 0 \\
S_1X & S_2Y & -S_3Z_1 & -Z_2 \\
D_{1c}X' & D_{1c}Y' & -D_{1r}Z_1' & 0 \\
S_1D_{2c}X' & S_2D_{2c}Y' & -S_3D_{2r}Z_1' & -D_{2r}Z_2'
\end{vmatrix} = 0. \qquad (8.55.1)
$$

This may be regarded as the critical equation for the two-group method for a reflected reactor. It should be clearly understood that in this determinant the X, Y, Z_1, and Z_2, and their derivatives, refer to the values at the core-reflector interface. Thus, for the slab, x is $\frac{1}{2}H$, whereas, for the sphere and the cylinder, r is equal to R in each case.

8.56. Since X and Y involve $\frac{1}{2}H$ or R, and Z_1 and Z_2 contain T or $T - R$, except for the infinitely thick reflector (see Table 8.51), an explicit solution of the determinant so as to give T as a function of R (or $\frac{1}{2}H$), or vice versa, is not possible. The general method of using the expression is thus somewhat as follows. Suppose that, for a given fuel, moderator, and reflector, with a specified fuel-moderator ratio, it is required to find the critical core radius R (or half-thickness $\frac{1}{2}H$) for a reflector of thickness T. An approximate value of R is first estimated, by means of the one-group method, for the thickness T. This is inserted in the determinant which is then evaluated, using the values S_1, S_2, S_3, κ_{1r}, κ_{2r}, μ^2, and ν^2 derived from the properties of the materials. The result, represented by the symbol Δ, is given by (8.55.1) as

$$
\Delta = \left(D_{1c}\frac{X'}{X} - D_{1r}\frac{Z_1'}{Z_1} \right)\left(S_2D_{2c}\frac{Y'}{Y} - S_3D_{2r}\frac{Z_1'}{Z_1} - (S_2 - S_3)D_{2r}\frac{Z_2'}{Z_2} \right)
$$
$$
- \left(D_{1c}\frac{Y'}{Y} - D_{1r}\frac{Z_1'}{Z_1} \right)\left(S_1D_{2c}\frac{X'}{X} - S_3D_{2r}\frac{Z_1'}{Z_1} - (S_1 - S_3)D_{2r}\frac{Z_2'}{Z_2} \right)
$$

and will, in general, differ from zero. A guess is then made at another value of the critical radius R, for the given reflector thickness T, and the determinant again evaluated. If this is still not zero, the two Δ's may be plotted against the R's, and an estimate made, by means of a linear plot, of the R which will make Δ zero. A final adjustment may then be necessary to give a more accurate value of R which satisfies the critical equation for the chosen reflector thickness. This is the core radius that will make the reflected reactor critical under the specified conditions.

8.57. The calculation may be repeated for several compositions of the fuel-moderator system, in order to find the minimum critical volume or mass of fuel material. An alternative approach is to assume a core radius and reflector thickness and make the fuel concentration the variable. In this case, the thermal diffusion length is the important quantity, and the requisite value to make the reactor critical for a given R and T can be determined.

8.58. By means of (8.49.1), (8.49.2), (8.52.1), and (8.52.2), an indication can be obtained of the spatial variation of the fast and slow group fluxes in the core and reflector. The results are indicated in Fig. 8.58, for a system in which the

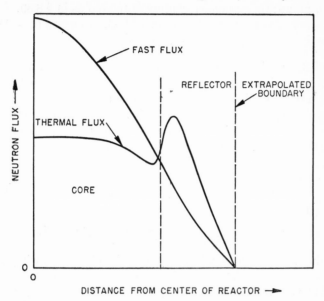

FIG. 8.58. Thermal and fast neutron flux distributions in core and reflector

reflector is the same material as the moderator in the core, with the properties of the latter not greatly affected by the fuel. It will be observed that the slow-neutron flux exhibits a maximum in the reflector at a short distance from the core-reflector interface. This arises from the fact that in the reflector slow neutrons are produced by the slowing down of fast ones, but they are absorbed very much less strongly in the reflector than in the core. Farther from the interface the slow-neutron flux, like the fast flux, falls off to zero at the extrapolated boundary of the reflector.

Multi-Group Treatment

8.59. The treatment by the method of groups may be improved by increasing the number of energy intervals, i.e., the number of groups, into which the neutrons are divided. Suppose there are n groups, namely, $1, 2, \ldots, i, \ldots, n,$ where 1 is the group of highest energy and n represents thermal energy. It is assumed that all the fission neutrons have the same energy and enter the first (fastest) group. The diffusion equation for any group, indicated by i, provided $i \neq 1$, i.e., the group of highest energy is excluded, is then [cf. (8.40.1)] given by

$$D_i \nabla^2 \phi_i - \Sigma_i \phi_i + \Sigma_{i-1} \phi_{i-1} = 0, \tag{8.59.1}$$

where Σ_i is the slowing down cross section in all cases except for $i = n$ (thermal neutrons), where it is the true absorption cross section.   The source term is taken as equal to the number of neutrons per cm^3 per sec, $\Sigma_{i-1}\phi_{i-1}$, slowed down from the $(i - 1)$th group; the resonance capture is treated as in § 8.39.

8.60. For the fission neutrons, i.e., those of highest energy $(n = 1)$, the diffusion equation is

$$D_1 \nabla^2 \phi_1 - \Sigma_1 \phi_1 + k\Sigma_n \phi_n = 0, \qquad (8.60.1)$$

where Σ_1 and Σ_n are the slowing down cross section of fission neutrons and the absorption cross section of thermal neutrons, respectively.   It will be noted that the absorption of thermal neutrons is the source of the fission neutrons.

8.61. In the two-group method, the solutions for ϕ_1 and ϕ_n, for both core and reflector, were expressed as linear combinations of functions μ and ν, where μ^2 and $-\nu^2$ are the positive and negative solutions, respectively, for B^2 of the characteristic equation (8.45.1).   A similar situation arises in the n-group treatment; each ϕ_i is an n-fold linear combination of functions B_n, there being a total of n values of B_n^2.   The condition that the solutions shall be nontrivial is found to be, for any value of B^2,

$$\frac{k}{(1 + L_1^2 B^2)(1 + L_2^2 B^2) \cdots (1 + L_n^2 B^2)} = 1, \qquad (8.61.1)$$

where L_n is the thermal diffusion length, and L_1, L_2, etc., are slowing down lengths (§ 8.44) for each group.   This equation is seen to be analogous to the critical equation (8.44.4) of the two-group treatment for a bare reactor.

8.62. In the limit, when the number of groups approaches infinity, i.e., $n \to \infty$, the group treatment would be expected to pass into the continuous slowing down (Fermi) model, since this postulates a continuous distribution of neutron energies.   This can be shown to be so, provided the sum of the (nonthermal) slowing down areas remains finite and equal to the age; thus,

$$\lim_{n \to \infty} \sum_{i=1}^{n-1} L_i^2 = \tau. \qquad (8.62.1)$$

Upon taking logarithms of both sides of (8.61.1) and rearranging, it is seen that

$$\ln k = \sum_{i=1}^{n-1} \ln (1 + L_i^2 B^2) + \ln (1 + L_n^2 B^2).$$

In the limit, when n becomes infinite, each L_i^2 becomes infinitesimally small, so that $\ln (1 + L_i^2 B^2)$ approaches $L_i^2 B^2$; hence, in the limit

$$\ln k = B^2 \sum_{i=1}^{n-1} L_i^2 + \ln (1 + L_n^2 B^2).$$

If the age, as given by (8.62.1), is now introduced, it follows that

$$\ln k = B^2 \tau + \ln (1 + L_n^2 B^2)$$

or

$$\frac{ke^{-B^2\tau}}{1 + L_n^2 B^2} = 1,$$

which is identical with the critical equation based on the Fermi model, since L_n is here the thermal diffusion length.

8.63. In the case of a large reactor, i.e., B^2 is small and $k - 1 \ll 1$, all terms in B^4 and of higher order in the critical equation (8.61.1) may be neglected, and so, upon multiplying out, this becomes

$$\frac{k}{1 + (L_1{}^2 + L_2{}^2 + \cdots L_i{}^2 + \cdots + L_n{}^2)B^2} = \frac{k}{1 + \sum_i L_i{}^2 B^2} = 1.$$

Hence, under these conditions,

$$B^2 \approx \frac{k - 1}{\sum_i L_i{}^2} = \frac{k - 1}{M^2},$$

where M^2 is the migration area. Equations of this form have been obtained for large bare reactors by other methods (cf. §§ 7.63, 12.50).

8.64. Returning now to the general problem, it is seen that the multi-group treatment leads to a set of n differential equations, $n - 1$ being of the type of (8.59.1), with (8.60.1) making up the set for the core. There will also be a set of n equations applicable to the reflector. In each case, the boundary conditions are that the neutron flux shall be zero at the outer (extrapolated) boundary, and that the flux and current shall be continuous across the core-reflector interface, for each neutron group. The solution of these equations is a major problem, and several methods have been described, e.g., solution in closed form, series expansion, method of iteration, or a combination of these methods. A detailed treatment of the subject is considered, however, to be beyond the scope of this book.

PROBLEMS

1. Calculate the critical mass of U^{235} and plot the fast and slow fluxes at room temperature for a spherical D_2O moderated reactor with a 75-cm core radius for three graphite reflector thicknesses, 25 cm, 50 cm, and infinite.

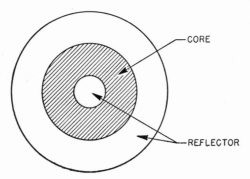

2. Obtain the critical determinant for a cylindrical assembly in which the fissionable material is in the annular region shown in the diagram.

Chapter IX

HETEROGENEOUS (NATURAL URANIUM) REACTORS*

THE FISSION CHAIN IN NATURAL URANIUM

INTRODUCTION

9.1. The treatment of the nuclear chain reaction in natural uranium is appropriately divided into two parts: microscopic theory and macroscopic theory. The microscopic theory is concerned essentially with the calculation of the infinite multiplication factor. This is an intensive property of the reactor system, since it is determined by the number of neutrons released in fission, the macroscopic cross sections for scattering and absorption processes, and the lattice structure, all of which are microscopic properties, independent of the overall size of the system. The extensive or macroscopic properties of the reactor, for example, its critical size, can then be obtained from the microscopic properties without further reference to the microscopic structure of the system.

9.2. In a natural uranium reactor four distinct capture processes compete for the available neutrons; they are:

(*a*) Absorption of fast neutrons above the fission threshold (about 1.1 Mev) of uranium-238; this is the main cause of the fast fission effect.

(*b*) Radiative capture in the resonance region (around 10 ev) of uranium-238 during slowing down.

(*c*) Radiative capture of slow neutrons in moderator and impurities; this is the so-called parasitic capture.

(*d*) Fission capture in uranium-235, mainly in the thermal region.

The determination of the infinite multiplication factor involves, essentially, computing the relative rates at which these processes occur.

---

* Most of the results presented in this chapter were obtained by the Theoretical Physics Group, led by E. P. Wigner, of the wartime Metallurgical Laboratory project at Chicago. A brief summary of the work of this group is given by E. P. Wigner, *J. Applied Phys.*, **17**, 857 (1946); MDDC–83.

THERMAL NEUTRON FISSION

9.3. Because of the nature of the variation with energy of the cross sections for the four reactions given above, the only possible chain reaction in a natural uranium system is one involving thermal neutrons with uranium-235 undergoing fission. Uranium-238 does not undergo appreciable fission with neutrons of energy less than 1.1 Mev, whereas the fission cross section for uranium-235 increases considerably with decreasing neutron energy. The use of slow neutrons for maintaining the chain reaction is, therefore, required. However, because of the large resonance absorption by uranium-238 in the vicinity of 10 ev, the proportion of neutrons taking part in fission is small in this energy region. Consequently, it is only in the thermal range, where the fission cross section for uranium-235 is 549 barns, as compared with 2.8 barns for the absorption of thermal neutrons by uranium-238, that a fission chain is possible in natural uranium. In spite of the fact that this material contains only 0.7 per cent of uranium-235, more than half of the neutrons absorbed in the thermal region cause fission.

9.4. In order to slow down the neutrons to thermal energies, the use of a moderator is necessary. As seen in Chapter VI, the best moderators are those having the largest values of $\xi\Sigma_s/\Sigma_a$. From the data in Table 6.25 and the accompanying discussion, it is evident that the only practical moderators for use in thermal reactors with natural uranium are heavy water, carbon (graphite), and beryllium (or beryllium oxide). The first successful reactor used graphite as moderator; this material was also employed in the so-called X-reactor at Oak Ridge, and in others. Several natural uranium reactors in which the moderator is heavy water have also been constructed.

9.5. Although 2.5 neutrons are produced, on the average, for each thermal neutron fission, the preponderance of uranium-238 in natural uranium causes a marked decrease in the value of η, the number of neutrons released per thermal neutron captured in fuel. If N^{238} and N^{235} represent the numbers of atoms of the two uranium isotopes per cm³ of natural uranium and σ_c^{238} and σ_c^{235} are the respective thermal neutron capture (nonfission) cross sections, while σ_f^{235} is the fission cross section of uranium-235, then, by (4.57.1),

$$\eta = \nu \frac{N^{235}\sigma_f^{235}}{N^{235}\sigma_f^{235} + N^{235}\sigma_c^{235} + N^{238}\sigma_c^{238}}$$
$$= \nu \frac{R\sigma_f^{235}}{R\sigma_f^{235} + R\sigma_c^{235} + \sigma_c^{238}}, \tag{9.5.1}$$

where ν is 2.5 neutrons per thermal fission, and R is the isotopic ratio of uranium-235 to uranium-238 in natural uranium, i.e., 0.00715. Utilizing the following values (see Table 4.57) for the thermal neutron cross sections:

$$\sigma_f^{235} = 549 \text{ barns}$$
$$\sigma_c^{235} = 101 \text{ barns}$$
$$\sigma_c^{238} = 2.8 \text{ barns},$$

it is found from (9.5.1) that $\eta = 1.3$.

9.6. It follows, therefore, that in a natural uranium reactor the maximum possible value of the infinite multiplication factor (k_∞) is 1.3 for thermal neutrons. This means that the product of the other three factors of k_∞, i.e., the fast fission factor ϵ, the thermal utilization f, and the resonance escape probability p, must exceed 1/1.3, i.e., 0.77, if a fission chain system is to be maintained.   For various reasons, which will be considered in Chapter XI, the multiplication factor in an actual reactor must be about 1.05, and so the value of $\epsilon p f$ must not be less than about 0.8.   Since ϵ is not very different from unity — about 1.03 in graphite lattices — it is necessary that the product of p and f should be greater than 0.78 for a fission chain reaction to be possible in natural uranium.

9.7. It will be seen shortly that it is not a simple matter for the condition derived above to be attained.   Any change in the composition or arrangement in a given type of natural uranium reactor resulting in an increase in the thermal utilization is accompanied by a decrease in the resonance escape probability. As a result, there is very little leeway possible, and the value of k_∞ for the system must be determined with greater precision than is necessary for enriched (homogeneous) reactors.

9.8. The evaluation of k_∞ is based on a combination of theory and experiment, in which the role of theory is to serve as a guide to experiment rather than as an exact instrument.   This course is dictated by the difficulty of the problem of calculating precisely the neutron events as a function of energy and position in a heterogeneous reactor system, and by the lack of, and inaccuracies in, cross-section data.

9.9. In addition to the experimental determination of ν and thermal cross sections, the measurement of the effective resonance integral (§ 9.11) in natural uranium is of major importance.   The result so obtained is combined with a relatively simple theoretical treatment to yield a reasonably good value for the resonance escape probability.   The data secured in this manner make possible a preliminary design of the fuel-moderator system in the thermal reactor.   This is subjected to a critical test by means of the exponential pile experiment in which the so-called "material" buckling is measured in a subcritical assembly.

RESONANCE CAPTURE IN NATURAL URANIUM

The Effective Resonance Integral

9.10. It was shown in Chapter VI that the resonance escape probability for neutrons of energy E in an absorbing system could be represented approximately by

$$p(E) = \exp\left[-\int_E^{E_0} \frac{\Sigma_a}{\bar{\xi}(\Sigma_s + \Sigma_a)} \cdot \frac{dE'}{E'} \right], \tag{9.10.1}$$

where E_0 is the fission neutron energy, Σ_s and Σ_a are the total macroscopic scattering and absorption cross sections, respectively, and $\bar{\xi}$ is the average of the logarithmic energy decrement per collision, defined in § 6.74. In general, it may be assumed that in a fuel-moderator system, the absorption cross section of the moderator is negligible compared to that of the fuel, so that Σ_a refers to the latter alone. Although (9.10.1) holds rigorously for hydrogen as moderator with an infinitely heavy absorber, its application to other moderators is restricted to absorbers with widely spaced resonances or to those exhibiting weak resonance capture.

9.11. If a system under consideration contains N_0 atoms per cm^3 of the resonance absorber, e.g., uranium-238, and σ_{a0} is the absorption cross section for neutrons of energy E, then Σ_a is equal to $N_0\sigma_{a0}$. It is thus possible to write

$$\frac{\Sigma_a}{\Sigma_s + \Sigma_a} = \frac{N_0\sigma_{a0}}{\Sigma_s} \cdot \frac{\Sigma_s}{\Sigma_s + \Sigma_a}. \tag{9.11.1}$$

In the resonance region, the scattering cross sections for both moderator and absorber may be taken to be independent of the neutron energy and hence, by combining (9.11.1) and (9.10.1), the result is

$$p(E) = \exp\left[-\frac{N_0}{\xi\Sigma_s} \cdot \int_E^{E_0} \left(\sigma_{a0}\frac{\Sigma_s}{\Sigma_s + \Sigma_a}\right)\frac{dE'}{E'}\right]. \tag{9.11.2}$$

The integral in (9.11.2) is called the *effective resonance integral*, i.e.,

$$\text{Effective Resonance Integral} \equiv \int_E^{E_0} \left(\sigma_{a0}\frac{\Sigma_s}{\Sigma_s + \Sigma_a}\right)\frac{dE'}{E'}$$

$$= \int_E^{E_0} (\sigma_{a0})_{\text{eff}}\frac{dE'}{E'}, \tag{9.11.3}$$

where $(\sigma_{a0})_{\text{eff}}$ is defined by

$$(\sigma_{a0})_{\text{eff}} \equiv \sigma_{a0}\frac{\Sigma_s}{\Sigma_s + \Sigma_a}, \tag{9.11.4}$$

and, like σ_{a0}, is a function of the neutron energy. Upon substituting (9.11.3) into (9.11.2), the resonance escape probability is

$$p(E) = \exp\left[-\frac{N_0}{\xi\Sigma_s} \int_E^{E_0} (\sigma_{a0})_{\text{eff}}\frac{dE'}{E'}\right]. \tag{9.11.5}$$

9.12. If Σ_a in (9.11.4) is replaced by $N_0\sigma_{a0}$, it follows, upon rearrangement, that

$$(\sigma_{a0})_{\text{eff}} = \frac{\sigma_{a0}}{1 + \dfrac{N_0\sigma_{a0}}{\Sigma_s}}. \tag{9.12.1}$$

The quantity Σ_s/N_0, that is, the total macroscopic scattering cross section divided by the number of atoms of uranium per cm^3, may be regarded as the *scattering cross section associated with each atom of absorber*. It is seen from (9.11.3),

(9.11.4), and (9.11.5) that the effective resonance integral and the resonance escape probability are dependent upon this quantity.   As the number of uranium atoms per cm^3 is increased, the scattering associated with each absorber atom is decreased, and $(\sigma_{a0})_{\mathrm{eff}}$ decreases correspondingly.   It follows, therefore, from (9.11.3) that the effective resonance integral also decreases.   The smallest value of the effective resonance integral is that for pure uranium in the absence of a moderator.

9.13. On the other hand, if the proportion of uranium is decreased, the scattering associated with each absorber atom is increased, i.e., Σ_s/N_0 becomes larger while N_0/N_1 becomes smaller.   Hence, $N_0\sigma_{a0}/\Sigma_s$ in the denominator of (9.12.1) will decrease and become negligible in comparison with unity; $(\sigma_{a0})_{\mathrm{eff}}$ will thus approach σ_{a0}.   Consequently, for an infinitely dilute mixture of absorber and moderator, the effective resonance integral becomes identical with the actual resonance integral; thus,

$$\lim_{\frac{\Sigma_s}{N_0}\to\infty} \int_E^{E_0} (\sigma_{a0})_{\mathrm{eff}} \frac{dE'}{E'} \to \int_E^{E_0} \sigma_{a0} \frac{dE'}{E'},$$

where the right-hand side is the actual (or ordinary) resonance integral.

9.14. It should be noted that Σ_s/N_0, or rather N_0/Σ_s, also appears in front of the effective resonance integral in the exponent of (9.11.5).   As far as this factor is concerned, it is apparent that a decrease in the scattering associated with each atom of uranium will result in a decrease in the resonance escape probability, for a given value of the effective resonance integral.   Thus the actual effect of a change in the scattering per uranium atom on the resonance escape probability will depend on which of the two opposing factors predominates.   For the infinitely dilute mixture the effective resonance integral has its maximum value, but since N_0 is then zero, the resonance escape probability is, of course, unity.

9.15. Although increase of temperature results in a broadening of resonance peaks, due to the so-called nuclear Doppler effect (§ 11.5), it can be shown, from the Breit-Wigner treatment (Chapter II), that the area under the peak — and hence the actual resonance integral — is independent of temperature, the value of $\int \sigma_a \, dE/E$ being $\frac{1}{2}\sigma_{a(\max)}\pi\Gamma$.   However, since $(\sigma_{a0})_{\mathrm{eff}}$ involves the absorption cross section σ_{a0} in both numerator and denominator, as may be seen in (9.12.1), the effective resonance integral does change with temperature.   For very dilute mixtures of uranium with moderator, the effective resonance integral is not very different from the actual resonance integral, and so the variation of the resonance escape probability with temperature in this case would be small.

9.16. For more concentrated mixtures, however, the effective resonance integral and the escape probability are both temperature dependent.   This temperature behavior of concentrated systems is important in connection with the transient behavior of reactors.   As the power level and, hence, the temperature change, the effective multiplication factor changes, since this depends, among other quantities, on the resonance escape probability. As a result, there may or may not be a tendency for the chain reaction to be stabilized, depending upon whether the effective multiplication decreases or increases, respectively, with increasing temperature.

9.17. The ratio of σ_{a0} to $(\sigma_{a0})_{\text{eff}}$, called the *volume advantage factor*, is given by (9.12.1) as

$$\frac{\sigma_{a0}}{(\sigma_{a0})_{\text{eff}}} = 1 + \frac{N_0 \sigma_{a0}}{\Sigma_s}. \tag{9.17.1}$$

If N_1 is the number of moderator atoms per cm^3, and σ_{s0} and σ_{s1} are the scattering cross sections of uranium and moderator, respectively, (9.17.1) may be written as

$$\frac{\sigma_{a0}}{(\sigma_{a0})_{\text{eff}}} = 1 + \frac{\sigma_{a0}}{\sigma_{s0} + \dfrac{N_1}{N_0} \sigma_{s1}}, \tag{9.17.2}$$

since Σ_s is equal to $N_0 \sigma_{s0} + N_1 \sigma_{s1}$. It is evident that the volume advantage factor increases as N_0/N_1, i.e., the proportion (or volume) of uranium to moderator, increases.

9.18. As indicated earlier, and as is apparent from (9.17.1) and (9.17.2), the actual resonance integral is larger than the effective resonance integral, the ratio increasing with the proportion of uranium in the system. The physical reason for this will be apparent from a consideration of the variation of the neutron flux with energy, in the region of a resonance.

9.19. For the present case of a single absorber and a single moderator, the collision density, by (6.71.1), is

$$F(E) = \int_E^{E/\alpha_0} \frac{\Sigma_{s0}\phi(E')}{E'(1 - \alpha_0)} \, dE' + \int_E^{E/\alpha_1} \frac{\Sigma_{s1}\phi(E')}{E'(1 - \alpha_1)} \, dE'. \tag{9.19.1}$$

The integrals represent the number of neutrons slowing down into unit energy range at E per cm^3 per second.

9.20. The flux $\phi(E)$ is related to the collision density $F(E)$, as shown in § 6.82, by

$$\phi(E) = \frac{F(E)}{\Sigma_a + \Sigma_s} = \frac{F(E)}{N_0\left(\sigma_{a0} + \sigma_{s0} + \dfrac{N_1}{N_0} \sigma_{s1}\right)}. \tag{9.20.1}$$

In the present case, $F(E)$, as given by (9.19.1), is a smoother function of E than is $\phi(E)$ because the former involves the sum of integrations over the intervals E to E/α_0 and E to E/α_1. It can be seen, therefore, from (9.20.1) that the flux will have a minimum roughly where σ_{a0} has a maximum, i.e., in a resonance, since σ_{s0} and σ_{s1} are small and vary slowly with energy. In general, the depression of the flux in the resonance will be greater the smaller the value of $N_1\sigma_{s1}/N_0$ i.e., Σ_{s1}/N_0, as shown qualitatively in Fig. 9.20.

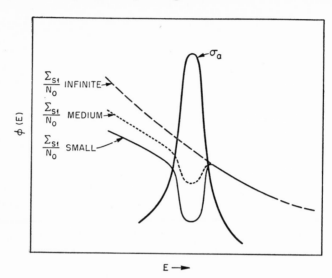

FIG. 9.20.   Dependence of neutron flux in resonance region on scattering cross section per atom of absorber

9.21. Comparison with (9.17.2) shows that the conditions for a large depression of the resonance flux are just those which will increase the value of the advantage factor.   The physical reason for the decrease in the effective resonance integral in a concentrated mixture of uranium with moderator is consequently the marked decrease in the resonance flux in such a mixture.   In a dilute system Σ_{s1}/N_0 is large, and the resonance flux will be almost the same as in the pure moderator, with no depression within the resonance (Fig. 9.20).   In these circumstances, the effective resonance integral has its maximum value being equal to the ordinary resonance integral.

9.22. The effective resonance integral as a function of scattering cross section per uranium atom has been measured in mixtures of UO_2 and various scatterers, namely, carbon, sugar, H_2O, and D_2O.   It was found that the effective resonance integral was essentially independent of the mass of the scattering nuclei, and that for values of the scattering cross section per uranium atom up to about 1000 barns, it could be expressed with fair accuracy by

$$\int (\sigma_{a0})_{\text{eff}} \frac{dE}{E} = 3.9 \left(\frac{\Sigma_s}{N_0}\right)^{0.415}.$$

The limiting value of the integral at great dilution is 240 barns.   Some of the results based on this equation are given in Table 9.22.

TABLE 9.22.   EFFECTIVE RESONANCE INTEGRAL AS FUNCTION OF SCATTERING
CROSS SECTION PER URANIUM ATOM

$\dfrac{\Sigma_s}{N_0}$	$\int (\sigma_{a0})_{\text{eff}} \dfrac{dE}{E}$
8.2 barns	9.3 barns
50	20
100	26
300	42
500	51
1000	69
∞	240

9.23. Using experimental data for the effective resonance integral, together with the thermal utilization, it can be shown that it is impossible to establish a self-sustaining chain reaction in a homogeneous mixture of natural uranium metal and graphite.   The thermal utilization in a uniform mixture is

$$ f = \frac{\Sigma_{a0}}{\Sigma_{a0} + \Sigma_{a1}} = \frac{N_0 \sigma_{a0}}{N_0 \sigma_{a0} + N_1 \sigma_{a1}}, $$

where σ_{a0} and σ_{a1} are here the absorption cross sections of natural uranium metal and graphite, respectively, for thermal neutrons.   The values of p and f for several different ratios N_1/N_0 are recorded in Table 9.23.   Since p decreases while f increases, the product pf passes through a maximum, as shown by the figures in the last column.   The highest value of pf is, however, less than 0.55, and this falls far short of the minimum (0.77) necessary to maintain a neutron chain reaction.   It is evident, therefore, that the construction of a homogeneous thermal reactor with natural uranium fuel and carbon moderator is not possible.

TABLE 9.23.   RESONANCE ESCAPE PROBABILITY AND THERMAL UTILIZATION
IN UNIFORM MIXTURES OF NATURAL URANIUM METAL WITH GRAPHITE

$\dfrac{N_1}{N_0}$	$\int (\sigma_{a0})_{\text{eff}} \dfrac{dE}{E}$	p	f	pf
200	72 barns	0.579	0.889	0.515
300	87	0.643	0.842	0.541
400	100	0.682	0.800	0.546
500	112	0.693	0.762	0.528

PROPERTIES OF HETEROGENEOUS SYSTEMS

Resonance Capture: Volume and Surface Absorptions

9.24. The suggestion was made by E. Fermi and L. Szilard in the early days of the Manhattan Project* that the resonance escape probability, for a given ratio of fuel to moderator, could be increased by using a heterogeneous lattice system consisting of lumps (or rods) of natural uranium arranged in a matrix of graphite. The neutrons which are slowed down to resonance energies in the moderator are largely absorbed in the outer layers of the uranium lump; the resonance neutron flux within the lump is consequently sharply depressed. As a result, the value of the effective absorption cross section for the fuel, i.e., $(\sigma_{a0})_{\text{eff}}$, in the center of the lump is less than for an equivalent uniform mixture of uranium and moderator. The resonance escape probability is increased accordingly. At the surface of the lump the neutron spectrum is essentially the same as within the moderator, and hence the resonance absorption will be approximately equal to that for uranium infinitely diluted with graphite.

9.25. The theoretical treatment of resonance absorption in a lump system has been simplified by the proposal† that the effective absorption cross section could be separated into two parts: (1) the volume absorption, proportional to the number of atoms of uranium per cm³, and (2) the surface absorption, proportional to the surface-to-mass ratio of the uranium lump, i.e.,

$$(\sigma_{a0})_{\text{eff}} = a(E) + b(E)\frac{S}{M},\qquad(9.25.1)$$

where the first term on the right-hand side represents the volume absorption cross section, and the second is the surface absorption cross section; S cm² is the surface area of the lump or rod and M grams is its mass. Experimental studies of the absorption of neutrons in uranium lumps of various sizes provide justification for the division into volume and surface contributions.

9.26. A simple procedure for deriving $a(E)$ and $b(E)$ has been given by A. M. Weinberg,‡ and this will be followed here. In the first place, the volume term $a(E)$ can be taken as equal to the effective absorption cross section *within the lump*, so that, from (9.11.4)

$$a(E) = \sigma_{a0}\frac{\Sigma_s}{\Sigma_s + \Sigma_a},\qquad(9.26.1)$$

where Σ_s and Σ_a are the macroscopic cross sections within the lump. An alternative form would be

$$a(E) = \sigma_{a0}\frac{N_0\sigma_{s0} + N_1\sigma_{s1}}{N_0\sigma_{s0} + N_1\sigma_{s1} + N_0\sigma_{a0}},\qquad(9.26.2)$$

---

* See H. D. Smyth, "Atomic Energy for Military Purposes," U. S. Government Printing Office, 1945, § 2.12.

† E. P. Wigner, unpublished; also, S. M. Dancoff and M. Ginsburg, unpublished.

‡ Private communication.

and for a lump of pure uranium metal this reduces to

$$a(E) = \frac{\sigma_{a0}\sigma_{s0}}{\sigma_{s0} + \sigma_{a0}}.$$

The ratio of $\int \sigma_{a0}\, dE/E$ to $\int a(E)\, dE/E$ is seen to be equal to the integrated volume advantage factor for the lump, as defined by (9.17.1). For pure uranium metal, this ratio is found to be about 26.

9.27. To derive an expression for the surface absorption coefficient $b(E)$, it is necessary to consider, first, the resonance flux within the lump. Neutrons having energies in the resonances of uranium will be rapidly absorbed in the outer layers of the lump. If there were no depletion of the resonance flux, the effective absorption cross section $a(E)$ would be σ_{a0}, as can be seen from the arguments presented earlier. Hence, from (9.26.1) the fraction $\Sigma_s/(\Sigma_s + \Sigma_a)$ is the factor by which the resonance flux is depleted in the interior of the lump due to neutron capture in the outer portions. The flux $\phi'(E)$ in the interior of the lump is thus given by

$$\phi'(E) = \frac{\Sigma_s}{\Sigma_s + \Sigma_a}\, \phi(E),$$

where $\phi(E)$ is the undepleted flux, equivalent to the flux incident on the lump. The difference between the undepleted flux and the depleted flux is then equal to the resonance flux at the surface of the lump; thus,

$$\phi_{\text{res}}(E) = \phi(E) - \phi'(E) = \frac{\Sigma_a}{\Sigma_s + \Sigma_a}\, \phi(E). \tag{9.27.1}$$

9.28. The neutrons represented by the flux ϕ_{res} are those with energies sufficiently close to the resonance absorption maximum that they will have a high probability of being absorbed in the outer layers of the lump. In other words, these neutrons are those which will contribute to the surface absorption in (9.25.1). The number of such neutrons striking the lump per cm² per sec is approximately $\frac{1}{4}\phi_{\text{res}}$. Upon introducing (9.27.1), it follows that

$$\text{Number of neutrons striking the surface of lump per cm}^2 \text{ per sec} = \frac{\Sigma_a}{4(\Sigma_s + \Sigma_a)}\, \phi(E).$$

9.29. The probability that a neutron will be absorbed on its first collision in the lump is $\Sigma_a/(\Sigma_s + \Sigma_a)$, and hence the total number of neutrons of energy E captured by surface absorption per cm² per unit flux is

$$\frac{\Sigma_a}{4(\Sigma_s + \Sigma_a)} \cdot \frac{\Sigma_a}{\Sigma_s + \Sigma_a} = \frac{1}{4}\left(\frac{\Sigma_a}{\Sigma_s + \Sigma_a}\right)^2.$$

The number of uranium atoms per gram of lump is N_0/d, where N_0 is the number of atoms per cm³, as before, and d is the density of the uranium lump. The surface absorption per atom per cm²/gram per unit flux, which is equal to $b(E)$, is then expressed by

$$b(E) = \frac{d}{4N_0} \left(\frac{\Sigma_a}{\Sigma_s + \Sigma_a}\right)^2. \tag{9.29.1}$$

The surface contribution to the effective absorption cross section is now obtained by multiplying this quantity by S/M, as in (9.25.1).

9.30. The effective resonance integral for a uranium lump is thus given by

$$\int (\sigma_{a0})_{\text{eff}} \frac{dE'}{E'} = \int a(E) \frac{dE'}{E'} + \frac{S}{M} \int b(E) \frac{dE'}{E'}, \tag{9.30.1}$$

where $a(E)$ and $b(E)$ are defined by (9.26.1) or (9.26.2) and (9.29.1), respectively.

9.31. The quantities $\int a(E) \frac{dE}{E}$ and $\int b(E) \frac{dE}{E}$ have been determined experimentally, by measuring the U^{239} activation in cadmium-covered uranium lumps. The resonance absorption may also be obtained by inserting cadmium-covered uranium lumps in a reactor and observing reactivity changes, which may be calibrated to give a measure of the resonance absorption. Experimental results obtained for uranium metal are:

$$\int a(E) \frac{dE}{E} = 9.25 \text{ barns}$$

$$\int b(E) \frac{dE}{E} = 24.7 \text{ barns gram/cm}^2.$$

$$\int (\sigma_{a0})_{\text{eff}} \frac{dE}{E} = 9.25 + 24.7 \frac{S}{M} \text{ barns.}$$

9.32. In the derivation of (9.29.1) it has been tacitly assumed that a resonance neutron suffering an elastic scattering collision in the outer layers of the lump will be thrown out of the resonance region. This will be true only if the resonances are narrow in comparison with the average change in energy of a neutron in an elastic collision in the lump, with uranium or any other element that may be present in addition. Actually, this is not the case for uranium, since a neutron loses about 1 per cent of its energy per collision, on the average. At 10 ev this is roughly equal to the half-width of the resonance.*

9.33. The expressions for $a(E)$ and $b(E)$ are strictly valid only for hydrogen moderator and a heavy absorber, since it is only then (§ 6.88) that $p(E)$ is given rigorously by (9.10.1). However, they do indicate roughly the dependence of $(\sigma_{a0})_{\text{eff}}$ on the scattering cross section per atom of uranium. To obtain a rigorous solution, the transport equation with energy loss must be solved for the case of rapidly varying cross sections with energy.

---

* More detailed calculations by E. P. Wigner and by S. M. Dancoff include the effect of elastic scattering collisions in the lump.

9.34. The dependence of the volume and surface absorptions on the scattering cross section per uranium atom, i.e., on Σ_s/N_0, may be seen by writing (9.26.1) and (9.29.1) in the alternative forms

$$a(E) = \frac{\dfrac{\Sigma_s}{N_0}}{\dfrac{\Sigma_s}{N_0} + \sigma_{a0}}\, \sigma_{a0} \qquad (9.34.1)$$

and

$$b(E) = \frac{d}{4N_0} \cdot \frac{\sigma_{a0}{}^2}{\left(\dfrac{\Sigma_s}{N_0} + \sigma_{a0}\right)^2}. \qquad (9.34.2)$$

It will be apparent that, whereas the volume absorption $a(E)$ increases with the scattering cross section per uranium atom, the surface absorption decreases. The physical interpretation of these results is as follows. The depression of resonance flux in a uranium lump decreases as Σ_s/N_0 increases, and this will mean an increase in the effective (volume) cross section. On the other hand, the larger the scattering per uranium atom, the greater the probability that a resonance neutron will be scattered rather than absorbed in a lump. The surface absorption will decrease correspondingly.

9.35. Attention may be called to the fact that the mass number of the scatterer does not enter into either of the expressions (9.34.1) and (9.34.2) for the volume and surface absorptions, respectively. This is strictly true, however, only if the width of the resonance is small in comparison with the average energy loss of a neutron per elastic collision. For uranium this average energy loss is about 0.8 per cent of the energy before collision. For a 10-ev neutron the average energy decrease, i.e., 0.08 ev, is of the same order as the resonance width, about 0.1 ev. Absorption at resonances above 10 ev will thus be dependent, to some extent, on the mass of the scattering nucleus.

RESONANCE ESCAPE PROBABILITY

9.36. It will be shown later (§ 9.51) that the regular arrangement of fuel lumps in a moderator may be regarded as made up of a lattice of equivalent unit cells. In each lattice cell the resonance escape probability depends on the spatial distribution of resonance neutrons, as well as on the structure and number of resonances. The total number of absorptions per sec per unit energy interval at E in the uranium lump is given by (9.25.1) as

$$A(E) = \bar{\phi}_0(E) N_0 V_0 a(E) + \bar{\phi}_s(E) N_0 V_0 b(E)\, \frac{S}{M}, \qquad (9.36.1)$$

where V_0 is the volume of the lump, per unit cell, and $\bar{\phi}_0(E)$ is the average flux at E per unit energy in the interior of the lump, defined by

$$\bar{\phi}_0(E) = \frac{1}{V_0} \int_{V_0} \phi(\mathbf{r}, E)\, dV,$$

and $\bar{\phi}_s(E)$ is the average flux at E per unit energy at the surface of the lump, defined by

$$\bar{\phi}_s(E) = \frac{1}{S} \int_S \phi(\mathbf{r}, E) \, dS.$$

9.37. The total number $Q(E)$ of neutrons slowing down past energy E per sec in the moderator present in the cell is given [cf. (6.67.1)] by

$$Q(E) = \bar{\phi}_1(E) V_1 \xi_1 \Sigma_{s1} E, \tag{9.37.1}$$

where V_1 is the volume of the moderator, per unit cell, and $\bar{\phi}_1(E)$ is the average flux at E per unit energy in the moderator, where

$$\bar{\phi}_1(E) = \frac{1}{V_1} \int_{V_1} \phi(\mathbf{r}, E) \, dV.$$

If more than one element is present in the moderator, ξ_1 is replaced by $\bar{\xi}$. The rate of change in $Q(E)$ with respect to E is equal to the absorption $A(E)$ in the uranium lump, so that

$$\frac{dQ(E)}{dE} = A(E). \tag{9.37.2}$$

9.38. Upon combining (9.36.1), (9.37.1), and (9.37.2) the result is

$$\frac{1}{Q} \cdot \frac{dQ}{dE} = \left[\frac{N_0 V_0 \bar{\phi}_0(E) a(E)}{V_1 \xi_1 \Sigma_{s1} \bar{\phi}_1(E)} + \frac{N_0 V_0 \bar{\phi}_s(E) b(E)}{V_1 \xi_1 \Sigma_{s1} \bar{\phi}_1(E)} \cdot \frac{S}{M} \right] \frac{1}{E}$$

and integration then gives

$$Q(E) = Q(E_0) \exp \left\{ - \frac{N_0 V_0}{V_1 \xi_1 \Sigma_{s1}} \left[\int_E^{E_0} \frac{\bar{\phi}_0(E')}{\bar{\phi}_1(E')} a(E') \frac{dE'}{E'} \right. \right.$$
$$\left. \left. + \frac{S}{M} \int_E^{E_0} \frac{\bar{\phi}_s(E')}{\bar{\phi}_1(E')} b(E') \frac{dE'}{E'} \right] \right\}.$$

The resonance escape probability $p(E)$ is equal to $Q(E)/Q(E_0)$, where $Q(E_0)$ is the number of neutrons slowing down into the resonance region per sec. Hence,

$$p(E) = \exp \left\{ - \frac{N_0 V_0}{V_1 \xi_1 \Sigma_{s1}} \left[\int_E^{E_0} \frac{\bar{\phi}_0(E')}{\bar{\phi}_1(E')} a(E') \frac{dE'}{E'} + \frac{S}{M} \int_E^{E_0} \frac{\bar{\phi}_s(E')}{\bar{\phi}_1(E')} b(E') \frac{dE'}{E'} \right] \right\}. \tag{9.38.1}$$

9.39. In the case of a homogeneous mixture of fuel and moderator, the ratios $\bar{\phi}_0/\bar{\phi}_1$ and $\bar{\phi}_s/\bar{\phi}_1$ are unity at all energies. At the same time V_0 and V_1 become identical, and (9.38.1) reduces, as it should, to (9.11.5). In general, however, for a heterogeneous assembly the evaluation of $p(E)$, assuming $a(E)$ and $b(E)$ to be known, depends on obtaining these flux ratios as functions of the energy.

9.40. In uranium lumps near the optimum size, in a graphite moderator, $\bar{\phi}_0/\bar{\phi}_1$ may be set equal to $\bar{\phi}_s/\bar{\phi}_1$ for simplicity. In the resonance region, if $\bar{\phi}_0/\bar{\phi}_1$

is assumed to be independent of energy, the resonance escape formula (9.38.1) becomes

$$p(E) \approx \exp\left[-\frac{N_0 V_0 \bar{\phi}_0}{V_1 \xi_1 \Sigma_{s1} \bar{\phi}_1} \int (\sigma_{a0})_{\text{eff}} \frac{dE'}{E'} \right]. \tag{9.40.1}$$

9.41. In this form $p(E)$ can be computed fairly easily, using experimental values for the effective resonance integral. The approximation is not as bad as it would at first appear, since to calculate the resonance escape probability to within 1 per cent error, for example, the value of $\bar{\phi}_0/\bar{\phi}_1$ need be known only to within about 10 per cent near the optimum ratio of the volumes of moderator to fuel, V_1/V_0. The ratio $\bar{\phi}_1/\bar{\phi}_0$ is called the *disadvantage factor* for resonance neutrons.

Advantages and Disadvantages of Heterogeneous System

9.42. The main advantage to be gained in the use of a heterogeneous assembly in a thermal reactor is the increase in the resonance escape probability due to the decrease in the effective resonance integral, for a given ratio of uranium to moderator. This arises largely from the absorption of resonance neutrons in the outer layers of the uranium lumps, so that the resonance flux in the interior is greatly decreased. Of the neutrons entering a uranium lump from the moderator only those with energies at, or very close to, resonance peaks will be captured. All others will have a high probability of passing through the lump, since they suffer little energy loss in collisions with uranium nuclei. Upon re-entering the moderator, the neutrons will undergo further slowing down, and they may pass through several resonances and reach thermal energies before being captured. The resonance escape probability is thus increased.

9.43. If the uranium resonances had been broad and low, the increase in the resonance escape probability due to lumping would be less. Because of the greater width of the resonance peak, neutrons covering a larger spread of energies would be absorbed upon entering a uranium lump (or rod). Thus, a smaller fraction of the neutrons incident on the lump would re-enter the moderator for further slowing down. In addition, since the resonances are wider, the probability that neutrons would be degraded from above to below the resonance range in a collision with a moderator nucleus would be greatly decreased.

9.44. A less important effect of lumping the uranium is a small increase in the resonance escape probability arising from the fact that some neutrons may be slowed down to thermal energies without ever entering a fuel rod. The effect is essentially geometrical, since it depends on the spacing of the rods, as well as on the slowing down length of the moderator. It amounts to a factor of about 1.04 in the Oak Ridge X-lattice.

9.45. In a heterogeneous system, there is also a small increase in the fast fission factor, as compared with a uniform mixture of the same composition. Since fission neutrons are produced within the uranium lump, in which they undergo very little slowing down, the probability of the capture of fast neutrons by uranium-238 nuclei, and thus causing fission, is greater than for a uniform mixture of uranium and moderator.

9.46. The chief disadvantage of the heterogeneous arrangement of uranium and moderator lies in the decrease in the thermal utilization. This is due largely to the depletion of the thermal flux within the uranium lump. The factors determining the thermal utilization in a lattice are considered in the next section.

CALCULATION OF THE THERMAL UTILIZATION*

9.47. The thermal utilization in a heterogeneous assembly, in which the fuel is separated from the moderator, is not a simple function of the macroscopic absorption cross sections, as it is for a homogeneous system (§ 7.66). It depends also on the thermal neutron flux in different parts of the lattice. By definition, the thermal utilization is

$$f = \frac{\int \Sigma_{a0}\phi(\mathbf{r})\, dV}{\int (\Sigma_{a0} + \Sigma_{a1})\phi(\mathbf{r})\, dV}, \tag{9.47.1}$$

where $\phi(\mathbf{r})$ is the thermal neutron flux at a particular point $\mathbf{r}$, and Σ_{a0} and Σ_{a1} are the macroscopic absorption cross sections, for the fuel and moderator respectively, for thermal neutrons. The integration is carried over the whole of the reactor. If the fuel is completely separated from the moderator, so that each region is homogeneous,

$$f = \frac{\Sigma_{a0} \int_{\text{Fuel}} \phi(\mathbf{r})\, dV}{\Sigma_{a0} \int_{\text{Fuel}} \phi(\mathbf{r})\, dV + \Sigma_{a1} \int_{\text{Moderator}} \phi(\mathbf{r})\, dV}. \tag{9.47.2}$$

9.48. Average thermal fluxes $\bar{\phi}_0$ and $\bar{\phi}_1$ in the fuel and moderator are defined (cf. § 9.36) by

$$\bar{\phi}_0 = \frac{1}{V_0} \int_{V_0} \phi(\mathbf{r})\, dV$$

and

$$\bar{\phi}_1 = \frac{1}{V_1} \int_{V_1} \phi(\mathbf{r})\, dV,$$

where V_0 is the volume of the fuel and V_1 is that of the moderator. The thermal utilization as expressed by (9.47.2) then becomes

$$f = \frac{\Sigma_{a0}}{\Sigma_{a0} + \Sigma_{a1} \dfrac{V_1}{V_0} \cdot \dfrac{\bar{\phi}_1}{\bar{\phi}_0}}. \tag{9.48.1}$$

---

* See A. M. Weinberg, in "The Science and Engineering of Nuclear Power" (edited by C. Goodman), Vol. II, Chapter 6, Addison-Wesley Press, 1949.

The ratio of the average thermal flux in the moderator to that in the fuel, i.e., $\bar{\phi}_1/\bar{\phi}_0$, is the disadvantage factor for thermal neutrons. The thermal flux is depressed in the fuel, so that the disadvantage factor is greater than unity. The thermal utilization is then smaller than for a corresponding homogeneous system with the same relative amounts of fuel and moderator.

9.49. In physical terms it may be stated that fast neutrons produced in the uranium lumps are slowed down significantly only in the moderator. Hence, thermal neutrons are produced only in the moderator and must diffuse into the fuel. The thermal neutron flux is, therefore, depressed in the center of the uranium lump because of absorption of thermal neutrons in the outer layers.

9.50. The calculation of the thermal utilization thus becomes essentially a matter of finding the thermal neutron flux distribution in the uranium-moderator system. In the following treatment, three assumptions (or approximations) will be made. It will be supposed, first, that the slowing down density is constant in the moderator and zero in the uranium. In other words, it is assumed that thermal neutrons are produced uniformly throughout the moderator but not at all in the uranium. This condition will hold, provided the separation of the lumps is not too large in comparison with the slowing down distance. If the slowing down densities, as calculated by the Fermi theory, due to point sources arranged in a lattice, are superimposed, the slow neutron production rate is found to be remarkably uniform, provided the lattice spacing is not greater than two or three slowing down lengths.

9.51. The second approximation is to divide the lattice up into a number of identical unit cells and to suppose that a square cross section can be replaced by a circular cross section of the same area. If the reactor consists of cylindrical rods of uranium, arranged in the manner shown in Fig. 9.51, each cell will consist

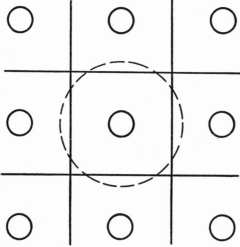

Fig. 9.51.   Unit cells in heterogeneous lattice

of a parallelepiped of square cross section. The equivalent cell of circular cross section, indicated by the dotted circle, will then be a long cylinder, with the fuel rod at the center. If the lattice consists of roughly spherical lumps, then the equivalent unit cell would be a sphere. The foregoing approximation, which is equivalent to that used by E. P. Wigner and F. Seitz in the theoretical treatment of crystal lattices, greatly simplifies the calculations.

9.52. The third assumption is that simple diffusion theory is applicable. This will be the case only if the dimensions of the system are large compared to the scattering mean free path of the neutrons, if the neutrons are not absorbed too strongly, and if there are no neutron sources present. None of these conditions is strictly satisfied, and estimates made by more accurate methods indicate that simple diffusion theory does result in some errors. However, in view of the simplicity of the calculations, the treatment is well worth while.

9.53. The theory will now be used to calculate the thermal utilization for a reactor with long cylindrical fuel rods, the cross section of the equivalent (cylindrical) unit cell being shown in Fig. 9.53. The radius of the fuel rod is R_0 and

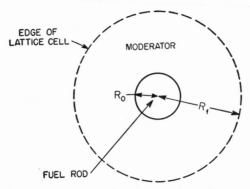

FIG. 9.53.   Cylindrical lattice cell

that of a unit cell in the reactor lattice is R_1. If the cell is long in comparison with its diameter, the neutron flux distribution becomes essentially a one-dimensional problem.

9.54. Since it has been assumed that the slowing down density is constant in the moderator and zero in the uranium, the neutrons may be treated as monoenergetic and the equations of the one-group method can be employed. Thus, the thermal diffusion equation for the fuel rod is

$$D_0 \nabla^2 \phi_0 - \Sigma_{a0} \phi_0 = 0, \tag{9.54.1}$$

where ϕ_0 represents the thermal neutron flux at any point in the uranium, and D_0 and Σ_{a0} are the corresponding diffusion coefficient and macroscopic absorption cross section, respectively. It will be noted that there is no thermal neutron source term in (9.54.1), since it had been postulated that there is no slowing down in the uranium.

9.55. For the moderator, the thermal diffusion equation is

$$D_1 \nabla^2 \phi_1 - \Sigma_{a1} \phi_1 + q = 0, \tag{9.55.1}$$

where the source term, equal to the number of neutrons becoming thermal in the moderator per cm^3 per sec, is constant because of the uniform slowing down density.

9.56. The boundary conditions which must be satisfied by solutions of the differential equations (9.54.1) and (9.55.1) are as follows:

(i) Continuity of neutron flux at the fuel rod-moderator boundary, i.e.,

$$\phi_0 = \phi_1 \text{ at } r = R_0.$$

(ii) Continuity of neutron current density at the boundary, i.e.,

$$D_0 \frac{d\phi_0}{dr} = D_1 \frac{d\phi_1}{dr} \text{ at } r = R_0.$$

(iii) No net flow of neutrons at the outside boundary of the cell, since just as many neutrons diffuse into any given unit cell as diffuse out of it, i.e.,

$$\frac{d\phi_1}{dr} = 0 \text{ at } r = R_1.$$

The r-coordinate is measured from the axis of the cylinder in a direction normal to its surface.

9.57. Upon dividing through (9.54.1) by D_0 and replacing Σ_{a0}/D_0 by κ_0^2, where κ_0 is the reciprocal of the thermal diffusion length in uranium, the result is

$$\nabla^2 \phi_0 - \kappa_0^2 \phi_0 = 0 \tag{9.57.1}$$

or, in cylindrical coordinates,

$$\frac{d\phi_0^2}{dr^2} + \frac{1}{r} \cdot \frac{d\phi_0}{dr} - \kappa_0^2 \phi_0 = 0.$$

Since κ_0^2 is positive, this expression is equivalent to a modified Bessel equation and the general solution (§ 7.54) is of the form

$$\phi_0 = A I_0(\kappa_0 r) + A' K_0(\kappa_0 r), \tag{9.57.2}$$

where I_0 and K_0 are zero order, modified Bessel functions of the first and second kinds, respectively. However, since K_0 would require the neutron flux to go to infinity at the axis of the uranium rod, where $r = 0$, the second term on the right-hand side of (9.57.2) may be eliminated, so that

$$\phi_0 = A I_0(\kappa_0 r). \tag{9.57.3}$$

9.58. The equation (9.55.1) for the moderator may be divided through by D_1 and Σ_{a1}/D_1 replaced by κ_1^2, so that

$$\nabla^2 \phi_1 - \kappa_1^2 \phi_1 + \frac{q}{D_1} = 0. \tag{9.58.1}$$

The homogeneous part of this equation is analogous to equation (9.57.1), and the solution of this part is

$$\phi_1(\text{homo}) = CI_0(\kappa_1 r) + FK_0(\kappa_1 r).$$

The K_0 function cannot be discarded in this case since the moderator region of the cell does not include the origin. The solution of the particular part of (9.58.1) may be obtained by setting ϕ_1 constant; it is, therefore, $q/D_1\kappa_1^2$, which is equal to q/Σ_{a1}, since $\kappa_1^2 = \Sigma_{a1}/D_1$. The complete solution of (9.58.1) is, therefore,

$$\phi_1 = CI_0(\kappa_1 r) + FK_0(\kappa_1 r) + \frac{q}{\Sigma_{a1}}. \tag{9.58.2}$$

9.59. The relationship between the arbitrary constants C and F is obtained from the boundary condition (iii); thus,

$$\frac{d\phi_1}{dr}\bigg|_{r=R_1} = \kappa_1[CI_1(\kappa_1 R_1) - FK_1(\kappa_1 R_1)] = 0,^*$$

and, consequently,

$$F = C\frac{I_1(\kappa_1 R_1)}{K_1(\kappa_1 R_1)}.$$

Introduction of this value for F into (9.58.2) then gives

$$\phi_1 = C[I_0(\kappa_1 r)K_1(\kappa_1 R_1) + K_0(\kappa_1 r)I_1(\kappa_1 R_1)] + \frac{q}{\Sigma_{a1}}, \tag{9.59.1}$$

where $K_1(\kappa_1 R_1)$ has been absorbed into the constant factor C.

9.60. The constants A and C may be evaluated by means of the boundary conditions (i) and (ii); thus, using (9.57.3) and (9.59.1) for ϕ_0 and ϕ_1, respectively, it follows from (i) that

$$AI_0(\kappa_0 R_0) = C[I_0(\kappa_1 R_0)K_1(\kappa_1 R_1) + K_0(\kappa_1 R_0)I_1(\kappa_1 R_1)] + \frac{q}{\Sigma_{a1}}$$

and from (ii),

$$D_0 A\kappa_0 I_1(\kappa_0 R_0) = D_1 C\kappa_1[I_1(\kappa_1 R_0)K_1(\kappa_1 R_1) - K_1(\kappa_1 R_0)I_1(\kappa_1 R_1)].$$

In the later development the value of C is not required, and in place of A, it is found more convenient to derive an expression for $1/A$. Algebraic treatment of the two foregoing equations leads to the result

$$\frac{1}{A} = \frac{\Sigma_{a1}}{q}\left\{ I_0(\kappa_0 R_0) - \frac{D_0\kappa_0 I_1(\kappa_0 R_0)[I_0(\kappa_1 R_0)K_1(\kappa_1 R_1) + K_0(\kappa_1 R_0)I_1(\kappa_1 R_1)]}{D_1\kappa_1[I_1(\kappa_1 R_0)K_1(\kappa_1 R_1) - K_1(\kappa_1 R_0)I_1(\kappa_1 R_1)]} \right\}. \tag{9.60.1}$$

9.61. With the information now available it is possible to express the thermal utilization f or, better, its reciprocal $1/f$, in terms of measurable quantities for

---

* Note that $dI_0(\kappa_1 r)/dr = \kappa_1 I_1(\kappa_1 r)$, and $dK_0(\kappa_1 r)/dr = -\kappa_1 K_1(\kappa_1 r)$, where I_1 and K_1 are first order modified Bessel functions.

the heterogeneous lattice.   Consider a cylindrical shell of radius r, thickness dr, and unit length, within the fuel rod, as indicated in Fig. 9.61.   The volume of

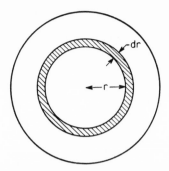

FIG. 9.61.   Calculation of thermal neutrons absorbed in fuel rod

this shell is $2\pi r\, dr$, and the number of thermal neutrons absorbed in it is $\Sigma_{a0}\phi_0(r)2\pi r\, dr$ per sec; $\phi_0(r)$ is the thermal neutron flux in the uranium at a radial distance r from the axis, as given by (9.57.3). The total number of thermal neutrons absorbed per sec in a unit length of the cylindrical fuel rod is then obtained by integration over values of r from zero to R_0, the radius of the rod. Hence,

$$\begin{aligned}\text{No. of thermal neutrons absorbed per} \atop \text{unit length of fuel rod per sec} &= \int_0^{R_0} \Sigma_{a0}\phi_0(r)2\pi r\, dr \\ &= 2\pi\Sigma_{a0}A \int_0^{R_0} rI_0(\kappa_0 r)\, dr \\ &= \frac{2\pi\Sigma_{a0}AR_0}{\kappa_0} I_1(\kappa_0 R_0).\end{aligned}$$

9.62. The number of thermal neutrons produced, by slowing down, in unit volume of the moderator per sec is q, and since the volume of unit length of the moderator in a cell is $\pi(R_1^2 - R_0^2)$, the total rate of thermal neutron production is $q\pi(R_1^2 - R_0^2)$ per unit length per sec.   The thermal utilization is the ratio of thermal neutrons absorbed in the uranium to the number produced, by slowing down, in the moderator.   Hence, the reciprocal, $1/f$, is given in the present case by

$$\frac{1}{f} = \frac{q\pi(R_1^2 - R_0^2)\kappa_0}{2\pi\Sigma_{a0}R_0 I_1(\kappa_0 R_0)} \cdot \frac{1}{A}. \tag{9.62.1}$$

Introducing the expression for $1/A$ in (9.60.1), and rearranging the result, it is found that

$$\frac{1}{f} = \frac{V_1\Sigma_{a1}}{V_0\Sigma_{a0}}\left[\frac{\kappa_0 R_0}{2} \cdot \frac{I_0(\kappa_0 R_0)}{I_1(\kappa_0 R_0)}\right] \tag{9.62.2}$$
$$+ \frac{\kappa_1(R_1^2 - R_0^2)}{2R_0}\left[\frac{I_0(\kappa_1 R_0)K_1(\kappa_1 R_1) + K_0(\kappa_1 R_0)I_1(\kappa_1 R_1)}{I_1(\kappa_1 R_1)K_1(\kappa_1 R_0) - K_1(\kappa_1 R_1)I_1(\kappa_1 R_0)}\right].$$

Defining the quantities F and E by

$$F \equiv \frac{\kappa_0 R_0}{2} \cdot \frac{I_0(\kappa_0 R_0)}{I_1(\kappa_0 R_0)}$$

and

$$E \equiv \frac{\kappa_1(R_1{}^2 - R_0{}^2)}{2R_0} \left[\frac{I_0(\kappa_1 R_0)K_1(\kappa_1 R_1) + K_0(\kappa_1 R_0)I_1(\kappa_1 R_1)}{I_1(\kappa_1 R_1)K_1(\kappa_1 R_0) - K_1(\kappa_1 R_1)I_1(\kappa_1 R_0)} \right],$$

the thermal utilization is represented by

$$\frac{1}{f} = 1 + \frac{V_1 \Sigma_{a1}}{V_0 \Sigma_{a0}} F + (E - 1). \tag{9.62.3}$$

9.63. The quantity F defined above can be shown to give the ratio of the neutron flux at the surface of the rod to the average flux in the interior. Consider the limiting case of an infinite diffusion coefficient in the moderator; then κ_1 is zero and E is unity, and (9.62.3) reduces to

$$\frac{1}{f} = 1 + \frac{V_1 \Sigma_{a1}}{V_0 \Sigma_{a0}} F$$

or

$$f = \frac{\Sigma_{a0}}{\Sigma_{a0} + \dfrac{V_1}{V_0} \Sigma_{a1} F}. \tag{9.63.1}$$

If the diffusion coefficient in the moderator is infinite, there can be no gradient of neutron flux, and hence the flux would be uniform throughout the moderator. The thermal neutrons produced uniformly in the moderator, and distributed

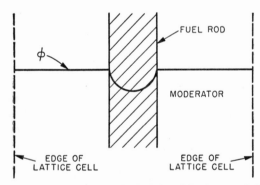

FIG. 9.63. Neutron flux distribution for infinite diffusion coefficient in moderator

isotropically, would travel in straight lines until they were absorbed in the moderator or left it to enter a fuel rod. The corresponding neutron distribution would then be as shown in Fig. 9.63.

9.64. Upon comparing (9.63.1) with (9.48.1), it is seen that

$$F = \frac{\bar{\phi}_1}{\bar{\phi}_0},$$

where $\bar{\phi}_1$ is now the neutron flux at the outer surface of the fuel rod. Since it is the same throughout the moderator,

$$F = \frac{\text{Thermal neutron flux at surface of rod}}{\text{Average thermal flux in interior of rod}}.$$

Actually, because the diffusion coefficient in the moderator is finite, the average thermal flux in the moderator is greater than the flux at the surface of the fuel

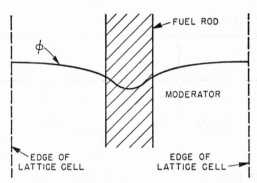

FIG. 9.64.   Neutron flux distribution for finite diffusion coefficient in moderator

rod (Fig. 9.64). This additional absorption is measured by the quantity $E - 1$, which is called the excess absorption.

9.65. By calculating $1/f$ for a given value of V_1/V_0 and of R_0, it is possible to obtain a series of curves in which $1/f$ is plotted as a function of V_1/V_0 for various R_0's. The general trend of these curves is shown in Fig. 9.65 for three values of the fuel rod radius, $R_{01} > R_{02} > R_{03}$. It is seen that the thermal utilization

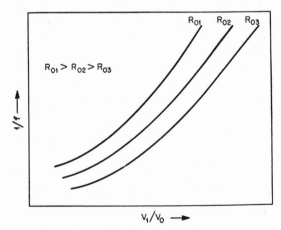

FIG. 9.65.   Reciprocal of thermal utilization as function of moderator-fuel rod volume ratio

decreases (a) with increasing radius of the rod at constant V_1/V_0, because the depression of the flux increases with the radius, and (b) with increasing V_1/V_0 at constant rod radius, because more neutrons are captured in the moderator.

9.66. Results similar to those derived for a cylindrical cell may be obtained for other types of lattice cells. The actual values of F and E, which have the same physical significance as derived above, depend on the geometry of the cells; the appropriate formulae for an infinite slab and a sphere are given in Table 9.66.

TABLE 9.66.   FUNCTIONS FOR LATTICE CALCULATIONS

Cell Geometry	F	E
Infinite Slab	$\kappa_0 R_0 \coth \kappa_0 R_0$	$\kappa_1(R_1 - R_0) \coth \kappa_1(R_1 - R_0)$
Sphere	$\dfrac{\kappa_0^2 R_0^2}{3} \cdot \dfrac{\tanh \kappa_0 R_0}{\kappa_0 R_0 - \tanh \kappa_0 R_0}$	$\dfrac{\kappa_1^2(R_1^3 - R_0^3)}{3R_0}\left[\dfrac{1 - \kappa_1 R_1 \coth \kappa_1(R_1 - R_0)}{1 - \kappa_1^2 R_1 R_0 - \kappa_1(R_1 - R_0) \coth \kappa_1(R_1 - R_0)}\right]$

For the slab cell, R_0 is the half-thickness of the fuel element and R_1 is that of the entire cell; for the spherical cell, R_0 is the radius of the fuel sphere and R_1 that of the whole cell. It is of interest to note that F contains only the constants of the fuel (κ_0) while E contains only that (κ_1) of the moderator. It is therefore possible to prepare tables of F and E, which facilitate lattice calculations.*

CALCULATION OF THE RESONANCE ESCAPE PROBABILITY†

9.67. The value of the resonance escape probability can be found from (9.40.1), provided the disadvantage factor for resonance neutrons, i.e., the ratio of the average value of the resonance flux in the moderator to that in the uranium, is known. In order to determine this factor, the resonance flux will be treated as a single neutron group, in a manner identical with that used for the fast neutron flux in the two-group reactor calculations (Chapter VIII). The problem is formally the same as the determination of the thermal utilization. Since very little slowing down occurs in the fuel, a uniform source of resonance neutrons may be assumed in the moderator. These neutrons then diffuse into the uranium, some of them being absorbed in the uranium-238 resonances.

9.68. The first and essential step in the calculations is to determine the appropriate group constants, namely, Σ_a and D. Since the energy range of the resonance region is not known exactly, estimates have been made in various ways. One of these is to compare the diffusion length of resonance neutrons in uranium oxide (U_3O_8) with the known transport mean free path, λ_t, and the total volume

* Such tables have been prepared under the supervision of J. A. Wheeler.
† R. F. Christy, A. M. Weinberg, and E. P. Wigner, unpublished.

absorption, $a(E)$.   The average absorption cross section, $\bar{\sigma}_a$, treating resonance neutrons as a single group, is given by

$$\bar{\sigma}_a = \frac{\overline{\Sigma}_{a0}}{N_0} = \frac{\int_{E_2}^{E_1} a(E) \frac{dE}{E}}{\ln (E_1/E_2)}, \tag{9.68.1}$$

but since $\overline{\Sigma}_{a0} \approx \lambda_{t0}/3L_0^2$, where L_0 is the diffusion length of resonance neutrons in the fuel (uranium oxide), it follows that

$$\ln \frac{E_1}{E_2} = \frac{3L_0^2 N_0 \int_{E_2}^{E_1} a(E) \frac{dE}{E}}{\lambda_{t0}}.$$

Since the integral, representing the total volume absorption, as well as L_0^2 and λ_{t0} can be determined experimentally, $\ln E_1/E_2$ can be evaluated.   The result, found to be in agreement with other estimates, was $\ln E_1/E_2 = 7.3$ for uranium oxide.

9.69. In uranium metal, $\ln E_1/E_2$ is smaller because the volume absorption is less than that in the oxide by a factor of 0.77; hence, for the metal $\ln E_1/E_2$ is 5.6. Since, for uranium, the volume absorption is equal to the effective resonance integral, (9.68.1) gives

$$\frac{\overline{\Sigma}_{a0}}{N_0} = \frac{\int_{E_2}^{E_1} (\sigma_{a0})_{\text{eff}} \frac{dE}{E}}{\ln (E_1/E_2)}, \tag{9.69.1}$$

where for the metal the effective resonance integral is given by (9.30.1).

9.70. The values of κ_0^2, equal to $3\Sigma_{t0}\overline{\Sigma}_{a0}$, with an appropriate transport theory correction (§ 14.40), may be obtained from

$$\kappa_0^2 \approx 3\Sigma_{t0}\overline{\Sigma}_{a0} \left(1 - \frac{4}{5} \cdot \frac{\overline{\Sigma}_{a0}}{\Sigma_0}\right),$$

where Σ_0 is the total cross section of the fuel.   A better procedure to estimate κ_0 is to measure the uranium-239 resonance activation in a fuel lump as a function of position; the data are then fitted to the appropriate solution of the diffusion equation.   For example, if the fuel element is a long rod, the activation should be proportional to $I_0(\kappa_0 r)$, where r is the distance from the axis [cf. (9.57.3)].   In uranium metal of density 18.7 grams per cm^3, κ_0 was found to be 0.42 cm^{-1}. Since $\overline{\Sigma}_{a0}$ and κ_0 are known, D_0 can be calculated.

9.71. The values of Σ_{a1}, κ_1, and D_1 for the moderator may be determined from experimental cross sections and diffusion lengths for resonance neutrons.   Some values, which may be used when uranium metal is the fuel, are given in Table 9.71.   If the fuel is uranium oxide (or other compound or mixture), some allowance must be made for the oxygen (or other element), because of the difference in the effective width of the resonance region.   For uranium oxide (U_3O_8), for example, $\Sigma_1 = 0.77\Sigma_1{}^*$ and $\kappa_1 = \sqrt{0.77}\kappa_1{}^* = 0.88\kappa_1{}^*$, where the starred values are those for the pure metal.

TABLE 9.71.   GROUP CONSTANTS OF VARIOUS MODERATORS FOR RESONANCE NEUTRONS

Moderator	Σ_1 cm^{-1}	κ_1 cm^{-1}
Water	0.241	0.583
Heavy water	0.0313	0.155
Beryllium	0.0276	0.237
Beryllium oxide	0.0150	0.138
Graphite	0.0108	0.1075

9.72. The problem is now formally identical with that of calculating the thermal utilization.   The resonance neutron diffusion equation for the fuel lump is

$$\nabla^2\phi_0 - \kappa_0{}^2\phi_0 = 0,$$

and for the moderator it is

$$\nabla^2\phi_1 - \kappa_1{}^2\phi_1 + S = 0,$$

where S is constant, as postulated above.   The boundary conditions are, as before, (i) continuity of flux and the normal component of the current at the moderator-fuel interface; and (ii) no net current in the direction normal to the surface of the lattice cell.

9.73. A resonance neutron utilization, f_r, may be defined, analogous to the thermal utilization; thus,

$$f_r = \frac{\text{Number of neutrons absorbed in uranium resonances}}{\text{Number of resonance neutrons produced}}.$$

Consequently, in accordance with (9.62.3),

$$\frac{1}{f_r} = 1 + \frac{V_1\Sigma_{a1}}{V_0\Sigma_{a0}} F + (E - 1), \tag{9.73.1}$$

where Σ_{a0} and Σ_{a1} now refer to resonance neutrons, the latter being effectively a slowing down cross section.   In this equation, F is the ratio of the resonance neutron density at the surface to the average density in the interior and $E - 1$ is the excess slowing down of neutrons out of the resonance region.   The expressions for F and E for various cell geometries are identical in form with those given above (§ 9.62, et seq.).

9.74. By transposing an expression similar to (9.48.1), the disadvantage factor for resonance neutrons, i.e., $\bar{\phi}_1/\bar{\phi}_0$, can be expressed by

$$\frac{\bar{\phi}_1}{\bar{\phi}_0} = \frac{V_0\Sigma_{a0}}{V_1\Sigma_{a1}}\left(\frac{1}{f_r} - 1\right),$$

and hence (9.40.1) for the resonance escape probability becomes

$$p(E) = \exp\left[-\frac{N_0\Sigma_{a1}}{\xi_1\Sigma_{s1}\Sigma_{a0}} \cdot \frac{f_r}{1 - f_r} \int (\sigma_{a0})_{\text{eff}} \frac{dE}{E}\right]. \tag{9.74.1}$$

From arguments similar to those in § 8.12, it follows that

$$\frac{\Sigma_{a1}}{\xi\Sigma_{s1}} = \frac{1}{\ln (E_1/E_2)}$$

and from (9.69.1)

$$\frac{\Sigma_{a0}}{N_0} = \frac{\int (\sigma_{a0})_{\text{eff}} \dfrac{dE}{E}}{\ln (E_1/E_2)},$$

so that

$$\frac{N_0\Sigma_{a1}}{\xi\Sigma_{s1}\Sigma_{a0}} \int (\sigma_{a0})_{\text{eff}} \frac{dE}{E} = 1.$$

Upon substituting in (9.74.1), the result is

$$p(E) = \exp\left(-\frac{f_r}{1 - f_r}\right).$$

9.75. By using (9.73.1) to obtain f_r, it is thus possible to calculate the resonance escape probability for any particular type of lattice cell, if the various group constants are known. The general nature of the dependence on V_1/V_0 of the resonance escape probability, or rather its reciprocal, for various fuel-rod radii is indicated in Fig. 9.75. The resonance escape probability increases (a) with

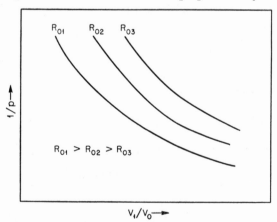

FIG. 9.75.   Reciprocal of resonance escape probability as function of moderator-fuel rod volume ratio

increasing radius at constant V_1/V_0, and (b) with increasing V_1/V_0 at constant radius of fuel rod. Thus, the conditions which favor increase of the resonance escape probability are just those which cause the thermal utilization to decrease (§ 9.65). The problem is, then, to find the arrangement which gives an optimum value of the product pf. This corresponds approximately to the V_1/V_0 and R_0 for which p and f are equal.*

* In the Oak Ridge (X-10) reactor the cylindrical fuel rods of natural uranium have a diameter of 1.1 in. and are arranged on 8-in. centers in a square lattice of graphite.

9.76. Fast neutrons with energies greater than about 1.1 Mev can cause fission in uranium-238. Thus, for every neutron produced in fission due to thermal neutrons, an additional number of fission neutrons, due to fast-neutron fission, will enter the system. For every fission neutron there will be a certain probability of causing fission, which will, in turn, produce more fission neutrons. The effect is thus a typical cascade process. The fast fission factor ϵ can be defined as the number of neutrons slowing down past the fission threshold of uranium-238 per primary fission neutron, i.e., per neutron produced by thermal fission. The computation of the fast fission factor must include the contribution of all the fission neutrons produced in the cascade.

9.77. The slowing down of fission neutrons produced in a uranium lump takes place in two ways. First, by inelastic collisions with uranium nuclei; because of the nature of such collisions, the neutron energy will be reduced well below the fission threshold. Second, by escape of fast neutrons into the moderator; it can be assumed to a good approximation that none of the neutrons entering the moderator will return to the uranium lump with energies exceeding the fission threshold. Elastic scattering within the lump will not change the neutron energy appreciably. Hence, elastic collisions will be regarded as leaving the neutron energy unchanged.

9.78. Let P be the probability that a primary fission neutron, as defined above, will make a collision inside the fuel lump in which it was created. Starting with one primary neutron, the following average values will hold on the first collision:

$$
\begin{aligned}
\text{Collisions in the lump} \quad &= P \\[4pt]
\text{Fission neutrons produced} \quad &= \frac{\nu P \sigma_f}{\sigma} \\[4pt]
\text{Elastic collisions in the lump} \quad &= P\frac{\sigma_e}{\sigma} \\[4pt]
\text{Neutrons escaping from the lump without collision} \quad &= 1 - P \\[4pt]
\text{Neutrons slowed down below threshold by inelastic collision} \quad &= P\frac{\sigma_i}{\sigma},
\end{aligned}
$$

where σ_f, σ_e, σ_i, and σ are the fission, elastic scattering, inelastic scattering, and total cross sections, respectively, for fast neutrons in the fuel. The total number of fast neutrons available in the lump after the first collision is the sum of the second and third quantities above, i.e., $P(\nu\sigma_f + \sigma_e)/\sigma$. If $(\nu\sigma_f + \sigma_e)/\sigma$ is represented by the symbol Z, thus

$$
Z \equiv \frac{\nu\sigma_f + \sigma_e}{\sigma},
$$

the number of neutrons available in the lump after the first collision is PZ.

* H. Castle, H. Ibser, G. Sacker, and A. M. Weinberg, unpublished.

9.79. Neutrons that have been scattered at least once within the fuel are distributed almost uniformly in the lump. But the primary fission neutrons are distributed like the thermal flux, which is depressed in the center of the lump. Since more primary neutrons are produced per unit volume in the outer layers than in the interior, the probability P' that second and higher generation fission neutrons will make a collision in the lump is greater than the probability for the primary neutrons.

9.80. The conditions for the second collision are as follows:

Collisions in the lump	$= P'PZ$
Fission neutrons produced	$= P'PZ \dfrac{\nu\sigma_f}{\sigma}$
Elastic collisions in the lump	$= P'PZ \dfrac{\sigma_e}{\sigma}$
Neutrons escaping from the lump without further collision	$= (1 - P')PZ$
Neutrons slowed down below threshold by inelastic scattering	$= P'PZ \dfrac{\sigma_i}{\sigma}.$

The total number of fast neutrons available in the lump after the second collision is thus $P'PZ^2$.

9.81. Continuing in the same manner, it is apparent that, after the $(n + 1)$th collision, the various terms will be:

Collisions in the lump	$= P(P'Z)^n$
Fission neutrons produced	$= P(P'Z)^n \dfrac{\nu\sigma_f}{\sigma}$
Elastic collisions in the lump	$= P(P'Z)^n \dfrac{\sigma_e}{\sigma}$
Neutrons escaping from the lump without further collision	$= \dfrac{1 - P'}{P'} P(P'Z)^n$
Neutrons slowed down below threshold by inelastic scattering	$= P(P'Z)^n \dfrac{\sigma_i}{\sigma}.$

9.82. The total number of neutrons slowing down past the fission threshold per primary fission neutron, which is equal to ϵ, is then obtained by summing the last two quantities for all the generations; thus,

$$\epsilon = 1 - P + P\frac{\sigma_i}{\sigma} + P\left(1 - P' + P'\frac{\sigma_i}{\sigma}\right)Z + PP'\left(1 - P' + P'\frac{\sigma_i}{\sigma}\right)Z^2 + \cdots$$

$$= 1 + P\left(\frac{\sigma_i}{\sigma} - 1\right) + \frac{P}{P'}\left[1 + P'\left(\frac{\sigma_i}{\sigma} - 1\right)\right]\sum_{n=1}^{\infty}(P'Z)^n$$

$$= 1 + P\left(\frac{\sigma_i}{\sigma} - 1\right) + \left[\frac{P}{P'} + P\left(\frac{\sigma_i}{\sigma} - 1\right)\right]\left[\frac{1}{1 - P'Z} - 1\right].$$

Noting that $\sigma = \sigma_f + \sigma_i + \sigma_e + \sigma_c$, where σ_c is the cross section for nonfission capture of fast neutrons by the fuel, so that

$$\sigma_i - \sigma = - (\sigma_f + \sigma_e + \sigma_c),$$

it is found that the expression for ϵ reduces to

$$\epsilon = 1 + \frac{\left[(\nu - 1) - \dfrac{\sigma_c}{\sigma_f} \right] \dfrac{\sigma_f}{\sigma} P}{1 - P' \left(\dfrac{\nu\sigma_f + \sigma_e}{\sigma} \right)}, \qquad (9.82.1)$$

recalling the definition of Z in § 9.78.

9.83. It should be mentioned that, in the foregoing derivation, it is assumed that all the fission neutrons are produced with energies above the threshold for fast-neutron fission. Because of the distribution of fission neutron energies, this will not be true. A proportion of the neutrons produced in fission will have energies below the threshold value. The net effect of this is to decrease $\epsilon - 1$ by about 3 per cent.

9.84. To complete the calculation of ϵ, the essentially geometric problem of computing P and P' will be outlined. The probability that a neutron originating at $\mathbf{r}_1$ will suffer a collision in the volume element $d\mathbf{r}_2$ at $\mathbf{r}_2$ in the fuel is

$$\frac{\Sigma e^{-\Sigma |\mathbf{r}_1 - \mathbf{r}_2|}}{4\pi |\mathbf{r}_1 - \mathbf{r}_2|^2} \, d\mathbf{r}_2,$$

where Σ is the total macroscopic cross section of the fuel. If $n(\mathbf{r}_1)$ is the neutron distribution in the fuel, i.e., the number of neutrons produced at $\mathbf{r}_1$ per cm^3 per sec, then

$$P = \frac{\Sigma}{4\pi} \cdot \frac{\displaystyle\int_{\mathbf{r}_2} \int_{\mathbf{r}_1} \frac{n(\mathbf{r}_1) e^{-\Sigma |\mathbf{r}_1 - \mathbf{r}_2|}}{|\mathbf{r}_1 - \mathbf{r}_2|^2} \, d\mathbf{r}_1 \, d\mathbf{r}_2}{\displaystyle\int_{\mathbf{r}_1} n(\mathbf{r}_1) \, d\mathbf{r}_1},$$

where the integrations are carried over the entire fuel lump. These integrals have been evaluated for lattice cells of various geometries. The value of P' can be obtained by letting the source distribution $n(\mathbf{r}_1)$ be a constant.

9.85. It is of interest to note that, in a large assembly, where $P' \approx 1$, a divergent fast chain reaction would be possible if $\nu\sigma_f + \sigma_e$ were equal to σ. It was found experimentally* that the maximum value of ϵ in uranium metal is about 1.2. The following average cross sections for fast neutrons in uranium metal give close agreement with the experimental results:

$$\sigma_f = 0.29 \text{ barn}$$
$$\sigma_i = 2.47 \text{ barns}$$
$$\sigma_e = 1.5 \ \text{ barns}$$
$$\sigma_c = 0.04 \text{ barn}$$

* A. H. Snell, unpublished.

so that σ is 4.3 barns.   The values of the fast fission factor for heterogeneous reactors of two types, with natural uranium as fuel, and either graphite or heavy water as moderator are given in Table 9.85.

TABLE 9.85.   FAST FISSION FACTOR FOR NATURAL URANIUM REACTORS

Reactor Type	Moderator	ϵ
CP–2 or "GLEEP"	Graphite	1.029
CP–3 or "ZEEP"	Heavy water	1.031

MACROSCOPIC REACTOR THEORY

CALCULATION OF THE MATERIAL BUCKLING

9.86. The preceding parts of this chapter may be regarded as covering what was called (§ 9.1) microscopic reactor (pile) theory.   A knowledge of the four quantities η, f, p, and ϵ for a particular fuel-moderator lattice of a certain composition permits evaluation of the infinite multiplication factor.   It is the main purpose of macroscopic theory, combined with experiment, to determine the critical size of the specified system.   The first step in this direction is to estimate appropriate values for the diffusion length and the age of thermal neutrons in the heterogeneous lattice.

9.87. Whereas microscopic theory is concerned with the variation of the neutron flux within a lattice cell and its effect on the infinite multiplication factor, macroscopic theory must take into consideration the variation of the average flux in a cell from cell to cell over the entire reactor.   The thermal neutron flux in a heterogeneous reactor can be considered as the product of two factors: one is an over-all cosine (or similar) distribution analogous to that in a homogeneous finite system (cf. § 7.61), and the other is the microscopic distribution within a lattice cell.   The thermal flux is thus given by

$$\phi(\mathbf{r}) = \phi_a(\mathbf{r})\phi_i(\mathbf{r}), \tag{9.87.1}$$

where the subscripts a and i refer to macroscopic and microscopic, respectively. The macroscopic flux is assumed to satisfy the diffusion equation

$$D \, \nabla^2 \phi_a - \Sigma_a \phi_a + S = 0, \tag{9.87.2}$$

where D is the average diffusion coefficient and Σ_a is the average macroscopic absorption cross section of thermal neutrons in the reactor, and S is the source term due to slowing down in the moderator.

9.88. The diffusion coefficient is not very different in fuel and moderator, and since the volume of moderator is large compared to that of the fuel, the average diffusion coefficient D in (9.87.2) may be taken to be equal to D_1, the diffusion coefficient in the moderator.   The absorption cross section, however, does differ appreciably in the two media, and the value, averaged according to the variation of flux in a lattice cell, is represented by

$$\Sigma_a = \frac{V_1 \Sigma_{a1} \bar{\phi}_1 + V_0 \Sigma_{a0} \bar{\phi}_0}{V_1 \bar{\phi}_1 + V_0 \bar{\phi}_0} = \frac{V_1 \Sigma_{a1} + V_0 \Sigma_{a0} \dfrac{\bar{\phi}_0}{\bar{\phi}_1}}{V_1 + V_0 \dfrac{\bar{\phi}_0}{\bar{\phi}_1}}. \tag{9.88.1}$$

From (9.48.1),

$$V_0 \Sigma_{a0} \frac{\bar{\phi}_0}{\bar{\phi}_1} = V_1 \Sigma_{a1} \frac{f}{1-f},$$

where f is the thermal utilization of the lattice, and so (9.88.1) becomes

$$\Sigma_a = \frac{\Sigma_{a1}}{1-f} \cdot \frac{V_1}{V_1 + V_0 \dfrac{\bar{\phi}_0}{\bar{\phi}_1}}. \tag{9.88.2}$$

In actual lattices V_1 is much greater than $V_0 \bar{\phi}_0 / \bar{\phi}_1$, and hence the average macroscopic absorption cross section becomes equal to the absorption cross section of the moderator divided by $1 - f$, i.e.,

$$\Sigma_a = \frac{\Sigma_{a1}}{1-f}. \tag{9.88.3}$$

The thermal diffusion length in the lattice is then given by

$$L = \sqrt{\frac{D}{\Sigma_a}} = \sqrt{\frac{D_1}{\Sigma_{a1}} (1-f)}$$
$$= L_1 \sqrt{1-f}, \tag{9.88.4}$$

where L_1 is the diffusion length in pure moderator.*

9.89. The next matter to consider is the Fermi age of the neutrons in the lattice. It would be expected to be somewhat larger than in the moderator alone because uranium is not effective in slowing down neutrons by elastic collisions. However, this increase in the thermal neutron age is opposed by the effect of inelastic scattering in the uranium. For all practical purposes, therefore, the age of thermal neutrons in the lattice may be taken as equal to that in the pure moderator.

9.90. Because η for natural uranium is 1.3, and p and f are both less than unity, while ϵ is about 1.03, it is evident that the infinite multiplication factor k is, at best, only slightly greater than unity. Consequently, in order to reduce the relative loss of neutrons from the assembly by leakage, a critical reactor, using natural uranium as fuel, will inevitably have to be large. For large reactors, the critical equation may be written (§ 7.63) as

$$\frac{k}{1 + M^2 B_m^2} = 1,$$

*It may be noted that (7.67.1) for a homogeneous reactor is equivalent to (9.88.4), so that this result is general.

so that the material buckling is given by

$$B_m{}^2 = \frac{k-1}{M^2}.$$ (9.90.1)

Since k may be regarded as known, and the migration area M^2 is defined by

$$M^2 = L^2 + \tau,$$

where the diffusion length L in the lattice is defined by (9.88.4) and the age τ of the thermal neutrons can be assumed to be the same as in the moderator, all the information may thus be regarded as available for the evaluation of the material buckling by (9.90.1). If this is set equal to the geometric buckling for a specified shape, the critical dimensions of the reactor can be determined (§ 7.26).

THE EXPONENTIAL EXPERIMENT*

9.91. Confirmation of the results given by the procedure described above is obtained by means of what has been called the *exponential pile experiment*. This involves construction of a subcritical assembly with exactly the same lattice as the proposed reactor but appreciably smaller. In a system of this type, a self-sustaining fission chain reaction will, of course, not be possible, but if an extraneous source is present, a steady state can be realized (§ 7.2). The flux distribution in such a system does not satisfy the wave equation for a critical reactor. Nevertheless, as will be shown later (§ 12.46), if the subcritical assembly is relatively large, as would be the case for a natural uranium system, the thermal neutron flux distribution, *at a distance from boundaries and from the extraneous source,* can be represented fairly closely by

$$\nabla^2\phi + B_m{}^2\phi = 0,$$ (9.91.1)

where $B_m{}^2$ is the material buckling of the given fuel-moderator system. Strictly speaking, the wave equation (9.91.1) applies to a homogeneous system. In a heterogeneous assembly, there will be local irregularities due to the lattice structure, as indicated earlier, but the wave equation will nevertheless give the large-scale or over-all neutron distribution.

9.92. The purpose of the exponential experiment is to determine the material buckling from measurements of the thermal flux distribution in the appropriate regions of a moderately large subcritical assembly in which a steady state is maintained by an extraneous neutron source. The critical dimensions of a reactor having the same composition and structure as the experimental assembly can then be obtained from the expression for the geometric buckling, as stated in § 9.90.

9.93. In the exponential arrangement, a portion of the reactor is constructed, with linear dimensions of the order of one-third or so of the critical reactor, on a

---

* The theory of the exponential pile is due to E. Fermi.

base from which emerges a supply of thermal neutrons. The latter may consist of a structure of graphite and uranium within which is placed a neutron source, such as radium-beryllium, or it may be part of an existing thermal reactor. In the case of a cubic or rectangular block reactor, the experimental system would be represented schematically as in Fig. 9.93, the origin of the coordinates being

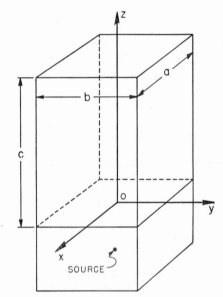

Fig. 9.93.   Assembly for exponential experiment in rectangular block

taken at the center of the bottom face of the reactor. The assembly has a number of vertical holes or tubes parallel to and near the z-axis of the coordinate system shown. In these holes can be placed indium foils or neutron counters by means of which the neutron flux at various distances from the bottom face can be determined.

9.94. To solve equation (9.91.1), the thermal flux ϕ is written as the product of the functions $X(x)$, $Y(y)$, $Z(z)$ of the respective single variables x, y, z. As in previous cases (§§ 5.71, 7.42), this leads to the expression

$$\frac{1}{X} \cdot \frac{d^2X}{dx^2} + \frac{1}{Y} \cdot \frac{d^2Y}{dy^2} + \frac{1}{Z} \cdot \frac{d^2Z}{dz^2} + B_m^2 = 0.$$

The terms in X, Y, and Z may then be set equal to the constants $-\alpha^2$, $-\beta^2$, and γ^2, respectively, so that

$$\alpha^2 + \beta^2 - \gamma^2 = B_m^2. \tag{9.94.1}$$

9.95. By the use of the flux symmetry condition, as before, it can be shown that α^2 and β^2 are positive quantities. Taking into account the usual boundary conditions, it is found (cf. § 5.76) that

$$\alpha^2 = \left(\frac{m\pi}{a}\right)^2 \quad \text{and} \quad \beta^2 = \left(\frac{n\pi}{b}\right)^2 \qquad (9.95.1)$$

and

$$X_m = A_m \cos \frac{m\pi x}{a}$$

$$Y_n = C_n \cos \frac{n\pi y}{b},$$

where A_m and C_n are constants, and m and n are odd integers. The smallest eigenvalues of α^2 and β^2 are those for which $m = 1$ and $n = 1$, respectively, so that

$$\alpha^2 = \left(\frac{\pi}{a}\right)^2 \quad \text{and} \quad \beta^2 = \left(\frac{\pi}{b}\right)^2. \qquad (9.95.2)$$

9.96. Although these results are formally similar to those obtained in connection with the rectangular block reactor (§ 7.43), it should be noted that the dimensions a and b of the block in the exponential pile experiment are considerably less than in the critical reactor. Hence, α^2 and β^2 in (9.95.2) are much greater than the corresponding components of the critical geometric buckling. In fact, in the exponential pile experiment, the dimensions of a and b are such that $\alpha^2 + \beta^2$ will exceed $B_m{}^2$. Consequently, it follows from (9.94.1) that γ^2 is also positive. Hence, as in § 5.77,

$$Z(z) = F \sinh \gamma(c - z). \qquad (9.96.1)$$

9.97. Upon inserting the values in (9.95.1) for α^2 and β^2 into (9.94.1), it follows that

$$\gamma_{mn}{}^2 = \left(\frac{m\pi}{a}\right)^2 + \left(\frac{n\pi}{b}\right)^2 - B_m{}^2. \qquad (9.97.1)$$

It is apparent that for each pair of m and n values there will be a definite value of γ, which may be indicated by γ_{mn}. Thus, from (9.96.1), the general solution for $Z(z)$ may be written as

$$Z_{mn} = F_{mn} \sinh \gamma_{mn}(c - z). \qquad (9.97.2)$$

9.98. The simplest solution of the wave equation (9.91.1) is a product of X, Y, and Z, but in view of the linear nature of this equation, the general solution is

$$\phi = \sum_{m=1}^{\infty} \sum_{n=1}^{\infty} A_{mn} \cos \frac{m\pi x}{a} \cos \frac{n\pi y}{b} \sinh \gamma_{mn}(c - z), \qquad (9.98.1)$$

where the arbitrary constants A_m, C_n, and F_{mn} have been combined into A_{mn}. In order to evaluate this constant, use must be made of the source condition, as in the treatment for the determination of the diffusion length in § 5.81, et seq. The source may be regarded as a point source of fast neutrons lying on the z-axis at some distance below the origin in Fig. 9.93. Then by solving the age equation for the slowing down density, evaluated at thermal energies, and combining with the diffusion treatment (cf. § 6.149), the thermal neutron source term in the x, y-plane through the origin could be determined. This could be expanded into a series of orthogonal functions, as in § 5.82. It would then be found that, at a distance of about two diffusion lengths from the source, the only term of (9.98.1) which makes any appreciable contribution to the neutron flux is the fundamental mode, i.e., when $m = 1$ and $n = 1$.

9.99. Hence, if the bottom of the experimental block, i.e., the x, y-plane through the origin, is about 100 cm or so from a fast neutron source, embedded in graphite, the contributions of the harmonic terms to the flux in the pile can be neglected. Consequently, under these conditions, it is not necessary to make the source calculations described above, but merely to write (9.98.1) in the form

$$\phi = A_{11} \cos \frac{\pi x}{a} \cos \frac{\pi y}{b} \sinh \gamma(c - z),$$

for $z > 0$. Since there is only one value of the constant A_{mn} which need be considered, there is, similarly, only one value of F_{mn} and one of γ_{mn}. The thermal flux distribution along any line parallel to the z-axis* is, therefore, given by the simplified form of (9.97.2), namely,

$$\phi(z) = F \sinh \gamma(c - z) \qquad (9.99.1)$$
$$= Ce^{-\gamma z}[1 - e^{-2\gamma(c-z)}], \qquad (9.99.2)$$

where $e^{\gamma c}$ has been included in the constant C.

9.100. Provided z does not approach c, i.e., at distances not too near the top of the rectangular block, the term in the brackets in (9.99.2) is not very different from unity, and then

$$\phi(z) = Ce^{-\gamma z}. \qquad (9.100.1)$$

This means that, in the experimental arrangement under consideration, along any line parallel to the z-axis, the thermal neutron flux falls off in an (approximately) exponential manner. For this reason, the system has been called an "exponential pile." The relaxation length of the neutrons, i.e., the distance within which the neutron flux falls off by a factor of e in the z-direction, is here seen to be $1/\gamma$.

9.101. In the foregoing it has been assumed that for $z > 0$, i.e., within the pile itself, the neutrons coming from the source have virtually all been thermalized in their passage through the graphite base. This will be essentially true, provided the fast neutron source is at a distance from the $z = 0$ plane of at least two or three slowing down lengths (§ 6.142), i.e., more than $2\sqrt{\tau}$ or $3\sqrt{\tau}$, where τ is the Fermi age of the thermal neutrons. Since the value of τ for thermal neutrons in graphite is about 300 cm, the minimum distance for virtually complete

---

* It is assumed, of course, that the line is not close to the vertical boundaries of the assembly.

thermalization is thus about 50 cm.   An experimental check on this assumption can be made by measuring the cadmium ratio (§ 3.89) at various points along the z-axis.   If there is no appreciable slowing down for $z > 0$, the cadmium ratio will be constant.

9.102. If the fluxes $\phi(z)$ at various distances z in the same vertical line near the central axis of the assembly are determined experimentally, e.g., by the irradiation of indium foil and subsequent determination of the (saturation) beta activity, then the plot of $\ln \phi(z)$, or rather a quantity proportional to $\ln \phi(z)$, against z should yield a straight line of slope $-\gamma$.   Actually, the plot will be linear only for points which are not too near the base nor too close to the top.*   In the former case higher harmonics, i.e., terms for which m or n, or both, are greater than unity, will make some contribution to the flux, and (9.100.1) will not be exact.   If necessary, corrections can be made for these harmonics, from measurements of the lateral distribution of the flux in the x, y-plane (see also, § 5.88).

9.103. The deviations from linearity of points representing measurements made near the top of the block are due to the neglect of the "end correction term," $1 - e^{-2\gamma(c-z)}$, in (9.99.2).   The experimental fluxes can be corrected by dividing by this quantity, which can be evaluated by the procedure described in connection with the measurement of diffusion length (§ 5.89).   From the best linear plot of the corrected values of $\ln \phi(z)$ against the vertical distance z, the slope, equal to $-\gamma$, is obtained.   Since this is really γ_{11}, it follows from (9.97.1) that

$$\left(\frac{\pi}{a}\right)^2 + \left(\frac{\pi}{b}\right)^2 - \gamma^2 = B_m{}^2.$$

9.104. In this case a and b are the extrapolated dimensions of the experimental block in the x- and y-directions, which may be obtained by adding $2 \times 0.71\lambda_t$ to the geometrical dimensions.   The actual values may be determined by measuring the lateral variation of the neutron flux and finding where it would become zero.   Alternatively, the difference between the extrapolated height, c, determined above, and the measured height may be used as a basis for applying a correction to the geometrical dimensions.   Thus, with a, b, and γ known, the material buckling of the multiplying medium constituting the assembly can be calculated.   The dimensions of the critical reactor can then be obtained from (7.44.1), since $B_m{}^2$ is equal to $B_g{}^2$ for the critical system.

Cylindrical Reactor

9.105. If it is required to design a cylindrical reactor, then the structure of the exponential experiment will also be cylindrical in shape (Fig. 9.105).   As

---

* It should be remembered that the diffusion equation (9.91.1), upon which the foregoing treatment is based, will represent the neutron flux distribution only at appreciable distances from the source and from boundaries.

in § 7.51, the solution ϕ of the wave equation is found to be separable into the product $\Theta(r)$ and $Z(z)$, where the former is a function of the variable r only and

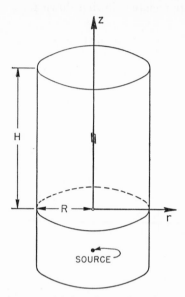

FIG. 9.105.   Exponential experiment in cylindrical assembly

the latter is a function of z only.   Thus, it is possible to write the wave equation in the form

$$f[\Theta(r)] + f'[Z(z)] + B_m{}^2 = 0.$$

If the function of $\Theta(r)$ is represented by the constant $-\alpha^2$, where α^2 is a positive quantity, and the function $Z(z)$ by the constant $-\gamma^2$, then γ^2 is a positive quantity, since

$$-\alpha^2 + \gamma^2 + B_m{}^2 = 0, \tag{9.105.1}$$

and $B_m{}^2$ is positive.   The solution of the differential equation in Θ, as seen earlier, is the zero order Bessel function of the first kind $J_0(\alpha r)$, but since the equation is linear, the general solution is given by a summation of terms; thus,

$$\Theta(r) = \sum_{n=1}^{\infty} A_n J_0(\alpha_n r), \tag{9.105.2}$$

where n may have any integral value.

9.106.   The differential equation in z is identical in form with (5.72.3), and the solution is

$$Z_n = C_n \sinh \gamma_n (H - z), \tag{9.106.1}$$

taking into account the boundary condition that the flux shall be zero at the (extrapolated) upper surface of the cylinder, where H is the extrapolated height.

9.107. The general solution of the wave equation is now

$$\phi(r, z) = \sum_{n=1}^{\infty} A_n J_0(\alpha_n r) \sinh \gamma_n(H - z), \qquad (9.107.1)$$

so that at the bottom face of the cylindrical pile, the flux distribution is given by $\phi(r, 0)$ which may be represented by $f(r)$, where

$$f(r) = \sum_{n=1}^{\infty} A_n' J_0(\alpha_n r). \qquad (9.107.2)$$

The Bessel functions J_0 form a complete orthogonal set in the interval of 0 to r, and so the Fourier theorem can be used, to determine the coefficients A_n', and hence A_n. It appears, however, from calculations and from experimental data that, provided measurements are made at distances not too close to the bottom face, the flux distribution can be represented with sufficient accuracy by the fundamental term ($n = 1$) alone of (9.107.2). Hence, (9.107.1) reduces to

$$\phi = A J_0(\alpha r) \sinh \gamma(H - z).$$

The expression for $\Theta(r)$ is then

$$\Theta(r) = A J_0(\alpha r),$$

and from the boundary condition that the flux shall be zero at the (extrapolated) surface of the cylinder.

$$\alpha = \frac{2.405}{R}, \qquad (9.107.3)$$

where R is the extrapolated radius.

9.108. Using only the fundamental term of (9.107.1), the flux variation along the z-axis may thus be represented by

$$\phi(z) = A' \sinh \gamma(H - z),$$

where H is the extrapolated height of the experimental cylinder. Extracting the exponential term, this becomes

$$\phi(z) = C e^{-\gamma z}[1 - e^{-2\gamma(H-z)}],$$

which is analogous to (9.99.2).

9.109. As in the case of the rectangular block arrangement, the neutron flux is measured at various distances from the bottom in a vertical line parallel to the z-axis. By determining the extrapolated height H, in a manner exactly similar to that described above, the slope $-\gamma$ of the plot of the logarithm of the corrected (exponential) flux, $\ln \phi(z)$, against the vertical distance z can be obtained. Only measurements made above about $2\sqrt{\tau}$ from the bottom are included, since the contributions of the harmonic terms for $n > 1$ are then small.

9.110. The results in Table 9.110 were obtained with an arrangement of rods of natural uranium suspended vertically in a cylindrical tank of heavy water.* The geometrical radius of the tank was 55.5 cm, and the water reached a height of 154.1 cm. The first column gives the distances from the bottom at which measurements were made. The second column shows the activity of indium foil in counts per minute, after allowing for natural decay; this is proportional to the neutron flux. The next two columns show the harmonic and end corrections,

TABLE 9.110.   RESULTS OF EXPONENTIAL EXPERIMENT

Height	Activity	Harmonic Correction	End Correction	Corrected Activity
21.4 cm	83,306	1.0181	1.0030	85,072
41.4	46,703	1.0053	1.0098	47,413
61.4	26,113	1.0015	1.0318	26,982
81.4	13,607	1.0004	1.1091	15,097

respectively; the fifth column represents the "corrected" activity, which is the product of the observed activity and the two correction terms. The natural logarithms of the corrected activity were plotted against the heights in the first column, and the best slope was estimated by the method of least squares.

9.111. The slope found in this way was -28.76×10^{-3} cm^{-1}, so that γ is 28.76×10^{-3}, and γ^2 is 827×10^{-6} cm^{-2}. The geometrical radius of the experimental cylinder is 55.5 cm, and taking the transport mean free path in heavy water as 2.4 cm, the extrapolated radius is 57.2 cm.† Hence, by (9.105.1) and (9.107.3),

$$B_m{}^2 = \alpha^2 - \gamma^2 = \left(\frac{2.405}{R}\right)^2 - \gamma^2$$
$$= \left(\frac{2.405}{57.2}\right)^2 - 827 \times 10^{-6} = 942 \times 10^{-6} \text{ cm}^{-2}.$$

The critical dimensions of a cylindrical reactor of minimum volume (§ 7.59) are given by

$$H = \frac{5.441}{B} \quad \text{and} \quad R = \frac{2.945}{B},$$

and, in the present case, these values are 177 cm height and 96 cm radius. The volume of the critical system would be 5190 liters. It should be noted that these results apply to a bare reactor, and that, by using a reflector, the critical dimen-

---

* The data refer to a CP–3 or "ZEEP" type of reactor.
† The extrapolation distance for the large cylinder is assumed to be 0.71λ_t, as for a plane slab.

sions would be reduced.   For a reactor having a 60-cm graphite reflector, the critical dimensions were found by experiment to be 122.5 cm (height) and 91.4 cm (radius), the volume being 3213 liters.

PROBLEMS

1. Calculate the minimum isotopic ratio of U^{235} to U^{238} that will make an infinite homogeneous water solution of uranyl sulphate just critical.   Repeat for graphite and D_2O moderators.

2. Calculate and plot the minimum critical mass of unreflected spherical reactors containing UO_2 and D_2O at room temperature as a function of the isotopic ratio of U^{235} to U^{238}.

Chapter X

TIME BEHAVIOR
OF A BARE THERMAL REACTOR*

TIME BEHAVIOR WITH PROMPT NEUTRONS

INTRODUCTION

10.1. The preceding discussion, with the exception of the treatment of the approach to critical in Chapter VII, has referred to reactors in the steady or stationary state where there was an exact balance between the neutrons lost by diffusion and absorption, on the one hand, and those gained form the source, i.e., fission, on the other hand. The neutron density was thus independent of time. The case will now be considered in which there is a change in the neutron density with time, resulting from a sudden change in the multiplication constant due to such factors as alteration in the position of a control rod, removal of fuel, removal of reflector, etc. The rate of gain of neutrons will then be greater or smaller than the rate of loss. It will be supposed, in the first instance, that all the neutrons emitted in the fission process appear within a very short time, about 10^{-15} sec; that is to say, it will be postulated that all the neutrons are released instantaneously as prompt neutrons.

10.2. In connection with the problem of neutron multiplication, the generation time is important; this is defined as the average time between successive generations of thermal neutron fissions (§ 7.34). It will, therefore, include the time required to slow down the neutron from fission to thermal energies, as well as the diffusion time of the thermal neutron before it is captured in a fission process. For the present purpose, however, the slowing down time will be assumed to be negligible in comparison with the diffusion time of the slow neutron (see Table 6.147). This is true for the natural uranium-graphite (X-10) reactor, but not for reactors in which an appreciable proportion of the fissions are due to neutrons in the intermediate energy range (§ 7.35).

10.3. The treatment will be restricted here to the homogeneous, bare, thermal reactor, although many of the general conclusions are applicable to heterogeneous

---

* The development of this subject is largely due to R. F. Christy and L. W. Nordheim (cf. MDDC–35).

and reflected reactors.   Further, it will be supposed that the system is near critical, so that all solutions other than the fundamental solution of the wave equation for the neutron flux can be neglected, as explained in Chapter VII.   Part of the discussion given below is, in effect, a simplified form of that in § 7.5, *et seq.*, using only the fundamental eigenfunction for the slowing down density and the flux of thermal neutrons.

The Nonequilibrium Diffusion Equation

10.4. The diffusion equation for thermal neutrons in a nonequilibrium system can be written as

$$D \, \nabla^2 \phi - \Sigma_a \phi + S = \frac{\partial n}{\partial t} = \frac{1}{v} \cdot \frac{\partial \phi}{\partial t}, \tag{10.4.1}$$

where v is the mean velocity of the thermal neutrons, so that ϕ is equal to nv. According to the Fermi age theory, the thermal neutron source term due to fissions is $pq \, (\tau_{\text{th}})$, and this is given by (7.22.3) as

$$S = k\Sigma_a \phi e^{-B^2\tau}, \tag{10.4.2}$$

where $k\Sigma_a \phi$ is the number of thermal neutrons per cm³ per sec that would result from fission in an infinite system, i.e., if there were no leakage, and $e^{-B^2\tau}$ represents the nonleakage probability during slowing down.*   Upon introducing (10.4.2) into (10.4.1), the result, in the absence of an extraneous source, is

$$D \, \nabla^2 \phi + \Sigma_a \phi (ke^{-B^2\tau} - 1) = \frac{1}{v} \cdot \frac{\partial \phi}{\partial t}.$$

Upon dividing through by Σ_a and making use of the fact that D/Σ_a is equal to L^2, where L is the thermal diffusion length, it is seen that

$$L^2 \, \nabla^2 \phi + (ke^{-B^2\tau} - 1)\phi = \frac{1}{\Sigma_a v} \cdot \frac{\partial \phi}{\partial t}$$
$$= l_0 \frac{\partial \phi}{\partial t}, \tag{10.4.3}$$

where $1/\Sigma_a v$ has been replaced by l_0, the infinite medium mean lifetime of thermal neutrons.

10.5. An attempt will now be made to solve this equation by separating the variables, i.e., by setting

$$\phi \equiv \phi(\mathbf{r}, t) = \phi(\mathbf{r})T(t), \tag{10.5.1}$$

---

* Although the treatment here is based on the Fermi (continuous slowing down) model, the same results can be obtained by the use of the generalized slowing down treatment, given in Chapter XII, which is independent of any particular model.

where $\mathbf{r}$ is the position vector of any point in the reactor and t is the time. Thus, $\phi(\mathbf{r})$ is a function of the space coordinates only, and $T(t)$ is dependent on the time only. Combining (10.5.1) with (10.4.3) gives

$$\frac{L^2 \, \nabla^2 \phi(\mathbf{r})}{\phi(\mathbf{r})} + ke^{-B^2\tau} - 1 = \frac{l_0}{T(t)} \cdot \frac{dT(t)}{dt}. \tag{10.5.2}$$

For the present treatment it will be supposed that the reactor has been operating in a steady state up to a time $t = 0$, when the multiplication factor k is made to undergo a small sudden or step change. It will be postulated that subsequently the value of k remains constant. In these circumstances the left-hand side of (10.5.2) contains no time variables, and the right-hand side no space variables, so that the variables have, in fact, been separated.

10.6. If the system is not far from critical, the spatial distribution of the flux is represented to a good approximation by the wave equation

$$\nabla^2 \phi(\mathbf{r}) + B^2 \phi(\mathbf{r}) = 0,$$

where B^2 is the geometric buckling (cf. § 7.11, *et seq.*). Hence, substituting $-B^2$ for $\nabla^2 \phi(\mathbf{r})/\phi(\mathbf{r})$ in (10.5.2), the latter becomes

$$-(1 + L^2 B^2) + ke^{-B^2\tau} = \frac{l_0}{T(t)} \cdot \frac{dT(t)}{dt},$$

and, dividing through by $1 + L^2 B^2$, the result is

$$\frac{ke^{-B^2\tau}}{1 + L^2 B^2} - 1 = \frac{l_0}{1 + L^2 B^2} \cdot \frac{1}{T(t)} \cdot \frac{dT(t)}{dt}. \tag{10.6.1}$$

The first term on the left-hand side is the effective multiplication factor, k_{eff} [cf. (7.27.1)], and the first factor on the right-hand side is the mean lifetime l of thermal neutrons in a finite medium (§ 7.34); thus, (10.6.1) reduces to

$$k_{\text{eff}} - 1 = \frac{l}{T(t)} \cdot \frac{dT(t)}{dt}. \tag{10.6.2}$$

10.7. The excess of k_{eff} over unity is called the *excess multiplication factor*, represented by k_{ex}, so that

$$k_{\text{ex}} \equiv k_{\text{eff}} - 1. \tag{10.7.1}$$

For a critical system, $k_{\text{eff}} = 1$, and so k_{ex} is a measure of how far the reactor is from critical. It is positive if the reactor is supercritical and negative if it is subcritical. Upon introducing the definition of k_{ex} into (10.6.2), it is seen that

$$k_{\text{ex}} = \frac{l}{T(t)} \cdot \frac{dT(t)}{dt}.$$

Integration of this expression gives

$$T(t) = A e^{k_{\mathrm{ext}}t/l},$$

so that, by (10.5.1),

$$\phi(\mathbf{r}, t) = A\phi(\mathbf{r})e^{k_{\mathrm{ext}}t/l}. \tag{10.7.2}$$

At zero time,

$$\phi(\mathbf{r}, 0) = A\phi(\mathbf{r}),$$

and if this is represented by ϕ_0, it follows from (10.7.2) that

$$\phi(\mathbf{r}, t) = \phi_0 e^{k_{\mathrm{ext}}t/l}, \tag{10.7.3}$$

where ϕ_0 is the thermal neutron flux at the position vector $\mathbf{r}$ in the steady state at zero time when the effective multiplication factor of the reactor was suddenly changed by an amount k_{ex}. It will be noted that (10.7.2) is equivalent to the general equation (7.17.1) in the absence of an extraneous source — so that the second term of the latter is zero — provided the spatial part of the flux can be expressed by a single eigenfunction which is a solution of the wave equation. As already mentioned, this is possible only if the reactor is near the critical state.

THE REACTOR PERIOD

10.8. The time required for the neutron flux (or neutron density) to change by a factor of e is called the *pile period* or *reactor period*, and is represented by T. This can be stated mathematically by writing

$$\phi(\mathbf{r}, t) \equiv \phi_0 e^{t/T}, \tag{10.8.1}$$

and comparison with (10.7.3) shows that in the present case, i.e., with all the neutrons emitted in the fission process assumed to be prompt neutrons,

$$T = \frac{l}{k_{\mathrm{ex}}}. \tag{10.8.2}$$

10.9. According to the foregoing treatment, it is seen that the thermal neutron flux of a reactor in a non-stationary state, i.e., $k_{\mathrm{ex}} \neq 0$, will increase (or decrease) in an exponential manner, the rate depending on the ratio of the average lifetime of the thermal neutron to the excess multiplication factor. That this result is to be expected has been seen from the general considerations in § 4.49. Since the time required for the neutrons to slow down has been assumed negligible, the average thermal lifetime is essentially the same as the generation time, and hence (4.49.2) is equivalent to (10.7.3). The reactor period is thus equal to the generation time divided by the excess multiplication factor. It may be noted that this result is completely general, and is independent of whether the neutrons liberated in fission are prompt or delayed. However, it is only when the fission neutrons are all prompt that the average thermal neutron lifetime can be identified with the generation time, as will be seen below.

10.10. As stated earlier, k_{ex} is positive, and hence the reactor period is positive, when the reactor is supercritical, i.e., $k_{eff} > 1$; then the neutron flux will increase exponentially, in accordance with (10.7.3). On the other hand, if the reactor is subcritical, k_{ex} is negative and so also is the period; the neutron flux will then decrease in an exponential manner.

10.11. An indication of the rate at which the neutron flux (or density) would increase according to the equations given above may be obtained by considering an actual example. Suppose that the effective multiplication factor is suddenly increased by 0.01, i.e., k_{ex} is 0.01. Since the thermal neutron lifetime in a large thermal reactor may be of the order of 0.001 sec, the reactor period given by (10.8.2) is then 0.001/0.01, i.e., 0.1 sec; hence the neutron flux would increase by a factor of e every 0.1 sec. In 1 sec the over-all increase would be by a factor of e^{10}, i.e., about 2×10^4.

TIME BEHAVIOR WITH DELAYED NEUTRONS

GENERAL CONSIDERATIONS

10.12. It is evident that, with such a rapid increase in the neutron flux, a reactor would be difficult to control. It should be remembered, however, that the foregoing derivations were based on the assumption that all the neutrons emitted in the fission process are released promptly. Fortunately, this is not the case. Of the total number of neutrons liberated in fission, something like 0.75 per cent are delayed neutrons which appear for an appreciable period of time following the actual nuclear fission, as seen in Chapter IV. It is the occurrence of these delayed neutrons which makes it possible to operate a reactor in such a manner that the rate of change of neutron flux is much less than would be the case if there were no delayed neutrons (cf. § 4.74, et seq.). As a result, the problem of control of a thermal reactor is greatly simplified.

10.13. It is apparent from the qualitative argument presented earlier (§ 10.9) that the reactor period, for a given excess multiplication, is proportional to the average generation time of the neutrons. Because some of the neutrons are delayed, the time between generations is increased, and the reactor period is increased accordingly. The general nature of the effect of the delayed neutrons may be seen in the following manner. The fact that t_i is the average life of the precursor* of the delayed neutrons of the ith group is equivalent to saying that each neutron of this group may be regarded as appearing *at an average time* of t_i after fission. If β_i is the fraction of the total fission neutrons in the ith delayed group, the mean delay time for this group is $\beta_i t_i$. The weighted mean delay time, which is the same as the weighted mean life of the precursors, is then equal to the sum of the $\beta_i t_i$ terms, i.e., to $\Sigma \beta_i t_i$, for all the delayed neutron groups.

---

* The term *precursor* is used to describe the species, e.g., Br [87] and I[137] (§§ 4.10, 4.11), whose rate of decay, by the emission of a beta particle, determines the neutron delay time. The decay product of the precursor expels the delayed neutron instantaneously.

Neglecting, as before, the time required to slow down the neutrons from fission to thermal energies, the average time $\bar{l}$ between generations, taking into account the fact that some of the neutrons are delayed, is given by

$$\bar{l} = \Sigma \beta_i t_i + l,$$

where l is the average lifetime already defined.

10.14. Upon multiplying each t_i by the corresponding β_i in Table 4.8 and adding the results, it is found that the weighted average delay time $\Sigma \beta_i t_i$ is 0.0942 sec, i.e., approximately 0.1 sec. Although l may be 10^{-3} sec for a large thermal reactor, this is negligible in comparison with the mean delay time, and so $\bar{l}$ is close to 0.1 sec. Thus, the reactor period is now roughly $0.1/k_{ex}$, instead of l/k_{ex} as would be the case if there were no delayed neutrons. In other words, it is increased by a factor of $0.1/l$. For k_{ex} equal to 0.01, as before, the reactor period becomes $0.1/0.01$, i.e., 10 sec. It would thus require something on the order of 10 sec for the neutron flux to increase by a factor of e, i.e., about 2.7. A period of this magnitude is sufficient to permit adequate control of the reactor.

THE DIFFUSION EQUATION WITH DELAYED NEUTRONS

10.15. The number of thermal neutrons absorbed per cm³ per sec is $\Sigma_a \phi$, and hence the over-all rate of production of fission neutrons, including both prompt and delayed, is equal to $(k/p)\Sigma_a \phi$ per cm³ per sec. Since β_i is the fraction of the total number of fission neutrons which are delayed neutrons belonging to the ith group, the rate of formation in the fission process of the nuclei which are the precursors of those neutrons is equal to $\beta_i(k/p)\Sigma_a \phi$ per cm³ per sec. If C_i is the concentration, in atomic nuclei per cm³, of the precursors from which the ith group of delayed neutrons arise, then the normal rate of radioactive decay is $\lambda_i C_i$ nuclei per cm³ per sec, where λ_i sec^{-1} is the appropriate decay constant. The net rate of formation of delayed neutron precursors of the ith group is consequently given by

$$\frac{\partial C_i(\mathbf{r}, t)}{\partial t} = -\lambda_i C_i(\mathbf{r}, t) + \frac{k}{p} \beta_i \Sigma_a \phi(\mathbf{r}, t). \tag{10.15.1}$$

10.16. The time-dependent, thermal neutron diffusion equation for the homogeneous, bare reactor has the same general form as before, namely, equation (10.4.1), but the source term must now be modified to allow for the delayed neutrons. The sum of the β_i values for the various delayed groups is represented by β, and hence, $1 - \beta$ is the fraction of fission neutrons which are emitted promptly. The corresponding (prompt neutron) source term is then $(1 - \beta)k\Sigma_a \phi e^{-B^2 \tau}$, which is the value given in (10.4.2) multiplied by $1 - \beta$.

10.17. The rate of formation of delayed neutrons in any group is equal to the rate of decay of the precursor, i.e., to $\lambda_i C_i$, and hence

$$\text{Total rate of formation of all} \atop \text{the delayed neutrons} = \sum_{i=1}^{m} \lambda_i C_i \text{ per cm}^3 \text{ per sec,}$$

where the summation is taken over all m values of i, i.e., for all the m groups of delayed neutrons. If this is multiplied by $e^{-B^2\tau}$, the nonleakage probability during the slowing down process, and also by the resonance escape probability p, the result, namely,

$$pe^{-B^2\tau} \sum_{i=1}^{m} \lambda_i C_i,$$

is the source term due to delayed neutrons. For simplicity, the approximation is made of taking the energy spectrum of the delayed neutrons to be the same as that of the prompt neutrons. Actually, the energies of the delayed neutrons are somewhat less than that of the prompt neutrons, but since a neutron spends most of its life, on the average, in the low energy regions, the difference is small.*

10.18. For the present case, therefore, the source term of (10.4.1) may be written as

$$S = (1 - \beta)k\Sigma_a\phi e^{-B^2\tau} + pe^{-B^2\tau} \sum_{i=1}^{m} \lambda_i C_i,$$

and consequently the appropriate thermal neutron diffusion equation is

$$D \nabla^2\phi(\mathbf{r}, t) - \Sigma_a\phi(\mathbf{r}, t) + (1 - \beta)k\Sigma_a\phi(\mathbf{r}, t)e^{-B^2\tau} + pe^{-B^2\tau} \sum_{i=1}^{m} \lambda_i C_i(\mathbf{r}, t)$$
$$= \frac{1}{v} \cdot \frac{\partial\phi(\mathbf{r}, t)}{\partial t}.$$

Dividing through by Σ_a and substituting L^2 for D/Σ_a, and l_0 for $1/\Sigma_a v$, as in § 10.4, this becomes

$$L^2 \nabla^2\phi(\mathbf{r}, t) + [(1 - \beta)ke^{-B^2\tau} - 1]\phi(\mathbf{r}, t) + \frac{pe^{-B^2\tau}}{\Sigma_a} \sum_{i=1}^{m} \lambda_i C_i(\mathbf{r}, t) = l_0 \frac{\partial\phi(\mathbf{r}, t)}{\partial t}.$$
$$(10.18.1)$$

10.19. If, as before, it is postulated that the reactor has been operating in the steady state and that the effective multiplication factor undergoes a small step change at time t equal to zero, after which it remains constant, it can be shown that the space and time variables in (10.18.1) are separable. Suppose the reactor is near enough to critical so that the neutron flux can be calculated satisfactorily from the fundamental mode of the wave equation, and let

$$\phi(\mathbf{r}, t) = \phi(\mathbf{r})T(t)$$

and

$$C_i(\mathbf{r}, t) = C_i(\mathbf{r})H_i(t).$$

Making these substitutions, (10.15.1) becomes

$$\frac{dH_i(t)}{dt} = -\lambda_i H_i(t) + \frac{k}{p} \beta_i \Sigma_a \frac{\phi(\mathbf{r})}{C_i(\mathbf{r})} T(t)$$

and consequently $C_i(\mathbf{r})/\phi(\mathbf{r})$ must be independent of $\mathbf{r}$.

---

* Taking the average energy of the prompt neutrons to be 2 Mev and that of the delayed neutrons to be 0.5 Mev (Table 4.8), it is found that the age of thermal neutrons in graphite is about 350 cm² in the former case and 333 cm² in the latter. For a large reactor, i.e., B^2 small, the difference in $e^{-B^2\tau}$ is very small.

10.20. With the same substitutions, for $\phi(\mathbf{r}, t)$ and $C_i(\mathbf{r}, t)$, equation (10.18.1) becomes

$$L^2 \frac{\nabla^2\phi(\mathbf{r})}{\phi(\mathbf{r})} + [(1 - \beta)ke^{-B^2\tau} - 1] + \frac{pe^{-B^2\tau}}{\Sigma_a} \sum_{i=1}^{m} \lambda_i \frac{C_i(\mathbf{r})H_i(t)}{\phi(\mathbf{r})T(t)} = \frac{l_0}{T(t)} \cdot \frac{dT(t)}{dt},$$

and, since $C_i(\mathbf{r})/\phi(\mathbf{r})$ is independent of $\mathbf{r}$, as shown above, it is seen that the variables have indeed been separated. It will be noted that this separability is due to the fact that $C_i(\mathbf{r})$, the concentration of each delayed neutron precursor, is everywhere proportional to the flux, $\phi(\mathbf{r})$; this is, of course, to be expected on physical grounds.

10.21. Because the space and time variables can be separated, it is possible to write, as before,

$$\nabla^2\phi(\mathbf{r}) + B^2\phi(\mathbf{r}) = 0.$$

However, since the Laplacian operator has no effect on the time-variable function $T(t)$, both sides of this equation may be multiplied by $T(t)$ to give the general wave equation

$$\nabla^2\phi(\mathbf{r}, t) + B^2\phi(\mathbf{r}, t) = 0, \tag{10.21.1}$$

where B^2 is the lowest eigenvalue resulting from the boundary condition that the thermal neutron flux shall be zero at the extrapolated boundary. Hence $\nabla^2\phi(\mathbf{r}, t)$ in (10.18.1) can be replaced by $-B^2\phi(\mathbf{r}, t)$.

10.22. The problem now is to solve the differential equations (10.15.1) and (10.18.1), taking into account (10.21.1). Since both of the former equations are linear and first order, and since the space and time variables are separable, solutions of the form

$$\phi(\mathbf{r}, t) = \phi_0 e^{t\omega} \tag{10.22.1}$$

and

$$C_i(\mathbf{r}, t) = C_{i0}e^{t\omega} \tag{10.22.2}$$

may be superimposed. It is then required to find the conditions on the parameters represented by ω, having the dimensions of a reciprocal time, which permit such solutions. It should be noted that ϕ_0 and C_{i0} are the values of the neutron flux and of the concentration of the precursor of the ith group of delayed neutrons, respectively, at time $t = 0$, at a point represented by the vector $\mathbf{r}$. The latter variable has been omitted from the symbols for simplicity of representation.

10.23. Upon substituting ϕ and C_i, as given by (10.22.1) and (10.22.2), respectively, into (10.15.1), the result is

$$C_{i0}\omega e^{t\omega} = -\lambda_i C_{i0}e^{t\omega} + \frac{k}{p} \beta_i \Sigma_a \phi_0 e^{t\omega},$$

and consequently

$$C_{i0} = \frac{k\beta_i\Sigma_a\phi_0}{p(\omega + \lambda_i)}. \tag{10.23.1}$$

Further, by introducing (10.21.1), (10.22.1), (10.22.2), and (10.23.1) into (10.18.1), the latter equation can be simplified to

$$-(L^2B^2 + 1) + (1 - \beta)ke^{-B^2\tau} + ke^{-B^2\tau} \sum_{i=1}^{m} \frac{\lambda_i\beta_i}{\omega + \lambda_i} = l_0\omega.$$

Dividing through by $1 + L^2B^2$, and recalling that $l_0/(1 + L^2B^2)$ is equal to l, the mean lifetime of the thermal neutrons in the finite reactor, it is seen that

$$(1 - \beta)\frac{ke^{-B^2\tau}}{1 + L^2B^2} - 1 + \frac{ke^{-B^2\tau}}{1 + L^2B^2} \sum_{i=1}^{m} \frac{\lambda_i\beta_i}{\omega + \lambda_i} = l\omega.$$

Upon introducing the definition of k_{eff}, as given by (7.27.1), this becomes

$$(1 - \beta)k_{\text{eff}} - 1 + k_{\text{eff}} \sum_{i=1}^{m} \frac{\lambda_i\beta_i}{\omega + \lambda_i} = l\omega. \tag{10.23.2}$$

The total fraction β of delayed neutrons is equal to the sum of the individual β_i's, by definition, and since $k_{\text{eff}} - 1$ is defined as k_{ex}, by (10.7.1), it follows that (10.23.2) may be written as

$$k_{\text{ex}} + k_{\text{eff}} \sum_{i=1}^{m} \left(\frac{\lambda_i\beta_i}{\omega + \lambda_i} - \beta_i\right) = l\omega$$

or

$$k_{\text{ex}} = l\omega + k_{\text{eff}} \sum_{i=1}^{m} \frac{\omega\beta_i}{\omega + \lambda_i}. \tag{10.23.3}$$

10.24. At this point it is convenient to introduce a quantity ρ, called the *reactivity*, and defined as

$$\rho \equiv \frac{k_{\text{ex}}}{k_{\text{eff}}} = \frac{k_{\text{eff}} - 1}{k_{\text{eff}}}, \tag{10.24.1}$$

the utility of which will be considered below. Hence, if (10.23.3) is divided through by k_{eff}, the result is

$$\rho = \frac{k_{\text{ex}}}{k_{\text{eff}}} = \frac{l\omega}{k_{\text{eff}}} + \sum_{i=1}^{m} \frac{\omega\beta_i}{\omega + \lambda_i}. \tag{10.24.2}$$

From (10.24.1), $k_{\text{eff}} = 1/(1 - \rho)$, and, if this is introduced into (10.24.2), the latter becomes

$$\rho = \frac{l\omega}{l\omega + 1} + \frac{1}{l\omega + 1} \sum_{i=1}^{m} \frac{\omega\beta_i}{\omega + \lambda_i}, \tag{10.24.3}$$

which is a convenient form for calculation purposes.

10.25. Equation (10.24.3) is the characteristic equation which relates the parameters ω to the nuclear properties of the substances constituting the reactor. It is an algebraic equation of degree $m + 1$ in ω, and consequently there are, in general, $m + 1$ values of ω corresponding to each value of the reactivity, ρ. The general nature of the solutions of (10.24.3) can best be understood by plotting ω as a function of ρ, as in Fig. 10.25. This is a purely qualitative representation,

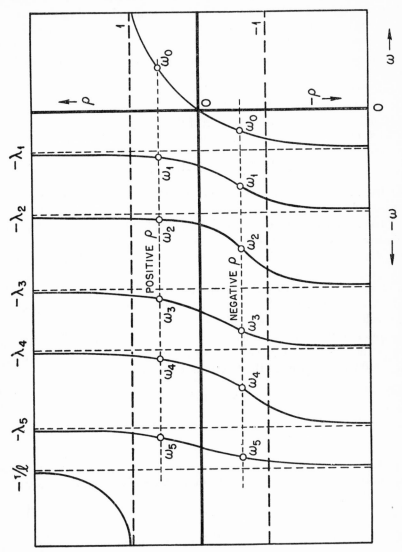

FIG. 10.25.   General plot of ω as a function of ρ

with $m = 5$, to correspond to five groups of delayed neutrons. It is seen that there are six poles, for ω values of $-\lambda_1, -\lambda_2, -\lambda_3, -\lambda_4, -\lambda_5,$ and $-1/l$. It should be noted that only a portion of Fig. 10.25 is significant from the reactor point of view; this is because the maximum value of $|\rho|$ having physical meaning is 1, as will be evident from the definition of ρ, by (10.24.1). The region between $\rho = 1$ and $\rho = -1$ is indicated by the horizontal dashed lines.

10.26. It is apparent from Fig. 10.25 that for positive values of ρ there are $m + 1$ roots of (10.24.3); of these m are negative and one is positive. Numerically each of the m negative values of ω is seen to be of the same order as one of the λ_i's, i.e., the decay constants of the delayed neutron precursors. Hence, the neutron flux at a point $\mathbf{r}$, as a function of time, may be represented by a linear combination of $m + 1$ solutions of the form of (10.22.1); thus,

$$\phi = A_0 e^{i\omega_0} + A_1 e^{i\omega_1} + \cdots + A_i e^{i\omega_i} + \cdots + A_m e^{i\omega_m}, \qquad (10.26.1)$$

where $\omega_0, \omega_1, \ldots, \omega_i, \ldots, \omega_m$ are the $m + 1$ roots of (10.24.3), ω_0 having a positive value, and $\omega_1, \ldots, \omega_m$ being approximately equal to $-\lambda_1, \ldots, -\lambda_m$, respectively. The A_0, A_1, etc., are constants determined by the initial conditions in the given reactor, as will be seen below.

10.27. Since all the terms beyond the first on the right-hand side of (10.26.1) have negative exponents, it is evident that as the time t following the sudden small change in reactivity increases, the contributions of these terms decrease rapidly to zero. These terms, therefore, make a transient contribution to the neutron flux, the values soon becoming negligible compared to the first term. Hence, after a short interval of time, which is of the order of something less than $1/\lambda_1$, where λ_1 is the smallest decay constant, i.e., corresponding to the most-delayed neutrons, (10.26.1) reduces to the first term only, i.e.,

$$\phi = A_0 e^{i\omega_0}.$$

In this case A_0 is evidently equal to ϕ_0, the flux at zero time, and so

$$\phi = \phi_0 e^{i\omega_0}.$$

Further, since ω_0, as seen above, has the dimensions of a reciprocal time, it may be set equal to $1/T$, so that

$$\phi = \phi_0 e^{t/T}. \qquad (10.27.1)$$

10.28. It is evident, from the definition of the reactor period as the time required for the neutron flux to increase by a factor of e, that T is here the reactor period after the lapse of sufficient time to permit the contributions of the transient terms to damp out. Hence, T, defined by

$$T \equiv \frac{1}{\omega_0}, \qquad (10.28.1)$$

is called the *stable reactor period*. The quantities $1/\omega_1$, $1/\omega_2$, etc., are sometimes referred to as *transient periods*, but they are negative in value and do not have any physical significance as reactor periods in the sense that $1/\omega_0$ does. They are the values of the parameter ω which satisfy the characteristic equation of the problem considered here. The dependence of ω_0 (or $1/T$) on the positive reactivity, as derived from (10.24.3), using the values of β_i and λ_i in Table 4.8, is shown in Fig. 10.28, for l equal to 10^{-3}, 10^{-4}, and 10^{-5} sec. It is seen that when ρ

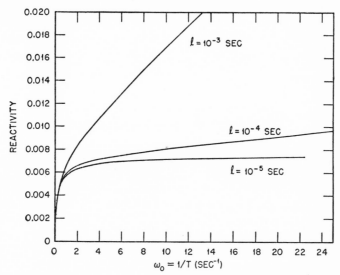

FIG. 10.28.   Reciprocal stable periods for positive values of reactivity

is small, e.g., less than about 0.005, the curves almost coincide. This means that, for systems having the same delayed neutron characteristics, the stable reactor period corresponding to a given reactivity is then virtually independent of l, the neutron lifetime. For higher reactivities, however, ω_0 increases, and hence the period decreases, with decreasing neutron lifetime. The physical interpretation of these results will be considered later.

The Inhour Formula

10.29. If ω in (10.24.2) is replaced by $1/T$, in accordance with (10.28.1), the former becomes

$$\rho = \frac{l}{Tk_{\text{eff}}} + \sum_{i=1}^{m} \frac{\beta_i}{1 + \lambda_i T},\tag{10.29.1}$$

so that the reactivity is related to the reactor period. The reactivity is sometimes expressed in terms of the "inverse hour" or "inhour" unit, this being defined as the reactivity which will make the reactor (stable) period equal to 1 hour, i.e., 3600 sec. Thus the value of the inhour unit is obtained by setting T in

(10.29.1) equal to 3600 sec, since λ_i is expressed in sec^{-1}. The reactivity of a reactor in inhours, represented by ρ_{ih}, is then obtained by dividing (10.29.1) by the corresponding value of the inhour unit; thus,

$$\rho_{ih} \equiv \frac{\dfrac{l}{Tk_{eff}} + \displaystyle\sum_{i=1}^{m} \frac{\beta_i}{1 + \lambda_i T}}{\dfrac{l}{3600k_{eff}} + \displaystyle\sum_{i=1}^{m} \frac{\beta_i}{1 + 3600\lambda_i}}. \tag{10.29.2}$$

This expression is known as the *inhour formula*, although (10.24.2), (10.24.3), and (10.29.1) are sometimes referred to by this name, since these equations are identical with (10.29.2) except for the fact that they express in different units the reactivity corresponding to a specified value of the reactor period.

One Group of Delayed Neutrons

10.30. Some indication of the relative importance of the stable and transient terms in (10.26.1) may be obtained by considering the simple case in which there is only one group of delayed neutrons with a decay constant λ equal to the properly weighted average for the five actual groups. For a single group of delayed neutrons, (10.24.2) becomes

$$\rho = \frac{l\omega}{k_{eff}} + \frac{\beta\omega}{\omega + \lambda}, \tag{10.30.1}$$

which is a quadratic equation in ω. In order to simplify the treatment without affecting the main conclusions, *it will be supposed that* k_{ex} *and* ρ *are small*, so that k_{eff} is approximately equal to unity. Equation (10.30.1) may then be written as

$$\rho \approx l\omega + \frac{\beta\omega}{\omega + \lambda} \tag{10.30.2}$$

or

$$l\omega^2 + (\beta - \rho + l\lambda)\omega - \lambda\rho \approx 0.$$

The solutions of this equation are

$$\omega = \frac{1}{2l}\left[-(\beta - \rho + l\lambda) \pm \sqrt{(\beta - \rho + l)^2 + 4l\lambda\rho}\right]$$

$$= -\frac{(\beta - \rho + l\lambda)}{2l}\left[1 \pm \sqrt{1 + \frac{4l\lambda\rho}{(\beta - \rho + l\lambda)^2}}\right].$$

If $(\beta - \rho + l\lambda)^2 \gg |2l\lambda\rho|$, this becomes

$$\omega \approx -\frac{(\beta - \rho + l\lambda)}{2l}\left\{1 \pm \left[1 + \frac{2l\lambda\rho}{(\beta - \rho + l\lambda)^2}\right]\right\},$$

and the two solutions are

$$\omega_0 \approx \frac{\lambda\rho}{\beta - \rho + l\lambda} \text{ and } \omega_1 \approx -\left(\frac{\beta - \rho + l\lambda}{l}\right),$$

where, in the case of ω_1, the second term in the square brackets has been neglected in comparison with unity, since $(\beta - \rho + l\lambda)^2 \gg |2l\lambda\rho|$.

10.31. For a thermal reactor, l may be 10^{-3} sec or less, and the average λ for the delayed neutrons is about 0.08 sec^{-1};[*] suppose the reactivity ρ is 0.0025, then $2l\lambda\rho$ is 0.4×10^{-6}.   Since β is 0.0075, it is seen that $(\beta - \rho + l\lambda)^2$ is 26×10^{-6}; and this is sufficiently greater than 0.4×10^{-6} for the present approximation to be applicable with fair accuracy for reactivities of 0.0025 or less.   Under these conditions $l\lambda$, which is about 8×10^{-5}, is appreciably less than $\beta - \rho$, i.e., 5×10^{-3} or more; the former may thus be neglected in comparison with the latter, and the two solutions of (10.30.2) become

$$\omega_0 \approx \frac{\lambda\rho}{\beta - \rho} \quad \text{and} \quad \omega_1 \approx -\left(\frac{\beta - \rho}{l}\right). \tag{10.31.1}$$

In cases of practical interest and, in any event, when ρ is small, as postulated above, $\beta > \rho$ so that $\beta - \rho$ is positive; hence, provided ρ is positive, ω_0 represents the positive solution of (10.30.2) and ω_1 is the negative solution.

10.32. The expression for the flux variation with time is

$$\phi = A_0 e^{t\omega_0} + A_1 e^{t\omega_1}, \tag{10.32.1}$$

while that for the delayed neutron precursor will be, by (10.22.2),

$$C = B_0 e^{t\omega_0} + B_1 e^{t\omega_1}. \tag{10.32.2}$$

It would appear, at first sight, that there are here four arbitrary constants, but actually only two are independent, because ϕ and C are related by (10.15.1). In the present case, this reduces to

$$\frac{\partial C}{\partial t} \approx -\lambda C + \frac{k}{p}\beta\Sigma_a\phi, \tag{10.32.3}$$

for one group of delayed neutrons.   Upon inserting the values of ϕ and C, given by (10.32.1) and (10.32.2), respectively, the result is

$$\frac{\partial C}{\partial t} = -\lambda(B_0 e^{t\omega_0} + B_1 e^{t\omega_1}) + \frac{k}{p}\beta\Sigma_a(A_0 e^{t\omega_0} + A_1 e^{t\omega_1}).$$

By differentiation of (10.32.2), it is found that

$$\frac{\partial C}{\partial t} = B_0\omega_0 e^{t\omega_0} + B_1\omega_1 e^{t\omega_1},$$

---

[*] The appropriate average decay constant is the reciprocal of the average mean life, defined by $\Sigma\beta_i t_i / \Sigma\beta_i$; hence λ is given by $\beta / \Sigma\beta_i t_i = 0.0075/0.094 = 0.08$.   The use of this definition gives (asymptotic) results equivalent to those obtained by taking the five groups of delayed neutrons into consideration (cf. § 10.43).

and comparison of the coefficients of $e^{t\omega_0}$ and $e^{t\omega_1}$ in the two foregoing expressions leads to

$$B_0 = \frac{k}{p} \cdot \frac{\beta\Sigma_a}{\omega_0 + \lambda} A_0 \quad \text{and} \quad B_1 = \frac{k}{p} \cdot \frac{\beta\Sigma_a}{\omega_1 + \lambda} A_1.$$

Upon introducing the values of ω_0 and ω_1 given by (10.31.1), these relationships become

$$B_0 = \frac{k}{p} \cdot \frac{(\beta - \rho)\Sigma_a}{\lambda} A_0 \quad \text{and} \quad B_1 = -\frac{k}{p} \cdot \frac{l\beta\Sigma_a}{\beta - \rho} A_1, \quad (10.32.4)$$

where, as before, λl has been neglected in comparison with $\beta - \rho$ in evaluating B_1.

10.33. It is evident from (10.32.4) that B_0 and B_1 are related to A_0 and A_1 by quantities which are determined by the microscopic properties of the reactor, and hence there are only two arbitrary constants to be determined. To evaluate them, therefore, two boundary conditions are required, and these are obtained as follows. First, in accordance with the postulates already made, before the sudden change in the effective multiplication factor at time $t = 0$, the reactor has been operating in the steady state, with a flux ϕ_0. Hence, by (10.32.1),

$$\phi(t = 0) = \phi_0 = A_0 + A_1. \quad (10.33.1)$$

10.34. Second, since the reactor has been in a steady (or equilibrium) state up to $t = 0$, the concentration of neutron precursors will be constant (C_0), and $\partial C/\partial t$ will be zero at time $t = 0$. Consequently, from (10.32.3), it follows that

$$0 = -\lambda C_0 + \frac{k}{p}\beta\Sigma_a\phi_0,$$

or

$$C_0 = \frac{k}{p} \cdot \frac{\beta}{\lambda}\Sigma_a\phi_0. \quad (10.34.1)$$

Further, from (10.32.2), at $t = 0$,

$$C(t = 0) = C_0 = B_0 + B_1. \quad (10.34.2)$$

10.35. Upon introducing into (10.34.2) the values for C_0, B_0, and B_1 given by (10.34.1) and (10.32.4) the result is

$$\frac{\beta}{\lambda}\Sigma_a\phi_0 = \frac{(\beta - \rho)\Sigma_a}{\lambda} A_0 - \frac{l\beta\Sigma_a}{\beta - \rho} A_1.$$

Replacing A_1 by $\phi_0 - A_0$, in accordance with (10.33.1), cancelling the Σ_a's and rearranging, it is found that

$$A_0 = \frac{\dfrac{\beta}{\lambda} + \dfrac{l\beta}{\beta - \rho}}{\dfrac{\beta - \rho}{\lambda} + \dfrac{l\beta}{\beta - \rho}} \phi_0 \approx \frac{\beta}{\beta - \rho} \phi_0, \quad (10.35.1)$$

where the second term in both numerator and denominator, which is of the order of 10^{-3}, has been neglected in comparison with the first, of the order of 10^{-1}, in each case. With the value of A_0 given by (10.35.1), equation (10.33.1) leads to

$$A_1 \approx - \frac{\rho}{\beta - \rho} \phi_0. \tag{10.35.2}$$

Introducing these results, together with (10.31.1), into (10.32.1), the final expression for the neutron flux at a given point as a function of time, in the special case of one group of delayed neutrons, and where the reactivity is small, is

$$\phi = \phi_0 \left[\frac{\beta}{\beta - \rho} e^{\frac{\lambda \rho t}{\beta - \rho}} - \frac{\rho}{\beta - \rho} e^{-\frac{(\beta - \rho)t}{l}} \right]. \tag{10.35.3}$$

It is of interest to note that since $\beta - \rho$ is positive, under the conditions that (10.35.3) is applicable, the second (or transient) term in the brackets has a negative coefficient, provided ρ is positive. The neutron flux is thus the difference of two terms, one of which increases while the other decreases with increasing time.

10.36. To illustrate the general behavior, a specific example will be considered. Suppose, as before, that l is 10^{-3} sec and ρ is 0.0025, while λ is 0.08 sec^{-1} and β is 0.0075; as already seen, these figures satisfy the conditions for which the foregoing approximations are applicable. Equation (10.35.3) then becomes

$$\phi = \phi_0(1.5e^{0.04t} - 0.5e^{-5t}),$$

and each term separately and their difference are plotted in Fig. 10.36.

10.37. There are a number of points of interest to which attention may be drawn. First, it is seen that the second (or transient) term dies

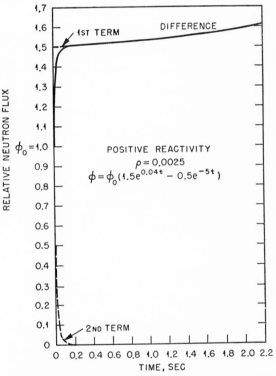

FIG. 10.36.   Change of neutron flux with time for positive reactivity

out within 1 sec; its contribution is then about 0.2 per cent of the total flux. In general, the time taken for the transient to damp out to negligible proportions is of the order of $5/|\omega_1|$, i.e., $5l/(\beta - \rho)$. Subsequently, the neutron flux is essentially equal to the first (or stable) term in (10.35.3). In these circumstances

$$\phi \approx \phi_0 \frac{\beta}{\beta - \rho} e^{\frac{\lambda \rho t}{\beta - \rho}},$$

and the stable reactor period is given by

$$T \approx \frac{\beta - \rho}{\lambda \rho}, \tag{10.37.1}$$

which is equal to 25 sec, in the example cited above. This may be compared with a calculated period of 0.4 sec for a reactivity of 0.0025 with all the neutrons liberated promptly. For very small reactivities, ρ may be neglected in comparison with β, and (10.37.1) gives

$$T \approx \frac{\beta}{\lambda \rho}, \tag{10.37.2}$$

for the stable period.

10.38. It will be noted, further, from Fig. 10.36 that immediately after the sudden change in the multiplication of the reactor, i.e., at times soon after $t = 0$, the flux rises rapidly. The rate approximates, in fact, that for the case in which all the neutrons are prompt. However, after a short time the effect of the delayed neutrons begins to be felt, and the flux increases more slowly.

10.39. The initial slope of the plot of ϕ against t may be obtained from (10.32.1) by differentiating with respect to time, and then setting $t = 0$. The result is

$$\frac{\partial \phi}{\partial t} \text{ (at } t = 0) = A_0 \omega_0 + A_1 \omega_1,$$

and introducing the values of A_0, A_1, ω_0, and ω_1, from (10.31.1), (10.35.1), and (10.35.2), it follows that

$$\frac{1}{\phi_0} \cdot \frac{\partial \phi_0}{\partial t} = \frac{\lambda \rho \beta}{(\beta - \rho)^2} + \frac{\rho}{l}. \tag{10.39.1}$$

From (10.27.1)

$$\frac{1}{\phi} \cdot \frac{d\phi}{dt} = \frac{1}{T},$$

and hence the left-hand side of (10.39.1) may be regarded as the reciprocal of the stable reactor period at $t = 0$. Representing this period by T_0, it is seen that

$$\frac{1}{T_0} = \frac{\lambda \rho \beta}{(\beta - \rho)^2} + \frac{\rho}{l}. \tag{10.39.2}$$

10.40. For moderately small values of ρ, the first term on the right-hand side of (10.39.2) may be neglected. In the example considered above, the first term in the equation would be equal to 0.06, while the second is 2.5. For smaller values of ρ, the relative difference is greater still.   Consequently, (10.39.2) may be written as

$$T_0 \approx \frac{l}{\rho} \approx \frac{l}{k_{ex}}, \qquad (10.40.1)$$

the final result being based on the fact that ρ is equal to k_{ex}/k_{eff}, by definition, while k_{eff} is not very different from unity.   It is seen that the reactor period is identical with that given by (10.8.2) for the case where all the fission neutrons are prompt neutrons.   Thus, for small reactivities, the initial rate of growth of the flux when there are delayed neutrons is almost the same as if all the neutrons were prompt.

10.41. The physical interpretation of this result is as follows.   The number of delayed neutrons contributed to the chain reaction at any instant is proportional to the neutron flux at some previous time, while the number of delayed neutron precursors produced by fissions, i.e., the number of neutrons being delayed, at the same instant is proportional to the flux at that given time.   For a short time after the change in multiplication, especially if the reactivity is small, the neutron flux will not change very greatly; the number of delayed neutrons contributed to the system will then not be appreciably less than those being delayed.   Hence, for a very short time, the reactor behaves as if all the fission neutrons were prompt, and the flux increases with a period of approximately l/k_{ex}.   However, as the neutron flux grows with time, fewer delayed neutrons enter the chain-reacting system than are being delayed, and the rate of increase of flux gradually falls off.   Ultimately, the rate of growth of the neutron flux is determined by the stable period, as given by (10.37.1), or by (10.37.2) if ρ is small.

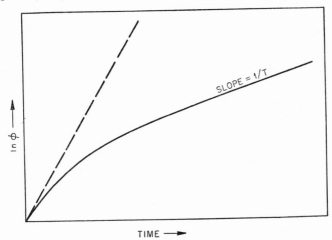

Fɪɢ. 10.42.   Effect of delayed neutrons on rate of increase of flux with time

10.42. The results derived above may be summarized by plotting $\ln \phi$ as a function of time, as in Fig. 10.42.   The actual variation of $\ln \phi$ is shown by the full curve, while that for the case in which all the fission neutrons are treated as prompt neutrons is indicated by the dotted line. The full curve becomes linear as the time increases, and its slope is equal to the reciprocal of the stable period of the reactor.

SMALL REACTIVITIES

10.43. Returning to the general problem of (10.24.2) and m groups of delayed neutrons, two extreme cases will be considered. In these cases it is possible to derive simple expressions for the stable period observed after the transient terms have damped out. First, suppose that k_{ex} and ρ are small; it will be evident from the plot of ρ against ω (Fig. 10.25), that ω_0 will then be small. Consequently, ω_0 may be neglected in comparison with the λ_i's in the denominators of the summation terms in (10.24.2). Hence, when the transients have damped out, this equation becomes

$$\rho \approx \frac{l\omega_0}{k_{eff}} + \omega_0 \sum_{i=1}^{m} \frac{\beta_i}{\lambda_i},$$

or, since ω_0 is equal to $1/T$,

$$\rho \approx \frac{l}{k_{eff}T} + \frac{1}{T} \sum_{i=1}^{m} \frac{\beta_i}{\lambda_i}.$$

Upon rearrangement, this gives

$$T \approx \frac{1}{\rho} \left[\frac{l}{k_{eff}} + \sum_{i=1}^{m} \frac{\beta_i}{\lambda_i} \right]$$
$$\approx \frac{1}{\rho} \left[\frac{l}{k_{eff}} + \sum_{i=1}^{m} \beta_i t_i \right], \tag{10.43.1}$$

where, as before, the t_i's are the mean lives of the delayed neutron precursors or the mean decay times of the delayed neutrons. For thermal reactors, l is of the order of 10^{-3} sec or less, and, since k_{eff} is not very different from unity, the first term in the bracket is about 10^{-3} sec or less. On the other hand, the second term, which is the weighted mean delay time, is about 0.1 sec, as seen earlier. Hence, l/k_{eff} may be neglected, and (10.43.1) becomes

$$T \approx \frac{1}{\rho} \sum_{i=1}^{m} \beta_i t_i. \tag{10.43.2}$$

It is of interest to observe that by defining the mean decay constant λ for a single (average) group of delayed neutrons as $\beta/\Sigma\beta_i t_i$, as was done above (§ 10.31, footnote), equations (10.37.2) and (10.43.2), for very small reactivities, become identical.

10.44. In the derivation of (10.43.1), and hence of (10.43.2), it was postulated that ω_0 is small in comparison with any of the λ_i's, and thus, in comparison with the smallest of them; this is equivalent to saying that T, equal to $1/\omega_0$, is taken to be large in comparison with the largest t_i. As seen from Table 4.8, this is about 80 sec, and as a rough indication it may be stated that the approximation represented by (10.43.1) will apply provided T is greater than about 250 sec. Upon inserting this value in (10.43.2) and recalling that $\Sigma\beta_i t_i$ is about 0.1, it follows that the approximations will be valid if

$$\rho < \frac{0.1}{250} < 0.0004.$$

In other words, for very small reactivities, about 0.0004 or less, (10.43.2) will be applicable. Since $\Sigma\beta_i t_i$ is a constant for a given fissionable material, it follows from this equation that, under these conditions, the reactor period T is inversely proportional to the reactivity. Consequently, for a given (small) reactivity, the reactor period will be the same, independent of the neutron lifetime, l, for any thermal reactor employing the same fuel material. It is because it leads to this useful result that the particular definition of reactivity given above was chosen.

10.45. For small reactivities, k_{eff} is close to unity, and ρ is not very different from k_{ex}; hence, from (10.43.2), the reactor period is seen to be equal to the weighted average delay time divided by k_{ex}. This is identical with the result obtained by the qualitative treatment in § 10.14. Physically, this means that when the reactivity is small, the rate of increase of neutron flux, for a given reactivity, is determined essentially by the neutron delay time, and is independent of the much shorter neutron lifetime.*

LARGE REACTIVITIES

10.46. The second asymptotic case to be considered is that in which the reactivity is large, that is, at the right of Fig. 10.25; ω_0 is then large in comparison with any of the λ_i's. After the transients have died out, (10.24.2) reduces to

$$\rho \approx \frac{l\omega_0}{k_{\text{eff}}} + \sum_{i=1}^{m} \beta_i$$
$$\approx \frac{l}{Tk_{\text{eff}}} + \beta. \tag{10.46.1}$$

Hence the stable period is now given by

$$T \approx \frac{l}{k_{\text{eff}}} \cdot \frac{1}{\rho - \beta}. \tag{10.46.2}$$

By its derivation, this equation can hold only when ρ is large and positive; in fact it has significance only when $\rho > \beta$, for otherwise T would have a negative value. If β can be neglected in comparison with ρ, equation (10.46.2) becomes

$$T \approx \frac{l}{k_{\text{eff}}\rho} = \frac{l}{k_{\text{ex}}}. \tag{10.46.3}$$

* While equation (10.43.2) holds only for very small reactivities, it can be seen from (10.37.1) that the reactor period, for a given reactivity, is still independent of the neutron lifetime for somewhat higher values of ρ, e.g., up to about 0.005 (see Fig. 10.28).

Hence, for reactivities, or excess multiplication, larger than β, that is, larger than 0.0075, the reactor period becomes very small, approaching that for the case in which there are no delayed neutrons [cf. equation (10.8.2)]. The reactor is then said to "outrun" the delayed neutrons. The reason why the latter no longer have any considerable influence is that, if $\rho > \beta$, the effective multiplication will exceed unity even if the delayed neutrons are disregarded entirely. Hence, the neutron flux can multiply rapidly due to the prompt neutrons alone, and the reactor then behaves virtually as if the reactivity is $\rho - \beta$ with no delayed neutrons. The actual neutron generation time (or lifetime) now determines the rate of increase of the flux, and hence the reactor period, in agreement with (10.46.2) or (10.46.3).

10.47. The state at which the reactor is critical on prompt neutrons alone is referred to as *prompt critical* (§ 4.78). The required condition can be obtained from (10.18.1). If the delayed neutron source term is ignored, this can be readily transformed into

$$(1 - \beta)k_{\text{eff}} - 1 = \frac{l}{\phi} \cdot \frac{\partial \phi}{\partial t}.$$

For the reactor to be critical, the flux must not vary with time, so that $\partial \phi / \partial t$ is zero; hence, the condition for prompt critical is

$$(1 - \beta)k_{\text{eff}} - 1 = 0$$

or

$$k_{\text{eff}} = \frac{1}{1 - \beta}. \tag{10.47.1}$$

It follows, therefore, from the definition of reactivity in (10.24.1) that at prompt critical

$$\rho = \beta,$$

so that the reactivity is then equal to the fraction of delayed neutrons. A thermal reactor in which the fissionable material is uranium-235 thus becomes prompt critical when the reactivity is 0.0075; the effective multiplication factor, as given by (10.47.1), is very close to 1.0075, i.e., $1 + \beta$. If k_{eff} exceeds this value, the neutron flux will increase with great rapidity and the reactor will soon go out of control.* If the effective multiplication factor is less than 1.0075, control of the reactor is feasible because of the delayed neutrons, although the period decreases as ρ approaches β, that is, as the reactivity approaches the value 0.0075.

NEGATIVE REACTIVITIES

10.48. The discussion of special cases has so far dealt with positive reactivity or excess multiplication resulting from an increase in the multiplication factor of the system. However, equation (10.7.3), for prompt neutrons, and (10.24.2),

---

* The reactivity of a reactor is sometimes expressed in terms of the "dollar" unit, proposed by L. Slotin. The "dollar" is the reactivity that will make a reactor prompt critical. A "cent" represents one-hundredth of the dollar reactivity.

which includes the effect of delayed neutrons, as well as those equations derived directly from the latter, e.g., (10.35.3) and (10.43.2),* hold for negative, as well as positive, values of the reactivity. In other words, they will apply when the effective multiplication factor of the reactor undergoes a sudden decrease. The case where all the neutrons produced in fission are prompt requires no special consideration, but that in which there are delayed neutrons merits examination.

10.49. It will be apparent from Fig. 10.25 that, in the general case, for a negative reactivity all $m + 1$ solutions of (10.24.2) have negative values. The expression for the flux as a function of time will then consist of a series of $m + 1$ terms with negative exponents, and the magnitude of each term will then decrease with increasing time. Although the first term, with the smallest numerical (negative) value of ω_0, will decrease at a slower rate, and ultimately yield a stable period, it will not be so dominant as when the reactivity is positive.

10.50. The effect of the delayed neutrons may be seen more clearly by considering the case in which there is one group of delayed neutrons with an average decay constant. Equation (10.35.3) will be applicable for almost any negative value of ρ, especially for large values, for the approximations made

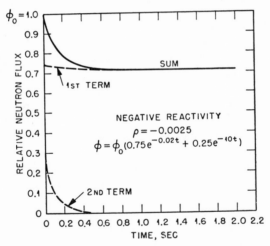

FIG. 10.50a.   Change of neutron flux with time for negative reactivity

in deriving this equation are more justifiable under these conditions.† Suppose now, that the reactivity is suddenly decreased by 0.0025, so that ρ is -0.0025; taking the same values for l and λ as before, (10.35.3) now becomes

$$\phi = \phi_0(0.75e^{-0.02t} + 0.25e^{-10t}).$$

---

* It should be noted that (10.46.2) and (10.46.3) hold only if ρ is large and positive.

† The main approximations are that $(\beta - \rho + l\lambda)^2 \gg |2l\lambda\rho|$ and that $\beta - \rho \gg l\lambda$. It is readily seen that, with l equal to 0.001 sec and λ to 0.08 sec^{-1}, these conditions are satisfied for almost any negative value of ρ.

It will be noted that the coefficients of both terms are now positive, whereas the exponents are both negative. However, the large negative exponent in the second term makes this damp out fairly rapidly, as shown in Fig. 10.50a. When this term ceases to be significant, the stable reactor period is $-1/0.02$, i.e., -50 sec, for ρ equal to -0.0025, compared with 25 sec when ρ is 0.0025 positive. If all the fission neutrons were prompt, the reactor periods would be -0.4 and 0.4 sec, respectively. Thus, although the presence of delayed neutrons slows down the rate of increase of the flux when the reactivity is positive, it slows down the rate of decrease to an even greater extent when the reactivity is negative (Fig. 10.50b). This makes it impossible to reduce the neutron flux

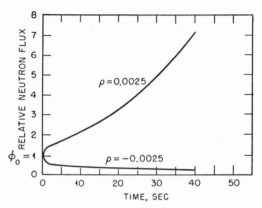

Fig. 10.50b.   Comparison of positive and negative reactivities

in a reactor more rapidly than is permitted by the longest delayed neutron period (cf. § 10.52).

10.51. Since the arguments leading to (10.40.1) apply irrespective of the sign of the reactivity, it follows that immediately after the effective multiplication factor of a reactor is suddenly decreased, after being in the steady state for some time, the rate of decrease of the neutron flux is the same as if all the fission neutrons were prompt. The physical interpretation is analogous to that given in § 10.41 for the case in which the effective multiplication is increased. After a short time, however, the delayed neutron effect causes a considerable slowing down of the rate of decrease of the flux.

10.52. The foregoing discussion is based on the approximation of one group of delayed neutrons. In the general case of m delayed groups, it can be seen from Fig. 10.25 that, when ρ has a large negative value, then ω_0, corresponding to the stable period, will approach $-\lambda_1$, where λ_1 is the smallest decay constant for the delayed neutron precursors. The stable period, equal to $1/\omega_0$, is then $-1/\lambda_1$, i.e., -80.2 sec (see Table 4.8). Consequently, if a reactor is shut down suddenly, by introducing a large negative reactivity, the flux will fall off rapidly at first, but in a short time, when the transient terms have damped out, it will decay exponentially with a period of -80 sec. Apart from the effects of secondary neutrons (cf. § 4.80), this period determines the maximum rate of shut-down of a reactor after the transients have died out.

PROBLEMS

1. Plot the thermal flux as a function of time for a reactor in which a step change in reactivity of 0.0025 is introduced. Assume the reactor to be in equilibrium initially, treat the delayed neutrons as a single group with constants $\lambda = 0.08$ sec^{-1} and $\beta = 0.0075$, and consider three cases with neutron lifetimes of 10^{-4}, 10^{-5}, and 10^{-6} sec.

2. Solve the time-dependent diffusion equation for an instantaneous plane source emitting one neutron per cm^2 to obtain the so-called *time-dependent diffusion kernel*. That is, let $S(x, t) = \delta(x)\delta(t)$. At what time after the source burst at any given point in the medium is the neutron intensity a maximum? At a distance of 200 cm from the source, what is this time lag in graphite?

3. If the source in Problem 2 is an oscillating source,

$$S(x, t) = \delta(x)e^{i\omega t},$$

obtain the neutron density as a function of space and time. The neutron density is propagated as a damped wave. Find the velocity of the wave, the wave length, and the attenuation distance of the wave, i.e., the distance in which its intensity is reduced by a factor of e.

Chapter XI

REACTOR CONTROL

DISTURBANCE OF NEUTRON ECONOMY

INTRODUCTION

11.1. If a reactor is to operate in a steady state, the effective multiplication factor must remain at unity, that is to say, the system must be exactly critical. However, if a reactor were constructed such that it was just critical, it would not stay in this condition very long. Several factors serve to change the effective multiplication of the system, most of them tending to cause a gradual reduction in the neutron flux and the power level with time. The main sources of disturbance of the neutron economy to be considered here are fuel depletion, fission product poisoning, and temperature effects. In addition, apparently extraneous factors, such as the barometric pressure, for example, in the case of a large air-cooled reactor, have some influence. Changes in the pressure are accompanied by changes in the thermal neutron absorption by the nitrogen ($\sigma_a = 1.5$ barns) of the air circulated through the reactor for cooling purposes.

11.2. As a reactor operates, the quantity of fissionable material in the core decreases. If operation is to continue for an appreciable time, therefore, more fuel material must be used than the minimum quantity required for the system to be critical. The amount of depletion or "burn-up" which a reactor can tolerate depends on a variety of conditions, such as the size, structure, composition, and radiation damage to the fuel units. In general, the maximum burn-up which can be tolerated in power reactors is 5 to 10 per cent, and this means that 5 to 10 per cent more fissionable material must be placed in the reactor when it is first put into operation. In other words, the reactor must have a few per cent extra reactivity built into it in order to allow for fuel depletion.

TEMPERATURE EFFECTS

11.3. When a reactor operates, its temperature rises because of the energy liberated. No matter how efficient the cooling, parts of the system will inevitably be at temperatures above those existing when the reactor is subcritical. Since the fuel and moderator materials expand upon heating, their densities

314

decrease.   One result is that the diffusion length and the age of thermal neutrons are increased.   The probability of neutron leakage during slowing down to thermal energies and before capture as thermal neutrons increases.   This means that the critical mass will be greater at the higher temperatures.   Sufficient fuel material, therefore, must be included in the reactor to allow for this extra requirement.

11.4. Further, one of the factors determining the critical mass of a reactor is the relationship among the fission, absorption, and scattering cross sections for thermal neutrons of fuel and moderator.   At the higher temperatures inside the reactor when it is in operation, the average energy of the thermal neutrons will be greater than at atmospheric temperatures at which the reactor is constructed. There will consequently be changes in the diffusion length, in the age of thermal neutrons, in the average number (η) of fast neutrons produced per thermal neutron captured, in the thermal utilization f, and in the resonance escape probability, all of which depend on the cross sections.

11.5. If the fission and absorption cross sections for thermal neutrons change according to the $1/v$ law, then η and f would be unaffected.   The resonance escape probability, however, will be influenced by the so-called nuclear "Doppler effect."*   Because of the increased kinetic energy of the target (uranium-238) nuclei with increasing temperature, the width of a resonance is increased, but the height of the peak is decreased, the total area beneath the resonance curve remaining constant.   If the resonance absorption cross sections are large, so that essentially all neutrons with energies in the resonance region are captured, the widening of the region will result in a decrease in the resonance escape probability as the reactor operates and the temperature rises.

EFFECT OF FISSION PRODUCTS

11.6. With continued operation of a reactor, the nuclides formed in fission and their many decay products accumulate; some of these may have large cross sections for the absorption of neutrons, and so they can act as poisons.   If such poisons are produced in appreciable amounts, either as direct fission fragments or as a result of radioactive decay, they will affect the neutron balance in the reactor.   Because decay products continue to form even after the power level of a reactor has been reduced, the concentration of a poison may increase to a maximum after shut-down.   In order to be able to start up a reactor at any time after shut-down, it may thus be necessary to include additional reactivity to "over-ride" the fission product poisoning.

11.7. Two nuclides, namely, xenon-135 and samarium-149, are of particular interest in this connection because of their large capture cross sections for thermal neutrons.   One of the direct products of fission, formed in 5.6 per cent of

* H. A. Bethe, *Rev. Mod. Phys.*, 9, 140 (1937).

the slow-neutron fissions of uranium-235, is tellurium-135; this undergoes a series of stages of negative beta decay, as follows:

$$\text{Te}^{135} \xrightarrow{2\text{m}} \text{I}^{135} \xrightarrow{6.7\text{h}} \text{Xe}^{135} \xrightarrow{9.2\text{h}} \text{Cs}^{135} \xrightarrow{2\times10^4\text{y}} \text{Ba}^{135} \text{ (stable)}.$$

Of these nuclides, xenon-135 has the high absorption cross section of about 3.5×10^6 barns for thermal neutrons at ordinary temperatures, and since it originates from tellurium-135, which is formed in relatively high yield in fission, the effect of xenon-135 on the neutron balance in a reactor can be quite considerable. Samarium-149 is a stable species, being the end-product of the decay chain

$$\text{Nd}^{149} \xrightarrow{1.7\text{h}} \text{Pm}^{149} \xrightarrow{47\text{h}} \text{Sm}^{149} \text{ (stable)},$$

which occurs in about 1.4 per cent of fissions. Its absorption cross section for thermal neutrons is about 5.3×10^4 barns. Although this is large, it is not as large as that of xenon-135, and since it is formed in smaller amounts, samarium-149 is a less important poison.

CONTROL RODS*

FUNCTIONS OF CONTROL RODS

11.8. It is apparent from the foregoing considerations that, if a reactor is to operate continuously for any period of time, or if it is to be started up soon after a shut-down, there must be available latent multiplication or reactivity to be called upon as required. This reactivity will not be necessary when the reactor is first operated, but it will have to be increasingly drawn upon as the temperature rises, the fuel material is burned up, and the fission products accumulate. The problem presented by these requirements is solved by building excess reactivity or excess multiplication into the reactor; this is achieved by putting more than the minimum critical amount of fissionable material into the core, and then compensating for the excess by means of *control rods*. For a thermal reactor these control rods consist of bars of cadmium or of boron steel, the isotopes Cd^{113} and B^{10} having large capture cross sections for thermal neutrons. When first set into operation the control rods are inserted into the reactor so that they absorb sufficient neutrons to keep the system just critical. As time goes on, and the effective multiplication factor of the reactor begins to fall below unity, due to the causes mentioned above, additional reactivity is provided by gradual withdrawal of the control rods. Thus, the decreased absorption of the rods exactly compensates for the decrease in multiplication due to fuel burn-up, temperature effects, and poisons.

11.9. The control rods are also of vital importance in the start-up and shut-down of the reactor. When not in operation, the rods are inserted so deeply into

---

* The theory of the effectiveness of control rods was worked out by F. L. Friedman, A. M. Weinberg, and J. A. Wheeler, and by L. W. Nordheim and R. Scalettar.

the core that the multiplication factor is well below unity.   In order to start up
the reactor, the control rods are gradually withdrawn until the reactivity is
slightly positive.   The reactor is then supercritical and the neutron flux increases, as shown in Chapter X.   When the desired power level is reached the
rods are driven into the reactor core to a position where $k_{\text{eff}} = 1$.   The flux and
power level then remain constant, except for statistical variations.   Conversely,
in order to shut down the reactor, the rods are dropped rapidly into the core,
thus increasing the parasitic capture of neutrons and decreasing the effective
multiplication factor below unity.   The effect of withdrawing the control rods
is thus to increase the reactivity, while insertion of the rods decreases it.   The
consequent over-all time effect on the neutron flux has been considered in the
preceding chapter.

11.10. In addition to increasing parasitic capture, a control rod has another
effect in reducing the effective multiplication factor.   Because of the strong absorption of neutrons in the rod, the thermal flux distribution in the reactor undergoes a marked change, as shown in Fig. 11.10.   The dotted line indicates the

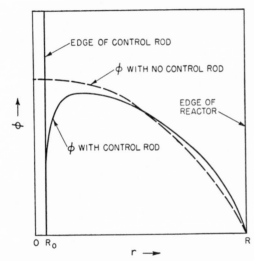

FIG. 11.10.   Neutron flux distribution in reactor with and without control rod

distribution in the absence of a control rod, and the full line shows the effect of
introducing the rod.   The flux now goes virtually to zero at the rod, as well as at
the extrapolated boundary of the reactor.   As seen in the figure, this leads to a
relatively higher thermal neutron flux near the boundary, and consequently the
probability of leakage of thermal neutrons is increased.   Physically, the absorption of thermal neutrons by the rod means that relatively more fissions take place
in the outer regions of the reactor, thus leading to an increase in the flux and the
leakage, and a decrease in the multiplication.

THEORY OF CONTROL RODS: ONE-GROUP TREATMENT*

11.11. The theoretical calculation of the reactivity equivalent of a control rod, in terms of known properties of a reactor, is relatively simple in the case of a large, finite, cylindrical, bare homogeneous reactor, of radius R and height H, with a cylindrical control rod, of radius R_0, at its axis (Fig. 11.11). In order to simplify

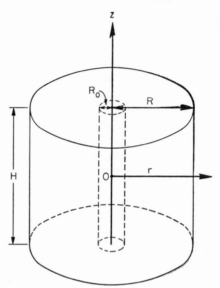

FIG. 11.11. Cylindrical reactor with central control rod

the treatment it will be supposed that, when the control rod is pushed in, it expels an equivalent cylinder of the reactor core, and that, when the rod is withdrawn, it does not leave a hole along the axis of the reactor core. The result of this assumption is to overestimate the effect of the control rod to some extent; pushing in the rod would not only introduce a strong neutron absorber, it would also remove some of the active material from the core.

11.12. The problem will be treated by the one-group method, in which all the neutrons are supposed to be produced, to diffuse, and be captured at one energy (§ 8.15). The modified one-group critical equation (8.16.4) is then

$$B^2 = \frac{k-1}{M^2},\tag{11.12.1}$$

where $M^2 = L^2 + \tau$ is the migration area, and B^2 is the buckling. Consequently, for the reactor to be critical

$$k = M^2B^2 + 1.\tag{11.12.2}$$

---

* See R. Scalettar and L. W. Nordheim, MDDC–42.

11.13. As seen earlier (§ 7.50, *et seq.*), in the treatment of a finite cylindrical reactor, the variables r and z may be separated, and B^2 may be written as

$$B^2 = \alpha^2 + \beta^2. \tag{11.13.1}$$

Since, with the control rod out, the reactor in the present case is just a finite cylinder of height H and radius R, the results obtained in Chapter VII may be used; thus,

$$\alpha^2 = \left(\frac{2.405}{R}\right)^2 \quad \text{and} \quad \beta^2 = \left(\frac{\pi}{H}\right)^2,$$

so that

$$B^2 = \left(\frac{2.405}{R}\right)^2 + \left(\frac{\pi}{H}\right)^2. \tag{11.13.2}$$

It will be recalled that the boundary conditions are that the neutron flux shall be finite and non-negative and go to zero at the (extrapolated) boundary of the reactor.*

11.14. When the control rod is inserted, the boundary conditions are changed. It is assumed, for the present treatment, that the control rod is "black" to thermal neutrons, so that every thermal neutron striking it is absorbed. Consequently, neutrons travel from the reactor into the rod, but none return. This introduces a new boundary condition, namely, that the neutron flux shall go to zero within the rod at R', where $R' = R_0 - d$, and d is the linear extrapolation distance for cylinders. According to transport theory, d may vary from $0.71\lambda_t$ for plane surfaces to $\frac{4}{3}\lambda_t$ for surfaces with radius of curvature small compared to λ_t (§ 14.56).

11.15. Since the r and z variables are separable, the introduction of the control rod will not affect the flux distribution $Z(z)$ dependent on z only; hence the value of the β^2 term in the buckling will be the same as before, namely, $(\pi/H)^2$. The value of the function $\Theta(r)$, however, will be changed.

11.16. As seen in (§ 7.53), the general solution of the equation for $\Theta(r)$ is given in this case by

$$\Theta(r) = AJ_0(\alpha r) + CY_0(\alpha r), \tag{11.16.1}$$

where A and C are arbitrary constants, and J_0 and Y_0 are zero-order Bessel functions of the first and second kinds, respectively. In the treatment of the cylindrical reactor, the second term was rejected because it required the flux to go to $-\infty$ at the axis. However, in the present case, this term cannot be excluded by the requirement that the flux shall be everywhere finite and non-negative, since the region is annular and does not include the axis of the cylinder.

11.17. Introducing the boundary condition that the neutron flux is zero at the extrapolated boundary, i.e., when $r = R$, it follows from (11.16.1) that

$$AJ_0(\alpha R) + CY_0(\alpha R) = 0.$$

* As before, the values of R and H are supposed to include the linear extrapolation distances.

This gives a relationship between A and C, namely,

$$C = -\frac{AJ_0(\alpha R)}{Y_0(\alpha R)},$$

and, hence (11.16.1) becomes

$$\Theta(r) = A\left[J_0(\alpha r) - \frac{J_0(\alpha R)}{Y_0(\alpha R)} Y_0(\alpha r)\right]. \tag{11.17.1}$$

The value of A, which is here merely a proportionality constant, is determined by the power level of the reactor.

11.18. In a large thermal reactor, where $R_0 \ll R$, the change in α required to make the reactor critical with the control rod inserted is small. Let α_0 be the value of α for the reactor without the control rod· then the difference may be written as

$$\alpha = \alpha_0 + \Delta\alpha, \tag{11.18.1}$$

where $\Delta\alpha$ is small. The zero-order Bessel functions can then be represented by

$$\begin{aligned} J_0(\alpha R) &= J_0[(\alpha_0 + \Delta\alpha)R] \\ &\approx J_0(\alpha_0 R) + \frac{dJ_0(\alpha_0 R)}{d(\alpha_0 R)} \Delta\alpha R \\ &\approx J_0(\alpha_0 R) - J_1(\alpha_0 R) \Delta\alpha R. \end{aligned} \tag{11.18.2}$$

For the critical reactor without control rod, $\alpha_0 R = 2.405$ (§ 7.56), so that

$$J_0(\alpha_0 R) = 0 \quad \text{and} \quad J_1(\alpha_0 R) = 0.519.$$

Hence, (11.18.2) gives

$$J_0(\alpha R) \approx -0.519 \Delta\alpha R. \tag{11.18.3}$$

Further, since $\alpha - \alpha_0$ is small,

$$Y_0(\alpha R) \approx Y_0(\alpha_0 R) = 0.510. \tag{11.18.4}$$

11.19. For small values of r, i.e., when αr is small, the following asymptotic expressions may be used:

$$J_0(\alpha r) \rightarrow 1 \tag{11.19.1}$$

$$Y_0(\alpha r) \rightarrow -\frac{2}{\pi}\left(0.116 + \ln\frac{1}{\alpha r}\right). \tag{11.19.2}$$

These, combined with (11.18.3) and (11.18.4) when substituted into (11.17.1), give for the flux distribution in the r-direction

$$\Theta(r) \approx A\left[1 - \frac{2\,\Delta\alpha}{\pi\alpha_0}2.44\left(0.116 + \ln\frac{1}{\alpha r}\right)\right]. \tag{11.19.3}$$

11.20. The excess multiplication Δk that is controlled by the rod is given by

$$\Delta k = k - k_0,$$

where k is the multiplication factor with the control rod in and k_0 is the value with it out. By (11.12.2) combined with (11.13.1),

$$k = M^2(\alpha^2 + \beta^2) + 1$$

and

$$k_0 = M^2(\alpha_0{}^2 + \beta^2) + 1,$$

so that

$$\Delta k = M^2(\alpha^2 - \alpha_0{}^2).$$

Dividing both sides of this equation by $\alpha_0{}^2$ and rearranging, the result is

$$\frac{\alpha^2 - \alpha_0{}^2}{\alpha_0{}^2} = \frac{\Delta k}{M^2\alpha_0{}^2}. \tag{11.20.1}$$

From (11.18.1), if $\Delta\alpha$ is small, as postulated above,

$$\frac{\alpha^2 - \alpha_0{}^2}{\alpha_0{}^2} = \frac{2\,\Delta\alpha}{\alpha_0},$$

and by comparison with (11.20.1) it follows that

$$\frac{2\,\Delta\alpha}{\alpha_0} = \frac{\Delta k}{M^2\alpha_0{}^2}.$$

Consequently, (11.19.3) can be written as

$$\Theta(r) = A\left[1 - \frac{2.44\,\Delta k}{\pi M^2\alpha_0{}^2}\left(0.116 + \ln\frac{1}{\alpha r}\right)\right]. \tag{11.20.2}$$

11.21. At this point the boundary condition given in § 11.14, i.e., that the flux shall go to zero at R' (the effective radius of the control rod), may be introduced. Since R' may be regarded as small, especially for a large thermal reactor, R' may be substituted for r in (11.20.2) and the result set equal to zero; upon solving for Δk it is seen that

$$\Delta k \approx \frac{7.5M^2}{R^2}\left(0.116 + \ln\frac{R}{2.4R'}\right)^{-1}, \tag{11.21.1}$$

where $R' = R_0 - d$, as defined in § 11.14. This expression gives an approximation to the maximum excess multiplication that can be controlled by a central rod for a large reactor. It should be borne in mind that the terms with zero subscripts in the foregoing development refer to the critical conditions with the control rod out and replaced by core material.

11.22. The simple one-group treatment given above is defective in three respects. First, if the control rod leaves a void when it is withdrawn, as is generally the case, the value of Δk derived here is an overestimate, since the void introduces neutron leakage losses that have a negative effect on reactivity. In actual practice, an estimate is made of the change in multiplication due to leakage out of the channel left when the control rod is withdrawn, and this is subtracted from the Δk given by (11.21.1). In the second place, the postulate that all the neutrons are in one energy group tends to overestimate the absorption of neutrons by the control rod.   This would also make the calculated Δk too large.   A better approximation can be obtained by using two groups of neutrons, as will be seen below; the fast neutrons are then treated as being scattered or absorbed weakly by the control rod.   Finally, it may be mentioned that, if the rod is smaller than two or three transport mean free paths in the core, diffusion theory is not reliable.

THEORY OF CONTROL RODS: TWO-GROUP TREATMENT

11.23. The calculation of the excess multiplication which can be taken up by a control rod can be improved by treating the neutrons as being in two groups, as in Chapter VIII.   The boundary conditions at the control rod are in this case different for the fast- and the slow-neutron fluxes, since fast neutrons are not absorbed appreciably by the rod.   At the surface of the control rod the gradient of the fast flux is zero, i.e., as many fast neutrons enter the rod as leave it; this is physically equivalent to the assumption that the control rod does not absorb fast neutrons.   The same boundary condition as in the one-group treatment holds for the slow-neutron flux.

11.24. The radial and longitudinal parts of the flux are separated, as before, and the radial parts of both slow- and fast-neutron flux satisfy the wave equation

$$\nabla^2\Theta(r) + \alpha^2\Theta(r) = 0,$$

where α^2 may have either of two values obtained from the solution of the characteristic equation exactly analogous to (8.45.1).   The values of α^2 are given [cf. (8.45.2) and (8.45.3)] by

$$\mu^2 = \frac{1}{2}\left[-\left(\frac{1}{\tau}+\frac{1}{L^2}\right) + \sqrt{\left(\frac{1}{\tau}+\frac{1}{L^2}\right)^2 + \frac{4(k-1)}{\tau L^2}}\right], \qquad (11.24.1)$$

where μ^2 is positive if $k > 1$, and

$$-\nu^2 = \frac{1}{2}\left[-\left(\frac{1}{\tau}+\frac{1}{L^2}\right) - \sqrt{\left(\frac{1}{\tau}+\frac{1}{L^2}\right)^2 + \frac{4(k-1)}{\tau L^2}}\right], \qquad (11.24.2)$$

where ν^2 is also positive.

11.25. The radial parts of both the fast flux and the slow flux are linear combinations of solutions of the equations.

$$\nabla^2 X_1 + \mu^2 X_1 = 0 \quad \text{and} \quad \nabla^2 X_2 - \nu^2 X_2 = 0. \qquad (11.25.1)$$

In the annular part of the reactor core under consideration, the solutions are, omitting multiplicative arbitrary constants,

$$X_1 = J_0(\mu r) + A Y_0(\mu r)$$
$$X_2 = C I_0(\nu r) + K_0(\nu r).$$

11.26. The boundary condition that the fast and slow flux both go to zero at the outside extrapolated boundary of the cylindrical reactor can be satisfied by making X_1 and X_2 equal to zero when $r = R$; thus,

$$X_1 = J_0(\mu r) - \frac{J_0(\mu R)}{Y_0(\mu R)} Y_0(\mu r), \tag{11.26.1}$$

which is analogous to (11.17.1), and

$$X_2 = K_0(\nu r) - \frac{K_0(\nu R)}{I_0(\nu R)} I_0(\nu r). \tag{11.26.2}$$

11.27. By postulating a large reactor, and writing

$$\mu = \mu_0 + \Delta\mu,$$

with $\Delta\mu$ small, where μ_0 is the value of μ in the critical reactor without the control rod, it can be shown, by a procedure exactly equivalent to that used in deriving (11.19.3), that (11.26.1) reduces to

$$X_1 \approx J_0(\mu r) + 2.44 \frac{\Delta\mu}{\mu_0} Y_0(\mu r). \tag{11.27.1}$$

Further, for small values of r the second term in (11.26.2) becomes negligible in comparison with the first, and hence, under these conditions,

$$X_2 \approx K_0(\nu r). \tag{11.27.2}$$

The radial part of the fast-neutron flux may be written as

$$\Theta_1 = X_1 + A X_2,$$

and hence, by (11.27.1) and (11.27.2),

$$\Theta_1 = J_0(\mu r) + 2.44 \frac{\Delta\mu}{\mu_0} Y_0(\mu r) + A K_0(\nu r). \tag{11.27.3}$$

11.28. The boundary condition that the gradient of the fast flux is zero at the surface of the control rod, i.e,

$$\frac{d\Theta_1}{dr} = 0 \text{ at } r = R_0,$$

can now be satisfied approximately in the following manner. Upon differentiating (11.27.3) with respect to r and setting the result equal to zero, it follows that

$$\cdot \mu J_1(\mu R_0) + 2.44 \frac{\Delta\mu}{\mu_0} Y_0'(\mu R_0) + A K_0'(\nu R_0) = 0,$$

where the primed quantities represent first derivatives with respect to r. Since $J_1(\mu R_0) \rightarrow 0$ for small values of the argument,

$$A = -2.44 \frac{\Delta\mu}{\mu_0} \cdot \frac{Y_0'(\mu R_0)}{K_0'(\nu R_0)}. \tag{11.28.1}$$

For small values of the argument, the asymptotic expression for $Y_0(\mu r)$ is given by (11.19.2), and that for $K_0(\nu r)$ is

$$K_0(\nu r) \rightarrow 0.116 + \ln \frac{1}{\nu r}. \tag{11.28.2}$$

Consequently,

$$\frac{Y_0'(\mu R_0)}{K_0'(\nu R_0)} = -\frac{\frac{2}{\pi R_0}}{\frac{1}{R_0}} = -\frac{2}{\pi}$$

for small arguments. If this result is inserted into (11.28.1), the approximate value of A required to satisfy the boundary condition is

$$A = 2.44 \frac{\Delta \mu}{\mu_0} \cdot \frac{2}{\pi}. \tag{11.28.3}$$

11.29. The radial part of the slow flux is

$$\Theta_2 = S_1 X_1 + A S_2 X_2, \tag{11.29.1}$$

where S_1 and S_2 are the coupling coefficients given by (8.47.4) and (8.48.2). In the large thermal reactors under consideration $k - 1$ is small compared with unity, and hence from (11.24.1) and (11.24.2)

$$\mu^2 \approx \frac{k - 1}{L^2 + \tau}$$

and

$$\nu^2 \approx \frac{1}{\tau} + \frac{1}{L^2}.$$

With these values for μ^2 and ν^2, the coupling coefficients become

$$S_1 = \frac{D_1 L^2}{D_2 \tau}$$

and

$$S_2 = -\frac{D_1}{D_2},$$

so that

$$\frac{S_2}{S_1} = -\frac{\tau}{L^2}. \tag{11.29.2}$$

11.30. By using the values of X_1 and X_2 from (11.27.1) and (11.27.2), that of A from (11.26.3), and S_2/S_1 from (11.29.2), the equation (11.29.1) gives

$$\frac{\Theta_2}{S_1} = J_0(\mu r) + 2.44 \frac{\Delta \mu}{\mu_0} \left[Y_0(\mu r) - K_0(\nu r) \frac{\tau}{L^2} \cdot \frac{2}{\pi} \right].$$

For small values of r the asymptotic expressions for $J_0(\mu r)$, $Y_0(\mu r)$, and $K_0(\nu r)$ are given by (11.19.1), (11.19.2), and (11.28.2), respectively. Hence, if r is small,

$$\frac{\Theta_2}{S_1} \approx 1 - 2.44 \frac{\Delta\mu}{\mu_0} \cdot \frac{2}{\pi} \left[0.116 + \ln\frac{1}{\mu r} + \frac{\tau}{L^2}\left(0.116 + \ln\frac{1}{\nu r}\right) \right]. \quad (11.30.1)$$

11.31. By a procedure similar to that used in § 11.20, it can be shown that

$$\frac{2\,\Delta\mu}{\mu_0} = \frac{\Delta k}{M^2\mu_0{}^2}.$$

This may be substituted into (11.30.1) and the boundary condition introduced that the slow flux shall go to zero at the effective boundary of the control rod, i.e., when $r = R'$. Thus, setting $\Theta_2(R') = 0$, and solving the resulting form of (11.30.1), it is found that

$$\Delta k \approx \frac{7.5M^2}{R^2} \left[0.116\left(1 + \frac{\tau}{L^2}\right) + \frac{\tau}{L^2}\ln\frac{L\sqrt{\tau}}{MR'} + \ln\frac{R}{2.4R'} \right]^{-1}, \quad (11.31.1)$$

which gives the maximum multiplication that can be controlled by a rod, according to the two-group calculation.

11.32. The values of Δk as derived from (11.21.1) and (11.31.1), i.e., by the one-group and two-group treatments, respectively, have been calculated for the case in which L^2 is equal to τ, and M/R is 0.20. The results in Fig. 11.32 are

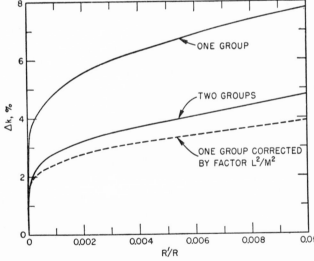

FIG. 11.32. One- and two-group calculations of effect of control rod

expressed as the percentage change in k plotted as a function of R'/R; R' is the effective radius of the control rod, i.e., $R_0 - d$, where d is the linear extrapolation distance. It can be seen that the one-group method overestimates the effectiveness of the control rod, for the second reason given in § 11.22, i.e., because it assumes that the control rod absorbs neutrons of all energies with the same efficiency.

11.33. It will be noted that the Δk value predicted by the two-group treatment [equation (11.31.1)] becomes identical with that given by the one-group method [equation (11.21.1)] when τ is zero. This will be obvious physically, since a zero value of τ implies that there are no fast neutrons. It might be expected, therefore, that the Δk given by the one-group treatment is too large by a factor of approximately $L^2/(L^2 + \tau)$, i.e., L^2/M^2, for control rods of small radii. In the case to which Fig. 11.32 is applicable L^2/M^2 is 0.5, and the results obtained by correcting the one-group values by this factor are represented by the dotted line. It is seen that this simple modification of the one-group equation (11.21.1), i.e.,

$$\Delta k \approx \frac{7.5L^2}{R^2}\left(0.116 + \ln\frac{R}{2.4R'}\right)^{-1},$$

gives values of Δk which can be taken up by a control rod, in fair agreement with those derived from the two-group calculations.

THEORY OF ECCENTRIC CONTROL ROD*

11.34. A control rod located eccentrically in a cylindrical thermal reactor may be considered to produce a singularity in the neutron flux at its position. The strength of the singularity is then determined by the boundary conditions at the surface of the rod. The problem is analogous to that of finding the electrical potential due to a point charge. In the latter case, the potential is e/r, where e is the charge and r is the distance from it. At the position of the charge, the potential has a $1/r$ singularity, the strength of which is measured by the charge e.

11.35. The strength of an absorber control rod is found from the boundary condition that the neutron flux shall go to zero at the extrapolated boundary within the "black" rod, as described in § 11.14. By restricting consideration to a large reactor, in which $k - 1 \ll 1$, the neutron flux in the reactor will satisfy the equation

$$\nabla^2\phi + B^2\phi = 0 \tag{11.35.1}$$

where

$$B^2 = \frac{k - 1}{M^2}. \tag{11.35.2}$$

A critical equation for the reactor, including the control rod, can then be derived and used in various ways. The simplest is to prescribe a certain value for k, for a reactor of given dimensions, and then find the radius of the control rod for which this particular reactor will be critical.

11.36. The neutron flux is a superposition of two solutions of the wave equation (11.35.1); one of these is nonsingular, while the other has a singularity at the control rod position. These solutions are obtained as follows. Let r be the distance from the axis of the reactor, of radius R, to a field point P, and let ρ be the

---

* The treatment given here follows that of R. Scalettar and L. W. Nordheim, unpublished.

distance from this field point to the axis of the control rod, of radius R_0. The
distance from the axis of the reactor to the axis of the rod is r_0.   The angles θ and
ψ are then defined as in Fig. 11.36.   The origin of the z-axis is taken at the mid-

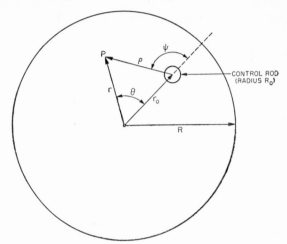

FIG. 11.36.   Cylindrical reactor with eccentric control rod

point of the axis of the reactor, as in Fig. 11.11, and the height of the reactor is
H, as before.

11.37. The general solution of (11.35.1) which is regular everywhere and is
symmetrical with respect to θ, is given [cf. (7.58.2)] by

$$\phi_r = \cos\frac{\pi z}{H} \sum_{n=0}^{\infty} A_n J_n(\mu r)\cos n\theta, \tag{11.37.1}$$

where

$$\mu^2 = B^2 - \left(\frac{\pi}{H}\right)^2. \tag{11.37.2}$$

11.38. The irregular solution of (11.35.1) may be found by solving this equation referred to the control rod as the center of the coordinate system and taking
only Y_m solutions.   The J_m terms, being finite at the axis of the control rod, do
not contribute to the strength of the absorber.   Thus, the irregular part of the
neutron flux is

$$\phi_i = \cos\frac{\pi z}{H} \sum_{m=0}^{\infty} Y_m(\mu\rho)[E_m\cos m\psi + F_n\sin m\psi]. \tag{11.38.1}$$

11.39. Considerable simplification may be achieved, at this point, if the variation of the flux with the angle θ over the surface of the control rod is small.*   This

---

* It may be noted that this approximation is rigorous if the rod is at the center of the reactor.
The results obtained will then be identical with those derived above.

means that ϕ_i is essentially independent of the angle ψ, so that (11.38.1) may be written as

$$\phi_i = \cos\frac{\pi z}{H}\, Y_0(\mu\rho). \tag{11.39.1}$$

The total flux is now obtained from (11.37.1) and (11.39.1) as

$$\phi = \phi_r + \phi_i = \cos\frac{\pi z}{H}\left[\sum_{n=0}^{\infty} A_n J_n(\mu r)\cos n\theta + Y_0(\mu\rho)\right]. \tag{11.39.2}$$

The function $Y_0(\mu\rho)$ may be expressed in terms of r and θ; thus for $r > r_0$,

$$Y_0(\mu\rho) = Y_0(\mu r)J_0(\mu r_0) + 2\sum_{n=1}^{\infty} Y_n(\mu r)J_n(\mu r_0)\cos n\theta. \tag{11.39.3}$$

11.40. Upon applying the boundary condition that the flux shall be zero at the extrapolated boundary of the reactor, i.e., when $r = R$, it follows from (11.39.2) and (11.39.3) that

$$\phi(R) = \cos\frac{\pi z}{H}\left[\sum_{n=0}^{\infty} A_n J_n(\mu R)\cos n\theta + Y_0(\mu R)J_0(\mu r_0)\right.$$
$$\left. + 2\sum_{n=1}^{\infty} Y_n(\mu R)J_n(\mu r_0)\cos n\theta\right] = 0,$$

so that

$$Y_0(\mu R)J_0(\mu r_0) + \sum_{n=0}^{\infty}[A_n J_n(\mu R) + 2Y_n(\mu R)J_n(\mu r_0)]\cos n\theta - 2Y_0(\mu R)J_0(\mu r_0) = 0.$$

This may be rewritten as

$$\sum_{n=0}^{\infty}[A_n J_n(\mu R) + \delta_n Y_n(\mu R)J_n(\mu r_0)]\cos n\theta = 0, \tag{11.40.1}$$

where
$$\delta_n = 1 \quad \text{for} \quad n = 0$$
$$= 2 \quad \text{for} \quad n > 0.$$

11.41. Since $\phi(R) = 0$ for all values of θ, equation (11.40.1) holds for all θ's, and consequently,

$$A_n = -\frac{\delta_n Y_n(\mu R)J_n(\mu r_0)}{J_n(\mu R)}.$$

This expression for A_n may now be inserted into (11.39.2), so that

$$\phi = \cos\frac{\pi z}{H}\left[-\sum_{n=0}^{\infty}\frac{\delta_n Y_n(\mu R)J_n(\mu r_0)}{J_n(\mu R)}J_n(\mu r)\cos n\theta + Y_0(\mu\rho)\right]. \tag{11.41.1}$$

11.42. The boundary condition that the flux shall go to zero at the extrapolation distance d within the control rod is now introduced. If R_0 is small in comparison with r_0, this requires that

$$\frac{1}{\phi}\cdot\frac{\partial\phi}{\partial\rho} = d, \tag{11.42.1}$$

when $r = r_0$, $\rho = R_0$, and $\theta = 0$. Since, from (11.41.1),

$$\frac{\partial \phi}{\partial \rho} = -\cos\frac{\pi z}{H}\,\mu Y_1(\mu\rho),$$

it follows from (11.41.1) and (11.42.1) that

$$\mu Y_1(\mu R_0) + Y_0(\mu R_0)d = \sum_{n=0}^{\infty} \frac{\delta_n Y_n(\mu R)J_n^2(\mu r_0)}{J_n(\mu R)}\,d. \tag{11.42.2}$$

This expression is the critical equation for a cylindrical reactor with an eccentric control rod.

11.43. The simplest procedure for the use of (11.42.2) is somewhat as follows. Suppose that it is desired to find the radius R_0 of the control rod that will result in a certain change in k. Then, from (11.35.2) and (11.37.2) the value of μ^2 may be obtained to correspond to the desired k, for a reactor of given dimensions, and hence of known B^2. Since R is known from the size of the reactor, and the position of the control rod specifies r_0, it is possible to solve (11.42.2) for R_0 by a process of iteration.

11.44. The problem of two control rods may be treated in a similar manner to that described above. Since a control rod depresses the flux in its vicinity, the effect of another rod will be a function of the spacing between rods as well as of their location in the reactor. Two important conclusions may be stated: (1) there is a separation of the rods for which their effectiveness is a maximum; and (2) beyond a certain separation, the total effectiveness of two rods is greater than the sum of the effects of each control rod separately.

11.45. The latter result can be explained qualitatively with the aid of Fig. 11.10. If a control rod is placed at the center of the reactor, the flux in the outer regions of the reactor is increased above that to be expected without a control rod. Thus, if a second rod is now placed in the region where the flux with the control rod is greater than without it, the effectiveness of the second rod is increased because of the initially larger thermal neutron flux.

FISSION PRODUCT POISONING

GENERAL CONSIDERATIONS

11.46. As stated above, when a reactor operates, certain nuclei with large cross sections for the capture of thermal neutrons are produced, so that they act as "poisons." These nuclei may be either direct fission products or they may result from the decay of the latter. The rate of formation depends on the fission rate in the reactor, while their removal is determined partly by natural radioactive decay, if radioactive, and partly by capture of neutrons which leads to a change of identity. In the cases of interest, namely, xenon-135 and samarium-149, the products, xenon-136 and samarium-150, respectively, have small cross sections for thermal neutron capture and so they may be neglected.

11.47. In the course of time there will be a balance between the rates of formation and of loss of the absorbing nuclei, so that an equilibrium concentration is attained in the reactor. However, when the reactor is shut down, substances like xenon-135 and samarium-149, which result mainly from the decay of other fission products, continue to be formed, although their rate of removal due to neutron capture is greatly decreased because of the diminution of the flux. There is consequently a possibility that the concentration of poison nuclei will actually increase and pass through a maximum, before finally decreasing because of natural decay. These aspects of fission product poisoning will now be considered analytically.

11.48. Xenon-135 is formed in a fractional yield (average number of atoms produced per fission) of 0.003 as a direct fission product, but a much larger amount results from the two-stage decay of the direct product tellurium-135, the fractional yield of which is 0.056. The half life of tellurium-135 is only 2 min, while its decay product, iodine-135, which is the parent of xenon-135, has a half life of 6.7 hr (§ 11.6). For purposes of simplifying the treatment, without introducing any appreciable error, it will be assumed, therefore, that iodine-135 is produced directly in fission with a fractional yield of 0.056.

IODINE CONCENTRATION

11.49. Consider first the net rate of formation of iodine-135. If I is the concentration of these nuclei per cm^3 at any instant, the natural rate of radioactive decay is $-\lambda_1 I$ nuclei per cm^3 per sec, where λ_1 is the ordinary decay constant. In addition iodine-135 will be lost as a result of neutron capture at a rate equal to $-\sigma_1\phi I$ nuclei per cm^3 per sec, where σ_1 is the microscopic cross section in cm^2 for the capture of thermal neutrons and ϕ is the thermal flux in neutrons per cm^2 per sec. The rate of formation, on the other hand, will depend on the number of fissions. If Σ_f is the macroscopic (thermal neutron) cross section for fission of the fuel material in the reactor, the rate of neutron capture as a result of fission, and hence the rate of fission, will be equal to $\Sigma_f\phi$ neutrons (or fissions) per cm^2 per sec. If γ_1 is the fractional yield of iodine-135 — actually of tellurium-135 — as a direct fission product, i.e., 0.056, then the rate of formation of iodine-135 is $\gamma_1\Sigma_f\phi$ nuclei per cm^3 per sec. It is thus possible to write the equation

$$\frac{dI}{dt} = -\lambda_1 I - \sigma_1\phi I + \gamma_1\Sigma_f\phi \tag{11.49.1}$$

for the net rate of increase of iodine-135 nuclei with time.

11.50. The microscopic cross section σ_1 for iodine-135 is about 7×10^{-24} cm^2, and, since ϕ is not likely to exceed 10^{15} neutrons per cm^2 per sec, the value of $\sigma_1\phi$ will be of the order of 10^{-8} or less. On the other hand, the decay constant λ_1 is 2.9×10^{-5} sec^{-1}, and hence in (11.49.1) the term $\sigma_1\phi I$ may be neglected in comparison with $\lambda_1 I$, so that

$$\frac{dI}{dt} \approx -\lambda_1 I + \gamma_1 \Sigma_f \phi. \tag{11.50.1}$$

If the reactor has been operating for some time the concentration of iodine-135 will have attained its equilibrium value, and dI/dt will be zero. Indicating the equilibrium concentration by I_0 and the corresponding (steady state) flux by ϕ_0, it follows from (11.50.1) that

$$\lambda_1 I_0 = \gamma_1 \Sigma_f \phi_0$$

or

$$I_0 = \frac{\gamma_1 \Sigma_f \phi_0}{\lambda_1}. \tag{11.50.2}$$

11.51. A general expression for $I(t)$, i.e., the concentration of iodine as a function of time, is now obtained by rewriting (11.50.1) in the form

$$\frac{dI}{dt} + \lambda_1 I = \gamma_1 \Sigma_f \phi$$

and then multiplying both sides of the differential equation by the integrating factor $e^{\lambda_1 t}\, dt$; thus,

$$e^{\lambda_1 t}\, dI + e^{\lambda_1 t} \lambda_1 I\, dt = \gamma_1 \Sigma_f \phi e^{\lambda_1 t}\, dt,$$

where the flux ϕ may be a function of time. The left-hand side of this equation is now a perfect differential, equal to $d(I e^{\lambda_1 t})$, so that

$$d(I e^{\lambda_1 t}) = \gamma_1 \Sigma_f \phi e^{\lambda_1 t}\, dt,$$

and upon integration this gives

$$I(t) = e^{-\lambda_1 t} \left[\gamma_1 \Sigma_f \int_0^t \phi e^{\lambda_1 t}\, dt + I(0) \right], \tag{11.51.1}$$

where $I(0)$ is the concentration of iodine at zero time.

11.52. If the rate of growth of iodine in a reactor is being studied, zero time may be taken as the time of start-up, and then $I(0)$ is zero. Suppose, for simplicity, the neutron flux is increased so rapidly that it attains the steady state value ϕ_0 in an extremely short interval of time compared with the growth of the iodine-135 concentration. Under these conditions, (11.51.1) becomes

$$I(t) = e^{-\lambda_1 t} \gamma_1 \Sigma_f \phi_0 \int_0^t e^{\lambda_1 t}\, dt$$

$$= \frac{\gamma_1 \Sigma_f \phi_0}{\lambda_1} (1 - e^{-\lambda_1 t}). \tag{11.52.1}$$

When t is large, this reduces to the value given by (11.50.2) for the limiting or equilibrium concentration.

11.53. Alternatively, (11.51.1) may be used to express the rate of decay of iodine-135 in a reactor which is shut down after running in a steady state for some time. If $t = 0$ is now the time of shut-down, $I(0)$ is the equilibrium concentration of iodine-135 as given by (11.50.2). Hence,

$$I(t) = e^{-\lambda_1 t}[\gamma_1 \Sigma_f \int_0^t \phi e^{\lambda_1 t} \, dt + I_0],$$ (11.53.1)

where ϕ is a function of t determined by the manner in which the reactor is shut down.

XENON CONCENTRATION

11.54. If X is the concentration of xenon-135 nuclei per cm³, at any instant, the rate of radioactive decay is $-\lambda_2 X$ and the rate of loss by neutron capture is $-\sigma_2 \phi X$, where λ_2 and σ_2 are, respectively, the decay constant and microscopic cross section for thermal neutron capture. On the other hand, xenon-135 is formed by decay of iodine-135, at a rate $\lambda_1 I$, and as a direct product of fission, at a rate of $\gamma_2 \Sigma_f \phi$, where γ_2 is the corresponding fractional fission yield, i.e., 0.003. The net rate of growth of the xenon concentration is then given by

$$\frac{dX}{dt} = \lambda_1 I + \gamma_2 \Sigma_f \phi - \lambda_2 X - \sigma_2 \phi X.$$ (11.54.1)

The mean life of xenon-135 in the nuclear reactor is seen to be $1/(\lambda_2 + \sigma_2 \phi_0)$, as compared with the natural decay mean life of $1/\lambda_2$, the decrease being due to neutron capture. The equilibrium or steady state concentration is obtained by setting dX/dt equal to zero; it is then readily found that

$$X_0 = \frac{\lambda_1 I_0 + \gamma_2 \Sigma_f \phi_0}{\lambda_2 + \sigma_2 \phi_0},$$

and introducing the value for I_0 from (11.50.2)

$$X_0 = \frac{(\gamma_1 + \gamma_2)\Sigma_f \phi_0}{\lambda_2 + \sigma_2 \phi_0}.$$ (11.54.2)

11.55. In order to obtain the concentration of xenon as a function of time, (11.54.1) is rearranged to give

$$\frac{dX}{dt} + (\lambda_2 + \sigma_2 \phi)X = \lambda_1 I + \gamma_2 \Sigma_f \phi,$$ (11.55.1)

where X, I, and ϕ are functions of time. The integrating factor for this differential equation is $\exp \left(\int_0^t A \, dt \right) dt$, where

$$A \equiv \lambda_2 + \sigma_2 \phi,$$

and consequently it follows, after multiplying both sides of (11.55.1) by this factor, that

$$d(X \exp \int A \, dt) = \exp \left(\int A \, dt \right)(\lambda_1 I + \gamma_2 \Sigma_f \phi) \, dt.$$

Upon integration it is seen that

$$X(t) = \exp \left(-\int A \, dt \right) \left\{ \int_0^t [\exp \left(\int A \, dt \right)(\lambda_1 I + \gamma_2 \Sigma_f \phi) \, dt] + X(0) \right\}, \quad (11.55.2)$$

where I, actually $I(t)$, is given by (11.51.1), in the general case.

11.56. As with the value of $I(0)$, considered above, the expression for $X(0)$ depends on the initial conditions. If (11.55.2) is to give the growth of the xenon concentration after start-up, then $X(0)$ will be zero. Assuming the neutron flux to have the steady-state value of ϕ_0, then, using (11.52.1) to give the required expression for I as a function of time, it is found from (11.55.2) that

$$X(t) = X_0 \left\{ 1 + \frac{1}{\gamma_1 + \gamma_2} \left(\frac{\gamma_1 \lambda_1}{\lambda_2 - \lambda_1 + \sigma_2 \phi_0} - \gamma_2 \right) e^{-(\lambda_2 + \sigma_2 \phi_0)t} \right.$$
$$\left. - \frac{\gamma_1}{\gamma_1 + \gamma_2} \left(\frac{\lambda_2 + \sigma_2 \phi_0}{\lambda_2 - \lambda_1 + \sigma_2 \phi_0} \right) e^{-\lambda_1 t} \right\}. \quad (11.56.1)$$

This equation gives the xenon build-up with time in terms of the steady state value of the neutron flux.

CALCULATION OF POISONING

11.57. The *poisoning*, P, of a reactor is defined as the ratio of the number of thermal neutrons absorbed by the poison to those absorbed in the fuel; thus, at time t,

$$P \equiv \frac{\Sigma_p}{\Sigma_u} = \frac{X(t)\sigma_2}{\Sigma_u}, \quad (11.57.1)$$

where Σ_p is the macroscopic thermal absorption cross section of poison at time t, and Σ_u is the corresponding value in fuel. Hence, the poisoning P_0 due to xenon-135 when the latter has reached its equilibrium value X_0 is given by

$$P_0 = \frac{X_0 \sigma_2}{\Sigma_u} = \frac{\sigma_2(\gamma_1 + \gamma_2)\Sigma_f \phi_0}{(\lambda_1 + \sigma_2 \phi_0)\Sigma_u}. \quad (11.57.2)$$

Since $\gamma_1 + \gamma_2 = 0.059$, $\sigma_2 = 3.5 \times 10^{-18}$ cm², $\lambda_2 = 2.1 \times 10^{-5}$ sec⁻¹, and Σ_f/Σ_u is 0.84 for uranium-235, this becomes

$$P_0 = \frac{1.7 \times 10^{-19} \phi_0}{2.1 \times 10^{-5} + 3.5 \times 10^{-18} \phi_0}. \quad (11.57.3)$$

11.58. If ϕ_0 is 10^{11} or less, the second term in the denominator in (11.57.3) may be neglected in comparison with the first; then

$$P_0 \approx 8 \times 10^{-15} \phi_0,$$

and hence, when ϕ_0 is 10^{11} or less, the poisoning will be negligible. Even for a flux of 10^{12} neutrons per cm^2 per sec, the poisoning is only 0.007, i.e., about 0.7 per cent of the thermal neutrons are absorbed by the equilibrium amount of xenon. However, for values of ϕ_0 of the order of 10^{13} or more, the poisoning increases rapidly, and, if the flux is greater than about 10^{15} neutrons per cm^2 per sec, λ_2 becomes negligible compared with $\sigma_2\phi_0$ and the poisoning, as given by (11.57.2), reaches a limiting value expressed by

$$P_{\text{lim}} \approx (\gamma_1 + \gamma_2)\frac{\Sigma_f}{\Sigma_u} = 0.059 \times 0.84$$
$$= 0.050,$$

for uranium-235 as fuel. This is the maximum value for the poisoning *during operation* of thermal reactors of high flux; about 5 per cent of the thermal neutrons are captured by the xenon poison under these conditions.*

11.59. The values of P_0 calculated from (11.57.3) for various steady state fluxes are given in Table 11.59 to two significant figures. It is seen that the

TABLE 11.59. EQUILIBRIUM VALUES OF XENON POISONING
DURING OPERATION OF REACTOR

Flux (ϕ_0)	Poisoning (P_0)
10^{12}	0.007
10^{13}	0.030
10^{14}	0.046
10^{15}	0.048

equilibrium poisoning is small for a flux of 10^{12} neutrons per cm^2 per sec, but increases rapidly at higher fluxes, approaching the limiting value at about 10^{15} neutrons per cm^2 per sec.

POISONING EFFECT ON REACTIVITY

11.60. The relationship between the poisoning as calculated above and the reactivity of the reactor may be derived as follows. Of the four factors which make up the infinite multiplication factor k, the thermal utilization is essentially the only one changed by the poison. Hence, if the leakage of neutrons is not affected by the poison, the effective multiplication factor will be proportional to the thermal utilization. Since fission product poisons are present in very small concentrations, the change in neutron scattering resulting from their presence is negligible. Consequently, in a bare thermal reactor the fast-neutron leakage will be unaltered. The thermal diffusion length, however, will be decreased by

---

* The foregoing calculations are based on the assumption of uniform distribution of flux and poison throughout the reactor. If ϕ_0 is taken as the average flux, the resulting error in P will probably be no more than 10 per cent. A more exact treatment should make use of statistical weights and perturbation theory (see Chapter XIII).

the additional neutron absorber, and so the thermal nonleakage probability, i.e., $1/(1 + L^2B^2)$, will change to a small extent. But in most thermal reactors $1 + L^2B^2$ is close to unity and is fairly insensitive to changes in L^2. Hence, it is reasonable to take the thermal utilization and the effective multiplication factor to be proportional, with or without poison.

11.61. Let f be the thermal utilization in the reactor without poison, and let f' be the value with poison; then, assuming a uniform flux,

$$f = \frac{\Sigma_u}{\Sigma_u + \Sigma_m} \quad \text{and} \quad f' = \frac{\Sigma_u}{\Sigma_u + \Sigma_m + \Sigma_p}, \qquad (11.61.1)$$

where Σ_u, Σ_m, and Σ_p are the macroscopic cross sections for the absorption of thermal neutrons in fuel, moderator, and poison, respectively. The ratio Σ_p/Σ_u has been defined above as the poisoning P, and, representing the ratio Σ_m/Σ_u by y, it follows that

$$f = \frac{1}{1 + y} \quad \text{and} \quad f' = \frac{1}{1 + y + P}.$$

If the effective multiplication factor of the reactor without poison is k_{eff} and that with poison is k_{eff}', then

$$\frac{k_{\text{eff}}' - k_{\text{eff}}}{k_{\text{eff}}'} = \frac{f' - f}{f'} = -\frac{P}{1 + y}. \qquad (11.61.2)$$

If the reactor was just critical without the poison, k_{eff} is unity, and the left-hand side of (11.61.2) becomes equivalent to the reactivity ρ due to the poison; thus,

$$\rho = -\frac{P}{1 + y}.$$

Since y is generally a small fraction of unity in an enriched reactor, it is seen that the negative reactivity resulting from the presence of fission products is roughly equal to the poisoning as defined above. Thus, the maximum reactivity due to the equilibrium concentration of xenon-135 is about -0.05.

BUILD-UP OF XENON AFTER COMPLETE SHUT-DOWN

11.62. A highly important aspect of poisoning due to xenon-135 arises because of the increase in the concentration of this species after a reactor is shut down. As stated earlier, the reason for this increase is that the iodine-135 present in the reactor at the time of shut-down continues to decay and form xenon-135. The latter is now lost by radioactive decay only, assuming the neutron flux to be so low that there is no appreciable removal of xenon-135 nuclei due to neutron capture. Since the half life of xenon-135 is greater than that of iodine-135, it is evident that the concentration of the former will increase at first. However, as the iodine-135 is not being regenerated when the reactor is shut down, the concentration of xenon will ultimately decrease after passing through a maximum.

11.63. It will be seen shortly that the maximum concentration of xenon-135 attained after shut-down may be several times the equilibrium value, especially if the neutron flux was high before shut-down. This results in a correspondingly large increase in the negative reactivity. An equivalent amount of multiplication, therefore, must be built into the reactor in order to make it possible to start up during a reasonable time interval after shut-down.

11.64. The variation of xenon concentration in a reactor after shut-down will be represented by (11.55.2) with $X(0)$, the xenon-135 concentration at zero time, equal to the equilibrium value X_0 given by (11.54.2). It is assumed, of course, that prior to shut-down the reactor has been operating for a sufficient length of time for the equilibrium concentration of xenon to be attained. The value of I, actually $I(t)$, is now given by (11.53.1).

11.65. Since (11.55.2) and (11.53.1) both involve ϕ, it is evident that the build-up of xenon after a reactor is shut down will depend on how the flux is decreased. In general, ϕ may be expressed as a function of t, and the required integrations may be carried out. A simple case, and one having some practical interest, is that in which the reactor is shut down as completely as possible. Taking into consideration the initial rapid drop and the subsequent stable negative period of 80 sec due to delayed neutrons (§ 10.52), it is found that a reactor can be shut down from a flux of 10^{12} to 10^3 neutrons per cm² per sec in about 20 min. This time is short compared with the several hours during which the xenon concentration builds up, and so very little error results from the assumption that the neutron flux drops immediately to zero at $t = 0$ and remains at this value during shut-down.

11.66. Consequently, setting ϕ equal to zero, (11.53.1) for the iodine concentration becomes merely

$$I(t) = I_0 e^{-\lambda_1 t} = \frac{\gamma_1 \Sigma_f \phi_0}{\lambda_1} e^{-\lambda_1 t}, \tag{11.66.1}$$

where ϕ_0 is the steady state flux before shut-down. Further, since $\phi = 0$, A is now equal to λ_2, and hence $\exp\left(\int A \, dt\right) = e^{\lambda_2 t}$. Thus, (11.55.2), with $X(0)$ given by (11.54.2), becomes

$$\begin{aligned}
X(t) &= e^{-\lambda_2 t}\left[\int_0^t (e^{\lambda_2 t}\gamma_1\Sigma_f\phi_0 e^{-\lambda_1 t})\, dt + \frac{(\gamma_1 + \gamma_2)\Sigma_f\phi_0}{\lambda_2 + \sigma_2\phi_0}\right] \\
&= e^{-\lambda_2 t}\left[\frac{\gamma_1\Sigma_f\phi_0}{\lambda_2 - \lambda_1}[e^{(\lambda_2 - \lambda_1)t} - 1] + \frac{(\gamma_1 + \gamma_2)\Sigma_f\phi_0}{\lambda_2 + \sigma_2\phi_0}\right].
\end{aligned} \tag{11.66.2}$$

The poisoning P, as defined by (11.57.1), is then

$$P = \frac{X(t)\sigma_2}{\Sigma_u} = \sigma_2\phi_0 \frac{\Sigma_f}{\Sigma_u}\left[\frac{\gamma_1}{\lambda_2 - \lambda_1}(e^{-\lambda_1 t} - e^{-\lambda_2 t}) + \frac{\gamma_1 + \gamma_2}{\lambda_2 + \sigma_2\phi_0}e^{-\lambda_2 t}\right]. \tag{11.66.3}$$

11.67. The values of P as a function of time, calculated from this equation, for various values, ϕ_0, of the steady-state flux before shut-down, are plotted in

Fig. 11.67. The concentration of xenon-135, which is proportional to P, is seen to increase to a maximum in each case. For fluxes of the order of 10^{13} neutrons per cm^2 per sec or less, the increase is negligible, but it assumes greater significance for higher fluxes. It is seen, for example, that, for ϕ_0 equal to 2×10^{14}, the poisoning due to xenon attains a value of over 0.35, compared with the equilibrium value of 0.05, when the reactor was in operation. The reactivity which can be tied up in this manner by the xenon is approximately 0.35. Consequently, this amount of excess multiplication must be built into a reactor to

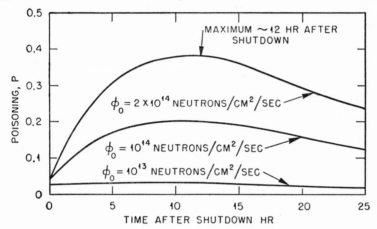

FIG. 11.67.   Change in xenon poisoning with time after shut-down

operate at a flux of 2×10^{14} neutrons per cm^2 per sec, if it is to be capable of being started up at any time after shut-down.   If this amount of reactivity is not available, then the reactor could be started up either before the xenon-135 had attained its maximum concentration or by waiting a sufficient time for the poison to decay to an adequate extent.   For a flux of 10^{15} neutrons per cm^2 per sec, the maximum poisoning, which occurs at about 12 hr after shut-down, is roughly 2.0.

11.68. In general, it can be seen that the problem of xenon poisoning is not very important for thermal reactors with fluxes of the order of 10^{12}, or possibly 10^{13}, either during operation or after shut-down.   Since the poisoning has a limiting equilibrium value of 0.050, it is not too serious while the reactor is operating.   But it is in connection with the start-up of a thermal reactor of high flux after shut-down that xenon poisoning becomes a matter to be considered in the design of the reactor.   It will be evident from the figure that, for fluxes exceeding 10^{14} neutrons per cm^2 per sec, the maximum poisoning after shut-down increases rapidly with the operating flux.

11.69. The foregoing discussion has referred to the special case of an instantaneous, and essentially complete, shut-down after the reactor has been operating in the steady state.   However, equation (11.55.2) may be solved for different types of shut-down, e.g., partial instantaneous shut-down, partial or complete shut-down in steps, or linear (or other) partial or complete shut-down. There is also the possibility that the reactor may be shut down before the xenon has attained its equilibrium concentration. The general results are the same as those described above, except that the more gradual and the less complete the shut-down, the smaller will be the maximum build-up of xenon. This is due, of course, to the fact that, for partial and gradual shut-downs, neutrons are available to be captured by, and hence to remove, the xenon-135.

SAMARIUM POISONING

11.70. The stable isotope samarium-149 is the product of the radioactive beta decay of promethium-149, half life 47 hr; the latter may be formed directly in fission and also by the decay of neodymium-149. Since the neodymium has a half life of 1.7 hr, which is relatively short in comparison with that of the promethium, it may be supposed that the 47-hr promethium-149 is a direct product of fission, its fractional yield being 0.014 (§ 11.7). The problem of the formation of promethium and samarium in a reactor is thus similar to that considered above for iodine and xenon. The thermal neutron absorption cross section σ_1 of promethium is very small, so that, as with iodine, $\sigma_1\phi$ may be neglected in comparison with λ_1 in (11.49.1). Hence, an equation of the same form as (11.50.2) will represent the promethium concentration at equilibrium. Similarly, all the equations derived above will be applicable with the appropriate values of the required physical constants. Thus, if promethium is indicated by the subscript 1 and samarium by 2, the fractional yield γ_1 is 0.014, the value of γ_2 being taken as zero. The decay constant λ_1 is 4.1×10^{-6} sec^{-1}, while λ_2 is zero, since samarium-149 is a stable nuclide. The absorption cross section σ_2 of the samarium for thermal neutrons is 5.3×10^{-20} cm^2.

11.71. Since λ_2 is zero, (11.54.2) for the equilibrium concentration of samarium is given by $\gamma_1\Sigma_f/\sigma_2$, so that it is independent of the neutron flux in the reactor. The time to attain equilibrium is roughly $5/\sigma_2\phi_0$ sec, and this would be about 11 days for a flux as high as 10^{14} neutrons per cm^2 per sec. The reactor poisoning at equilibrium is equal $\gamma_1\Sigma_f/\Sigma_u$, i.e., $0.014 \times 0.84 = 0.012$, independent of the flux; hence, the maximum reactivity due to samarium under steady-state conditions is about -0.012.

11.72. The expression for the poisoning as a function of time after instantaneous complete shut-down, i.e., equation (11.66.3), now becomes

$$P = \sigma_2\phi_0 \frac{\Sigma_f}{\Sigma_u}\left[\frac{\gamma_1}{\lambda_1}(1 - e^{-\lambda_1 t}) + \frac{\gamma_1}{\sigma_2\phi_0}\right]$$

$$= \sigma_2\phi_0 \frac{\Sigma_f}{\Sigma_u}\left[\frac{\gamma_1}{\lambda_1}(1 - e^{-\lambda_1 t})\right] + \gamma_1\frac{\Sigma_f}{\Sigma_u}. \qquad (11.72.1)$$

It can be seen from this expression that, after shut-down, the poisoning due to samarium increases from its initial value of $\gamma_1\Sigma_f/\Sigma_u$ to a limit, when t is large, represented by

$$P_{\text{lim}} = \frac{\sigma_2 \phi_0 \gamma_1}{\lambda_1} \cdot \frac{\Sigma_f}{\Sigma_u} + \gamma_1 \frac{\Sigma_f}{\Sigma_u}$$
$$= 1.5 \times 10^{-16} \phi_0 + 0.012.$$

For a steady-state flux of the order of 10^{12} neutrons per cm^2 per sec or less, $1.5 \times 10^{-16} \phi_0$ is negligible in comparison with 0.012, and the poisoning due to samarium remains almost constant after shut-down. If the steady state flux is 2×10^{14}, which appears to be the practical limit for thermal reactors unless means are provided for the removal of xenon, the limiting samarium poisoning after instantaneous, complete shut-down is 0.030+0.012, i.e., 0.042. It is apparent, therefore, that the presence of samarium among the fission products requires an addition of no more than about 0.04 to the reactivity of a thermal reactor of high flux.

REACTIVITY TEMPERATURE COEFFICIENTS

Effects of Temperature on Reactivity

11.73. In a nuclear reactor a considerable amount of energy, depending on the power output, is released in the form of heat, and, although some form of heat transfer mechanism is used to cool the reactor, the temperature will inevitably experience variations during operation. An increase of temperature will affect the reactivity for at least two reasons: first, the mean energy of the thermal neutrons increases and hence their absorption will be affected because the nuclear cross sections vary with energy; and, second, the mean free paths and the non-leakage probabilities are functions of the density, which changes with temperature.

11.74. The practical operation of a reactor requires the temperature coefficient of the reactivity to be small, so that a steady state can be maintained by means of the control rods. The reactor will then remain stable in spite of moderate fluctuations in temperature. If the temperature coefficient is negative, i.e., the reactivity decreases with increasing temperature, the reactor will be stable. Positive temperature coefficients, however, result in instability, since the critical reactor will become supercritical when the temperature rises. For large thermal reactors the temperature coefficient of reactivity can conveniently be separated into two main parts, namely, the *nuclear temperature coefficient*, which is determined by the effect on the nuclear cross sections, and the *density temperature coefficient*, due to changes in volume and density of the system. These aspects will be examined in turn.

Nuclear Temperature Coefficients

11.75. Consider a reactor consisting of fuel and moderator only, and assume that the absorption cross sections follow the $1/v$ law in the thermal energy region. Since the kinetic energy ($\frac{1}{2}mv^2$) of a neutron is proportional to the absolute

(Kelvin) temperature, T, this means that the thermal cross sections will vary as $1/T^{\frac{1}{2}}$. Hence, if σ_a is the absorption cross section at the temperature T, and σ_{a0} is the value at T_0, then

$$\sigma_a = \sigma_{a0} \left(\frac{T_0}{T}\right)^{\frac{1}{2}} = \sigma_{a0}\theta^{-\frac{1}{2}}, \tag{11.75.1}$$

where θ is the ratio of the absolute temperatures, i.e.,

$$\theta \equiv \frac{T}{T_0}. \tag{11.75.2}$$

The scattering cross sections do not change so rapidly with increasing temperature as do the absorption cross sections; if σ_s is the scattering cross section at the absolute temperature T, and σ_{s0} is that at T_0, then it is possible to represent the effect of temperature by

$$\sigma_s = \sigma_{s0} \left(\frac{T_0}{T}\right)^{x} = \sigma_{s0}\theta^{-x}, \tag{11.75.3}$$

where x may be of the order of 0.1. A relationship similar to (11.75.3) applies to transport cross sections.

11.76. The square of the diffusion length is given by $L^2 = D/\Sigma_a$ or $1/3\Sigma_a\Sigma_t$, where Σ_t, equal to $1/\lambda_t$, is the macroscopic transport cross section. Hence, it follows that

$$L^2 = \frac{1}{3\Sigma_a\Sigma_t} = \frac{1}{3\Sigma_{a0}\Sigma_{t0}} \cdot \frac{1}{\theta^{-(x+\frac{1}{2})}}$$
$$= L_0^2\theta^{x+\frac{1}{2}}. \tag{11.76.1}$$

An expression for the age, from fission energies to thermal, can be obtained, similarly, by writing [cf. (6.130.1)]

$$\tau = \int_{E_{\text{th}}}^{E_0} \frac{D}{\xi\Sigma_s} \cdot \frac{dE}{E} = \int_{E_{\text{th}}}^{E_0} \frac{1}{3\xi\Sigma_s\Sigma_t} \cdot \frac{dE}{E},$$

so that

$$\tau = \tau_0 - \int_{E_{\text{th}_0}}^{E_{\text{th}}} \frac{1}{3\xi\Sigma_s\Sigma_t} \cdot \frac{dE}{E}, \tag{11.76.2}$$

where τ and τ_0 are the ages of the thermal neutrons at the temperatures T and T_0, respectively, and the corresponding thermal energies are E_{th} and E_{th_0}. If $|x|$, defined by (11.75.3), is $\ll 1$, it can be shown from (11.76.2) that

$$\tau = \tau_0 - \left(\frac{1}{3\xi\Sigma_s\Sigma_t}\right)_0 \ln \theta. \tag{11.76.3}$$

11.77. Since the thermal cross sections of all absorbers present in the reactor may be supposed to obey (11.75.1), it is evident that the thermal utilization will be independent of temperature. The resonance escape probability may decrease somewhat as the temperature is raised, but on the whole it may be assumed that the infinite multiplication factor is independent of temperature.

11.78. For a large reactor, the effective multiplication factor is given by

$$k_{eff} = \frac{k}{1 + M^2 B^2},$$

where k may be regarded as being independent of temperature. The reactivity, ρ, which is $(k_{eff} - 1)/k_{eff}$, is then

$$\rho = \frac{k - 1 - M^2 B^2}{k} \tag{11.78.1}$$

$$= \frac{k - 1 - B^2(L^2 + \tau)}{k}. \tag{11.78.2}$$

A general expression for ρ as a function of temperature can now be obtained by inserting (11.76.1) and (11.76.3) for L^2 and τ, respectively; the result is

$$\rho = \frac{k - 1}{k} - \frac{B^2}{k}\left[\tau_0 - \left(\frac{1}{3\xi\Sigma_s\Sigma_t}\right)_0 \ln \theta + L_0^2\theta^{x+\frac{1}{2}}\right]. \tag{11.78.3}$$

11.79. The nuclear temperature coefficient, i.e., the temperature coefficient of ρ due to changes in the cross sections, at constant density, d, is given by*

$$\left(\frac{\partial\rho}{\partial T}\right)_d = \frac{\partial\rho}{\partial\theta}\cdot\frac{\partial\theta}{\partial T} = \frac{1}{T_0}\cdot\frac{\partial\rho}{\partial\theta},$$

since $\partial\theta/\partial T$ is $1/T_0$ by (11.75.2). Hence, from (11.78.3),

$$\left(\frac{\partial\rho}{\partial T}\right)_d = -\frac{B^2}{kT_0}\left[-\left(\frac{1}{3\xi\Sigma_s\Sigma_t}\right)_0\theta^{-1} + (x + \tfrac{1}{2})\theta^{x-\frac{1}{2}}L_0^2\right].$$

At the temperature T_0, i.e., when $T = T_0$ so that θ is unity, this becomes

$$\left(\frac{\partial\rho}{\partial T}\right)_d = -\frac{B^2}{kT_0}\left[-\left(\frac{1}{3\xi\Sigma_s\Sigma_t}\right)_0 + (x + \tfrac{1}{2})L_0^2\right]. \tag{11.79.1}$$

11.80. The foregoing treatment does not take into account a nuclear temperature coefficient that may arise from changes in the fission product poisoning. As a general rule, increase of temperature will result in a decrease in the absorption cross sections of the poisons for thermal neutrons because of the increase in the energy of the latter. There is consequently a decrease in the poisoning and a corresponding increase in reactivity of the reactor; this will produce a positive temperature coefficient of reactivity. Unless the other nuclear temperature coefficients have large negative values, to compensate for the positive contribution of the fission product poisoning, the reactor may be unstable to temperature changes. Of course, if increase of temperature brought the energy of the thermal neutrons close to a resonance, the absorption cross section of the poison might be increased, and the effect on the reactivity temperature coefficient would be reversed.

---

* The partial differential notation used here is that commonly employed in thermodynamics. A subscript, e.g., d in this case, is used to indicate the variable maintained constant.

DENSITY TEMPERATURE COEFFICIENTS

11.81. Increase of temperature causes expansion of the reactor materials, and this affects the reactivity in two ways: first, by changing the mean free paths for absorption and scattering and, second, by an over-all change in the size of the system. In some reactors a further change may occur due to the extrusion of material, e.g., liquid metal coolant in a reactor with stationary fuel elements.

11.82. The macroscopic absorption cross sections are proportional to the number of atoms per unit volume, and consequently such cross sections, apart from changes in the microscopic cross sections considered above, are directly proportional to the density. It, therefore, can be shown, from the definitions of L^2 and τ, that these quantities are inversely proportional to the square of the density. In a homogeneous system, where density changes affect all components in the same manner, it is possible to write

$$L^2 + \tau = L_0^2 \left(\frac{d_0}{d}\right)^2 + \tau_0 \left(\frac{d_0}{d}\right)^2$$

or

$$M^2 = M_0^2 \left(\frac{d_0}{d}\right)^2,$$

where M^2 and d are the migration area and density at the temperature T, and M_0^2 and d_0 are the values at T_0. If this result is substituted into (11.78.1), it follows that

$$\rho = \frac{k-1}{k} - \frac{B^2 M_0^2}{k}\left(\frac{d_0}{d}\right)^2.$$

If the volume is held constant, B^2 is constant, and if the microscopic cross sections are constant, as assumed above, then

$$\left(\frac{\partial \rho}{\partial T}\right)_{B^2, \sigma_a, \sigma_s} = \frac{2B^2 M_0^2}{k} \cdot \frac{d_0^2}{d^3} \cdot \frac{\partial d}{\partial T}. \tag{11.82.1}$$

11.83. If α is the coefficient of linear expansion of the material, i.e., $l = l_0[1 + \alpha(T - T_0)]$, then $V = V_0[1 + \alpha(T - T_0)]^3$, so that

$$d = \frac{d_0}{[1 + \alpha(T - T_0)]^3},$$

and, hence,

$$\frac{\partial d}{\partial T} = -\frac{3\alpha d_0}{[1 + \alpha(T - T_0)]^4}.$$

Insertion of this result into (11.82.1) then gives

$$\left(\frac{\partial \rho}{\partial T}\right)_{B^2, \sigma_a, \sigma_s} = -\frac{6B^2 M_0^2}{k} \cdot \frac{d_0^3}{d^3} \cdot \frac{\alpha}{[1 + \alpha(T - T_0)]^4}.$$

At $T = T_0$ this becomes

$$\left(\frac{\partial\rho}{\partial T}\right)_{B^2,\,\sigma_a,\,\sigma_s} = -\frac{6\alpha B^2 M_0^2}{k}$$

$$= -\frac{6(k-1)}{k}\alpha, \tag{11.83.1}$$

replacing $B^2 M_0^2$ by $k - 1$.

11.84. The reactivity change due to an over-all change in size of the reactor is small, especially if the reactor is constrained. The effect would be due to a change in the buckling; thus, from (11.78.1),

$$\left(\frac{\partial\rho}{\partial B}\right)_{\Sigma_a,\,\Sigma_s} = -\frac{2BM^2}{k} = -\frac{2(k-1)}{kB}, \tag{11.84.1}$$

since $M^2 = (k-1)/B^2$. If the reactor is spherical, $B = \pi/R$, and $R = R_0[1 + \alpha(T - T_0)]$, where R and R_0 refer to the radius of the reactor; hence,

$$\frac{dR}{dT} = \alpha R_0$$

and

$$\frac{dB}{dT} = -\frac{\pi}{R^2}\cdot\frac{dR}{dT} = -\frac{\alpha\pi}{R}.$$

Consequently, from (11.84.1),

$$\left(\frac{\partial\rho}{\partial T}\right)_{\Sigma_a,\,\Sigma_s} = \frac{\partial\rho}{\partial B}\cdot\frac{\partial B}{\partial T}$$

$$= \frac{2(k-1)\alpha\pi}{kBR}$$

$$= \frac{2(k-1)}{k}\alpha. \tag{11.84.2}$$

11.85. In order to illustrate the general magnitudes of the temperature coefficients derived here, the case will be considered of a graphite-moderated, thermal reactor with an operating temperature of 400° Kelvin, for which k is 1.05. For graphite, L^2 is 2850 cm² at 400°K and if the thermal utilization is taken as 0.9, it follows from (9.88.4) that L_0^2 in the reactor is 285 cm². The Fermi age, τ_0, is essentially that of the moderator, i.e., 350 cm², so that $M_0^2 = L_0^2 + \tau_0$ is 635 cm², and $B^2 \approx (k-1)/M_0^2$ is 7.8×10^{-5} cm⁻². Suppose $1/\xi\Sigma_s\Sigma_t$ is 1.38, the coefficient of linear expansion α is 10^{-5} per °C and let x be zero (§ 11.75); then from (11.79.1), (11.83.1), and (11.84.2), respectively, it is found that

$$\left(\frac{\partial\rho}{\partial T}\right)_d = -2.6 \times 10^{-5} \text{ per } °C$$

$$\left(\frac{\partial\rho}{\partial T}\right)_{B^2,\,\sigma_a,\,\sigma_s} = -0.29 \times 10^{-5} \text{ per } °C$$

and

$$\left(\frac{\partial\rho}{\partial T}\right)_{\Sigma_a,\,\Sigma_s} = 0.095 \times 10^{-5} \text{ per } °C.$$

The only positive temperature coefficient is the last, and this is the smallest of the three, so that the over-all temperature coefficient is negative. Such a reactor would be stable to temperature fluctuations. The total temperature coefficient for homogeneous, water-solution, enriched reactors may be as large negative as -10^{-3} per °C. This is due mainly to the expansion of the water which carries fuel with it.

PROBLEMS

1. Derive the critical equation for a bare cylindrical reactor containing two control rods placed on a single diameter.

2. Find the critical atomic ratio of hydrogen to uranium in a spherical bare reactor of 30-cm radius containing a water solution of 100% enriched uranyl sulphate at 20°C, 100°C, 175°C, and 250°C. Assume that a strong pressure shell surrounds the reactor and that the pressure on the solution is held to 1000 p.s.i. Calculate the reactivity temperature coefficient at 250°C.

3. If the reactor in Problem 2 is being operated at 175°C and the reactivity is increased 0.25%, what is the new steady state operating temperature?

Chapter XII

GENERAL THEORY OF
HOMOGENEOUS MULTIPLYING SYSTEMS*

INFINITE SLOWING DOWN KERNELS

GAUSSIAN (FERMI AGE) KERNELS

12.1. A general approach to the theory of bare thermal reactors which does not involve, although it can be adapted to, the continuous slowing down model. is based on the use of slowing down kernels. It was shown in § 5.92, *et seq.*, that the flux distribution from a distributed source of monoenergetic neutrons could be expressed in the form of an integral equation, using the appropriate diffusion kernels. Similarly, the slowing down density from a distributed source can be written in terms of the *slowing down kernels*. The form of these kernels for an infinite medium, on the basis of the continuous slowing down (Fermi age) model, will first be considered.

12.2. Since the age equation (6.128.2) is linear, the slowing down density at $\mathbf{r}$ due to a distributed source in an infinite medium is the sum of the slowing down densities due to the separate sources. Hence, it is possible to write in general, for an infinite medium,

$$q = \int_{\substack{\text{all} \\ \text{space}}} S(\mathbf{r}_0) P \, d\mathbf{r}_0,$$

where $S(\mathbf{r}_0)$ represents the distributed source, P is the appropriate slowing down kernel, and $d\mathbf{r}_0$ is a volume element at the field point $\mathbf{r}_0$.

12.3. For a point source in an infinite medium the slowing down kernel, according to the Fermi age theory, is given by a more general form of (6.138.1); thus,

$$P_{\text{pt}} = \frac{e^{-|\mathbf{r}-\mathbf{r}_0|^2/4(\tau-\tau_0)}}{[4\pi(\tau - \tau_0)]^{\frac{3}{2}}}, \tag{12.3.1}$$

---

* Some of the techniques employed in this chapter were first developed by S. F. Frankel and E. C. Nelson. Use of the concept of "image piles" was proposed by F. L. Friedman, and the generalization and organization of the material are due to A. M. Weinberg.

where $\mathbf{r}_0$ represents the position of the point source emitting neutrons of age τ_0. This expression reduces to (6.138.2) if the source neutrons are fission neutrons, so that their age is zero. The point kernel is, physically, the slowing down density of neutrons of age τ at a field point $\mathbf{r}$, due to a unit point source of neutrons of age τ_0 at the point $\mathbf{r}_0$. In other words, it gives the probability per unit volume that a neutron emitted with age τ_0 at $\mathbf{r}_0$ will slow down to an age τ at the field point $\mathbf{r}$.

12.4. For plane sources, the slowing down kernel, according to the age treatment, is obtained similarly, from (6.135.1); thus, for an infinite medium,

$$P_{\text{pl}} = \frac{e^{-|x-x_0|^2/4(\tau-\tau_0)}}{[4\pi(\tau-\tau_0)]^{\frac{1}{2}}}, \tag{12.4.1}$$

where x is the coordinate of the field point and x_0 that of the source which emits neutrons of age τ_0.

12.5. Because the kernels given above, in (12.3.1) and (12.4.1), derived from the Fermi continuous slowing down model, are of the same form as the Gauss functions, they are often referred to as *Gaussian slowing down kernels*. As stated in § 6.122, the supposition that the neutron energy can be treated as a continuous function of the time, which leads to the results given above, is applicable only when the slowing down medium does not contain very light nuclei. If the moderator is ordinary water or heavy water, the Gaussian kernels must be replaced by other kernels, as will be shown later (§ 12.61).

Group-Diffusion Kernels

12.6. Another approach to the problem of determining the spatial distribution of the slowing down density of neutrons in an infinite medium, as a function of their energy, is the group-diffusion method. This is somewhat more involved than the continuous slowing down treatment given above, but it is important because it can be applied to cases, such as when the moderator is ordinary or heavy water, for which the continuous slowing down model is quite unsatisfactory. In the group method, it is postulated, as in Chapter VIII, that the energy of neutrons is divided into a finite set of groups.

12.7. Suppose the neutron energy range from E_0, the fission energy, down to E_{th}, the thermal energy, is divided into $n + 1$ groups, the last, $(n + 1)$th, group being the thermal group. The probability per unit volume that a source neutron (energy E_0), i.e., one in the first group, at $\mathbf{r}_0$, in an infinite medium will enter the second group (energy E_1) at a field point $\mathbf{r}_1$ may be represented, in general, by the infinite-medium slowing down kernel $P_1(|\mathbf{r}_1 - \mathbf{r}_0|)$ for the first neutron group. This has been written as a displacement kernel (§ 5.96), since in an infinite medium it is dependent only on the distance from the source to the field point. Similarly, the probability per unit volume that a neutron in the second group (energy E_1), at $\mathbf{r}_1$, will enter the third group (energy E_2), at $\mathbf{r}_2$, is represented by

$P_2(|\mathbf{r}_2 - \mathbf{r}_1|)$, which is the slowing down kernel for the second group. Analogous symbols may be used for all the groups, the last kernel for slowing down from the nth group to the thermal $(n + 1)$th group being $P_n(|\mathbf{r}_n - \mathbf{r}_{n-1}|)$.

12.8. The number of source neutrons, originating at $\mathbf{r}_0$, entering the second group (energy E_1) in a volume element $d\mathbf{r}_1$ at the field point $\mathbf{r}_1$ is equal to $P_1(|\mathbf{r}_1 - \mathbf{r}_0|) \, d\mathbf{r}_1$, assuming a single source neutron; the probability per unit volume that these will enter the third group is then $P_1(|\mathbf{r}_1 - \mathbf{r}_0|) \cdot P_2(|\mathbf{r}_2 - \mathbf{r}_1|) \, d\mathbf{r}_1$. The total number of source neutrons per cm³ per sec, starting at $\mathbf{r}_0$, which will cross the energy level E_2 and pass into the third group at the field point $\mathbf{r}_2$ is consequently obtained by integrating over all space, since this sums up the contributions of all the volume elements $d\mathbf{r}_1$ for the second group; for unit source this is equivalent to the kernel $P(|\mathbf{r}_2 - \mathbf{r}_0|)$, so that

$$P(|\mathbf{r}_2 - \mathbf{r}_0|) = \int_{\substack{\text{all} \\ \text{space}}} P_1(|\mathbf{r}_1 - \mathbf{r}_0|) \cdot P_2(|\mathbf{r}_2 - \mathbf{r}_1|) \, d\mathbf{r}_1. \tag{12.8.1}$$

12.9. By pursuing this treatment throughout the whole series of energy groups, the probability that a fission neutron starting at $\mathbf{r}_0$ will become thermal at $\mathbf{r}_n$ is found to be given by

$$P(|\mathbf{r}_n - \mathbf{r}_0|) = \underset{\text{all space}}{\int\int \cdots \int} P_1(|\mathbf{r}_1 - \mathbf{r}_0|) \cdot P_2(|\mathbf{r}_2 - \mathbf{r}_1|) \cdots$$
$$P_n(|\mathbf{r}_n - \mathbf{r}_{n-1}|) \, d\mathbf{r}_1 \, d\mathbf{r}_2 \cdots d\mathbf{r}_{n-1}, \tag{12.9.1}$$

where, in general, the P's are different for each energy group. This represents a general slowing down kernel in an infinite medium for neutrons starting with fission energy (E_0) at $\mathbf{r}_0$ and slowing down to thermal energy (E_{th}) at $\mathbf{r}_n$.

12.10. In order to derive expressions for the slowing down kernels on the basis of the group-diffusion theory, it will be supposed, in the first place, that there are only two energy groups. Thus, thermal neutrons will represent one group; all neutrons of higher energy, the other (fast) group, as in Chapter VIII. If there is assumed to be no absorption of neutrons in the fast group, it may be supposed that the fast flux, ϕ_1, satisfies the diffusion equation

$$D_1 \nabla^2 \phi_1 - \Sigma_1 \phi_1 + S = 0, \tag{12.10.1}$$

where D_1 is the average diffusion coefficient, defined by (8.13.1), and Σ_1 is the slowing down cross section, considered in § 8.12. The first term gives the fast-neutron leakage, the second is the loss of neutrons per cm³ per sec due to degradation into the slow group, and the third is the source of fast neutrons. Upon dividing through by D_1 and replacing D_1/Σ_1 by L_1^2, where L_1 is a fictitious diffusion length, (12.10.1) becomes

$$\nabla^2 \phi_1 - \frac{\phi_1}{L_1^2} + \frac{S}{D_1} = 0. \tag{12.10.2}$$

The homogeneous part of this differential equation is similar to (5.44.2), except that $1/L_1^2$ is used, for convenience, in place of κ_1^2. Hence, for a unit point source of fast neutrons, the flux [cf. (5.49.1)], away from the source, is

$$\phi_1 = \frac{e^{-r/L_1}}{4\pi D_1 r}. \tag{12.10.3}$$

If $L_1^2\Sigma_1$ is substituted for D_1, to which it is equivalent, it follows that

$$\Sigma_1\phi_1 = \frac{e^{-r/L_1}}{4\pi L_1^2 r}. \tag{12.10.4}$$

12.11. This result can now be used to construct the infinite-medium diffusion slowing down kernel for two groups. As seen above, the quantity $\Sigma_1\phi_1$ represents the number of neutrons crossing from the fast group to the slow group per cm^3 per sec, and hence the right-hand side of (12.10.4) gives the probability that a source neutron at $\mathbf{r}_0 = 0$ will become thermal at the field point $\mathbf{r}$, per cm^3 per sec. Consequently, if a point source is at $\mathbf{r}_0$ and the field point at $\mathbf{r}$, in an infinite homogeneous medium, the probability per unit volume, which represents the two-group slowing down kernel, can be written as

$$P(|\mathbf{r} - \mathbf{r}_0|) = \frac{e^{-|\mathbf{r}-\mathbf{r}_0|/L_1}}{4\pi L_1^2 |\mathbf{r} - \mathbf{r}_0|}. \tag{12.11.1}$$

12.12. The foregoing treatment for one fast and one slow group may be extended to the general case, discussed in § 8.59, et seq., of n groups of neutrons with energies exceeding the thermal values. Thus, consideration of the slowing down from the ith group to the $(i + 1)$th group leads to the diffusion equation

$$D_i \nabla^2\phi_i(\mathbf{r}) - \Sigma_i\phi_i(\mathbf{r}) + S_i = 0, \tag{12.12.1}$$

where the source term S_i is given by the number of neutrons which have been degraded from the $(i - 1)$th group into the ith group. In accordance with the method used for two groups, it is readily seen that, in an infinite medium, the diffusion slowing down kernel for the ith group, which is the probability per unit volume for a neutron at $\mathbf{r}_i$ in the ith group to enter the $(i + 1)$th group at $\mathbf{r}_{i+1}$, is given by

$$P_i(|\mathbf{r}_{i+1} - \mathbf{r}_i|) = \frac{e^{-|\mathbf{r}_{i+1}-\mathbf{r}_i|/L_i}}{4\pi L_i^2 |\mathbf{r}_{i+1} - \mathbf{r}_i|}, \tag{12.12.2}$$

where L_i is equal to D_i/Σ_i; here D_i is the diffusion coefficient of neutrons in the ith group, and Σ_i is defined by an expression analogous to (8.12.3), viz.,

$$\Sigma_i = \frac{\overline{\Sigma}_s}{\dfrac{1}{\xi} \ln \dfrac{E_i}{E_{i+1}}}. \tag{12.12.3}$$

If the number of groups is sufficiently large, $\overline{\Sigma}_s$ may be taken as equal to the scattering cross section of neutrons with energy E_i; otherwise, it might be averaged over the range from E_i to E_{i+1}, according to (8.11.3).

12.13. By inserting expressions of the form of (12.12.2) for the individual group kernels, $P_1, P_2, \ldots, P_n$ into the general equation (12.9.1), it is possible to determine the infinite-medium diffusion slowing down kernel for fission neutrons originating at $\mathbf{r}_0$ and becoming thermal at $\mathbf{r}_n$. It will be shown later (§ 12.63) how the group-diffusion kernels for slowing down can be combined with certain experimental data to permit the development of an analytical expression for the slowing down density of neutrons in water. As pointed out earlier, the Fermi continuous slowing down model fails when either light or heavy water is the moderator, and the approach indicated here provides a satisfactory solution of the problem.

12.14. It is important to note that, in the derivation and application of the slowing down kernels, the possibility of absorption of the neutrons during the slowing down process has been neglected. The necessary correction can be made, however, by multiplying the slowing down kernels, as given by (12.3.1), etc., by the resonance escape probability.

THE GENERAL REACTOR EQUATION

THE SLOWING DOWN DENSITY

12.15. The probability, per unit volume, that a source (fission) neutron released at $\mathbf{r}_0$ will reach the field point $\mathbf{r}$ as a neutron of energy E may be represented by the slowing down kernel $P(\mathbf{r}, \mathbf{r}_0, E)$.* When E is equal to the thermal energy E_{th}, the slowing down kernel $P(\mathbf{r}, \mathbf{r}_0, E_{\text{th}})$ becomes the slowing down density at thermal energy at $\mathbf{r}$ due to a point source at $\mathbf{r}_0$. Since the resonance escape probability $p(E)$ is the fraction of the source neutrons, in an infinite medium, which actually reach energy E, it follows that the slowing down kernel can be normalized so that

$$\int_{\substack{\text{all} \\ \text{space}}} P(\mathbf{r}, \mathbf{r}_0, E) \, d\mathbf{r} = p(E), \qquad (12.15.1)$$

where $d\mathbf{r}$ is a volume element at the field point $\mathbf{r}$.

12.16. It was seen in § 7.7 that the number of fast neutrons per cm³ per sec produced at a point $\mathbf{r}_0$ by fissions in a multiplying medium, e.g., in a reactor, is $(k/p)\Sigma_a\phi(\mathbf{r}_0)$. Hence, in a volume element $d\mathbf{r}_0$ at the point $\mathbf{r}_0$, the number of source neutrons created per sec is $(k/p)\Sigma_a\phi(\mathbf{r}_0) \, d\mathbf{r}_0$. The number of source neutrons originating in the volume element $d\mathbf{r}_0$ which are slowed down past energy E

---

*A general symbol is used here, as the slowing down kernels may apply to a finite medium and are then not displacement kernels.

at $\mathbf{r}$ per cm^3 per sec, in a system with no extraneous source, assuming the fission (source) neutrons to be monoenergetic, is thus

$$\text{Neutrons from } dr_0 \text{ slowed down to energy } E \text{ at } \mathbf{r} = \frac{k}{p} \Sigma_a \phi(\mathbf{r}_0) P(\mathbf{r}, \mathbf{r}_0, E) \, d\mathbf{r}_0.$$

The total number of neutrons per cm^3 per sec at the field point $\mathbf{r}$ slowed down to energy E, which is equal to the slowing down density $q(\mathbf{r}, E)$, is then obtained by summing the contributions from all volume elements in the reactor; thus,

$$q(\mathbf{r}, E) = \int_{\substack{\text{volume} \\ \text{of reactor}}} \frac{k}{p} \Sigma_a \phi(\mathbf{r}_0) P(\mathbf{r}, \mathbf{r}_0, E) \, d\mathbf{r}_0. \tag{12.16.1}$$

The slowing down density given by (12.16.1) includes allowance for absorption during slowing down, since a proper estimate of the slowing down kernel must take into account loss of neutrons by resonance capture, etc., during the slowing down process. This will be apparent from (12.15.1), where the integral of the slowing down kernel is identified with the resonance escape probability.

12.17. The slowing down density at thermal energies $q(\mathbf{r}, E_{th})$ is obtained by substituting E_{th} for E in (12.16.1), and this is equal to the thermal neutron source term in the diffusion equation; hence,

$$q(\mathbf{r}, E_{th}) = \int_{\substack{\text{volume} \\ \text{of reactor}}} \frac{k}{p} \Sigma_a \phi(\mathbf{r}_0) P(\mathbf{r}, \mathbf{r}_0, E_{th}) \, d\mathbf{r}_0, \tag{12.17.1}$$

where $P(\mathbf{r}, \mathbf{r}_0, E_{th})$ is the slowing down kernel for fission neutrons to thermal energy. Since, as pointed out above, the expression for $q(\mathbf{r}, E)$ already includes allowance for absorption during slowing down, it is not necessary to multiply by p, as was done in § 7.6. If an extraneous source of fast neutrons, represented by $S(\mathbf{r}_0)$, with the same energy as the fission neutrons, is present in the system, an additional term must be included in (12.17.1), which now becomes

$$q(\mathbf{r}, E_{th}) = \int_{\substack{\text{volume} \\ \text{of reactor}}} \left[\frac{k}{p} \Sigma_a \phi(\mathbf{r}_0) + S(\mathbf{r}_0) \right] P(\mathbf{r}, \mathbf{r}_0, E_{th}) \, d\mathbf{r}_0. \tag{12.17.2}$$

The General Diffusion Equation

12.18. If the general value for $q(\mathbf{r}, E_{th})$ given by (12.17.2) is inserted into the thermal diffusion equation, in which the possibility of a change in the neutron density with time is included, the result is

$$D \, \nabla^2 \phi(\mathbf{r}, t) - \Sigma_a \phi(\mathbf{r}, t) + \int_{\substack{\text{volume} \\ \text{of reactor}}} \left[\frac{k}{p} \Sigma_a \phi(\mathbf{r}_0) + S(\mathbf{r}_0) \right] P(\mathbf{r}, \mathbf{r}_0, E_{th}) \, d\mathbf{r}_0 = \frac{\partial n}{\partial t}$$

$$= \frac{1}{v} \cdot \frac{\partial \phi(\mathbf{r}, t)}{\partial t}, \tag{12.18.1}$$

where the neutron density n is replaced by ϕ/v, with v being the average speed of thermal neutrons. The thermal neutron flux is then given by the solution of this equation satisfying the condition that it goes to zero at the extrapolated boundary. As mentioned above, it has been assumed, for simplicity, that all fission and source neutrons are released with the same energy. The generalization to a fission spectrum can be made without difficulty. In addition, it is supposed that all the fission neutrons are emitted promptly; neglect of the delayed neutrons does not affect the main argument.

12.19. In the subsequent treatment it will be postulated that the transport mean free path — and hence the extrapolation distance for the neutron flux — is independent of the energy. This means that the position of the extrapolated boundary, where the flux goes to zero, is the same for neutrons of all energies. This assumption is particularly satisfactory for large reactors, since the neutron flux is not changed appreciably by small variations in the extrapolation distance.

12.20. To solve the boundary value problem analytically, it will be postulated that the slowing down kernels employed shall be restricted to those obtained from the solution of linear, homogeneous differential equations. For example, in the continuous slowing down treatment, the slowing down kernel is the solution of the (linear and homogeneous) age equation, under suitable conditions. The three kernels in general use in reactor theory are the Gaussian, diffusion, and transport kernels, and the two latter, like the first, are derived from linear, homogeneous equations.

12.21. For a bare, homogeneous reactor a solution of the diffusion equation (12.18.1) may be attempted by assuming the space part to be equivalent to the space form of the wave equation. Hence, solutions of the wave equation

$$\nabla^2 Z(\mathbf{r}) + B^2 Z(\mathbf{r}) = 0 \qquad (12.21.1)$$

that go to zero at the extrapolated boundary of a finite multiplying medium may be considered. The condition that $Z = 0$ on the boundary results in a set of eigenvalues B_n^2; that is to say, Z will go to zero on the boundary only for discrete values of B_n^2. The corresponding eigenfunctions, of which Z_n is the nth member, form a complete orthogonal set of functions. Consequently, the space part of the neutron flux, the slowing down density, and certain extraneous sources can be expanded in terms of an infinite series of eigenfunctions Z_n.

12.22. If the space and time variables are separable in $\phi(\mathbf{r}, t)$, it is possible to write

$$\phi(\mathbf{r}, t) = \sum_n A_n Z_n(\mathbf{r}) T_n(t) \qquad (12.22.1)$$

and

$$q(\mathbf{r}, E) = \int_{\substack{\text{volume} \\ \text{of reactor}}} \sum_n Q_n Z_n(\mathbf{r}_0) P(\mathbf{r}, \mathbf{r}_0, E) \, d\mathbf{r}_0, \qquad (12.22.2)$$

for the flux and the slowing down density, respectively, while the extraneous source is represented by

$$S(\mathbf{r}) = \sum_n S_n Z_n(\mathbf{r}).$$ (12.22.3)

Upon insertion of these results into (12.17.2), it is found that

$$Q_n = \frac{k}{p} \Sigma_a A_n T_n(t) + S_n.$$ (12.22.4)

The coefficients A_n and S_n can be obtained from the orthogonality condition, that is, by expressing them as coefficients of a Fourier series.

12.23. As can be seen from § 12.3, *et seq.*, the infinite-medium slowing down kernels are displacement kernels, since they are functions only of the distance from the source to the field point. If the medium is finite, however, the presence of a boundary changes the slowing down kernel. This is apparent on physical grounds, since neutrons originating near a boundary have a higher probability of escaping than those produced in the interior of the medium. The finite-medium slowing down kernels, $P(\mathbf{r}, \mathbf{r}_0, E)$, appearing in the equations given above, are thus very complex. In order to solve the reactor equation it is desirable to replace them by infinite kernels, and this is achieved by means of the concept of an image source.

FINITE AND INFINITE KERNELS

12.24. Consider a semi-infinite slab with a vacuum at its (extrapolated) boundary; a plane source of fast neutrons is supposed to be within the medium

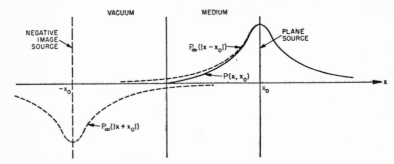

FIG. 12.24.   Negative image source in evaluation of finite kernels

at a distance x_0 from the boundary (Fig. 12.24). The infinite-medium (Gaussian) slowing down kernel is given by (12.4.1) as

$$P_\infty(|\,x - x_0\,|, E) = \frac{e^{-|\,x-x_0\,|^2/4\tau(E)}}{[4\pi\tau(E)]^{\frac{1}{2}}},$$ (12.24.1)

the resonance escape probability being omitted as it is not essential to the present argument. The finite or, rather, semifinite slowing down kernel that satisfies the condition that the slowing down density, and hence the kernel, shall be zero at the boundary, i.e., when $x = 0$, is then

$$P(x, x_0, E) = \frac{1}{[4\pi\tau(E)]^{\frac{1}{2}}} [e^{-|x-x_0|^2/4\tau(E)} - e^{-|x+x_0|^2/4\tau(E)}]. \qquad (12.24.2)$$

This finite kernel is seen to be the difference of two infinite-medium kernels; the first term is that due to a plane source at x_0, while the second corresponds to a negative image source at $-x_0$, shown by the dotted line in Fig. 12.24. Thus, a finite kernel can be obtained from the superposition of infinite-medium kernels, arising from a real source and a distributed image source that makes $q = 0$ on the extrapolated boundary.

12.25. The result just obtained will now be applied to a consideration of the source integral in the diffusion equation, and the semi-infinite slab will again be used for purposes of illustration. Suppose the flux distribution is as indicated by the full curve in Fig. 12.25; the dotted curve for negative values of x is defined

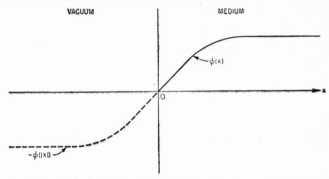

Fig. 12.25. Analytical continuation of flux distribution to represent image source

as $-\phi(|x|)$, which is an analytical continuation of $\phi(x)$, and will represent the image source. Omitting $(k/p)\Sigma_a$, the source integral in (12.17.1) may be expressed in the form

$$I = \int \phi(x_0)P(x, x_0, E) \, dx_0, \qquad (12.25.1)$$

where $P(x, x_0, E)$ is the finite-medium (slowing down) kernel corresponding to the given geometry, i.e., the semi-infinite slab. Hence, from (12.24.2)

$$I = \frac{1}{(4\pi\tau)^{\frac{1}{2}}} \int_0^\infty \phi(x_0)[e^{-|x-x_0|^2/4\tau} - e^{-|x+x_0|^2/4\tau}] \, dx_0,$$

where the first term in the brackets corresponds to the real source and the second to a negative image source at $-x_0$. Since $\phi(x_0)$ is analytically continued as $-\phi(|x_0|)$, the integral can be written as

$$I = \frac{1}{(4\pi\tau)^{\frac{1}{2}}} \left[\int_0^\infty \phi(x_0)e^{-|x-x_0|^2/4\tau} \, dx_0 + \int_{-\infty}^0 \phi(x_0)e^{-|x-x_0|^2/4\tau} \, dx_0 \right],$$

where the limits of integration have been reversed in the second integral and x_0 in the exponent replaced by $-x_0$, since it is always negative in the range of integration and the absolute value of $x - x_0$ is involved; consequently,

$$I = \frac{1}{(4\pi\tau)^{\frac{1}{2}}} \int_{-\infty}^{\infty} \phi(x_0)e^{-|x-x_0|^2/4\tau} \, dx_0. \tag{12.25.2}$$

Comparison of (12.25.1) and (12.25.2) shows that the finite kernel in the former has been replaced by an infinite-medium kernel in the latter; at the same time, the source distribution has been analytically continued to obtain a distributed image source.

SOLUTION OF THE REACTOR EQUATION*

12.26. The results obtained above are quite general and can be applied in solving the reactor equation with its associated boundary conditions. The eigenfunctions Z_n of the wave equation (12.21.1) are continued analytically to infinity, beyond the extrapolated boundary of the reactor. This represents a distributed image source system analogous to the simple case considered above. The finite kernels in equations (12.16.1), etc., can then be replaced by infinite-medium kernels, and the integration of the source term extended over all space. This provides a valuable method for the solution of the general problem of a finite multiplying medium with fast neutron sources.

12.27. Applying the procedure to (12.22.2), the result is

$$q(\mathbf{r}, E) = \int_{\substack{\text{all} \\ \text{space}}} \sum_n Q_n Z_n(\mathbf{r}_0) P_\infty(|\mathbf{r} - \mathbf{r}_0|, E) \, d\mathbf{r}_0, \tag{12.27.1}$$

where the finite kernel has been substituted by the infinite kernel; at the same time, the functions $\phi(\mathbf{r}_0, t)$ and $S(\mathbf{r}_0)$ have been analytically continued, and the integration extended over all space. Equation (12.27.1) for the slowing down density can now be written in a more convenient form employing Fourier transforms.†

---

* The procedure followed is essentially that of A. M. Weinberg, unpublished.

† The three-dimensional Fourier transform of $Z_n(\mathbf{r})$ is $\bar{Z}_n(\boldsymbol{\alpha})$ defined by

$$\bar{Z}_n(\boldsymbol{\alpha}) = \int_{\substack{\text{all} \\ \text{space}}} e^{i\boldsymbol{\alpha} \cdot \mathbf{r}} \, Z_n(\mathbf{r}) \, d\mathbf{r},$$

while the inverse transformation is

$$Z_n(\mathbf{r}) = \frac{1}{(2\pi)^3} \int_{\substack{\text{all } \alpha \\ \text{space}}} e^{-i\boldsymbol{\alpha} \cdot \mathbf{r}} \, \bar{Z}_n(\boldsymbol{\alpha}) \, d\boldsymbol{\alpha},$$

where $\boldsymbol{\alpha} = \mathbf{i}\alpha_x + \mathbf{j}\alpha_y + \mathbf{k}\alpha_z$ is a vector integration variable. The Fourier transform of a function is indicated by a line over the symbol.

12.28. The Fourier transform of (12.21.1) is

$$-\alpha^2 \bar{Z}_n(\boldsymbol{\alpha}) + B_n^2 \bar{Z}_n(\boldsymbol{\alpha}) = 0,$$

so that

$$(B_n^2 - \alpha^2)\bar{Z}_n(\boldsymbol{\alpha}) = 0. \tag{12.28.1}$$

Consequently, $\bar{Z}_n(\boldsymbol{\alpha})$ is zero everywhere except when $B_n^2 = \alpha^2$. The inverse Fourier transform of $\bar{Z}_n(\boldsymbol{\alpha})$ can then be written as

$$Z_n(\mathbf{r}) = \frac{1}{(2\pi)^3} \int_{\substack{\text{all } \alpha \\ \text{space}}} e^{-i\mathbf{B}_n \cdot \mathbf{r}}\, \bar{Z}_n(\boldsymbol{\alpha})\, d\boldsymbol{\alpha}, \tag{12.28.2}$$

where $\mathbf{B} = \mathbf{i}B_x + \mathbf{j}B_y + \mathbf{k}B_z$ is the buckling vector. With this result, (12.27.1) for $q(\mathbf{r}, E)$ becomes

$$q(\mathbf{r}, E) = \int_{\substack{\text{all} \\ \text{space}}} \sum_n Q_n \frac{1}{(2\pi)^3} \int_{\substack{\text{all } \alpha \\ \text{space}}} e^{-i\mathbf{B}_n \cdot \mathbf{r}_0} \bar{Z}_n(\boldsymbol{\alpha})\, d\boldsymbol{\alpha} P_\infty(|\mathbf{r} - \mathbf{r}_0|, E)\, d\mathbf{r}_0. \tag{12.28.3}$$

The volume element $d\mathbf{r}_0$ is equivalent to $d(\mathbf{r}_0 - \mathbf{r})$ at $\mathbf{r}_0$, provided the appropriate limits are chosen so that the integration extends over all space, and since $\mathbf{r}_0 = \mathbf{r} - (\mathbf{r} - \mathbf{r}_0)$, equation (12.28.3) can be written as

$$q(\mathbf{r}, E) = \int_{\substack{\text{all} \\ \text{space}}} \sum_n Q_n \frac{1}{(2\pi)^3} \int_{\substack{\text{all } \alpha \\ \text{space}}} e^{-i\mathbf{B}_n \cdot \mathbf{r}} \bar{Z}_n(\boldsymbol{\alpha})\, d\boldsymbol{\alpha}\; e^{i\mathbf{B}_n \cdot (\mathbf{r} - \mathbf{r}_0)} P_\infty(|\mathbf{r} - \mathbf{r}_0|, E)\, d(\mathbf{r}_0 - \mathbf{r}).$$

The second integral is the inverse Fourier transform of $\bar{Z}_n(\mathbf{r})$, so that this equation becomes

$$q(\mathbf{r}, E) = \sum_n Q_n Z_n(\mathbf{r}) \int_{\substack{\text{all} \\ \text{space}}} e^{i\mathbf{B}_n \cdot (\mathbf{r} - \mathbf{r}_0)} P_\infty(|\mathbf{r} - \mathbf{r}_0|, E)\, d(\mathbf{r}_0 - \mathbf{r}). \tag{12.28.4}$$

12.29. The three-dimensional Fourier transform of the infinite slowing down kernel $P_\infty(|\mathbf{r} - \mathbf{r}_0|, E)$, represented by $\bar{P}_\infty(E, B_n^2)$, is given by

$$\bar{P}_\infty(E, B_n^2) = \int_{\substack{\text{all} \\ \text{space}}} e^{i\mathbf{B}_n \cdot (\mathbf{r} - \mathbf{r}_0)} P_\infty(|\mathbf{r} - \mathbf{r}_0|, E)\, d(\mathbf{r}_0 - \mathbf{r}), \tag{12.29.1}$$

and hence (12.28.4) may be written as

$$q(\mathbf{r}, E) = \sum_n Q_n Z_n(\mathbf{r}) \bar{P}_\infty(E, B_n^2). \tag{12.29.2}$$

This equation, in which the slowing down density is related to the three-dimensional Fourier transform of an infinite slowing down kernel, is fundamental to generalized reactor theory. It may be noted that the expansion of $q(\mathbf{r}, E)$ in the form of a series, as in (12.29.2), is possible only if the differential equation in q, e.g., the Fermi age equation, is linear and homogeneous.

SIGNIFICANCE OF THE FOURIER TRANSFORM

12.30. As a purely mathematical concept, the neutrons of any particular energy E may be regarded as being divided into n modes; then the slowing down density for the nth mode is given by (12.29.2) as

$$q_n(\mathbf{r}, E) = Q_n Z_n(\mathbf{r}) \bar{P}_\infty(E, B_n^2).$$

This gives the number of neutrons in the nth mode, per cm^3 per sec, that slow down past energy E. The number of fast neutrons, with energy E_0, that start out from the source in this mode is then

$$q_n(\mathbf{r}, E_0) = Q_n Z_n(\mathbf{r}) \bar{P}_\infty(E_0, B_n^2),$$

so that the ratio of the number of neutrons in the nth mode reaching energy E to the number leaving the source at energy E_0 in this mode, is given by

$$\frac{\text{No. of } n\text{th mode neutrons reaching energy } E}{\text{No. of } n\text{th mode neutrons leaving source}} = \frac{q_n(\mathbf{r}, E)}{q_n(\mathbf{r}, E_0)}$$
$$= \frac{\bar{P}_\infty(E, B_n^2)}{\bar{P}_\infty(E_0, B_n^2)}. \quad (12.30.1)$$

12.31. The denominator of this equation is equal to unity, as may be shown by choosing a suitable infinite slowing down, e.g., Gaussian, kernel, based on a linear, homogeneous differential equation. A general expression for the Fourier transform is then obtained, and the result is evaluated for E_0 to give the required Fourier transform for the source neutrons. For example, it will be shown later (§ 12.54) that, when the Gaussian slowing down kernel is used, $\bar{P}_\infty(E, B_n^2)$ is equal to $pe^{-B_n^2 \tau}$, where p is the resonance escape probability and τ is the Fermi age of the neutrons of energy E. For the source neutrons τ is zero and p is unity; hence, the value of $\bar{P}_\infty(E_0, B_n^2)$ is unity. This result is quite general and so it can be concluded from (12.30.1) that

$$\frac{\text{No. of } n\text{th mode neutrons reaching energy } E}{\text{No. of } n\text{th mode neutrons leaving source}} = \bar{P}_\infty(E, B_n^2). \quad (12.31.1)$$

Thus, $\bar{P}_\infty(E, B_n^2)$ is the probability that nth mode source neutrons will reach energy E in the assembly without escaping from the system or being absorbed at higher energies.

APPROACH TO CRITICAL

GENERAL BEHAVIOR OF MULTIPLYING SYSTEMS

12.32. Consider a finite system built up of fissionable material and moderator, containing a point source of fast neutrons at $\mathbf{r}_0$, represented by $S\delta(\mathbf{r} - \mathbf{r}_0)$, where δ is a delta function. To simplify the problem without serious loss of generality, it will be assumed, as above, that the neutrons produced by fission and the extraneous source neutrons are released with the same energy.

12.33. If the nth terms of the expansions in equations (12.21.1), (12.22.1), (12.22.3), and (12.29.2) are inserted into the general diffusion equation (12.18.1), the latter becomes, for thermal neutrons of the nth mode,

$$-DB_n{}^2 A_n T_n(t) Z_n(\mathbf{r}) - \Sigma_a A_n T_n(t) Z_n(\mathbf{r})$$
$$+ \left[\frac{k}{p}\Sigma_a A_n T_n(t) + S_n\right] Z_n(\mathbf{r}) \bar{P}_\infty(B_n{}^2) = \frac{1}{v} A_n Z_n(\mathbf{r}) \frac{dT_n(t)}{dt}, \quad (12.33.1)$$

where $\nabla^2 Z_n(\mathbf{r})$ has been replaced by $-B_n{}^2 Z_n(\mathbf{r})$ in accordance with (12.21.1), and the symbol E has been omitted from the argument in $\bar{P}_\infty(E, B_n{}^2)$, since the energy is assumed to be thermal. Dividing through (12.33.1) by $\Sigma_a A_n T_n Z_n$, and recalling that $D/\Sigma_a = L^2$ and $l_0 = 1/\Sigma_a v$, where L is the diffusion length and l_0 is the infinite-medium lifetime of the nth mode thermal neutrons, the result is

$$\frac{k}{p}\bar{P}_\infty(B_n{}^2) - (1 + L^2 B_n{}^2) + \frac{S_n \bar{P}_\infty(B_n{}^2)}{\Sigma_a A_n T_n(t)} = \frac{l_0}{T_n(t)} \cdot \frac{dT_n(t)}{dt}.$$

12.34. Upon dividing through by $(1 + L^2 B_n{}^2)$, and replacing $l_0/(1 + L^2 B_n{}^2)$ by the finite-medium lifetime l_n for the nth mode, it follows that

$$\left[\frac{k\bar{P}_\infty(B_n{}^2)}{p(1 + L^2 B_n{}^2)} - 1\right] + \frac{S_n \bar{P}_\infty(B_n{}^2)}{\Sigma_a(1 + L^2 B_n{}^2) A_n T_n(t)} = \frac{l_n}{T_n(t)} \cdot \frac{dT_n(t)}{dt}.$$

The solution of this differential equation for $T_n(t)$ in terms of t is

$$T_n(t) = \text{const.} \times e^{(k_{n\text{eff}}-1)\frac{t}{l_n}} + \frac{S_n \bar{P}_\infty(B_n{}^2)}{A_n \Sigma_a(1 + L^2 B_n{}^2)(1 - k_{n\text{eff}})},$$

where $k_{n\text{eff}}$ is defined by

$$k_{n\text{eff}} = \frac{k\bar{P}_\infty(B_n{}^2)}{p(1 + L^2 B_n{}^2)}. \quad (12.34.1)$$

12.35. The total neutron flux in the assembly is then given by (12.22.1) as

$$\phi(\mathbf{r}, t) = \sum_n \left[A_n' Z_n(\mathbf{r}) e^{(k_{n\text{eff}}-1)\frac{t}{l_n}} + \frac{S_n Z_n(\mathbf{r}) \bar{P}_\infty(B_n{}^2)}{\Sigma_a(1 + L^2 B_n{}^2)(1 - k_{n\text{eff}})}\right], \quad (12.35.1)$$

where A_n' is a combined constant. This equation is the general solution for the behavior of the thermal neutron flux in a finite multiplying medium with an extraneous source, irrespective of whether the system is in a steady state or not. The first term gives the flux due to fissions, and the second term is the contribution made by the extraneous source.

12.36. From the presence of $k_{n\text{eff}}$ in the second term, it is evident that the fast extraneous source neutrons are multiplied by fissions. If no fissionable material were present, so that k and, hence, $k_{n\text{eff}}$ would be zero, (12.35.1) would reduce to

$$\phi(\mathbf{r}) = \sum_n \frac{S_n Z_n(\mathbf{r}) \bar{P}_\infty(B_n{}^2)}{\Sigma_a(1 + L^2 B_n{}^2)}.$$

The effect of fissions is, therefore, to multiply each mode of the thermal neutron flux that would result from a given source in a nonmultiplying medium by $1/(1 - k_{n_{\text{eff}}})$, the geometry, scattering, and slowing down being assumed to be the same in both cases.

12.37. Returning to the general equation (12.35.1), it will be shown how this can be used to prove the existence of a specific, critical geometry for a given multiplying system. Imagine, for example, a rectangular parallelepiped, with dimensions a, b, c, containing a point source of fast neutrons at its center. Such a system is symmetrical with respect to the Cartesian coordinate axes, x, y, z, selected with their origin at the center of the parallelepiped and parallel to its edges. The eigenfunctions are therefore even functions, i.e.,

$$Z_n = \cos\frac{u\pi x}{a}\cos\frac{v\pi y}{b}\cos\frac{w\pi z}{c},$$

and the corresponding eigenvalues that satisfy the boundary condition (§ 12.21) are

$$B_n{}^2 = \pi^2\left[\left(\frac{u}{a}\right)^2 + \left(\frac{v}{b}\right)^2 + \left(\frac{w}{c}\right)^2\right], \tag{12.37.1}$$

where u, v, and w are positive odd integers. If the assembly is very subcritical, e.g., due to its being too small, $B_n{}^2$ is large; in fact, as $a = b = c \to 0$, $B_n{}^2 \to \infty$.

12.38. Consider now equation (12.34.1) which defines $k_{n_{\text{eff}}}$. As the dimensions of the system are increased from the very small magnitude considered above, $B_n{}^2$ decreases until at some point $k_{n_{\text{eff}}}$ is equal to unity. The $B_n{}^2$'s form a sequence of values that, for a fixed a, b, c, increase monotonically with increasing n, the smallest value being that for which $u = v = w = 1$ [cf. (12.37.1)]; this will then correspond to the largest value of $k_{n_{\text{eff}}}$. These values of u, v, w give the lowest of the eigenvalues corresponding to solutions of the wave equation that satisfy the boundary condition that $\phi = 0$ on the extrapolated boundary.

12.39. As long as $k_{n_{\text{eff}}}$ is less than unity for all n, the first term in (12.35.1) implies an exponential decay of the flux with time, since $k_{n_{\text{eff}}} - 1$ is negative for all n. Hence, the only way that a steady state can be obtained is if an extraneous source of neutrons is present. In this event, the fission chain reaction in the assembly is not self-sustaining; the leakage of neutrons is too large, or the multiplication factor k is too small. In either case, extraneous source neutrons are required to maintain a neutron balance, and the steady state flux, after a sufficient time for the exponential term to decay, is

$$\phi(\mathbf{r}) = \sum_n \frac{S_n Z_n(\mathbf{r})\bar{P}_\infty(B_n{}^2)}{\Sigma_a(1 + L^2 B_n{}^2)(1 - k_{n_{\text{eff}}})}. \tag{12.39.1}$$

THE CRITICAL STATE

12.40. Suppose next that the assembly of given fuel and moderator is increased in size until

$$k_{0_{\text{eff}}} = 1,$$

where $k_{0_{eff}}$ is the largest $k_{n_{eff}}$, which refers to $u = v = w = 1$, and corresponds to the fundamental eigenvalue B_0^2. The first term in (12.35.1) then becomes constant for $n = 0$. Now, however, the second term becomes infinite if an extraneous source is present. Hence, to have a steady state, this source must be removed. This is the condition for a critical self-sustaining reaction. The *critical equation* is consequently

$$k_{0_{eff}} = \frac{k \bar{P}_\infty(B_0^2)}{p(1 + L^2 B_0^2)} = 1. \tag{12.40.1}$$

12.41. Since $k_{0_{eff}}$ is the largest $k_{n_{eff}}$, all others, for $n > 0$, are less than unity; hence, the corresponding values of the first term in (12.35.1) decay exponentially in time, and for a true steady state all must be zero. Therefore, when a chain reaction is critical, without an extraneous source, the Fourier series expansion for the flux reduces to only the fundamental term. The steady state flux in the rectangular parallelepiped considered above is represented by

$$\phi(x, y, z) = A \cos \frac{\pi x}{a} \cos \frac{\pi y}{b} \cos \frac{\pi z}{c}. \tag{12.41.1}$$

An equivalent statement is that the flux satisfies the wave equation

$$\nabla^2 \phi + B^2 \phi = 0,$$

with $\phi = 0$ on the boundary, where

$$\frac{k \bar{P}_\infty(B^2)}{p(1 + L^2 B^2)} = 1, \tag{12.41.2}$$

is the critical equation; and, for the geometry under consideration, the buckling is given by (12.37.1) as

$$B^2 = \left(\frac{\pi}{a}\right)^2 + \left(\frac{\pi}{b}\right)^2 + \left(\frac{\pi}{c}\right)^2.$$

The zero subscript has now been dropped from B^2, since only one value has significance in the critical state. The essential result of the preceding argument is, therefore, that in critical or near critical assemblies, the neutron flux can be expressed by means of the fundamental mode of the wave equation whose solution goes to zero at the extrapolated boundary.

12.42. It may be mentioned that, when $k_{0_{eff}}$ is greater than unity, the assembly becomes supercritical, and the flux increases with time, because of the exponential increase of the first term in (12.35.1). If the system is not far from critical, so that $k_{0_{eff}} - 1$ is small, the rate of increase will be determined essentially by this quantity in the numerator of the exponent. If the effective multiplication factor is appreciably in excess of unity, then $k_{1_{eff}}$ may also exceed unity, and two terms of the series will increase with time. This situation has no practical significance, for the condition in which a reactor is supercritical to such an extent must be avoided.

The Asymptotic Reactor Equation and Material Buckling

12.43. If a steady state is maintained in a multiplying system in the absence of an extraneous source, so that the reactor is in the critical state, the thermal diffusion equation (12.18.1) reduces to

$$D \nabla^2 \phi(\mathbf{r}) - \Sigma_a \phi(\mathbf{r}) + \frac{k}{p} \Sigma_a \int_{\substack{\text{volume} \\ \text{of reactor}}} \phi(r_0) P(\mathbf{r}, \mathbf{r}_0, E) \, d\mathbf{r}_0 = 0. \qquad (12.43.1)$$

The reactor is assumed to be uniform so that k, p, and Σ_a are independent of position and can be taken out of the integral. The solution of this equation can be obtained by the method of § 12.26, *et seq.*, on the assumption that the extrapolation distance is independent of the neutron energy (§ 12.19). As a result, the image system is given by the analytical continuation of the eigenfunctions Z_n of the wave equation (12.21.1). If the extrapolation distance varies with the neutron energy, this image system cannot satisfy the boundary conditions on $q(\mathbf{r}, E)$ for all energies. In general, by replacing the finite-medium slowing down kernel by an infinite-medium kernel, and extending the integration over all space, there is obtained an asymptotic equation

$$D \nabla^2 \phi(\mathbf{r}) - \Sigma_a \phi(r) + \frac{k}{p} \Sigma_a \int_{\substack{\text{all} \\ \text{space}}} \phi(\mathbf{r}_0) P_\infty(|\mathbf{r} - \mathbf{r}_0|) \, d\mathbf{r}_0 = 0. \qquad (12.43.2)$$

In a finite system $\phi(\mathbf{r}_0)$ falls off to zero at the extrapolated boundary, and $P_\infty(|\mathbf{r} - \mathbf{r}_0|)$ decreases rapidly with increasing $|\mathbf{r} - \mathbf{r}_0|$. Consequently, if the system is large, (12.43.2) gives an asymptotic solution to (12.43.1) which is valid far from boundaries.

12.44. By means of the Fourier transform method used in §§ 12.28, 12.29, it can be shown that

$$\int_{\substack{\text{all} \\ \text{space}}} \phi(\mathbf{r}_0) P_\infty(|\mathbf{r} - \mathbf{r}_0|) \, d\mathbf{r}_0 = \phi(\mathbf{r}) \bar{P}_\infty(B^2),$$

where $\bar{P}_\infty(B^2)$ is the three-dimensional Fourier transform defined by (12.29.1) with E equal to the thermal energy. Upon making the substitution for the integral in (12.43.2), this equation becomes

$$D \nabla^2 \phi(\mathbf{r}) - \Sigma_a \phi(\mathbf{r}) + \frac{k}{p} \Sigma_a \phi(\mathbf{r}) \bar{P}_\infty(B)^2 = 0. \qquad (12.44.1)$$

If B^2 is a solution of the wave equation

$$\nabla^2 \phi(\mathbf{r}) + B^2 \phi(\mathbf{r}) = 0, \qquad (12.44.2)$$

then it readily follows from (12.44.1) that

$$\frac{k \bar{P}_\infty(B^2)}{p(1 + L^2 B^2)} = 1. \qquad (12.44.3)$$

This means that the asymptotic reactor equation is satisfied by any solution of the wave equation (12.44.2), provided B^2 is a root of the critical equation (12.44.3).

12.45. Since k, p, L^2, and $\bar{P}_\infty(B^2)$ are microscopic properties of the multiplying system, it is evident that for a given reactor composition there is only one value of B^2 which satisfies (12.44.3). This is the material buckling $B_m{}^2$, previously defined in terms of the continuous slowing down model (§ 7.24). Hence, the asymptotic equation for a critical reactor will be satisfied by only one solution of the wave equation (12.44.2) for the flux distribution, namely,

$$\nabla^2\phi(\mathbf{r}) + B_m{}^2\phi(\mathbf{r}) = 0. \tag{12.45.1}$$

In general, the asymptotic reactor equation and its asymptotic solution are valid only at distances from boundaries that are large in comparison with the slowing down length of the neutrons. If the extrapolation distance is independent of neutron energy, the asymptotic solution becomes identical with the solution of the exact equation (12.43.1), as given in §§ 12.40, 12.41.

12.46. For a large assembly which is subcritical, but is maintained in a steady state by an extraneous source of neutrons, the thermal neutron balance in a region *far from the source*, where essentially all the neutrons have resulted from fissions, can still be represented fairly closely by (12.43.1), the integration being carried over the prescribed region only. Provided the region is more than a slowing down length from the boundaries of the assembly, the slowing down density can be expressed by means of the infinite-medium kernel, and the integration extended over all space, as in (12.43.2). Consequently, from the arguments presented above, the steady state thermal flux distribution in a large, subcritical assembly, in regions well away from sources and boundaries, is given, to a good approximation, by (12.45.1), where $B_m{}^2$ is the material buckling of the particular multiplying medium of which the assembly is composed. In the exponential experiment described in Chapter IX, the value of $B_m{}^2$ is obtained from the flux distribution measured in a subcritical assembly in the steady state. By setting $B_m{}^2$ equal to the (critical) geometric buckling, the dimensions of the critical reactor, having the same microscopic properties as the experimental assembly, can be determined. It should be noted that the exponential experiment method for determining the material buckling cannot be used for enriched uranium systems, for the subcritical assembly will generally be too small for the asymptotic solution to hold at any point.

THE CRITICAL EQUATION FOR VARIOUS SLOWING DOWN KERNELS

The Nonleakage Probability during Slowing Down

12.47. It was shown in § 12.31 that the fraction of the source neutrons, in any mode, which actually reach the energy E is equal to the Fourier transform of the infinite slowing down kernel for that mode. When the reactor is critical, and only the lowest eigenvalue is significant, all the neutrons may be regarded as being in one mode. If E is taken as the thermal energy, it follows from (12.31.1) that

$$\frac{\text{No. of neutrons becoming thermal}}{\text{No. of neutrons leaving source}} = \bar{P}_\infty(B^2), \qquad (12.47.1)$$

where $\bar{P}_\infty(B^2)$ is identical with $\bar{P}_\infty(B_0{}^2)$ in (12.40.1) or with $\bar{P}_\infty(B^2)$ in the critical equation (12.41.2). If there were no leakage of neutrons from the reactor, i.e., in an infinite medium, the fraction represented by (12.47.1) would be identical with the resonance escape probability p (cf. § 12.14). For a finite system, however, $\bar{P}_\infty(B^2)$ is the total probability that the neutrons will not leak out or be captured while slowing down. The nonleakage probability during slowing down to thermal energies is thus $\bar{P}_\infty(B^2)/p$. This is a completely general result and is independent of any theory concerning the slowing down process. It will be seen later that, by the use of a slowing down kernel based on the Fermi continuous slowing down model, the value of $\bar{P}_\infty(B^2)/p$ is found to be $e^{-B^2\tau}$, in agreement with the result obtained in Chapter VII. However, when the Fermi model is not applicable, the nonleakage probability can be obtained by using more appropriate kernels.

MOMENT FORM OF THE CRITICAL EQUATION

12.48. The critical equation can be written in a convenient form which can be directly related to a measured slowing down density in a given medium. In the critical (steady) state, the three-dimensional Fourier transform of the infinite-medium slowing down kernel $P_\infty(|\,\mathbf{r} - \mathbf{r}_0\,|)$ for thermal neutrons is given by (12.29.1) as

$$\bar{P}_\infty(B^2) = \int_{\substack{\text{all}\\\text{space}}} e^{i\mathbf{B}\,\cdot\,(\mathbf{r}-\mathbf{r}_0)} P_\infty(|\,\mathbf{r} - \mathbf{r}_0\,|)\, d(\mathbf{r}_0 - \mathbf{r}), \qquad (12.48.1)$$

where B^2 is the lowest eigenvalue of the wave equation, i.e., $B_0{}^2$, all others being now insignificant (§ 12.41). In polar coordinates this becomes

$$\bar{P}_\infty(B^2) = 4\pi \int_0^\infty P_\infty(r)\, \frac{\sin Br}{Br}\, r^2\, dr, \qquad (12.48.2)$$

where r is equal to $|\,\mathbf{r} - \mathbf{r}_0\,|$, and $P_\infty(r)$ is the slowing down kernel for an infinite medium. Upon expanding $\dfrac{\sin Br}{Br}$ in a Taylor series, and integrating term by term, the expression for the transform of the slowing down kernel becomes

$$\bar{P}_\infty(B^2) = 4\pi \sum_{n=0}^\infty \frac{(-1)^n}{(2n+1)!}\, B^{2n} \int_0^\infty r^{2n} P_\infty(r) r^2\, dr. \qquad (12.48.3)$$

12.49. The $2n$th moment of the slowing down density distribution is represented by

$$\overline{r^{2n}} = \frac{\int_0^\infty r^{2n} P_\infty(r) 4\pi r^2 \, dr}{\int_0^\infty P_\infty(r) 4\pi r^2 \, dr}. \tag{12.49.1}$$

Since the slowing down kernel is normalized to yield the resonance escape probability, according to (12.15.1), it follows that

$$4\pi \int_0^\infty P_\infty(r) r^2 \, dr = p, \tag{12.49.2}$$

where p is the resonance escape probability at thermal energy. Hence, from (12.49.1)

$$\int_0^\infty r^{2n} P_\infty(r) r^2 \, dr = \frac{p}{4\pi} \overline{r^{2n}},$$

and (12.48.3) becomes

$$\bar{P}_\infty(B^2) = p \sum_{n=0}^\infty \frac{(-1)^n}{(2n+1)!} B^{2n} \overline{r^{2n}}. \tag{12.49.3}$$

The critical equation (12.40.1) can then be written in terms of the $2n$th, i.e., even, moments of the slowing down distribution at the thermal energy; thus,

$$\frac{k}{1 + L^2 B^2} \sum_{n=0}^\infty \frac{(-1)^n}{(2n+1)!} B^{2n} \overline{r^{2n}} = 1, \tag{12.49.4}$$

which is the moment form of the critical equation.

12.50. If the reactor is large compared to $\sqrt{\overline{r^2}}$, the square root of the mean square slowing down distance, the buckling B^2 is small compared to $1/\overline{r^2}$, and terms beyond $n = 1$ in (12.49.4) may be neglected. In these circumstances

$$\sum_{n=0}^\infty \frac{(-1)^n}{(2n+1)!} B^{2n} \overline{r^{2n}} \approx 1 - \frac{1}{6} B^2 \overline{r^2}, \tag{12.50.1}$$

where $\overline{r^2}$ is the mean square distance a fission neutron travels from its source to where it is thermalized in an infinite medium, and hence it is equal to the quantity represented by $\overline{r_s^2}$ (§ 7.63). Making the substitution in the critical equation (12.49.4), the latter becomes

$$\frac{k}{1 + L^2 B^2} (1 - \tfrac{1}{6} B^2 \overline{r_s^2}) = 1. \tag{12.50.2}$$

If $\frac{1}{6} B^2 \overline{r_s^2}$ is small in comparison with unity, this expression may be written, approximately, as

$$\frac{k}{(1 + L^2 B^2)(1 + \tfrac{1}{6} B^2 \overline{r_s^2})} \approx \frac{k}{1 + B^2(L^2 + \tfrac{1}{6} \overline{r_s^2})} = 1. \tag{12.50.3}$$

Since $L^2 + \frac{1}{6}\overline{r_s^2}$ is equal to the migration area, M^2, this result may be expressed as

$$\frac{k}{1 + M^2 B^2} = 1,$$

in agreement with (7.63.2) derived from the continuous slowing down theory for a large reactor. Thus, as is to be expected, the nonleakage probability for large reactors is independent of the particular slowing down model used and becomes essentially a function of the migration area.

12.51. The experimental determination of $\overline{r^{2n}}$ involves the measurement of the slowing down density in the moderator at various distances r from a fast neutron source, and then fitting the results empirically by means of a suitable slowing down kernel $P_\infty(r)$, e.g., one based on the Fermi treatment or on the group-diffusion method. The kernel is then inserted into (12.49.1) and the integral evaluated to give $\overline{r^{2n}}$ for several values of n. When n is 2, the result is $\overline{r_s^2}$, where $\frac{1}{6}\overline{r_s^2}$ is identified with the Fermi age, although it is equivalent to the latter only if the continuous slowing down model is applicable. The experimental values of $\overline{r^{2n}}$ are then inserted into (12.49.4), and a critical equation is obtained which is independent of any specific slowing down kernel.

12.52. In practice, the evaluation of the higher order moments for the purpose of deriving a critical equation is difficult for, at least, two reasons. First, it is necessary that measurements be made at large distances from the source, where the neutron intensity is very weak; and, second, the use of indium foil means that slowing down densities are measured at about 1.4 ev, the indium resonance level, and corrections must be applied to obtain values at thermal energy. In addition, measurements should be made in a region with the same resonance absorption as the reactor; this requirement can be satisfied by adding the proper amount of absorber uniformly to the medium.

FERMI AGE (GAUSSIAN) KERNELS AND THE CRITICAL EQUATION

12.53. The solution of the Fermi age, continuous slowing down, equation for a unit point source in an infinite nonabsorbing medium was seen in § 6.138 to be

$$q(r, E_{\text{th}}) = \frac{e^{-r^2/4\tau}}{(4\pi\tau)^{\frac{3}{2}}},$$

where the origin of the coordinate system is taken to be at the source and τ is the age of thermal neutrons from a monoenergetic fission source. The slowing down density in an absorbing medium is obtained upon multiplying by the resonance escape probability p (§ 6.159), so that the corresponding (infinite) slowing down kernel is

$$P_\infty(r) = \frac{pe^{-r^2/4\tau}}{(4\pi\tau)^{\frac{3}{2}}}. \tag{12.53.1}$$

The Fourier transform of $P_\infty(r)$ is then given by (12.48.2) as

$$\bar{P}_\infty(B^2) = 4\pi \int_0^\infty \frac{pe^{-r^2/4\tau}}{(4\pi\tau)^{\frac{3}{2}}} \cdot \frac{\sin Br}{Br} r^2 \, dr$$

$$= \frac{p}{(4\pi)^{\frac{1}{2}}\tau^{\frac{3}{2}}B} \int_0^\infty e^{-r^2/4\tau} r \sin Br \, dr. \qquad (12.53.2)$$

12.54. In order to integrate by parts, let

$$u \equiv \sin Br, \qquad du = B \cos Br \, dr$$

and

$$v \equiv -2\tau e^{-r^2/4\tau}, \qquad dv = re^{-r^2/4\tau} \, dr.$$

Consequently, (12.53.2) becomes

$$\bar{P}_\infty(B^2) = \frac{p}{(4\pi)^{\frac{1}{2}}\tau^{\frac{3}{2}}B} \left[-2\tau e^{-r^2/4\tau} \sin Br \big|_0^\infty + 2\tau B \int_0^\infty e^{-r^2/4\tau} \cos Br \, dr \right]. \qquad (12.54.1)$$

The first term in the brackets is zero, and the definite integral can be obtained from tables; substituting the appropriate values, (12.54.1) becomes

$$\bar{P}_\infty(B^2) = pe^{-B^2\tau}. \qquad (12.54.2)$$

As seen above, the nonleakage probability during slowing down to thermal energy is equal to $\bar{P}_\infty(B^2)/p$, which is $e^{-B^2\tau}$ in the present case. This is, of course, the result obtained by means of the Fermi age equation (§ 7.29). Using the value of the Fourier transform, based on the continuous slowing down model, as given by (12.54.2), the critical equation (12.41.2) becomes

$$\frac{ke^{-B^2\tau}}{1 + L^2B^2} = 1, \qquad (12.54.3)$$

as derived in Chapter VII.

GAUSSIAN KERNEL CRITICAL EQUATION AND FISSION SPECTRUM SOURCE

12.55. In the preceding case it was supposed that the fission source neutrons were monoenergetic; the treatment will now be extended so as to allow for the energy spectrum of fission neutrons (§ 4.7). For moderators in which the continuous slowing down model may be used, the generalized slowing down kernel is obtained by superposing the Gaussian (age) kernels integrated over the fission spectrum.

12.56. Let $s(E_0) \, dE_0$ be the fraction of fission neutrons created with energy between E_0 and $E_0 + dE_0$, so that the function $s(E_0)$ may be regarded as the analytical expression of the fission spectrum. The age $\tau(E_0, E)$ of the neutrons at energy E may be written as

$$\tau(E_0, E) = \int_E^{E_0} \frac{D}{\xi\Sigma_s} \cdot \frac{dE'}{E'}, \qquad (12.56.1)$$

and the slowing down kernel, analogous to (12.53.1), is then

$$P_\infty(r, E) = p(E) \int_{E\text{th}}^{\infty} \frac{e^{-r^2/4\tau(E_0, E)}}{[4\pi\tau(E_0, E)]^{\frac{3}{2}}} s(E_0) \, dE_0, \tag{12.56.2}$$

where $p(E)$ is the resonance escape probability for neutrons of energy E. By using a procedure similar to that described above, the Fourier transform of (12.56.2) is found to be

$$\bar{P}_\infty(r, E) = p(E) \int_{E\text{th}}^{\infty} e^{-B^2\tau(E_0, E)} s(E_0) \, dE_0. \tag{12.56.3}$$

It may be noted that since the fission spectrum is effectively zero below 0.1 Mev, i.e., virtually all fission neutrons have energy in excess of this value, it follows that the resonance escape probability at a given energy will be the same for all fission neutrons. This is because the resonance capture takes place almost exclusively at energies well below 0.1 Mev. Consequently, it is permissible to write $p(E)$ as a function of the energy at which $\bar{P}_\infty(r, E)$ is calculated.

12.57. The nonleakage probability while slowing down for thermal neutrons is equal, in the present case, to $\bar{P}_\infty(r, E\text{th})/p(E\text{th})$, and hence the critical equation is

$$\frac{k}{1 + L^2 B^2} \int_{E\text{th}}^{\infty} e^{-B^2\tau(E_0, E\text{th})} s(E_0) \, dE_0 = 1. \tag{12.57.1}$$

If all the fission neutrons are created with the same energy, so that $s(E_0)$ is a Dirac delta function, (12.57.1) reduces to the monochromatic critical equation (12.54.3) derived above.

12.58. In order to allow for the fission energy spectrum in criticality estimates, the proper average age, $\bar{\tau}$, must be used. This can be obtained by defining it so that

$$e^{-B^2\bar{\tau}} \equiv \int_{E\text{th}}^{\infty} e^{-B^2\tau(E_0, E\text{th})} s(E_0) \, dE_0. \tag{12.58.1}$$

The critical equation may then be written as

$$\frac{ke^{-B^2\bar{\tau}}}{1 + L^2 B^2} = 1. \tag{12.58.2}$$

12.59. The moment form of (12.58.1) can be obtained by expanding $e^{-B^2\tau(E_0, E\text{th})}$ in a power series; thus, the integral becomes

$$\int_{E\text{th}}^{\infty} e^{-B^2\tau(E_0, E\text{th})} s(E_0) \, dE_0 = 1 - B^2 \int_{E\text{th}}^{\infty} \tau(E_0, E\text{th}) s(E_0) \, dE_0$$
$$+ \frac{B^4}{2!} \int_{E\text{th}}^{\infty} \tau^2(E_0, E\text{th}) s(E_0) \, dE_0 - \cdots.$$

Similarly, expansion of the left-hand side of (12.58.1) gives

$$e^{-B^2\bar{\tau}} = 1 - B^2\bar{\tau} + \frac{B^4}{2!} \bar{\tau}^2 - \cdots.$$

If the reactor is large, so that the series may be cut off after the second term in each case (cf. § 12.50), comparison of the expansions shows that

$$\bar{\tau} = \int_{E_{\text{th}}}^{\infty} \tau(E_0, E_{\text{th}}) s(E_0) \, dE_0,$$

the right-hand side being the arithmetic mean of the age of the fission neutrons from source to thermal energy. This result gives the physical significance of the average age defined by (12.58.1).

12.60. Using the first two terms only in the expansion of $e^{-B^2\bar{\tau}}$, it follows that for a large reactor

$$e^{-B^2\bar{\tau}} \approx 1 - B^2\bar{\tau} \approx (1 + B^2\bar{\tau})^{-1}.$$

The critical equation (12.58.2) now becomes, as in §12.50,

$$\frac{k}{1 + M^2 B^2} \approx 1$$

with M^2 defined by

$$M^2 \equiv L^2 + \bar{\tau},$$

where $\bar{\tau}$ is the arithmetic mean age of the thermal neutrons taking into account the fission spectrum.

GROUP-DIFFUSION SLOWING DOWN KERNELS: TWO GROUPS

12.61. The infinite-medium slowing down kernel, in terms of diffusion theory, as applied to two groups of neutrons, is given by (12.11.1), provided there is no resonance absorption. To allow for the latter, the kernel should be multiplied by the resonance escape probability p of the neutrons in the first (high-energy) group. Hence, if the neutron source is at the origin of the coordinates, it follows that the slowing down kernel from fission to thermal energies is

$$P_\infty(r) = \frac{p e^{-r/L_1}}{4\pi L_1^2 r}, \tag{12.61.1}$$

where, as before, $L_1 = D_1/\Sigma_1$, the Σ_1 being a slowing down cross section (§ 8.12). The Fourier transform of $P_\infty(r)$, represented by $\bar{P}_\infty(B^2)$, is [cf. (12.48.2)] consequently

$$\begin{aligned}
\bar{P}_\infty(B^2) &= 4\pi \int_0^\infty \frac{p e^{-r/L_1}}{4\pi L_1^2 r} \cdot \frac{\sin Br}{Br} r^2 \, dr \\
&= \frac{p}{L_1^2 B} \int_0^\infty e^{-r/L_1} \sin Br \, dr \tag{12.61.2} \\
&= \frac{p}{L_1^2 B} \cdot \frac{B}{\dfrac{1}{L_1^2} + B^2} \\
&= \frac{p}{1 + L_1^2 B^2}. \tag{12.61.3}
\end{aligned}$$

Upon inserting this result into the general critical equation (12.41.2), the two-group critical equation becomes

$$\frac{k}{(1 + L^2B^2)(1 + L_1^2B^2)} = 1,$$
(12.61.4)

which is equivalent to (8.44.3).

12.62. The second moment of the slowing down density distribution is given by

$$\overline{r_s^2} = \frac{\int_0^\infty r^2 \frac{e^{-r/L_1}}{4\pi L_1^2 r} 4\pi r^2 \, dr}{\int_0^\infty \frac{e^{-r/L_1}}{4\pi L_1^2 r} 4\pi r^2 \, dr} = 6L_1^2,$$
(12.62.1)

and comparison with (6.141.1) shows that L_1^2 in the two-group treatment has the same physical significance as the Fermi age, τ, namely, one-sixth of the mean square distance a neutron travels from its source as a fission neutron to where it becomes thermal (cf. § 8.44). Hence, the critical equation (12.61.4) may be written as

$$\frac{k}{(1 + L^2B^2)(1 + \frac{1}{6}\overline{r_s^2}B^2)} = \frac{k}{(1 + L^2B^2)(1 + \tau B^2)} = 1.$$
(12.62.2)

If the critical reactor is large, so that B^2 is small, or, in general, if $k - 1$ is small, the denominator can be replaced by $1 + B^2(L^2 + \frac{1}{6}\overline{r_s^2})$; then (12.62.2) becomes

$$\frac{k}{1 + B^2(L^2 + \frac{1}{6}\overline{r_s^2})} = \frac{k}{1 + M^2B^2} = 1.$$

CONVOLUTION OF DIFFUSION SLOWING DOWN KERNELS: SLOWING DOWN IN WATER

12.63. In § 12.6, *et seq.*, an expression was derived for the slowing down kernel, from fission energy to thermal energy, by imagining the neutrons to be divided into $n + 1$ energy groups. The result was a convolution of functions, each of which was a slowing down kernel for one of the n groups with energy above the thermal value.

12.64. It can be shown that the Fourier transform of a convolution of functions is equal to the product of the transforms of the separate functions. Hence, (12.9.1) leads to the result

$$\bar{P}_\infty(B^2) = \bar{P}_1(B_1^2) \cdot \bar{P}_2(B_2^2) \cdots \bar{P}_n(B_n^2),$$

where $\bar{P}_\infty(B^2)$ is the Fourier transform of the over-all slowing down kernel, and $\bar{P}_1(B_1^2)$, $\bar{P}_2(B_2^2)$, etc., are the transforms of the kernels for the individual energy groups. The critical equation (12.41.2) then becomes

$$\frac{k}{p(1 + L^2B^2)} \bar{P}_1(B_1^2) \cdot \bar{P}_2(B_2^2) \cdots \bar{P}_n(B_n^2) = 1.$$
(12.64.1)

The advantage of the foregoing procedure is that it permits the use of any convenient number of kernels, which may be of the same or of different types. In this way it is possible to introduce several parameters with which to fit the analytical slowing down density distribution to an experimental distribution. This was essentially the technique used* to obtain a slowing down kernel for the homogeneous, water-moderated, enriched reactor known as the "water boiler."

12.65. The calculations were based on measured neutron slowing down densities to indium resonance in water, for which the results are plotted in Fig. 12.65. The ordinates are proportional to $r^2 q(r)$, where $q(r)$ is the experimental slowing down density at a distance r from the source. Measurements were made up to 30 cm, and the distribution was continued by the function $r^{-2}e^{-r/9}$. Various analytical slowing down kernels, sometimes called *synthetic kernels*, were fitted to the experimental distribution with the following conditions being satisfied: (i) the analytical value for $\frac{1}{6}\overline{r_s^2}$ should be equal to the experimental value; and (ii) the total area under the analytical curves in Fig. 12.65 should be the same as for the experimental curve.

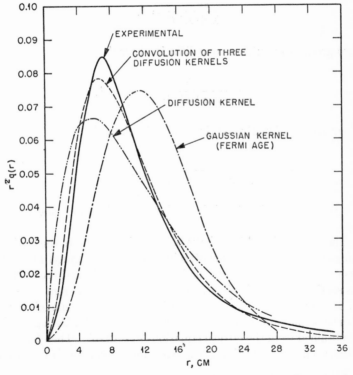

FIG. 12.65. Experimental and calculated distribution of slowing down density in water

* E. Greuling, unpublished.

12.66. Three analytical curves are shown in the figure; the first is for a Gaussian (continuous slowing down) kernel, as given in (12.53.1), with τ equal to 33 cm^2 (cf. § 6.145); the second is for a single diffusion kernel, as in (12.61.1), with L_1 equal to 5.69 cm; and the third is for a convolution of three diffusion kernels with $L_1 = 4.49$ cm, $L_2 = 2.05$ cm, and $L_3 = 1.00$ cm.* It is seen that the continuous slowing down model is not applicable to water as moderator. The curve for the Gaussian distribution is displaced to the right, as compared with the experimental results; this is because, as indicated in Chapter VI, a neutron can lose energy in collisions with hydrogen nuclei at a faster rate than would be expected on the basis of continuous slowing down. The use of a convolution of three diffusion kernels to give the slowing down in water is seen to provide a very close representation of the experimental distribution of the slowing down density.

12.67. Utilizing the three-dimensional Fourier transforms $\bar{P}_\infty(B^2)$ of the infinite slowing down kernels developed earlier in this chapter, it is seen that the critical equations corresponding to various slowing down kernels are as follows:

(i) Gaussian slowing down

$$\frac{ke^{-B^2\tau}}{1 + L^2B^2} = 1.$$

(ii) Two groups of neutrons: one diffusion kernel

$$\frac{k}{(1 + L^2B^2)(1 + L_1^2B^2)} = 1.$$

(iii) Four groups of neutrons: three diffusion kernels

$$\frac{k}{(1 + L^2B^2)(1 + L_1^2B^2)(1 + L_2^2B^2)(1 + L_3^2B^2)} = 1,$$

where L is the diffusion length of thermal neutrons in water, and B^2 is the buckling.

12.68. The results given above have been used to calculate the critical geometric bucklings for finite cylinders containing solutions of uranyl fluoride in water at various concentrations. From the known H/U ratio and the nuclear absorption cross sections, the multiplication factor k for the different solutions can be obtained, as shown in § 7.66. The solutions were dilute enough for τ and the various L's to be the same as in pure water, and so from the data given in § 12.66, B^2 can be obtained from the critical equations in § 12.67. Then from the expression for the geometric buckling for a bare, finite cylinder (§ 7.58), the critical

---

* In deriving these curves the resonance escape probability was omitted from the slowing down kernels, since the quantity of interest is $\bar{P}_\infty(B^2)/p$. It is apparent from the cases considered above that the p's cancel out in the critical equation in any event.

height of the solution, for cylinders of a given radius, can be readily determined in each case. The results are plotted in Fig. 12.68. Since a convolution of three diffusion kernels gives a reasonably good representation of the slowing down

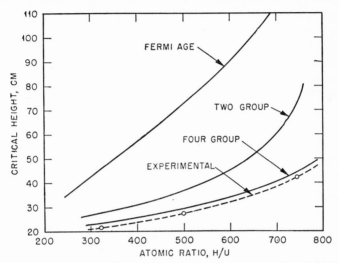

FIG. 12.68.　Comparison of critical calculations using different kernels

density distribution in water (Fig. 12.65), it is found, as expected, that the critical heights given by the four-group calculation are in close agreement with those obtained by experiment. The observed differences are probably due, at least in part, to the neglect of fast-neutron fissions in the calculations. It appears, therefore, that, when the continuous slowing down model is not applicable, the critical properties of a bare, thermal reactor can be determined, to a fair degree of accuracy, by the development of a synthetic (empirical) slowing down kernel based on observed slowing down density measurements in the moderator.

Chapter XIII

PERTURBATION THEORY*

GENERAL THEORY

MULTI-GROUP TREATMENT

13.1. The effect of changes in a reactor structure resulting, for example, from localized poisons or temperature changes is most readily determined by means of perturbation theory. The perturbation will produce a change in the stable period of the reactor, which can usually be related to a change in reactivity corresponding to the perturbation. However, most calculations using perturbation theory are made to determine small compensatory changes that will leave a reactor critical. For example, it may be required to find the change in fuel necessary to compensate for the additional poisoning due to an increase in the jacket thickness of a fuel rod. In calculations of this sort, the effect of delayed neutrons need not be considered.

13.2. In the multi-group treatment of a nuclear reactor, not necessarily in a state of equilibrium, the equation for the ith group may be written in the general form

$$\sum_{j=1}^{m} \mathbf{M}_{ij}\phi_i = \frac{\partial \phi_i}{\partial t},$$
(13.2.1)

where $\mathbf{M}_{ij}$ is an operator and ϕ_i is the neutron flux in the ith group. For the whole system of m groups, the equation can be represented by

$$\mathbf{M}\phi = \frac{\partial \phi}{\partial t},$$
(13.2.2)

where $\mathbf{M}$ is the appropriate matrix operator and ϕ represents the vector set (ϕ_1, $\phi_2, \ldots \phi_m$).

13.3. Consider solutions of (13.2.2) that depend in an exponential manner on the time, i.e.,

$$\phi_i = \phi_{i0}e^{\omega_i t}$$
(13.3.1)

so that

$$\frac{\partial \phi_i}{\partial t} = \omega_i \phi_i.$$
(13.3.2)

* The use of perturbation theory in reactor calculations is due to E. P. Wigner.

Since the group equations are coupled by the fission chain reaction and by the slowing down from group to group, all the ω_i's for the various energy groups are equal.   Hence, (13.2.2) may be written as

$$\mathbf{M}\phi = \omega\phi, \tag{13.3.3}$$

where ω, having the same value for each group, is actually the reciprocal of the reactor period (§ 10.28).   The general solution of (13.3.3) gives a series of eigenvalues, ω_k, and the corresponding eigenfunctions, ϕ_k.   Of these eigenvalues, only one will be positive, corresponding to the stable period of the reactor, and this can usually be related in a simple way to the reactivity of the reactor.   The negative eigenvalues are not of interest here, since they represent transients which damp out with time.   In the steady state of a critical reactor, ω is, of course, zero, and the perturbations to be considered cause relatively small changes in ω.

13.4. Suppose that a small change occurs in a reactor such as, for example, the introduction of an absorber.   Let this change be represented by an operator **P**.   The neutron flux will now be ϕ', and the reciprocal period will change from ω to ω'.   The reactor equation will then be

$$(\mathbf{M} + \mathbf{P})\phi' = \omega'\phi', \tag{13.4.1}$$

where ϕ' is the perturbed flux and ω' represents the new eigenvalues.   A general formula for $\omega' - \omega$, which is basic to all applications of perturbation theory to be given here, will now be derived.

SELF-ADJOINT AND ADJOINT OPERATORS

13.5. If the eigenfunctions of (13.3.3) form a complete orthogonal set, the operator **M** is said to be *self-adjoint*.   An example of this is to be found in the case of one-group theory of a bare reactor, when the neutron flux satisfies the equation

$$\nabla^2\phi + B^2\phi = \frac{1}{v} \cdot \frac{\partial\phi}{\partial t},$$

and the boundary condition that it vanish on the extrapolated surface of the reactor.   The solution of this problem leads to a complete set of eigenfunctions that are orthogonal over the volume of the reactor enclosed by the extrapolated boundary.   In this case the operator **M** is self-adjoint and satisfies an important theorem.

13.6. Consider two particular eigenfunctions of (13.3.3), namely, ϕ_k and ϕ_l, so that

$$\mathbf{M}\phi_k = \omega_k\phi_k \quad \text{and} \quad \mathbf{M}\phi_l = \omega_l\phi_l.$$

Multiply the former by ϕ_l and the latter by ϕ_k and integrate each over the whole volume of the reactor; the results are

$$\int \phi_l\mathbf{M}\phi_k \, dV = \omega_k \int \phi_k\phi_l \, dV$$

and

$$\int \phi_k \mathbf{M}\phi_l \, dV = \omega_l \int \phi_k \phi_l \, dV.$$

Upon subtracting, it is seen that

$$\int \phi_l \mathbf{M}\phi_k \, dV - \int \phi_k \mathbf{M}\phi_l \, dV = (\omega_k - \omega_l) \int \phi_k \phi_l \, dV. \qquad (13.6.1)$$

If the eigenfunctions ϕ_k and ϕ_l are orthogonal, then

$$\int \phi_k \phi_l \, dV = C_k \quad \text{if} \quad k = l$$
$$= 0 \quad \text{if} \quad k \neq l,$$

and so it follows from (13.6.1) that

$$\int \phi_k \mathbf{M}\phi_l \, dV = \int \phi_l \mathbf{M}\phi_k \, dV. \qquad (13.6.2)$$

In this case the operator $\mathbf{M}$ is said to be self-adjoint.

13.7. Suppose the eigenfunctions do not form an orthogonal set, as is the case for a reactor with reflector; then an *adjoint operator* $\mathbf{M}\dagger$ may be defined by

$$\int \phi_k\dagger \mathbf{M}\phi_l \, dV = \int \phi_l \mathbf{M}\dagger\phi_k\dagger \, dV, \qquad (13.7.1)$$

where the $\phi_k\dagger$'s, called the *adjoint functions*, are the eigenfunctions of the adjoint equation

$$\mathbf{M}\dagger\phi\dagger = \omega^*\phi\dagger, \qquad (13.7.2)$$

where ω^* is the complex conjugate of ω.

13.8. In general, the adjoint operator $\mathbf{M}\dagger$ is obtained by replacing each element $\mathbf{M}_{kl}$ of $\mathbf{M}$ by its complex conjugate and then interchanging the rows and columns in the matrix, i.e., each $\mathbf{M}_{kl}$ becomes $\mathbf{M}_{lk}^*$. For the equation of a reactor, the elements are all real, so that the adjoint operator $\mathbf{M}\dagger$ is obtained merely by interchanging rows and columns in the matrix $\mathbf{M}$; at the same time, ω^* is equal to ω.

13.9. By starting with one solution of (13.7.2) and one of (13.3.3), namely,

$$\mathbf{M}\dagger\phi_k\dagger = \omega_k\phi_k\dagger \quad \text{and} \quad \mathbf{M}\phi_l = \omega_l\phi_l,$$

multiplying the former by ϕ_l and the latter by $\phi_k\dagger$, integrating each and subtracting, the result, analogous to (13.6.1), is

$$\int \phi_l \mathbf{M}\dagger\phi_k\dagger \, dV - \int \phi_k\dagger \mathbf{M}\phi_l \, dV = (\omega_k - \omega_l) \int \phi_k\dagger\phi_l \, dV.$$

Upon introducing the condition, expressed by (13.7.1), that $\mathbf{M}\dagger$ and $\mathbf{M}$ are adjoint, it is seen that if $k \neq l$, so that $\omega_k - \omega_l$ is not zero,

$$\int \phi_k\dagger\phi_l \, dV = 0 \quad \text{for} \quad k \neq l.$$

It is evident, therefore, that the adjoint functions $\phi_k\dagger$ are orthogonal to the original functions ϕ_k.

13.10. An expression for the change in the reciprocal period of the reactor due to a small perturbation can now be derived. Upon multiplying (13.4.1) by $\phi\dagger$ and (13.7.2) by ϕ', integrating over the reactor volume in each case and subtracting the results, it is found that

$$\int \phi\dagger\mathbf{M}\phi' \, dV - \int \phi'\mathbf{M}\dagger\phi\dagger \, dV + \int \phi\dagger\mathbf{P}\phi' \, dV = (\omega' - \omega)\int \phi\dagger\phi' \, dV.$$

Since $\mathbf{M}$ and $\mathbf{M}\dagger$ are adjoint operators, the first two integrals on the left are equal in magnitude, and hence it follows that

$$\omega' - \omega = \frac{\int \phi\dagger\mathbf{P}\phi' \, dV}{\int \phi\dagger\phi' \, dV}.$$

If the perturbation $\mathbf{P}$ is small, ϕ' may, in the first order of approximation, be replaced by ϕ, so that the first order perturbation solution for the change in the reciprocal of the reactor period, i.e., $\omega' - \omega = \Delta\omega$, is given by

$$\Delta\omega = \frac{\int \phi\dagger\mathbf{P}\phi \, dV}{\int \phi\dagger\phi \, dV}. \tag{13.10.1}$$

Finally, if $\mathbf{M}$ is self-adjoint, the change in ω is represented by

$$\Delta\omega = \frac{\int \phi\mathbf{P}\phi \, dV}{\int \phi^2 \, dV}. \tag{13.10.2}$$

APPLICATIONS OF PERTURBATION THEORY

APPLICATION TO ONE-GROUP TREATMENT

13.11. A bare reactor having a stable period $1/\omega$ satisfies the one-group equation

$$v \, \mathrm{div} \, D \, \mathrm{grad} \, \phi + \alpha\phi = \omega\phi \tag{13.11.1}$$

where

$$\alpha \equiv (k - 1)\Sigma_a v.$$

The operator $\mathbf{M}$ is then

$$\mathbf{M} = v \, \mathrm{div} \, D \, \mathrm{grad} + \alpha. \tag{13.11.2}$$

Suppose now that the reactor is perturbed by a small change, δv, δD, $\delta \alpha$, in any or all of the parameters.   The operator $\mathbf{M} + \mathbf{P}$ is then

$$\mathbf{M} + \mathbf{P} = (v + \delta v) \text{ div } (D + \delta D) \text{ grad } + \alpha + \delta \alpha. \qquad (13.11.3)$$

13.12. Making use of the identity

$$\text{div } S\mathbf{V} = \text{grad } S \cdot \mathbf{V} + S \text{ div } \mathbf{V}, \qquad (13.12.1)$$

where S is a scalar and $\mathbf{V}$ is a vector, it is seen that

$$\text{div } (D + \delta D) \text{ grad } = \text{grad } (D + \delta D) \cdot \text{grad } + (D + \delta D) \, \nabla^2. \quad (13.12.2)$$

Using this result, (13.11.2) and (13.11.3) may be written as

$$\mathbf{M} = v \text{ grad } D \cdot \text{grad } + vD \, \nabla^2 + \alpha \qquad (13.12.3)$$

and

$$\mathbf{M} + \mathbf{P} = (v + \delta v)[\text{grad } (D + \delta D) \cdot \text{grad } + (D + \delta D) \, \nabla^2] + \alpha + \delta \alpha. \quad (13.12.4)$$

Subtracting (13.12.3) from (13.12.4) and assuming that products of the variations are small compared to the first variation, the result is

$$\mathbf{P} = \delta v[\text{grad } D \cdot \text{grad } + D \, \nabla^2] + v[\text{grad } \delta D \cdot \text{grad } + \delta D \, \nabla^2] + \delta \alpha. \quad (13.12.5)$$

13.13. The change in ω, according to (13.10.2), is then

$$\Delta\omega = \frac{1}{\int \phi^2 \, dV} \int [\phi \, \delta v \text{ grad } D \cdot \text{grad } \phi + \phi v \text{ grad } \delta D \cdot \text{grad } \phi + \phi \delta \, (Dv) \, \nabla^2 \phi + \delta \alpha \phi^2] \, dV.$$
$$(13.13.1)$$

Again making use of the identity (13.12.1), it follows that

$$\text{div } (\phi D \text{ grad } \phi) = \text{grad } \phi D \cdot \text{grad } \phi + \phi D \, \nabla^2 \phi$$
$$= D| \text{ grad } \phi|^2 + \phi D \, \nabla^2 \phi + \phi \text{ grad } D \cdot \text{grad } \phi, \quad (13.13.2)$$

which may be solved for $\phi \text{ grad } D \cdot \text{grad } \phi$, to give

$$\phi \text{ grad } D \cdot \text{grad } \phi = \text{div } (\phi D \text{ grad } \phi) - D| \text{ grad } \phi|^2 - \phi D \, \nabla^2 \phi. \quad (13.13.3)$$

This result may be substituted into the first term of the integrand in (13.13.1). However, before doing so, it may be noted that the integral

$$\int \text{div } (\phi D \text{ grad } \phi) \, dV$$

vanishes by applying Gauss's theorem; thus,

$$\int_V \text{div } (\phi D \text{ grad } \phi) \, dV = \int_S \phi D \text{ grad}_n \, \phi \, dS = 0,$$

because ϕ is zero on the surface of the reactor.

13.14. Apart from the factor v, the second term in the integrand, applying the same technique as in § 13.13, is

$$\phi \operatorname{grad} \delta D \cdot \operatorname{grad} \phi = \operatorname{div} (\phi \, \delta D \operatorname{grad} \phi) - \delta D| \operatorname{grad} \phi|^2 - \phi \, \delta D \, \nabla^2 \phi. \quad (13.14.1)$$

Substituting (13.13.3) and (13.14.1) into (13.13.1), the result is

$$\Delta \omega = \frac{\int [\delta \alpha \phi^2 - \delta(Dv)| \operatorname{grad} \phi|^2] \, dV}{\int \phi^2 \, dV}. \quad (13.14.2)$$

It is interesting to note that changes in absorption or in multiplication factor are weighted by the square of the flux, whereas the change in the diffusion coefficient is weighted by the gradient of the flux squared, as appears reasonable.

13.15. The change in reactivity due to a perturbation over the whole reactor can be obtained from (13.14.2) and the time-dependent diffusion equation. If it is assumed that the perturbation is small, then the flux is given by (cf. § 10.7)

$$\frac{\delta k_{\text{eff}}}{l} \phi' = \frac{d\phi'}{dt} \quad (13.15.1)$$

or

$$k\Sigma_a v \frac{\delta k_{\text{eff}}}{k_{\text{eff}}} \phi' = \omega \phi'. \quad (13.15.2)$$

Multiplying (13.15.2) by the unperturbed flux, ϕ, dropping second order terms, and integrating over the volume of the reactor, the result is

$$\frac{\delta k_{\text{eff}}}{k_{\text{eff}}} = \omega \frac{\int \phi^2 \, dV}{\int k\Sigma_a v \phi^2 \, dV}.$$

Substituting for ω from (13.14.2), since $\Delta \omega = \omega$ if the reactor was initially just critical, then

$$\frac{\delta k_{\text{eff}}}{k_{\text{eff}}} = \frac{\int \{\delta[(k-1)\Sigma_a v]\phi^2 - \delta(Dv)| \operatorname{grad} \phi|^2\} \, dV}{\int k\Sigma_a v \phi^2 \, dV}, \quad (13.15.3)$$

after introducing the expression for α in § 13.11.

13.16. In many problems, it is desirable to calculate the joint effect of two or more changes in the nuclear parameters, namely, D, Σ_a, k, that leave the reactor just critical. For example, the effect of an absorber placed in a reactor may be counterbalanced by the addition of fuel to keep the reactor critical. From (13.10.2) it is evident that the condition that the reactor remain critical is

$$\int \phi \mathbf{P} \phi \, dV = 0 \quad (13.16.1)$$

or, from (13.14.2),

$$\int \{\delta[(k-1)\Sigma_a v]\phi^2 - \delta(Dv)|\operatorname{grad}\phi|^2\}\, dV = 0. \qquad (13.16.2)$$

In calculations of this kind, delayed neutrons do not usually play any part (§ 13.1), and hence (13.16.2) is somewhat more general than (13.15.3).

STATISTICAL WEIGHT

13.17. The *statistical weight* of a region R of a large bare reactor is defined as

$$W(R) = \frac{\int_R \phi^2\, dV}{\int_V \phi^2\, dV}. \qquad (13.17.1)$$

If a reactor is made of two different materials having bucklings B_1^2 and B_2^2, respectively, it can be shown that the buckling of the entire reactor is given by

$$B^2 = B_1^2 W(R_1) + B_2^2 W(R_2). \qquad (13.17.2)$$

In a large thermal reactor, $\nabla^2\phi + B^2\phi = 0$, where $B^2 = (k-1)/M^2$, so that in the steady state, the operator $\mathbf{M}$ is

$$\mathbf{M} = \nabla^2 + B^2.$$

If the reactor is just critical, then from (13.16.1)

$$\int_V \phi \mathbf{P} \phi\, dV = 0. \qquad (13.17.3)$$

13.18. In the region with buckling B_1^2, $\mathbf{M} = \nabla^2 + B_1^2$ and $\mathbf{P} = B_1^2 - B^2$; in the region with buckling B_2^2, $\mathbf{M} = \nabla^2 + B_2^2$ and $\mathbf{P} = B_2^2 - B^2$. Substitution into (13.17.3) gives the criticality condition as

$$\int_{R_1}(B_1^2 - B^2)\phi^2\, dV + \int_{R_2}(B_2^2 - B^2)\phi^2\, dV = 0.$$

Since the B^2's are independent of position in each region, it follows from (13.17.1) and (13.17.2) that

$$B^2 = B_1^2 \frac{\int_{R_1}\phi^2\, dV}{\int_V \phi^2\, dV} + B_2^2 \frac{\int_{R_2}\phi^2\, dV}{\int_V \phi^2\, dV}. \qquad (13.18.1)$$

The statistical weights of concentric regions in cubic, cylindrical, and spherical reactors are given in Fig. 13.18; $r(R)$ is the radius of the region and $r(V)$ is that of the whole system. For a cube, $r(V)$ represents half the edge length.

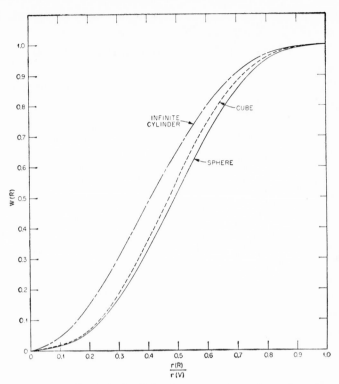

FIG. 13.18.   Statistical weights in concentric regions of reactors

POISONING OF A REACTOR AND DANGER COEFFICIENTS

13.19. If a thermal neutron absorber is added to a cell in a heterogeneous, natural uranium reactor, the reactivity will decrease due to the decrease in the thermal utilization. From (13.15.3) the change in reactivity, neglecting any changes in Dv, is

$$\frac{\delta k_{\text{eff}}}{k_{\text{eff}}} = \frac{\delta[(k-1)\Sigma_a]}{k\Sigma_a} W(R_1). \tag{13.19.1}$$

To apply (13.19.1) to a heterogeneous assembly, the interpretation of the equation must be modified. The statistical weight for the cell is calculated from the over-all cosine distribution of the flux. The constants k and Σ_a must be averaged over the cell according to the flux distribution in the cell.

13.20. To find the change in reactivity by means of (13.19.1), it is convenient to write

$$\frac{\delta[(k-1)\Sigma_a]}{k\Sigma_a} = \frac{\delta k}{k} + \frac{k-1}{k} \cdot \frac{\delta\Sigma_a}{\Sigma_a}. \tag{13.20.1}$$

In the present case Σ_a is equivalent to the total neutron absorption in a lattice cell, i.e., $\Sigma_{a0}\bar{\phi}_0 + \Sigma_{a1}\bar{\phi}_1$, where the subscripts 0 and 1 refer to the fuel and moderator, respectively, and the $\bar{\phi}$'s are the average unperturbed fluxes. Representing the total neutron absorption by A, (13.20.1) becomes

$$\frac{\delta[(k-1)\Sigma_a]}{k\Sigma_a} = \frac{\delta k}{k} + \frac{k-1}{k} \cdot \frac{\delta A}{A}. \tag{13.20.2}$$

The quantities $\delta k/k$ and $\delta A/A$ are obtained as follows.

13.21. The thermal utilization in the cell with the poison is

$$f' = \frac{1}{1 + \frac{\Sigma_{a1}}{\Sigma_{a0}} d' + \frac{\Sigma_{ai}}{\Sigma_{a0}} d_i},$$

where the subscript i refers to the impurity (poison); d' and d_i are defined by

$$d' = \frac{\bar{\phi}_1'}{\bar{\phi}_0'} = \text{perturbed thermal disadvantage factor}$$

and

$$d_i = \frac{\bar{\phi}_i'}{\bar{\phi}_0'} = \frac{\text{average flux in impurity}}{\text{average flux in fuel}}.$$

Consequently,

$$\frac{\delta f}{f} = -\frac{\Sigma_{ai}}{\Sigma_{a0}} f d_i,$$

correct to first order terms. Since the change in k is essentially due to that in f, it follows that

$$\frac{\delta k}{k} = \frac{\delta f}{f} = -\frac{\Sigma_{ai}}{\Sigma_{a0}} f d_i. \tag{13.21.1}$$

13.22. Turning next to $\delta A/A$, this may be expressed as

$$\frac{\delta A}{A} = \frac{\delta(A/\Sigma_{a0}\bar{\phi}_0)}{A/\Sigma_{a0}\bar{\phi}_0} = f\delta\left(\frac{A}{\Sigma_{a0}\phi_0}\right), \tag{13.22.1}$$

where f is the thermal utilization in the unperturbed system. If A' is the value of the total neutron absorption in the presence of poison, then,

$$\frac{A'}{\Sigma_{a0}\bar{\phi}_0'} = 1 + \frac{\Sigma_{a1}}{\Sigma_{a0}} d' + \frac{\Sigma_{ai}}{\Sigma_{a0}} d_i. \tag{13.22.2}$$

Similarly, for the unperturbed reactor,

$$\frac{A}{\Sigma_{a0}\bar{\phi}_0} = 1 + \frac{\Sigma_{a1}}{\Sigma_{a0}} d, \tag{13.22.3}$$

where d is the disadvantage factor, equal to $\bar{\phi}_1/\bar{\phi}_0$. If, to a first order approximation, d' is assumed to be not very different from d, subtraction of (13.22.3) from (13.22.2) and insertion of the result into (13.22.1) lead to

$$\frac{\delta A}{A} = \frac{\Sigma_{ai}}{\Sigma_{a0}} f d_i. \tag{13.22.4}$$

13.23. If (13.21.1) and (13.22.4) are now inserted into (13.20.2), the result is

$$\frac{\delta[(k-1)\Sigma_a]}{k\Sigma_a} = -\frac{\Sigma_{ai}}{\Sigma_{a0}} fd_i + \frac{k-1}{k} \cdot \frac{\Sigma_{ai}}{\Sigma_{a0}} fd_i$$

$$= -\frac{\Sigma_{ai}}{\Sigma_{a0}} \cdot \frac{fd_i}{k}.$$

The change in reactivity is then, by (13.19.1),

$$\frac{\delta k_{\text{eff}}}{k_{\text{eff}}} = -\frac{\Sigma_{ai}}{\Sigma_{a0}} \cdot \frac{fd_i}{k} W(R_1). \tag{13.23.1}$$

If there are M_i grams of impurity per gram of fuel, then from the definition of the macroscopic cross section (§ 3.44), it is found that

$$\frac{\Sigma_{ai}}{\Sigma_{a0}} = \frac{\sigma_{ai}}{\sigma_{a0}} \cdot \frac{A_0}{A_i} M_i,$$

where A_0 and A_i are the atomic weights of fuel and impurity, respectively. The *danger coefficient*, K_d, of an impurity may be defined as

$$K_d \equiv \frac{\sigma_{ai}}{\sigma_{a0}} \cdot \frac{A_0}{A_i},$$

and so it follows from (13.23.1) that

$$\frac{\delta k_{\text{eff}}}{k_{\text{eff}}} = -\frac{fd_i}{k} W(R_1) M_i K_d. \tag{13.23.2}$$

This expression may be used to calculate the change in reactivity resulting from the introduction of a given impurity, e.g., a coolant or an aluminum can for the fuel rod, in each cell of a heterogeneous reactor. In this case, the total change in reactivity will be given by the sum of the $\delta k_{\text{eff}}/k_{\text{eff}}$ for all cells in the reactor. Since all the terms in (12.23.2), except $W(R_1)$, are essentially the same, the total change in reactivity will be given by

$$\frac{\delta k_{\text{eff}}}{k_{\text{eff}}} = -\frac{fd_i}{k} M_i K_d, \tag{13.23.3}*$$

since the sum of the $W(R_1)$ for all cells is unity.

APPLICATION TO THE TWO-GROUP TREATMENT

13.24. In the two-group treatment, as outlined in Chapter VIII, the operator **M** [cf. (8.39.1) and (8.40.1)] is

$$\mathbf{M} = \begin{pmatrix} v_1[\text{div } D_1 \text{ grad} - \Sigma_1] & v_1 k\Sigma_2 \\ v_2\Sigma_1 & v_2[\text{div } D_2 \text{ grad} - \Sigma_2] \end{pmatrix}.$$

---

* The danger coefficient of a substance in a reactor is sometimes defined as $-\delta k_{\text{eff}}/k_{\text{eff}}$, which is seen to be approximately proportional to K_d.

The adjoint operator may be found from $\mathbf{M}$ by applying the definition (13.7.1). If $\mathbf{M}\phi$ and $\mathbf{M}\dagger\phi\dagger$ are written in the forms,

and

$$\mathbf{M}\phi = \begin{pmatrix} \mathbf{M}_{11} & \mathbf{M}_{12} \\ \mathbf{M}_{21} & \mathbf{M}_{22} \end{pmatrix}\begin{pmatrix} \phi_1 \\ \phi_2 \end{pmatrix}$$

$$\mathbf{M}\dagger\phi\dagger = \begin{pmatrix} \mathbf{M}_{11}\dagger & \mathbf{M}_{12}\dagger \\ \mathbf{M}_{21}\dagger & \mathbf{M}_{22}\dagger \end{pmatrix}\begin{pmatrix} \phi_1\dagger \\ \phi_2\dagger \end{pmatrix},$$

it is found that

$$\phi\dagger\mathbf{M}\phi = \mathbf{M}_{11}\phi_1\phi_1\dagger + \mathbf{M}_{12}\phi_2\phi_1\dagger + \mathbf{M}_{21}\phi_1\phi_2\dagger + \mathbf{M}_{22}\phi_2\phi_2\dagger$$

and

$$\phi\mathbf{M}\dagger\phi\dagger = \mathbf{M}_{11}\dagger\phi_1\dagger\phi_1 + \mathbf{M}_{12}\dagger\phi_2\dagger\phi_1 + \mathbf{M}_{21}\dagger\phi_1\dagger\phi_2 + \mathbf{M}_{22}\dagger\phi_2\dagger\phi_2.$$

Applying (13.7.1) and comparing the terms of these two expressions it is evident that $\mathbf{M}_{11}\dagger = \mathbf{M}_{11}$, $\mathbf{M}_{22}\dagger = \mathbf{M}_{22}$, $\mathbf{M}_{21}\dagger = \mathbf{M}_{12}$, and $\mathbf{M}_{12}\dagger = \mathbf{M}_{21}$, since each term in $\mathbf{M}$ is self-adjoint. Thus, the adjoint operator is

$$\mathbf{M}\dagger = \begin{pmatrix} v_1[(\text{div } D_1 \text{ grad } - \Sigma_1)] & v_2\Sigma_1 \\ v_1 k\Sigma_2 & v_2[\text{div } D_2 \text{ grad } - \Sigma_2] \end{pmatrix}.$$

13.25. The general procedure in a group calculation consists of obtaining the actual fluxes as described in Chapter VIII. The adjoint fluxes are obtained in an analogous manner by solving the equations (13.7.2) for the steady state, i.e., ω equal to zero, subject to the same boundary conditions as apply to the real fluxes. The appropriate weighting functions for various perturbations may then be obtained in the manner outlined below.

13.26. The perturbation matrix in which v_1, v_2, D_1, D_2, Σ_1, and Σ_2 may all change is

$$\mathbf{P} = \begin{pmatrix} \delta v_1[\text{grad } D_1 \cdot \text{grad } + D_1 \nabla^2] - \delta(v_1\Sigma_1) & \delta(v_1 k\Sigma_2) \\ + v_1[\text{grad } \delta D_1 \cdot \text{grad } + \delta D_1 \nabla^2] & \delta v_2[\text{grad } D_2 \cdot \text{grad } + D_2 \nabla^2] - \delta(v_2\Sigma_2) \\ \delta(v_2\Sigma_1) & + v_2[\text{grad } D_2 \cdot \text{grad } + \delta D_2 \nabla^2] \end{pmatrix}.$$

In general, an expression for the change in ω may be obtained by performing the operations indicated in § 13.10 and applying the same procedure as used in the one-group treatment to reduce the $\mathbf{P}_{11}$ and $\mathbf{P}_{22}$ terms; the change in ω is found to be

$$\Delta\omega = \frac{1}{\chi}\left[-\int \delta(v_1\Sigma_1)\phi_1\dagger\phi_1 \, dV + \int \delta(v_1 k\Sigma_2)\phi_1\dagger\phi_2 \, dV \right.$$

$$+ \int \delta(v_2\Sigma_1)\phi_2\dagger\phi_1 \, dV - \int \delta(v_2\Sigma_2)\phi_2\dagger\phi_2 \, dV$$

$$\left. - \int \delta(D_1 v_1) \text{ grad } \phi_1\dagger \cdot \text{grad } \phi_1 \, dV - \int \delta(v_2 D_2) \text{ grad } \phi_2\dagger \cdot \text{grad } \phi_2 \, dV \right],$$

where

$$\chi = \int (\phi_1\dagger\phi_1 + \phi_2\dagger\phi_2) \, dV.$$

If an impurity that effectively changes only the thermal neutron absorption cross section, Σ_2, is added to the reactor, the change in ω reduces to

$$\Delta\omega = -v_2 \frac{\int \delta\Sigma_2 \phi_2 \dagger \phi_2 \, dV}{\int (\phi_1 \dagger \phi_1 + \phi_2 \dagger \phi_2) \, dV}.$$

The contribution to $\Delta\omega$ from the second integral is zero in this case since $k\Sigma_2$ remains essentially constant when Σ_2 changes.

PROBLEMS

1. Find the two-group adjoint fluxes for the reactor described in Problem 1, Chapter VII, having a 50-cm graphite reflector. Plot the statistical weight for a thermal neutron absorber as a function of position in the system.

2. If the coolant air in the X-lattice is replaced with a 0.5-cm water coolant jacket surrounding the fuel rod, what is the approximate change in k_∞ of the system, using one-group perturbation theory?

Chapter XIV

TRANSPORT THEORY
AND NEUTRON DIFFUSION*

DEVELOPMENT OF THE TRANSPORT EQUATION

INTRODUCTION

14.1. In Chapter V the problems associated with the motion of neutrons from regions of higher to those of lower neutron density were treated by means of diffusion theory. As stated in § 5.4, this represents an approximation based on the postulate that the angular distribution of the neutron velocity vectors is isotropic, or nearly isotropic. The equation expressing the conservation of neutrons thus did not include the direction of these vectors as a variable. The transport theory treatment, some aspects of which will be outlined here, takes into account the instantaneous velocity vectors of all the neutrons contained in a given volume element. In this way, the neutron distribution is characterized more completely than it is by the use of the total (or scalar) flux, as is the case in diffusion theory.

14.2. The objective of this chapter is limited to determining some of the conditions of validity of the elementary diffusion approximation as applied to monoenergetic neutrons. In particular, it will be shown that diffusion theory is an asymptotic form of transport theory which holds in regions away from boundaries and sources where the angular distribution of neutron velocity vectors is, in fact, nearly isotropic. In addition, more precise formulae will be derived for the diffusion coefficient and the diffusion length, and some corrections to elementary diffusion theory for regions near boundaries will be developed. For the present purpose it will be supposed that the neutrons are monoenergetic; this is sometimes referred to as "one-velocity" transport theory.

---

* This chapter is based largely on material made available by A. M. Weinberg, cf. AECD–3405. Some of the methods used here are essentially those described by W. Bothe, *Zeit. für Physik*, **118**, 401 (1942). A summary of the work of many authors is given by R. E. Marshak, *Rev. Mod. Phys.*, **19**, 185 (1947).

The One-Velocity Transport Equation

14.3. The expression for the neutron current given in Chapter V was derived on the assumption that the total or scalar neutron flux was a slowly varying function of the space coordinates in a medium. In this event, the higher terms in the Taylor series expansion of the flux may be neglected, as was done in § 5.12. However, if the neutron flux varies in such a manner that grad ϕ changes appreciably in a distance of two or three mean free paths, then this approximation is no longer justifiable. To understand the nature of the deviations from elementary diffusion theory, it is necessary to consider the directions in which neutrons are traveling, as well as their space coordinates. In other words, a correct theory will describe the neutron diffusion process in terms of a phase space consisting of three position coordinates and three velocity components along the coordinate axes.

14.4. For this purpose, two new dependent variables are introduced. Let n $(\mathbf{r}, \boldsymbol{\Omega})\, d\mathbf{r}\, d\boldsymbol{\Omega}$ be the number of neutrons in a volume element $d\mathbf{r}$ at $\mathbf{r}$ whose directions of motion lie in the element of solid angle $d\boldsymbol{\Omega}$ about the direction $\boldsymbol{\Omega}$, where $\boldsymbol{\Omega}$ is a unit directional vector. As stated above, it will be assumed that all neutrons have the same velocity v, but that they may change their directions when scattered. The ordinary or scalar neutron density $n(\mathbf{r})$ is then given by

$$n(\mathbf{r}) = \int_{\boldsymbol{\Omega}} n(\mathbf{r}, \boldsymbol{\Omega})\, d\boldsymbol{\Omega}, \qquad (14.4.1)$$

where the symbol $\boldsymbol{\Omega}$ at the bottom of the integral sign implies integration over all values of $\boldsymbol{\Omega}$, i.e., over all directions.

14.5. Further, the *vector flux*, which is defined by

$$\mathbf{F}(\mathbf{r}, \boldsymbol{\Omega}) = n(\mathbf{r}, \boldsymbol{\Omega})v\boldsymbol{\Omega}, \qquad (14.5.1)$$

is a vector whose magnitude $F(\mathbf{r}, \boldsymbol{\Omega})\boldsymbol{\Omega}$ is the number of neutrons traveling in direction $\boldsymbol{\Omega}$ that cross a unit area normal to $\boldsymbol{\Omega}$ in unit time. The total or scalar flux is then

$$\phi(\mathbf{r}) = \int_{\boldsymbol{\Omega}} F(\mathbf{r}, \boldsymbol{\Omega})\, d\boldsymbol{\Omega}. \qquad (14.5.2)$$

14.6. In order to derive the transport equation from the conservation of neutrons, consider a volume element $dx\, dy\, dz$ at $\mathbf{r}$ and an element of solid angle $d\boldsymbol{\Omega}$ at $\boldsymbol{\Omega}$. The number of neutrons in $d\boldsymbol{\Omega}$ that enter the volume element per second through the $dy\, dz$-face at x, y, z, is equal to the x-component of $\mathbf{F}(\mathbf{r}, \boldsymbol{\Omega})$, multiplied by $dy\, dz\, d\boldsymbol{\Omega}$, i.e.,

$$\text{Number of neutrons entering volume element through } dy\, dz \text{ per sec} = F_x(x, y, z, \boldsymbol{\Omega})\, dy\, dz\, d\boldsymbol{\Omega}.$$

Similarly, the number of neutrons leaving the volume element per second through the $dy\,dz$-face is

$$\text{Number of neutrons leaving volume} \atop \text{element through } dy\,dz \text{ per sec} = F_x(x + dx, y, z, \mathbf{\Omega})\,dy\,dz\,d\mathbf{\Omega}.$$

Consequently, the net number of neutrons entering $dx\,dy\,dz$ through the $dy\,dz$ faces of the cube per second is

$$\text{Net number of neutrons entering} \atop \text{volume element through } dy\,dz \text{ per sec} = -\frac{\partial F_x(x, y, z, \mathbf{\Omega})}{\partial x}\,dx\,dy\,dz\,d\mathbf{\Omega}.$$

The net number of neutrons in $d\mathbf{\Omega}$ entering the volume element per second through all the faces due to diffusion is then

$$\text{Net number of neutrons entering} \atop \text{volume element per sec} = -\left(\frac{\partial F_x}{\partial x} + \frac{\partial F_y}{\partial y} + \frac{\partial F_z}{\partial z}\right) dx\,dy\,dz\,d\mathbf{\Omega}$$

$$= -\operatorname{div} \mathbf{F}(\mathbf{r}, \mathbf{\Omega})\,d\mathbf{r}\,d\mathbf{\Omega}. \qquad (14.6.1)$$

14.7. Neutrons may enter the phase element $d\mathbf{r}\,d\mathbf{\Omega}$ by being scattered from $d\mathbf{r}\,d\mathbf{\Omega}'$ to $d\mathbf{r}\,d\mathbf{\Omega}$; that is to say, neutrons in the volume element may be scattered into $d\mathbf{\Omega}$ from directions different to the direction under consideration. Let $\Sigma_s(\mathbf{\Omega}, \mathbf{\Omega}')\,d\mathbf{\Omega}\,d\mathbf{\Omega}'$ be defined as the differential macroscopic scattering cross section from $d\mathbf{\Omega}'$ about $\mathbf{\Omega}'$ to $d\mathbf{\Omega}$ about $\mathbf{\Omega}$; then $\Sigma_s(\mathbf{\Omega}, \mathbf{\Omega}')F(\mathbf{r}, \mathbf{\Omega}')\,d\mathbf{\Omega}\,d\mathbf{\Omega}'$ is the number of neutrons whose velocity vectors lie in $d\mathbf{\Omega}'$ that are scattered into $d\mathbf{\Omega}$ per cm³ per sec at $\mathbf{\Omega}$. The number of neutrons entering the phase element $d\mathbf{r}\,d\mathbf{\Omega}$ due to scattering collisions per second is then

$$\text{Number of neutrons scattered into} \atop \text{volume element per sec} = d\mathbf{r}\,d\mathbf{\Omega} \int_{\mathbf{\Omega}'} N_s \sigma_s(\mathbf{\Omega}, \mathbf{\Omega}')F(\mathbf{r}, \mathbf{\Omega}')\,d\mathbf{\Omega}', \quad (14.7.1)$$

where N_s is the number of scattering nuclei per cm³ and $\sigma_s(\mathbf{\Omega}, \mathbf{\Omega}')$ is the cross section for the scattering from $d\mathbf{\Omega}'$ into $d\mathbf{\Omega}$.

14.8. The total macroscopic cross section Σ for the removal of neutrons from $d\mathbf{\Omega}$ is

$$\Sigma = N_a \sigma_a + N_s \sigma_s,$$

where N_a is the number per cm³ of absorber nuclei and σ_a is the absorption cross section. The (total) scattering cross section σ_s is related to $\sigma_s(\mathbf{\Omega}, \mathbf{\Omega}')$ by

$$\sigma_s = \int_{\mathbf{\Omega}'} \sigma_s(\mathbf{\Omega}, \mathbf{\Omega}')\,d\mathbf{\Omega}'.$$

The total number of neutrons removed from the phase element $d\mathbf{r}\,d\mathbf{\Omega}$ per second by absorption and scattering is then

$$\text{Total number of neutrons} \atop \text{removed per sec} = \Sigma(\mathbf{\Omega})F(\mathbf{r}, \mathbf{\Omega})\,d\mathbf{r}\,d\mathbf{\Omega}. \qquad (14.8.1)$$

14.9. Finally, if $S(\mathbf{r}, \boldsymbol{\Omega})\, d\mathbf{r}\, d\boldsymbol{\Omega}$ is the number of source neutrons emitted in $d\mathbf{r}\, d\boldsymbol{\Omega}$ per sec, the conservation of neutrons requires for a steady state that

$$-\operatorname{div} \mathbf{F}(\mathbf{r}, \boldsymbol{\Omega}) + \int_{\Omega'} N_s \sigma_s(\boldsymbol{\Omega}, \boldsymbol{\Omega}') F(\mathbf{r}, \boldsymbol{\Omega}')\, d\boldsymbol{\Omega}' - \Sigma(\boldsymbol{\Omega}) F(\mathbf{r}, \boldsymbol{\Omega}) + S(\mathbf{r}, \boldsymbol{\Omega}) = 0 \quad (14.9.1)$$

or rearranging the terms, the one-velocity *transport equation* becomes

$$\operatorname{div} \mathbf{F}(\mathbf{r}, \boldsymbol{\Omega}) + \Sigma(\boldsymbol{\Omega}) F(\mathbf{r}, \boldsymbol{\Omega}) = \int_{\Omega'} N_s \sigma_s(\boldsymbol{\Omega}, \boldsymbol{\Omega}') F(\mathbf{r}, \boldsymbol{\Omega}')\, d\boldsymbol{\Omega}' + S(\mathbf{r}, \boldsymbol{\Omega}). \quad (14.9.2)$$

THE ONE-DIMENSIONAL TRANSPORT EQUATION

14.10. Considerable simplification in notation can be achieved, with little loss in generality for the present purpose, by considering the one-dimensional transport equation. It is assumed that $F(\mathbf{r}, \boldsymbol{\Omega})$ and $S(\mathbf{r}, \boldsymbol{\Omega})$ are functions only of x

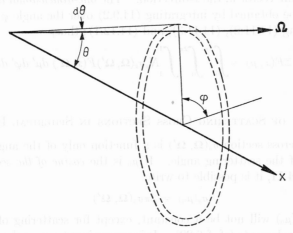

Fɪɢ. 14.10.   Derivation of one-dimensional transport equation

and of the angle between the x-axis and $\boldsymbol{\Omega}$; in other words, it is assumed that the source is symmetric about the x-axis. Let θ be the angle between $\boldsymbol{\Omega}$ and the x-axis (Fig. 14.10); then all the neutrons in an element $d\theta$ may be treated as equivalent.

14.11. For convenience, let $\cos\theta$ be represented by μ, and suppose $F(x, \mu)$ is the number of neutrons with direction cosines between μ and $\mu + d\mu$ crossing a ring element of area 2π per second. If φ is the azimuthal angle indicated in Fig. 14.10, then

$$d\boldsymbol{\Omega} = d\mu\, d\varphi,$$

and hence,

$$F(x, \mu)\, d\mu = d\mu \int_0^{2\pi} F(x, \boldsymbol{\Omega})\, d\varphi \quad (14.11.1)$$

or

$$F(x, \mu) = 2\pi F(x, \boldsymbol{\Omega}). \tag{14.11.2}$$

Similarly, if $S(x, \mu)$ is defined in an analogous manner,

$$S(x, \mu) = 2\pi S(x, \boldsymbol{\Omega}). \tag{14.11.3}$$

14.12. By using the identity in (13.12.1) for the divergence of the product of a scalar and a vector quantity, the first term in the transport equation leads to

$$\text{div } [F(x, \boldsymbol{\Omega})\boldsymbol{\Omega}] = \boldsymbol{\Omega} \cdot \hat{x}\, \frac{\partial F(x, \boldsymbol{\Omega})}{\partial x}$$

$$= \mu \frac{\partial F(x, \boldsymbol{\Omega})}{\partial x}, \tag{14.12.1}$$

since

$$\text{grad } F = \frac{\partial F}{\partial x}\, \hat{x},$$

where $\hat{x}$ is a unit vector in the x-direction. The *one-dimensional transport equation* can now be obtained by integrating (14.9.2) over the angle φ from 0 to 2π and introducing (14.11.2), (14.11.3), and (14.12.1); thus,

$$\mu \frac{dF(x, \mu)}{dx} + \Sigma F(x, \mu) = \int_0^{2\pi} \int_0^{2\pi} \int_{-1}^1 N_s \sigma_s(\boldsymbol{\Omega}, \boldsymbol{\Omega}') F(x, \boldsymbol{\Omega}')\, d\mu'\, d\varphi'\, d\varphi + S(x, \mu). \tag{14.12.2}$$

Expansion of Scattering Cross Sections in Spherical Harmonics

14.13. The cross section $\sigma_s(\boldsymbol{\Omega}, \boldsymbol{\Omega}')$ is a function only of the angle between $\boldsymbol{\Omega}$ and $\boldsymbol{\Omega}'$, i.e., of the scattering angle. If μ_0 is the *cosine of the scattering angle*, then, as in § 14.11, it is possible to write

$$\sigma_s(\mu_0) = 2\pi \sigma_s(\boldsymbol{\Omega}, \boldsymbol{\Omega}').$$

In general, $\sigma_s(\mu_0)$ will not be a constant, except for scattering of neutrons by nuclei of heavy elements (cf. § 6.20). It is convenient to expand $\sigma_s(\mu_0)$ in spherical harmonics, $P_l(\mu_0)$*; thus, let

$$\sigma_s(\mu_0) = \sum_{l=0}^{\infty} \frac{2l+1}{2}\, \sigma_{sl} P_l(\mu_0) \tag{14.13.1}$$

where

$$\sigma_{sl} = \int_{-1}^1 \sigma_s(\mu_0) P_l(\mu_0)\, d\mu_0. \tag{14.13.2}$$

14.14. The first two σ_{sl}'s in the expansion (14.13.1) are, respectively, the total scattering cross section, i.e.,

$$\sigma_{s0} = \int_{-1}^1 \sigma_s(\mu_0)\, d\mu_0, \tag{14.14.1}$$

---

* A few values of the spherical harmonics for low l's are as follows: $P_0(\mu) = 1$; $P_1(\mu) = \mu$; $P_2(\mu) = \frac{1}{2}(3\mu^2 - 1)$.

and the total scattering cross section times the average cosine of the scattering angle, $\bar{\mu}_0$, i.e.,

$$\sigma_{s1} = \int_{-1}^{1} \mu_0 \sigma_s(\mu_0) \, d\mu_0 = \bar{\mu}_0 \, \sigma_{s0}. \tag{14.14.2}$$

14.15. To permit the integral in (14.12.2) to be evaluated, $\sigma_s(\mu_0)$ must now be expressed as a function of φ', φ, μ', and μ; this is done by using the addition theorem for Legendre polynomials, viz.,

$$P_l(\mu_0) = P_l(\mu)P_l(\mu') + 2\sum_{m=1}^{l} \frac{(l-m)!}{(l+m)!} P_l^m(\mu)P_l^m(\mu') \cos m(\varphi - \varphi'), \tag{14.15.1}$$

where the P_l^m's are associated Legendre functions. Consequently,

$$\sigma_s(\Omega, \Omega') = \frac{1}{2\pi}\left[\sum_{l=0}^{\infty} \frac{2l+1}{2} \sigma_{sl}P_l(\mu)P_l(\mu')\right.$$
$$\left. + \sum_{l=0}^{\infty}\sum_{m=1}^{l} \frac{(l-m)!}{(l+m)!}(2l+1)\sigma_{sl}P_l^m(\mu)P_l^m(\mu') \cos m(\varphi' - \varphi)\right]. \tag{14.15.2}$$

14.16. Upon substituting (14.15.2) into the integral in (14.12.2) and performing the integration with respect to φ, it is evident that each term in the double sum integrates to zero and that the factor 2π is cancelled in the first term. Then, integrating with respect to φ', the final result is

$$\mu\frac{dF(x,\mu)}{dx} + \Sigma F(x,\mu) = \sum_{l=0}^{\infty} \frac{2l+1}{2} N_s\sigma_{sl}P_l(\mu)\int_{-1}^{1} P_l(\mu')F(x,\mu') \, d\mu' + S(x,\mu). \tag{14.16.1}$$

THE TRANSPORT EQUATION AND DIFFUSION THEORY

ELEMENTARY DIFFUSION APPROXIMATION

14.17. A standard procedure for solving (14.16.1) is the so-called spherical harmonics method. The angular distribution of the flux and the source are expanded in Legendre polynomials; thus,

$$F(x,\mu) = \sum_{l=0}^{\infty} \frac{2l+1}{2} F_l(x)P_l(\mu) \tag{14.17.1}$$

and

$$S(x,\mu) = \sum_{l=0}^{\infty} \frac{2l+1}{2} S_l(x)P_l(\mu) \tag{14.17.2}$$

where

$$F_l(x) = \int_{-1}^{1} F(x,\mu)P_l(\mu) \, d\mu \tag{14.17.3}$$

and

$$S_l(x) = \int_{-1}^{1} S(x,\mu)P_l(\mu) \, d\mu. \tag{14.17.4}$$

14.18. For a given source distribution the source harmonics may be evaluated. The problem is then to determine the $F_l(x)$ in the expansion (14.17.1). The procedure is to approximate the angular distribution by a finite number of terms in the expansion for $F(x, \mu)$. Then, by operating on the transport equation, a system of linear, first order differential equations for the $F_l(x)$ may be obtained and solved.

14.19. The elementary diffusion approximation, as will be shown below, corresponds to taking all $F_l(x)$ with $l > 1$ equal to zero. That is, the angular distribution is represented by only the first two terms in the spherical harmonics expansion. These two terms have a direct physical interpretation; thus,

$$F_0(x) = \int_{-1}^{1} F(x, \mu) \, d\mu \tag{14.19.1}$$

is the scalar neutron flux usually represented by $\phi(x)$*, whereas

$$F_1(x) = \int_{-1}^{1} \mu F(x, \mu) \, d\mu \tag{14.19.2}$$

is the net neutron current, $J(x)$. The angular distribution, using only the first two terms of (14.17.1), thus becomes

$$F(x, \mu) = \tfrac{1}{2}F_0(x)P_0(\mu) + \tfrac{3}{2}F_1(x)P_1(\mu) \tag{14.19.3}$$
$$= \tfrac{1}{2}F_0(x) + \tfrac{3}{2}\mu F_1(x) \tag{14.19.4}$$
$$= \tfrac{1}{2}\phi(x) + \tfrac{3}{2}\mu J(x), \tag{14.19.5}$$

since $P_0(\mu) = 1$ and $P_1(\mu) = \mu$.

14.20. To obtain the diffusion equation from the rigorous transport equation (14.16.1), use is made of the general method for generating the differential equations for $F_l(x)$ in the spherical harmonics method. The equation (14.16.1) is first integrated with respect to μ from -1 to 1. This is equivalent to multiplying by $P_0(\mu)$ and integrating with respect to μ; the result is

$$\int_{-1}^{1} \mu \frac{dF(x, \mu)}{dx} \, d\mu + \Sigma \int_{-1}^{1} F(x, \mu) \, d\mu$$
$$= \int_{-1}^{1} \sum_{l=0}^{\infty} \frac{2l+1}{2} N_s \sigma_{sl} P_l(\mu) \, d\mu \int_{-1}^{1} P_l(\mu') F(x, \mu') \, d\mu' + \int_{-1}^{1} S(x, \mu) \, d\mu. \tag{14.20.1}$$

14.21. Using the orthogonality relations for Legendre polynomials

$$\int_{-1}^{1} P_l(\mu) P_n(\mu) \, d\mu = 0 \quad \text{if} \quad l \neq n$$
$$= \frac{2}{2l+1} \quad \text{if} \quad l = n,$$

---

* Although $F_0(x)$ is identical with the ordinary flux $\phi(x)$, the former symbolism is retained for consistency.

equation (14.20.1) becomes

$$\frac{dF_1(x)}{dx} + \Sigma F_0(x) = N_s \sigma_{s0} F_0(x) + S_0(x), \tag{14.21.1}$$

in which $S_0(x)$ is the total source strength. As seen in § 14.14, σ_{s0} is the total scattering cross section, so that $N_s \sigma_{s0}$ is equal to Σ_s, the macroscopic scattering cross section. Further, since Σ is the total macroscopic cross section for absorption and scattering, $\Sigma - \Sigma_s$ is equal to Σ_a the macroscopic cross section for absorption only. Consequently, (14.21.1) can be written as

$$\frac{dF_1(x)}{dx} + \Sigma_a F_0(x) - S_0(x) = 0. \tag{14.21.2}$$

14.22. Upon multiplying (14.16.1) by $P_1(\mu)$ and integrating over μ from -1 to 1, it is found that

$$\frac{d}{dx} \int_{-1}^{1} \mu P_1(\mu) F(x, \mu)\, d\mu + \Sigma F_1(x) = N_s \sigma_{s1} F_1(x), \tag{14.22.1}$$

the source term here being zero, if the source is assumed to be isotropic. Equation (14.19.3) is now substituted into the integrand, and by the use of the relations

$$\int_{-1}^{1} \mu P_n(\mu) P_l(\mu)\, d\mu = 0 \text{ if } l \neq n + 1$$

$$= \frac{n+1}{2n+1} \cdot \frac{2}{2(n+1)+1} \text{ if } l = n+1,$$

the integral in (14.22.1), neglecting all terms beyond $P_1(\mu)$, becomes

$$\int_{-1}^{1} \mu P_1(\mu) [\tfrac{1}{2} F_0(x) P_0(\mu) + \tfrac{3}{2} F_1(x) P_1(\mu)] = \tfrac{1}{3} F_0(x).$$

Thus, (14.22.1) reduces to

$$\frac{1}{3} \cdot \frac{dF_0(x)}{dx} + (\Sigma - N_s \sigma_{s1}) F_1(x) = 0. \tag{14.22.2}$$

14.23. By combining (14.21.2) and (14.22.2), $F_1(x)$ may be eliminated, the result being

$$\frac{1}{3(\Sigma - N_s \sigma_{s1})} \cdot \frac{d^2 F_0(x)}{dx^2} - \Sigma_a F_0(x) + S_0(x) = 0. \tag{14.23.1}$$

This expression is obviously of the form of the familiar diffusion equation used in earlier chapters, the diffusion coefficient for neutron flux being now represented by

$$D = \frac{1}{3(\Sigma - N_s \sigma_{s1})}.$$

If the medium is a weak absorber, Σ may be replaced by $N_s\sigma_{s0}$ (or Σ_s) and, since σ_{s1} is equal to $\bar{\mu}_0\sigma_{s0}$, by (14.14.2), the expression for the diffusion coefficient becomes

$$D = \frac{1}{3N_s\sigma_{s0}(1 - \bar{\mu}_0)} = \frac{1}{3\Sigma_s(1 - \bar{\mu}_0)}. \qquad (14.23.2)$$

$$= \tfrac{1}{3}\lambda_t. \qquad (14.23.3)$$

The quantity $1/N_s\sigma_{s0}(1 - \bar{\mu}_0) = 1/\Sigma_s(1 - \bar{\mu}_0)$ is the transport mean free path, λ_t, referred to in § 5.24. It may be concluded, therefore, that when the conditions are such that the angular distribution of the flux can be represented by the first two terms of the spherial harmonics expansion, simple diffusion theory is applicable, with the diffusion coefficient defined by (14.23.2) or (14.23.3).

14.24. If the scattering were isotropic in the laboratory system, the net neutron current for a given gradient of the neutron flux would be a minimum. As $\bar{\mu}_0$ increases, i.e., as the scattering in the forward direction predominates, the net neutron current is increased. Hence, $1/(1 - \bar{\mu}_0)$ is a measure of the forward scattering in the laboratory system.

GENERALIZED FICK'S LAW AND APPLICABILITY OF ELEMENTARY DIFFUSION THEORY

14.25. Since $F_1(x)$ is equivalent to the net neutron current $J(x)$, as pointed out in § 14.19, and, noting that $P_1(\mu)$ is equal to μ, (14.22.1) can be put in the form

$$J(x) = -\frac{1}{\Sigma - N_s\sigma_{s1}} \cdot \frac{d}{dx} \int_{-1}^{1} \mu^2 F(x, \mu)\, d\mu. \qquad (14.25.1)$$

The mean square cosine $\overline{\mu^2}$ of the neutron angular distribution is defined by

$$\overline{\mu^2} = \frac{\int_{-1}^{1} \mu^2 F(x, \mu)\, d\mu}{\int_{-1}^{1} F(x, \mu)\, d\mu}, \qquad (14.25.2)$$

and so (14.25.1) becomes

$$J(x) = -\frac{1}{\Sigma - N_s\sigma_{s1}} \cdot \frac{d}{dx} [\overline{\mu^2} F_0(x)]. \qquad (14.25.3)$$

This equation is a generalized form of Fick's law, as applied to the diffusion of neutrons, derived from transport theory. It should be noted that this result is quite general and does not depend upon the restriction of the spherical harmonics expansion to any particular number of terms.

14.26. The coefficient in (14.25.3) has the dimensions of length and is called the *diffusion mean free path*; then,

$$\lambda_d = \frac{1}{\Sigma - N_s\sigma_{s1}} = \frac{1}{N_a\sigma_a + N_s\sigma_{s0}(1 - \bar{\mu}_0)}, \qquad (14.26.1)$$

so that (14.25.3) may be written as

$$J(x) = -\lambda_d \frac{d}{dx} [\overline{\mu^2} F_0(x)]. \tag{14.26.2}$$

If the capture of neutrons by the diffusion medium is negligible, the diffusion mean free path becomes identical with the transport mean free path as defined in § 14.23.

14.27. Elementary diffusion theory is based on the assumption that Fick's law in the simple form $J(x) = -D$ grad $F_0(x)$ is applicable to neutrons. It is evident, therefore, from (14.26.2) that elementary diffusion theory can hold rigorously for monoenergetic neutrons only if $\overline{\mu^2}$ is independent of position, for then (14.26.2) becomes

$$J(x) = -\lambda_d \overline{\mu^2} \frac{dF_0(x)}{dx},$$

and $\lambda_d \overline{\mu^2}$ is equal to D, the diffusion coefficient.

14.28. The mean square cosine of the neutron angular distribution can be obtained as follows. From the values of $P_0(\mu)$, $P_1(\mu)$, and $P_2(\mu)$, given in § 14.13, footnote, it is seen that

$$\mu^2 = \tfrac{1}{3} P_0(\mu) + \tfrac{2}{3} P_2(\mu),$$

and then, using (14.17.1), (14.25.2) gives

$$\overline{\mu^2} = \frac{1}{F_0(x)} \int_{-1}^{1} [\tfrac{1}{3} P_0(\mu) + \tfrac{2}{3} P_2(\mu)] \sum_{l=0}^{\infty} \frac{2l+1}{2} F_l(x) P_l(\mu) \, d\mu.$$

Upon integrating and applying the orthogonality conditions, the result is

$$\overline{\mu^2} = \frac{1}{3} + \frac{2}{3} \cdot \frac{F_2(x)}{F_0(x)},$$

so that if $F_2(x)/F_0(x)$ is independent of x, elementary diffusion theory, based on the proportionality of the net neutron current and the gradient of the neutron flux, will be rigorously correct.

ASYMPTOTIC SOLUTION OF TRANSPORT EQUATION IN NONABSORBING MEDIUM

14.29. There are two special cases in which $F_2(x)/F_0(x)$ is independent of position: one applies to a nonabsorbing medium and the other to an absorbing medium. It will be shown that in each case elementary diffusion theory is applicable. Near a source or a boundary between two different media, the neutron angular distribution is highly anisotropic, since it is influenced by the presence of the source or boundary. A number of terms are then required in the spherical harmonics expansion of the angular distribution. At some distance from sources and boundaries, i.e., in the so-called asymptotic case, however, their effect is lost, and the angular distribution can be adequately represented by the first two harmonics only, i.e., by $F_0(x)$ and $F_1(x)$. Since $F_2(x)$ is now zero, it is evident that $F_2(x)/F_0(x)$ must be independent of x, and elementary diffusion theory should be applicable. That this is so, provided the medium is a nonabsorber, may be shown as follows. The treatment is alternative to that in § 14.22, *et seq.*, and has some points of interest.

14.30. Termination of the spherical harmonics for the angular distribution after the second term is equivalent to expressing the scalar flux, i.e., $F_0(x)$, by means of a Taylor series in which all terms containing derivatives of the second and higher orders are taken as zero, as in § 5.12. Thus, $F_0(x)$ must be a linear function of x. As given in § 14.19, the angular distribution of the flux, using only two harmonics, is

$$F(x, \mu) = \tfrac{1}{2}F_0(x) + \tfrac{3}{2}F_1(x)\mu, \qquad (14.30.1)$$

and, since $F_0(x)$ must be linear in x, a general solution for the angular distribution will be of the form

$$F(x, \mu) = A + Bx + C\mu, \qquad (14.30.2)$$

where

$$F_0(x) = 2A + 2Bx \qquad (14.30.3)$$

and

$$F_1(x) = \tfrac{2}{3}C. \qquad (14.30.4)$$

14.31. The transport equation (14.16.1) in a source-free medium is

$$\mu \frac{dF(x, \mu)}{dx} + \Sigma F(x, \mu) = \sum_{l=0}^{\infty} \frac{2l + 1}{2} N_s\sigma_{sl}P_l(\mu) \int_{-1}^{1} P_l(\mu')F(x, \mu')\, d\mu'. \quad (14.31.1)$$

Upon substituting (14.30.2) into (14.31.2) and integrating, the result is

$$\mu B + \Sigma(A + Bx + C\mu) = N_s\sigma_{s0}(A + Bx) + N_s\sigma_{s1}\mu C.$$

Replacing Σ by $\Sigma_a + \Sigma_s$ and $N_s\sigma_{s0}$ by Σ_s, it is found that

$$C = -\frac{\mu B + \Sigma_a(A + Bx)}{(\Sigma - N_s\sigma_{s1})\mu}. \qquad (14.31.2)$$

Since A and B in (14.30.3) are both arbitrary, that is to say, the specification of the flux level and the slope is arbitrary, Σ_a must be zero if C is to be a constant. In other words, the conditions require that the medium should be nonabsorbing. In this case, (14.31.2) becomes

$$C = -\frac{B}{\Sigma_s(1 - \mu_0)} = -\lambda_t B. \qquad (14.31.3)$$

14.32. Differentiation of (14.30.3) with respect to x gives

$$\frac{dF_0(x)}{dx} = 2B,$$

and consequently (14.31.3) becomes

$$C = -\tfrac{1}{2}\lambda_t \frac{dF_0(x)}{dx}.$$

Finally, utilizing (14.30.4), and the fact that $F_1(x)$ is equivalent to $J(x)$, there is obtained the result

$$F_1(x) = J(x) = -\tfrac{1}{3}\lambda_t \frac{dF_0(x)}{dx}, \tag{14.32.1}$$

which is the expression of Fick's law in diffusion theory with $D = \tfrac{1}{3}\lambda_t$, as in § 14.23. Thus, elementary diffusion theory is rigorously correct for mono-energetic neutrons in a nonabsorbing medium away from sources and boundaries. By inserting (14.32.1) into (14.30.1), and writing $F_0'(x)$ for the derivative of $F_0(x)$, the equation for $F(x, \mu)$ in the asymptotic case becomes

$$F(x, \mu) = \tfrac{1}{2}F_0(x) - \tfrac{1}{2}\lambda_t\mu F_0'(x). \tag{14.32.2}$$

Asymptotic Solution of Transport Equation in Absorbing Medium

14.33. In the case of a medium which captures neutrons to an appreciable extent, the conditions for diffusion theory to be applicable may be derived if the angular distribution $F(x, \mu)$ can be treated as a product of two functions, one of which is dependent upon x only and the other upon μ only. In these circumstances, all the harmonics bear a constant ratio to $F_0(x, \mu)$ for all values of x. Thus, in particular, $F_2(x)/F_0(x)$ is independent of x, and elementary diffusion theory should hold. The expression for the diffusion coefficient is, however, different from that derived above.

14.34. If the expansion of the scattering cross section in § 14.13 can be terminated after the first two terms, as is the case if the scattering is not highly anisotropic, the transport equation (14.31.1) in a source-free medium can be written as

$$\mu\frac{dF(x, \mu)}{dx} + \Sigma F(x, \mu) = \tfrac{1}{2}N_s\sigma_{s0} \int_{-1}^{1} F(x, \mu')\, d\mu' + \tfrac{3}{2}\mu N_s\sigma_{s1} \int_{-1}^{1} \mu'F(x, \mu')\, d\mu'$$

$$= \Sigma_s\left[\tfrac{1}{2} \int_{-1}^{1} F(x, \mu')\, d\mu' + \tfrac{3}{2}\mu\bar{\mu}_0 \int_{-1}^{1} \mu'F(x, \mu')\, d\mu'\right], \tag{14.34.1}$$

since $N_s\sigma_{s0} = \Sigma_s$ and $\sigma_{s1} = \bar{\mu}_0\sigma_{s0}$. Upon substituting for $F(x, \mu)$ a trial separable solution, represented by

$$F(x, \mu) = e^{\pm\kappa x}f(\mu), \tag{14.34.2}$$

the result is

$$(\Sigma \pm \kappa\mu)f(\mu) = \Sigma_s\left[\tfrac{1}{2} \int_{-1}^{1} f(\mu')\, d\mu' + \tfrac{3}{2}\mu\bar{\mu}_0 \int_{-1}^{1} \mu'f(\mu')\, d\mu'\right]. \tag{14.34.3}$$

The separable solution (14.34.2) will then satisfy (14.34.1) if a value of $f(\mu)$ can be found which will satisfy (14.34.3).

14.35. A solution for $f(\mu)$ of the form

$$f(\mu) = \text{const.} \times \frac{A + \mu\bar{\mu}_0}{\Sigma \pm \kappa\mu}, \tag{14.35.1}$$

may be tried. This will, in general, not satisfy (14.34.3), but it will do so for particular values of A and κ. These characteristic values may be obtained as follows. Upon substituting (14.35.1) into (14.34.3) and making use of standard integrals, it is found that

$$A + \mu\bar{\mu}_0 = A\,\frac{\Sigma_s}{2\kappa}\ln\,\zeta \pm \frac{\Sigma_s\bar{\mu}_0}{2}\left(\frac{2}{\kappa} - \frac{\Sigma}{\kappa^2}\ln\,\zeta\right)$$
$$\pm A\,\frac{3\Sigma_s\mu\bar{\mu}_0}{2}\left(\frac{2}{\kappa} - \frac{\Sigma}{\kappa^2}\ln\,\zeta\right) + \frac{3\Sigma_s\mu\bar{\mu}_0^2}{2}\left(-\frac{2\Sigma}{\kappa^2} + \frac{\Sigma^2}{\kappa^3}\ln\,\zeta\right),$$

where

$$\zeta \equiv \frac{\Sigma + \kappa}{\Sigma - \kappa}.$$

This is an identity in μ and hence coefficients of powers of μ may be equated; thus,

$$A = \pm\,\frac{\dfrac{\Sigma_s\bar{\mu}_0}{2}\left(\dfrac{2}{\kappa} - \dfrac{\Sigma}{\kappa^2}\ln\,\zeta\right)}{1 - \dfrac{\Sigma_s}{2\kappa}\ln\,\zeta} \tag{14.35.2}$$

and

$$\frac{\Sigma_s}{2\kappa}\ln\,\zeta = \frac{1 + \dfrac{3\Sigma_a\Sigma_s}{\kappa^2}\bar{\mu}_0}{1 + \dfrac{3\Sigma\Sigma_s}{\kappa^2}\bar{\mu}_0}, \tag{14.35.3}$$

where $\Sigma = \Sigma_a + \Sigma_s$.

14.36. For isotropic scattering in the laboratory system, $\bar{\mu}_0$ is zero, and κ is determined, from (14.35.3), as the root of

$$\frac{\Sigma_s}{2\kappa}\ln\,\zeta = \frac{\Sigma_s}{2\kappa}\ln\,\frac{\Sigma + \kappa}{\Sigma - \kappa} = 1. \tag{14.36.1}$$

This equation has one pair of real roots, $\pm\kappa$, with absolute value less than Σ; there is also an infinite set of imaginary roots, which are of no consequence for the present purpose. It may be noted that, for the form of (14.35.1) for $f(\mu)$ to be valid, it is indeed necessary for $|\kappa|$ to be less than Σ. If this were not so, $f(\mu)$ would have singularities for those values of μ at which the denominator of (14.35.1) vanishes.

14.37. The quantity A, as expressed by (14.35.2), is indeterminate for the isotropic case, i.e., when $\bar{\mu}_0$ is zero; nevertheless, it can be shown to be finite, although the actual value is not required here. For isotropic scattering the angular distribution is given by (14.34.2) and (14.35.1) as

$$F(x, \mu) = \text{const.} \times \frac{e^{\pm\kappa x}}{\Sigma \pm \kappa\mu}, \tag{14.37.1}$$

and from (14.25.2) it is found that

$$\overline{\mu^2} = \frac{\Sigma\Sigma_a}{\kappa^2}. \tag{14.37.2}$$

In the diffusion theory approximation, the diffusion coefficient, D, is equal to $\lambda_d\overline{\mu^2}$ (§ 14.27), and since, for isotropic scattering, $\overline{\mu}_0$ is zero, this is equivalent to $\overline{\mu^2}/\Sigma$. Consequently, it follows from (14.37.2) that in the present case

$$D = \frac{\Sigma_a}{\kappa^2}. \tag{14.37.3}$$

14.38. When the absorption is very small compared to the scattering, κ is small compared to Σ. It is then permissible to expand the denominator of (14.37.1) and retain only the first two terms; thus,

$$F(x, \mu) \approx Ce^{\pm\kappa x}\left(1 \mp \frac{\kappa}{\Sigma}\mu\right), \tag{14.38.1}$$

where C is a composite constant. This is essentially an expression for the angular distribution containing only the first two spherical harmonics, and so it represents the distribution in elementary diffusion theory. Applying (14.19.1) and (14.19.2), it is seen that

$$F_0(x) = 2Ce^{\pm\kappa x} \tag{14.38.2}$$

and

$$F_1(x) = \mp \tfrac{2}{3}C\frac{\kappa}{\Sigma}e^{\pm\kappa x}. \tag{14.38.3}$$

Upon substituting these values into (14.19.3) the result is identical with (14.38.1). It is thus evident that in a weak absorber, the angular distribution of elementary diffusion theory is a good approximation to the (asymptotic) distribution (14.37.1).

14.39. The angular distribution as given by (14.37.1) or (14.38.1) contains a single multiplicative constant. It is consequently not sufficiently general to satisfy arbitrary boundary conditions of the kind that would apply to the neutron angular distribution near sources or boundaries. Thus, the separable solution postulated for an absorbing medium, like the two-harmonic solution applicable to the nonabsorbing medium, can hold only at considerable distances from sources and boundaries. The solutions given, which satisfy elementary diffusion theory, are thus asymptotic solutions of the transport equation in absorbing and non-absorbing media, respectively. It may be concluded, therefore, that elementary diffusion theory, based on Fick's law, holds strictly only for conditions where asymptotic solutions of the transport equation are valid. In other words, only when the neutron distribution approaches the asymptotic distribution, i.e., a few transport mean free paths away from sources and boundaries, can elementary diffusion theory be used.

The Diffusion Length

14.40. Since the neutron flux in an absorbing medium can be represented by the exponential expression (14.37.1), it follows by the procedure given in (§ 5.63) that the mean square distance a neutron travels before it is absorbed is equal to $6/\kappa^2$. Consequently, the κ in the preceding treatment is identical with that used in Chapter V and is the reciprocal of the diffusion length. The latter may thus be regarded as being defined by the transcendental equation (14.35.3). If Σ_a is small in comparison with Σ_s, the equation may be solved by series expansion. The result, correct to terms in the first degree in Σ_a/Σ, is then found to be

$$\kappa^2 = \frac{1}{L^2} = 3\Sigma\Sigma_a(1 - \bar{\mu}_0)\left(1 - \frac{4}{5}\cdot\frac{\Sigma_a}{\Sigma} + \frac{\Sigma_a}{\Sigma}\cdot\frac{\bar{\mu}_0}{1 - \bar{\mu}_0} + \cdots\right). \quad (14.40.1)$$

If the scattering is isotropic, i.e., $\bar{\mu}_0$ is zero, this reduces to

$$\kappa^2 = \frac{1}{L^2} = 3\Sigma\Sigma_a\left(1 - \frac{4}{5}\cdot\frac{\Sigma_a}{\Sigma}\right). \quad (14.40.2)$$

On the other hand, for weak capture, so that Σ_a/Σ can be neglected, and Σ replaced by Σ_s, (14.40.1) becomes

$$\kappa^2 = \frac{1}{L^2} = 3\Sigma_s\Sigma_a(1 - \bar{\mu}_0). \quad (14.40.3)$$

Since, by (14.37.3), the diffusion coefficient is equal to Σ_a/κ^2, it follows from (14.40.3) that

$$D = \frac{1}{3\Sigma_s(1 - \bar{\mu}_0)} = \frac{1}{3}\lambda_t,$$

as given by (14.23.2) from elementary diffusion theory.

RIGOROUS SOLUTION OF TRANSPORT EQUATION

Infinite Plane Isotropic Source in Infinite Medium*

14.41. The transport equation can be solved relatively easily for an infinite plane isotropic source in an infinite medium. There is no loss of generality, since the solution can be transformed to that for a point source (cf. § 6.136) and the solution for a general source distribution obtained by integrating the resulting kernel over the source distribution. Let a unit plane source be placed at $x = 0$. If the scattering is isotropic in the laboratory system, the transport equation is

$$\mu\frac{dF(x, \mu)}{dx} + \Sigma F(x, \mu) = \tfrac{1}{2}N_s\sigma_{s0}\int_{-1}^{1} F(x, \mu)\,d\mu + \tfrac{1}{2}\delta(x), \quad (14.41.1)$$

* E. P. Wigner, unpublished.

where the delta function, $\delta(x)$, represents the plane source. To solve this equation $F(x, \mu)$ and $\delta(x)$ are expanded in terms of the Fourier integral; thus,

$$\delta(x) = \frac{1}{2\pi} \int_{-\infty}^{\infty} e^{i\omega x} \, d\omega \tag{14.41.2}$$

and

$$F(x, \mu) = \frac{1}{2\pi} \int_{-\infty}^{\infty} \frac{A(\omega) e^{i\omega x}}{\Sigma + i\omega\mu} \, d\omega, \tag{14.41.3}$$

where the constant term $\Sigma + i\omega\mu$ has been used as the denominator in (14.41.3) in order to simplify the algebra.

14.42. Upon substituting (14.41.3) into (14.41.1) it is found that

$$A(\omega) = \frac{1}{2\left[1 - \dfrac{\Sigma_s}{2i\omega} \ln \zeta\right]} \tag{14.42.1}$$

where

$$\zeta \equiv \frac{\Sigma + i\omega}{\Sigma - i\omega}. \tag{14.42.2}$$

The complete solution of (14.41.1) is then

$$F(x, \mu) = \frac{1}{4\pi} \int_{-\infty}^{\infty} \frac{e^{i\omega x}}{1 - \dfrac{\Sigma_s}{2i\omega} \ln \zeta} \cdot \frac{d\omega}{\Sigma + i\omega\mu}. \tag{14.42.3}$$

The total (scalar) flux is obtained upon integrating (14.42.3) with respect to μ; thus,

$$F_0(x) = \frac{1}{4\pi} \int_{-\infty}^{\infty} \frac{e^{i\omega x}}{i\omega\left(1 - \dfrac{\Sigma_s}{2i\omega} \ln \zeta\right)} \ln \zeta \, d\omega. \tag{14.42.4}$$

Asymptotic and Nonasymptotic Solutions

14.43. The integral in (14.42.4) has a simple pole where

$$\frac{\Sigma_s}{2i\omega} \ln \zeta = \frac{\Sigma_s}{2i\omega} \ln \frac{\Sigma + i\omega}{\Sigma - i\omega} = 1.$$

Comparing with (14.36.1), it is seen that the simple pole occurs where $i\omega$ is equal to $\pm\kappa$, the reciprocal of the diffusion length. It also has an essential singularity at $i\omega = \pm\Sigma$. The contribution to the integral from the residue at the pole is, from Cauchy's theorem,

$$F_0(x)_{\text{as.}} = \alpha \frac{\kappa}{2\Sigma_a} e^{-\kappa|x|}, \tag{14.43.1}$$

where

$$\alpha \equiv \frac{2\Sigma_a}{\Sigma_s} \cdot \frac{\Sigma^2 - \kappa^2}{\kappa^2 - \Sigma\Sigma_a}. \tag{14.43.2}$$

This is the asymptotic solution which holds beyond a few mean paths away from the source.

14.44. The nonasymptotic part of the solution, which comes from the essential singularity, can be expressed as a real integral; thus,

$$F_0(x)_{\text{n.as.}} = 2\Sigma^2 \int_0^\infty \frac{(1 + \eta)e^{-(1+\eta)\Sigma x} \, d\eta}{\left[2\Sigma(1 + \eta) - \Sigma_s \ln\left(1 + \dfrac{2}{\eta}\right)\right]^2 + \pi^2 \Sigma_s^2}.$$

It can be shown that $F_0(x)_{\text{n.as.}}$ falls off much more rapidly with increasing distance from the source plane than does $F_0(x)_{\text{as.}}$.

14.45. If the asymptotic solution (14.43.1) is compared with the corresponding solution from elementary diffusion theory, e.g., equation (5.51.2), which is equivalent to $\dfrac{\kappa}{2\Sigma_a} e^{-\kappa x}$, it is seen that diffusion theory gives the correct asymptotic solution except for the factor α. This can be interpreted as a reduction in the effective source strength, and the procedure for correcting elementary diffusion theory is then merely to multiply the actual source strength by the factor

$$\frac{2\Sigma_a}{\Sigma_s} \cdot \frac{\Sigma^2 - \kappa^2}{\kappa^2 - \Sigma\Sigma_a} \approx 1 - \frac{4}{5} \cdot \frac{\Sigma_a}{\Sigma} \quad \text{if} \quad \frac{\Sigma_a}{\Sigma} \ll 1. \tag{14.45.1}$$

14.46. The reason for the apparent reduction in source strength is that the additional term $F_0(x)_{\text{n.as.}}$ shows that the absorption near the source is greater than given by elementary diffusion theory. For neutrons diffusing in ordinary water, for example, $1 - \dfrac{4}{5} \cdot \dfrac{\Sigma_a}{\Sigma}$ is about 0.990, so that the discrepancy is not large in this case. However, in homogeneous, enriched chain reactors, the absorption by fuel will result in more significant source corrections.

BOUNDARY CONDITIONS

INTERFACE BETWEEN TWO MEDIA

14.47. At the interface between two media, the neutron flux distribution must be continuous for all values of μ. If $F(x, \mu)$ were discontinuous at a boundary, the number of neutrons having a given value of μ reaching the boundary from the right would not be the same as the number, having the same value of μ, leaving toward the left. This would be possible only if there were a neutron source or an absorber at the interface which would account for the difference in the neutron currents to and from the boundary.

14.48. Suppose neutrons diffuse in a system consisting of two media with different scattering and absorption properties. The coordinate of the planar interface between the media will be taken as $x = 0$, and $+$ and $-$ signs will be used to distinguish the media. The boundary condition of continuity derived qualitatively in the preceding paragraph then means that

$$F^+(0, \mu) = F^-(0, \mu)$$

for all values of μ. In view of the spherical harmonics expansion in (14.17.1), this condition may be stated in the form, that

$$F_l^+(0) = F_l^-(0) \tag{14.48.1}$$

for all values of l.

14.49. If neither of the media absorbs neutrons, then the asymptotic solution (14.32.2) away from sources, namely,

$$F(x, \mu) = \tfrac{1}{2}F_0(x) - \tfrac{1}{2}\lambda_t\mu\, F_0'(x), \tag{14.49.1}$$

where $F_0(x) = 2A + 2Bx$ [cf. (14.29.1)], holds even at the interface. The reason for this is that (14.48.1) is automatically satisfied if the arbitrary constants A^+ and B^+ and A^- and B^- for the two media are chosen so that

$$F_0^+(0) = F_0^-(0) \tag{14.49.2}$$

and

$$F_1^+(0) = F_1^-(0), \tag{14.49.3}$$

the latter condition being equivalent to

$$\lambda_t^+ \frac{dF_0^+(0)}{dx} = \lambda_t^- \frac{dF_0^-(0)}{dx}. \tag{14.49.4}$$

The boundary condition (14.49.2) means that the total flux of neutrons is continuous, while (14.49.3) requires that the net diffusion current shall also be continuous at the boundary. Since $F_0(x)$ in elementary diffusion theory is the solution of a second order differential equation, it is possible to specify both $F_0(x)$ and $F_0'(x)$ at an interface. Thus, when neither medium absorbs neutrons, the boundary conditions (14.49.2) and (14.49.3) lead to a rigorously correct solution.

14.50. If one of the media is an absorber, then continuity of flux and of current at the interface are not rigorously correct boundary conditions. The nonasymptotic distribution in an absorbing medium involves all the spherical harmonics, whereas continuity of flux and current means only that the coefficients of the first two harmonics are continuous. To satisfy the rigorous boundary condition (14.48.1) a large number of nonasymptotic solutions, which die away beyond one or two mean free paths from the interface, must be included. Since this procedure is complicated, it is usual to employ the elementary diffusion theory boundary conditions of continuity of flux and current. This insures that there is continuity as far as the $P_0(\mu)$ and $P_1(\mu)$ terms are concerned, and that there is no discontinuity in the net flow of neutrons, although there may possibly be discontinuities for flow in particular directions.

14.51. The diffusion coefficient in a medium with capture is equal to Σ_a/κ^2 by (14.37.3). Hence, for absorbing media, the boundary condition (14.49.4) becomes

$$\left(\frac{\Sigma_a}{\kappa^2}\right)^+ \frac{dF_0^+(0)}{dx} = \left(\frac{\Sigma_a}{\kappa^2}\right)^- \frac{dF_0^-(0)}{dx}. \tag{14.51.1}$$

Since the identification of the diffusion coefficient with Σ_a/κ^2 is based on the asymptotic distribution, which breaks down near an interface, it is not certain that (14.51.1) represents a consistent approximation. An alternative procedure would be to assume that the two-harmonic solution (14.49.1) applies to an absorbing medium, since it represents a good approximation if the absorption is weak. The diffusion coefficient would then be equal to $\frac{1}{3}\lambda_t$, and (14.51.1) would be replaced by

$$\lambda_t^+ \frac{dF_0^+(0)}{dx} = \lambda_t^- \frac{dF_0^-(0)}{dx}. \tag{14.51.2}$$

Without an exact solution of the transport equation, it is, in general, not possible to decide whether (14.51.1) or (14.51.2) is a better approximation; both have been used in neutron diffusion theory.

Interface Between a Medium and Vacuum

14.52. If one of the media in the foregoing treatment is a vacuum, or a perfect absorber, the boundary conditions derived become meaningless. In a vacuum there are no collisions, and hence there will be no net diffusion current from the vacuum to the medium. Thus, a vacuum acts as a perfect absorber. Since no neutrons can return from a perfect absorber, the rigorous boundary condition must be

$$F(0, \mu) = 0 \quad \text{for} \quad \mu \leqq 0. \tag{14.52.1}$$

This condition cannot be satisfied by diffusion theory, and so it is replaced by the condition requiring that there shall be no *net* current of neutrons back from the vacuum. In other words, there is an implication that neutrons may be reflected back from the vacuum in certain directions, provided they are compensated for by increasing the flow into the vacuum from other directions. This is much less stringent than (14.52.1) which denies the possibility of any neutrons returning from the vacuum. The diffusion theory boundary condition can then be expressed (cf. § 14.19) as

$$J^-(0) = \int_0^{-1} \mu F(0, \mu) \, d\mu = 0,$$

noting that $\mu \leqq 0$.

The Extrapolation Distance

14.53. In a nonabsorbing medium the asymptotic, or elementary diffusion theory, distribution is given by (14.49.1), and hence

$$J^-(x) = \int_0^{-1} \mu F(x, \mu) \, d\mu$$
$$= \tfrac{1}{4}F_0(x) + \tfrac{1}{6}\lambda_t F_0{}'(x),$$

which is equivalent to the diffusion theory equation (5.28.3). If $J^-(0)$ is to be zero, then

$$\frac{F_0(0)}{F_0{}'(0)} = -\frac{2}{3}\lambda_t.$$

Consequently, at a planar boundary between a nonabsorbing medium and a vacuum, the asymptotic distribution of the neutron flux should extrapolate to zero at a distance $\tfrac{2}{3}\lambda_t$ beyond the surface of the medium (§ 5.39).

14.54. A more accurate calculation, in which all the nonasymptotic solutions are used to satisfy (14.52.1) rigorously, gives $0.7104 \, \lambda_t$ as the extrapolation distance for a noncapturing medium. In the exact transport theory treatment, it is the asymptotic flux distribution which extrapolates linearly to zero at $0.7104\lambda_t$ beyond the boundary; the actual flux falls below the asymptotic distribution close to the boundary (cf. Fig. 5.41). The linear extrapolation of the asymptotic flux is represented by $c(x - 0.7104\lambda_t)$, where c is a constant and x is the distance from the actual boundary. The asymptotic flux at the boundary is consequently proportional to $0.7104\lambda_t$. The correct value from transport theory is $\lambda_t/\sqrt{3}$, i.e., $0.577\lambda_t$, and so the ratio of the actual flux to the asymptotic flux is $0.577/0.710 = 0.81$. Physically, the reason why the flux falls off faster near the boundary than in the interior is that close to the boundary neutrons arrive at a given point almost entirely from one side, whereas in the interior they come from both sides.

14.55. The extrapolation distance of $0.71\lambda_t$ is correct only for a planar boundary of a nonabsorbing medium. If the medium absorbs neutrons, the expression for the extrapolation distance becomes more complicated. It has been found that, for a relatively weak absorber, the extrapolation distance is roughly equal to $0.71\lambda_t\Sigma/\Sigma_s$, so that it is increased by the ratio of the total to the scattering cross sections.

14.56. For curved boundaries, the extrapolation distance is greater than $0.71\lambda_t$. In the limit of vanishingly small radius of curvature of the boundary — corresponding to an extremely small spherical perfect (or "black") absorber embedded in a scattering medium — the extrapolation distance is $\tfrac{4}{3}\lambda_t$.

Index

Accelerators, and nuclear reactions, 2.5, 3.9
  and neutron production, 3.9
Adjoint function, 13.7
  operator, 13.7
Age, 6.128
  and diffusion coefficient, 6.129
  average for fission spectrum, 12.58–12.60
  experimental determination, 6.143–6.145
    results, 6.145
  in heterogeneous system, 9.89
  physical significance, 6.141
  and slowing down length, 6.142
    time, 6.127
  temperature effect, 11.76, 11.82
  values of, 6.145
Age equation, with capture, 6.155–6.159
  without capture, 6.123–6.130
    solutions of, 6.131–6.142
      plane source, 6.131–6.135, 6.149–6.154
      point source, 6.136–6.140
Age theory and slowing down kernels, 12.1–12.5
  and thermal reactor, 7.5–7.24
Albedo, 5.97–5.113
  as boundary condition, 5.106–5.108
  and boundary crossings, 5.109–5.111
  definition, 5.98
  and diffusion coefficient, 5.98
    properties, 5.105
  experimental determination, 5.112, 5.113
  for finite slab, 5.100
  for infinite slab, 5.99
  for sphere, 5.103
  values of, 5.102
Alpha particle, 1.12
  emission, 1.19
  in slow-neutron reactions, 3.29–3.34
Amu, 1.4

Asymptotic reactor equation, 12.43–12.46
Atomic mass unit, 1.4
  energy equivalent, 1.28
Atomic number, 1.6
  and isotopes, 1.8
Augmentation distance, *see* Extrapolation distance

Barn, definition, 3.39
Beryllium, age in, 6.145
  albedo, 5.102
  diffusion properties, 5.91
  moderating ratio, 6.25, 6.26
  as moderator, 4.56
  as neutron source, 3.1–3.3, 3.5
  photoneutrons and shut-down, 4.80, 10.52
  resonance neutron constants, 9.71
  scattering properties, 6.24
  slowing down power, 6.25
Bessel equation, 7.52, 7.53
  functions, 7.53–7.55
Beta particle, 1.12
  emission, 1.16–1.18
    by fission products, 4.16, 4.23
  negative, 1.16, 1.17
  positive, 1.18
Binding energy, 1.23–1.44
  and fission energy, 4.19–4.21
  and mass defect, 1.25–1.29
  and nuclear forces, 1.32
  per nucleon, 1.30, 1.44, 4.19
  semi-empirical calculation, 1.35–1.44
  spin effect, 1.40
    and fission, 4.41, 4.45
  surface tension effect, 1.37
Boron, in control rods, 4.72
  cross sections, 3.76, 3.77
  as neutron detector, 3.84
  as neutron source, 3.2
  reaction with slow neutrons, 3.32

405

Boundary conditions, and diffusion theory, 5.36–5.40, 5.106–5.108
  and transport theory, 14.47–14.56
Breit-Wigner formula, 2.38–2.47, 2.54, 3.68, 3.77
  and hydrogen, 3.81
  and resonance absorption, 2.44, 3.74
  and resonance scattering, 3.54
Buckling, 7.23
  geometric, 7.24–7.27, 7.36–7.60
    and effective multiplication factor, 7.27
    for finite cylinder, 7.50–7.60
    for infinite slab, 7.37–7.40, 7.60
    and nonleakage probability, 7.32
    for rectangular parallelepiped, 7.41–7.46, 7.60
    for sphere, 7.47–7.49, 7.60
  material, 7.24–7.27, 12.45, 12.46
    and exponential experiment, 9.90–9.111
    and macroscopic theory, 9.86–9.89
  vector, 12.28
Burn-up, 11.2

Cadmium, in control rods, 4.72
  cross sections, 3.69
  ratio, 3.89, 5.86
  as shield, 3.89
Carbon, see Graphite
Center of mass (C) system, 5.20, 6.4
  scattering in, 6.4–6.11
Chain reaction, 4.46–4.80
  multiplication factor, 4.47–4.51, 4.57–4.79
    and power level, 4.48
    in natural uranium, 4.56–4.65, see also Uranium
    and neutron balance, 4.52–4.54, 7.33
  self-sustaining, 4.46
    conditions for, 4.47–4.51, 7.3–7.20, 7.31–7.33, 12.32–12.42
Characteristic equation, see Critical equation
Chemical energy and nuclear energy, 1.2
  reactions and nuclear reactions, 2.1–2.5
Collision density, 6.33
  in carbon, 6.55
  in deuterium, 6.55
  in hydrogen, with capture, 6.82–6.86
    without capture, 6.32–6.39, 6.55

in mixtures, 6.69–6.73
  in other media, with capture, 6.89–6.92
    without capture, 6.44–6.66
Collisions, neutron, 6.4–6.24
  to thermalize, 6.24
  see also Scattering
Compound nucleus, 2.10–2.30
  disintegration, 2.11, 2.18
  emission of radiation, 2.21, 3.21–3.28
  excited, 2.11–2.21, 3.21–3.28
  in fission, 4.27, 4.37
  formation, 2.11
  ground state, 2.15
  mean life, 2.12, 2.20, 2.26, 2.29, 2.30
Continuous slowing down model, 6.117–6.122
Control, reactor, 4.72, 10.12, 11.8–11.45
  and delayed neutrons, 4.74–4.80, 10.13–10.52
  rods, 4.72
    eccentric, theory of, 11.34–11.45
    effect on flux, 11.10, 11.45
    function of, 11.8–11.10
    one-group theory, 11.11–11.22, 11.32
      modified, 11.33
    two-group theory, 11.23–11.33
Critical assembly, 7.72–7.78
Critical composition, calculation, 7.26, 7.65–7.69
Critical energy for fission, 4.25–4.35
Critical equation, 7.20, 7.23, 7.31, 8.62, 12.40–12.68
  Gaussian (age) form, 7.20, 7.23, 12.53, 12.54
    and fission spectrum, 12.55–12.60
  general form, 12.40
  and group-diffusion kernels, 12.61–12.68
  for large reactor, 7.62, 7.63, 8.63, 9.88, 12.50, 12.60, 12.62
  for reflected reactor, 8.16, 8.44, 8.61, see also Group-diffusion method
  for uranium-water system, 12.67, 12.68
Critical mass and composition, 7.79–7.81
Critical reactor, flux distribution, 7.22, 7.24, 7.25, 7.40, 7.43, 7.49, 7.57, 7.61
  minimum volume, 7.60

Critical size, 4.69, 4.70, *see also* Buckling
  calculation of, 7.26, 7.65, 7.71
  and composition, 7.79–7.81
  experimental determination, 7.72–7.78
Critical state, 7.2, 7.20–7.22, 7.33, 12.40–12.42
  approach to, 7.11–7.19, 12.32–12.39
Cross sections, 2.38–2.47, 3.38–3.82
  absorption, 3.53, 3.60–3.65, 3.69–3.79
    values, 3.79
  Breit-Wigner formula, 2.38–2.47, 3.68, 3.71, 3.74, 3.77
  experimental determination, 3.57–3.64
    activation method, 3.60–3.64
    results, 3.65–3.82
    transmission method, 3.57–3.59
  fast neutron, 3.75
    in natural uranium, 9.25
  fission, 4.57
  macroscopic, 3.42–3.52, *see also* Macroscopic cross sections
  and mean free path, 3.45–3.47
  microscopic, 3.42
  and neutron energy, 2.39–2.47, 3.65–3.82
  and relaxation length, 3.47
  in resonance region, 3.69–3.74
  scattering, 3.54–3.56
    values, 3.79
  significance of, 3.38–3.40
  slowing down, 8.12
  temperature effect, 11.3, 11.5, 11.74, 11.75
  thermal neutron, 3.79
  $1/v$ law, 2.43, 2.46, 3.53, 3.68, 3.76, 3.77
Current density, 5.9–5.19, 5.26, 5.28
  and albedo, 5.98
  and boundary conditions, 5.38, 5.39
  definition, 5.11

Danger coefficient, 13.23
Decay constant, 1.20
  and half life, 1.21
  and mean life, 1.22
Delayed neutrons, 4.6, 4.8–4.10
  and generation time, 10.13
  and perturbation theory, 13.1, 13.16
  precursors, 4.10, 4.11

and reactor control, 4.74–4.80, 10.12, 10.14, 10.47
  and time behavior of reactor, 10.13–10.52
Delta function, 5.81
Density temperature coefficient, 11.74, 11.81–11.85
Deuterium, collision density in, 6.55
  and continuous slowing down model, 6.118, 6.122
  moderating ratio, 6.25, 6.26
  as neutron source, 3.9
  scattering properties, 6.29
  slowing down power, 6.25
Deuterium oxide, *see* Water, heavy
Diffusion coefficient, 5.7
  and albedo, 5.98
  and transport mean free path, 5.24, 5.28
  and transport theory, 5.22, 14.40
  values, 5.91
Diffusion equation, 5.4, 5.35, 5.43–5.61, 14.17–14.24
  boundary conditions, 5.36–5.40
  and Fick's law, 5.7, 5.28, 14.27
  general form, 12.18
  integral form, 5.92, 5.93
  with slowing down, 6.149–6.152
  solution of, 5.46–5.61
    plane source, 5.50–5.61
    point source, 5.46–5.49
    time-dependent, 10.4–10.20
  and transport theory, 14.17–14.24
Diffusion kernels, 5.93–5.95
Diffusion length, 5.57, 5.62–5.91
  experimental determination, 5.67–5.90
    end correction, 5.89
    harmonic correction, 5.88
    results, 5.91
  in heterogeneous system, 9.88
  physical significance, 5.64
  and temperature, 11.76, 11.82
  values, 5.91
Diffusion mean free path, 14.26
Diffusion theory, 5.1–5.113
  applicability of, 14.32, 14.39
  extrapolation distance, 5.39
  and Fick's law, 5.7, 5.28, 14.27
  and transport theory, 5.3, 5.4, 14.17–14.28

Diffusion theory (*Continued*)
    corrections, 5.20–5.29
Diffusion time, 6.146, 6.148
Dirac function, 5.81
Disadvantage factor, 9.41, 9.67, 9.74
    perturbed, 13.21
Displacement kernels, 5.96, 12.23
Doppler effect, 9.15, 11.5

Effective multiplication factor, 4.71, 7.27, 7.32, 10.6, 12.34
Effective resonance integral, *see* Resonance integral
Eigenfunction, 7.12
Eigenvalue, 7.12
Einstein mass-energy equation, 1.27
Electron volt, 1.28
Electrostatic repulsion of protons, 1.39, 1.44, 4.21, 4.32, 4.33
End correction, diffusion length, 5.89
    exponential experiment, 9.103, 9.110
Energy, binding, *see* Binding energy
    critical, for fission, 4.25–4.35
    excitation, 2.13–2.20
    of fission, 4.17–4.24
    logarithmic decrement, 6.21–6.24
Energy levels, *see* Nuclear energy levels
Epithermal neutrons, 3.13
Ev, 1.28
Excess multiplication factor, 10.7
Excitation energy, compound nucleus, 2.13–2.17
    statistical distribution, 2.18–2.20
Exponential (pile) experiment, 9.90–9.111
Extrapolated boundary, 5.40
Extrapolation distance, 5.39–5.41, 14.53–14.56

Fast fission factor, 4.58, 9.45, 9.76–9.85
Fast neutrons, 3.10
    cross sections, 3.75
        in natural uranium, 9.85
    detection, 3.87
    fission by, 3.37, 4.36–4.45
    reactions, 3.36, 3.37
Fast reactor, 4.55, 4.56
Fermi age treatment, 6.117–6.159, *see also* Age
Fick's law, 5.7, 5.28, 14.27
    generalized form, 14.25

Fission, 2.22, 2.35, 3.37
    beta and gamma rays, 4.16
    chain reaction, 4.46–4.80, *see also* Chain reaction
    characteristics of, 4.1–4.45
    critical energy of, 4.25–4.35
    cross sections, 4.57
    for detection of neutrons, 3.86
    energy, 4.17–4.24
        and binding energy, 4.19–4.21
        experimental determination, 4.22
        and proton repulsion, 4.21
    fast-neutron, 3.37, 4.36–4.45
    fragments, 4.4, 4.12
        energy of, 4.22, 4.23
    liquid-drop model, 4.26, 4.33, 4.34
    mechanism of, 4.25–4.35
    neutron emission in, 4.4–4.11, 4.57
        delayed, 4.6, 4.8–4.10
            precursors, 4.10, 4.11
        prompt, 4.6, 4.7
            energy spectrum, 4.7
        and time behavior of reactor, *see* Time behavior
    and nuclear type, 4.45
    products, 4.12–4.16
        poisoning by, 11.6, 11.7, 11.46–11.72, *see also* Samarium, Xenon
        over-ride, 11.6
        and reactivity, 11.60, 11.61
        radioactivity, 4.15, 4.16
        yield, 4.13
    slow-neutron, 3.35, 4.36–4.45
    spectrum, 4.7
    spontaneous, 4.2, 4.31, 4.35
Flux, *see* Neutron flux
Four-factor formula, 4.61
Fourier integral, 6.133
    transform, 12.27–12.29
        and convolution of functions, 12.64
        in polar coordinates, 12.48, 12.53, 12.61
        significance of, 12.30, 12.31, 12.47
Fuel, 4.54
    burn-up, 11.2
    enriched, 4.56, 4.65, 4.70

Gamma rays, 1.13
    capture, 3.24
    from fission products, 4.16, 4.23
    and neutron production, 3.4–3.8

Gamma rays (*Continued*)
  in nuclear reactions, 2.21, 3.21–3.28
Gaussian kernels, 12.1–12.5
Generation time, 4.49, 6.146, 7.34, 7.35, 10.2, 10.9, 10.13
Graphite, age in, 6.145
  albedo, 5.102
  collision density in, 6.55
  constants for resonance neutrons, 9.71
  cross section, 3.79
  diffusion properties, 5.91
  moderating ratio, 6.25, 6.26
  as moderator, 4.56
  scattering properties, 6.24
  slowing down power, 6.25
Group constants, 8.9–8.13
Group-diffusion method, 8.7–8.14
  and reflected reactors, 8.15–8.64
    multi-group treatment, 8.59–8.64
    one-group treatment, 8.15–8.37
    two-group treatment, 8.38–8.58
Group-diffusion slowing down kernels, 12.6–12.14
    and critical equation, 12.61–12.68

Half life, for delayed neutron emission, 4.8
  radioactive, 1.21
Harmonic correction, diffusion length, 5.88
  exponential experiment, 9.103, 9.110
Heavy water, *see* Water
Heterogeneous reactors, 9.24–9.11, *see also* Nuclear reactors
  advantages and disadvantages, 9.42–9.46
  age in, 9.88
  diffusion length in, 9.88
  and effective resonance integral, 9.30, 9.31
  fast fission factor, 9.45, 9.76–9.86
  lattice cell, 9.26, 9.51–9.53
  macroscopic properties, 9.1, 9.86–9.111
  material buckling, 9.86–9.89
    experimental determination, 9.90–9.111
  microscopic properties, 9.1, 9.36–9.86

neutron flux in, 9.24, 9.27, 9.64
  resonance escape probability, 9.24, 9.36–9.41, 9.43, 9.44, 9.67–9.75
  surface and volume absorption, 9.25–9.35
  thermal utilization, 9.47–9.66
Homogeneous reactors, bare, 7.1–7.81, *see also* Nuclear reactors
  critical equation, 7.20, 7.23, 7.31, 12.40–12.68
  large, 7.62, 7.63, 8.63, 12.50, 12.60, 12.62
  time behavior, *see* Time behavior
  reflected, 8.1–8.64
    multi-group treatment, 8.59–8.64
    one-group treatment, 8.15–8.37
      infinite slab, 8.19–8.30
      sphere, 8.31–8.34
    two-group treatment, 8.38–8.58
Hydrogen, collision density in, 6.32–6.39
  with capture, 6.82–6.86
  and continuous slowing down model, 6.118, 6.122
  diffusion properties, *see* Water
  heavy, *see* Deuterium
  moderating ratio, 6.25, 6.26
  resonance escape probability in, 6.86–6.88
  scattering cross section, 3.80–3.82
  scattering properties, 6.24
  slowing down in, 6.32–6.43, 6.55
    with capture, 6.80–6.88
  slowing down density in, 6.40–6.43
    with capture, 6.87, 6.88
  slowing down power, 6.25
  -uranium system, *see* Uranium

Image, source, 12.24, 12.25
Incident particle, 2.10
Indium, neutron capture in, 3.25
    cross sections, 3.69
  as neutron detector, 3.88, 3.89
Infinite multiplication factor, 4.66
Inhour formula, 10.29
  unit, 10.29
Intermediate reactor, 4.55
  generation time in, 7.35
Iodine in reactor, 11.49–11.53
Isotopes, definition, 1.8
  radioactive, 1.12–1.15
  stable and unstable, 1.9

Kernels, diffusion, 5.93–5.95
  displacement, 5.96, 12.23
  slowing down, 12.1–12.14
    finite, 12.24, 12.25
    Gaussian (age), 12.1–12.5
      and critical equation, 12.53–12.60
    group-diffusion, 12.6–12.14
    synthetic, 12.65
Kinetics, *see* Time behavior

Laboratory (or L) system, 5.20, 6.4
  scattering in, 6.4–6.11
Laplacian operator, 5.31, 5.32
Lattice cell, 9.36, 9.51–9.53
  and perturbation theory, 13.19–13.23
Leakage, neutron, 4.52, 4.53, 4.66–4.70, 5.2, 5.30–5.35, 7.5
  while slowing down, 7.27, 7.28, 7.30–7.33, 7.70
  while thermal, 7.29–7.33, 7.70
  and lifetime, 7.34
Legendre functions, associated, 14.14
Legendre polynomials, 14.14
  orthogonality, 14.21
Lethargy, 6.27–6.29
Lifetime, thermal neutron, 6.148, 7.34, 7.35
    effective, 4.75
    in finite medium, 7.34, 7.35
    and generation time, 7.34, 10.9, 10.13
    and neutron leakage, 7.34
    and reactor period, 10.8, 10.28, 10.39, 10.40, 10.46
    and time behavior of reactor, 4.49, 10.12, 10.52
Liquid-drop model, 1.31–1.34
  and binding energy, 1.35–1.44
  and fission, 4.26, 4.33, 4.34
  and nuclear surface tension, 1.37
Lithium, cross sections, 3.76, 3.77
  as neutron detector, 3.84
  reaction with slow neutrons, 3.33
Lumping in reactors, 9.24
  advantages and disadvantages, 9.42–9.46

Macroscopic and microscopic theory, 9.1, 9.86

Macroscopic cross sections, 3.42
    average, 3.52
    and mean free path, 3.45–3.47
    and rates of processes, 3.48, 3.49, 3.51
    scattering, 3.54–3.56
    of several nuclides, 3.44
    significance, 3.43
    slowing down, 8.12
Macroscopic reactor theory, 9.86–9.111
Mass defect, 1.26
  and binding energy, 1.25–1.29
Mass-energy equivalence, 1.27, 1.28
Mass number, 1.7
Mass unit, *see* Atomic mass unit
Maxwell-Boltzmann distribution, 3.14–3.17
  and cross sections, 3.53
Mean free path, 3.45–3.47
  diffusion, 14.26
  scattering, 3.55, 3.56, 5.24–5.29
  transport, 5.24–5.29
Mean life, delayed neutron, 4.8
  of excited nuclei, 2.26
  radioactive, 1.22
Mev, 1.28
Migration area, 7.63, 7.64, 8.63, 9.89, 12.50, 12.60, 12.62
  and temperature, 11.82
Migration length, 6.154, 7.64
Million electron volts, 1.28
Moderating ratio, 6.25, 6.26
Moderator, 3.12, 4.52, 4.54–4.56
  albedo, 5.102
  age, 6.145
  diffusion properties, 5.91
  for natural uranium reactors, 9.4
  resonance neutron properties, 9.71
  scattering properties, 6.24
  slowing down power, 6.25
Moment form of critical equation, 12.45–12.52
Multigroup treatment, perturbation theory, 13.1–13.10
  reflected reactor, 8.59–8.64
Multiplication factor, 4.47–4.51, 4.57–4.79
  calculation, 7.66
  effective, 4.71, 7.27, 7.32, 10.6, 12.34
  excess, 10.7
  and fast fission factor, 4.57

Multiplication factor (*Continued*)
four-factor formuia, 4.61
infinite, 4.66
in natural uranium reactors, 9.6–9.8
and neutron density, 4.49
and power level, 4.48
and resonance escape probability, 4.59
and thermal utilization, 4.60

Natural uranium reactor, *see* Uranium
Neptunium, fission, 4.43
formation, 3.26
Neutron (or neutrons), 1.3
age, *see* Age
attenuation, 3.41
balance in reactor, 4.52–4.54, 7.27–7.33
conservation of, 5.2
cross sections, *see* Cross sections
current density, 5.9–5.19, 5.26, 5.28, *see also* Current density
cycle, 7.33
delayed, 4.6, 4.8–4.10
precursors, 4.10, 4.11
and reactor control, 4.74–4.80, 10.12, 10.14, 10.47
density, 3.48
detection, 3.83–3.89
diameter, effective, 2.9
diffusion theory, 5.1–5.113, *see also* Diffusion theory
emission in fission, 4.4–4.11
delayed, 4.6, 4.8–4.11
prompt, 4.6, 4.7
epithermal, 3.13
fast, 2.7, 3.10, *see also* Fast neutrons
flux, 3.49, 3.50, *see also* Scalar flux, Vector flux
distribution, bare reactor, 7.22, 7.24, 7.25, 7.61
reflected reactor, 8.2, 8.19, 8.20, 8.36, 8.37, 8.58
measurement, 3.63
forces, 1.24
generation time, *see* Generation time
interaction with nuclei, 2.6, 2.7, *see also* Neutron reactions
leakage, *see* Leakage
lifetime, *see* Lifetime
mass, 1.5
moderation, *see* Moderator

polyenergetic, 3.50–3.53
production of, 3.1–3.9
prompt, 4.6, 4.7
energy spectrum, 4.7
-proton forces, 1.24
-to-proton ratio and nuclear stability, 1.15, 1.45–1.48
and radioactivity, 1.16–1.19
reactions, 2.6, 2.7, 2.13–2.17, 3.20–3.27
radiative capture, 2.14, 3.21–3.28
rates, and cross sections, 348, 349, 3.51
scattering, 5.9–5.112, 6.1–6.116, *see also* Scattering, Slowing down
slow, 2.6, 3.10, *see also* Slow neutrons
slowing down, 6.30–6.116, *see also* Slowing down, Scattering
thermal, 3.13
velocity selector, 3.66
wave length, 2.8, 2.9
Nonleakage probability, 4.67–4.70
and effective multiplication factor, 4.67, 4.71, 7.32
in large reactors, 12.50
while slowing down, 7.27, 7.28, 7.30–7.33, 12.47, 12.57
while thermal, 7.29–7.33
Nuclear binding energy, *see* Binding energy
Nuclear cross sections, *see* Cross sections
Nuclear density, 1.39
Nuclear energy levels, 2.23–2.30
and resonance absorption, 2.32–2.37
spacing, 2.24, 2.25, 2.36, 2.37, 2.40
width, 2.26–2.30, 2.39–2.47
partial, 2.27
physical significance, 2.28
Nuclear forces, 1.23, 1.24, 1.32, 1.33
attractive, 1.36, 1.46
and binding energy, 1.35–1.44
and nuclear stability, 1.45–1.47
repulsive, 1.39, 1.45
and nuclear reactions, 2.3
spin effect, 1.40
surface tension effect, 1.37
Nuclear radii, 1.33, 1.34
Nuclear reactors, 1.1, 2.10, 4.54
control, 4.72–4.80, 10.12, 11.8–11.45, *see also* Control
critical size, 4.69, 4.70, *see also* Critical size, etc.

Nuclear reactors (*Continued*)
  fast, 4.55
  and fission chain, 4.46–4.79
  fuel, 4.54
  heterogeneous, 4.64, 9.24–9.111, *see also* Heterogeneous reactors
  homogeneous, 7.1–7.81, *see also* Homogeneous reactors
  reflected, 8.1–8.64
  intermediate, 4.55
  kinetics, *see* Time behavior
  moderators, 3.12, 4.52, 4.54–4.56, *see also* Moderators
  neutron balance, 4.52–4.54, 7.33
  neutron leakage, 4.52, 4.66–4.70, 7.27–7.33, 7.70
  poisoning, 4.52, *see also* Poisoning
  power level, 4.48
  prompt critical, 4.78, 10.47
  resonance capture in, 4.52
  steady state, 4.71, *see also* Critical state
  subcritical, 4.71, 7.25, 7.33
  supercritical, 4.71, 7.25, 7.33
  thermal, 4.55
  time behavior, *see* Time behavior
  types, 4.55
Nuclear stability, and neutron-proton ratio, 1.15–1.19, 1.45–1.48
  and nuclear forces, 1.45–1.47
Nuclear temperature coefficient, 11.74–11.80, 11.85
Nucleon, 1.3
  and binding energy, 1.30, 1.44
Nucleus, 1.2
  binding energy of, *see* Binding energy
  compound, *see* Compound nucleus
  excited, 1.13, 2.11–2.21
  liquid-drop model, 1.31–1.34
    and binding energy, 1.45–1.47
  radius of, 1.33, 1.34
  recoil, 2.11
  stability range, 1.15, 1.45–1.47, *see also* Nuclear forces
  structure of, 1.3–1.7
  target, 2.10
Nuclide, 1.11

One-group treatment, control rod, 11.11–11.22, 11.32
    modified, 11.33

perturbation theory, 13.11–13.23
reflected reactor, 8.15–8.37
Over-ride, 11.6

Periods, stable and transient, *see* Reactor period
Perturbation theory, 13.1–13.26
  multi-group treatment, 13.1–13.10
  one-group treatment, 13.11
  and reactor poisoning, 13.19–13.23
  statistical weight, 13.17, 13.18
Photon, 2.11
Photoneutron sources, 3.4–3.8
Photoneutrons, effect in shut-down, 4.80, 10.52
Photonuclear reactions, 3.4–3.8
Pile, *see* Nuclear reactor
Pile period, *see* Reactor period
Planck's constant, 2.8
Plane diffusion kernel, 5.94, 5.95
Plane source, diffusion, finite medium, 5.54–5.58
  infinite medium, 5.50–5.53
  two finite media, 5.59–5.61
  slowing down density distribution, 6.131–6.135
  slowing down and diffusion, 6.149–6.154
Plutonium, fission, 3.35, 4.2, 4.36, 4.42, 4.56
  formation, 3.26, 3.27
Point diffusion kernel, 5.93, 5.95
Point source, diffusion, 5.46–5.49, 5.92
  superposition, 5.52, 5.53
  slowing down density distribution, 6.136–6.140
Poisoning, 11.57
  over-ride, 11.6
  and perturbation theory, 13.19–13.23
  and reactivity, 11.60, 11.61
  reactor, 4.52, 11.1, 11.2, 11.6, 11.7, 11.46–11.72, *see also* Samarium, Xenon
  temperature effect, 11.80
Projectile, nuclear, 2.10
Prompt critical reactor, 4.78, 10.47
Prompt neutrons, 4.5–4.7
  and time behavior of reactor, 10.1–10.12
Proton, 1.3
  charge, 1.4

Proton (*Continued*)
  formation in neutron reactions, 3.34
  mass, 1.4
  -neutron forces, 1.24
  -to-neutron ratio, and nuclear stability, 1.15, 1.45–1.48
    and radioactivity, 1.16–1.19
  -proton forces, 1.24, 1.39, 1.44, 4.21, 4.32, 4.33

Radiative capture, 2.21, 3.21–3.28
Radioactive decay, 1.16–1.19
  constant, 1.20
  half life, 1.21
  mean life, 1.22
  rate of, 1.20–1.22
Radioactive isotopes, 1.12, 1.14
Radioactivity, 1.12–1.22
  alpha, 1.19
  beta, negative, 1.16, 1.17
  positive, 1.18
Reactivity, 10.24
  and danger coefficient, 13.23
  perturbation effect, 13.15, 13.16, 13.19–13.23
  poisoning effect, 11.60, 11.61
  and reactor period, 10.28, 10.29, 10.37, 10.43–10.46, 10.50–10.52
  temperature coefficient, 11.73–11.85
    density, 11.81, 11.85
    nuclear, 11.75–11.80, 11.85
    poisoning, 11.80
  and time behavior, 10.24–10.52
Reactor equation, asymptotic form, 12.43–12.46
Reactor kinetics, *see* Time behavior
Reactor, nuclear, *see* Nuclear reactor
Reactor period, 10.8
  effect of delayed neutrons, 10.14
  and neutron lifetime, 10.28, 10.45, 10.46
  and reactivity, 10.28, 10.29, 10.37, 10.43–10.46, 10.50–10.52
  stable, 10.28, 10.37, 10.40, 10.43, 10.46
  negative, 10.49, 10.52
  transient, 10.28
Recoil nucleus, 2.11
Reflection coefficient, *see* Albedo
Reflector, general properties, 8.1–8.6

group treatment, 8.15–8.64, *see also* Homogeneous reactor, reflected
savings, 8.25
  infinite slab reactor, 8.25–8.30
  spherical reactor, 8.31–8.34
Relaxation length, 3.47
Reproduction factor, *see* Multiplication factor
Resonance absorption (or capture), 2.31–2.47, 3.69–3.74
  and Breit-Wigner formula, 2.38–2.47, 3.74
  conditions for, 2.31–2.37
  peaks, 2.44, 3.69, 3.70
    half width, 2.45
  in reactor, 4.52
  region, 3.69
Resonance escape probability, 4.59, 9.10
  in heterogeneous system, 9.36–9.41, 9.43, 9.44, 9.67–9.75
  in homogeneous system, 9.23
  in hydrogen moderator, 6.86–6.88
  for infinitely large cross section, 6.103
  for slowly varying capture, 6.105–6.111
  and temperature, 9.16
  for weak capture, 6.113–6.116
  for widely spaced resonances, 6.94–6.104
Resonance flux, 9.20
Resonance integral, 9.13
  and temperature, 9.15, 9.16
Resonance integral, effective, 9.11–9.23
  in natural uranium, 9.22–9.31
  and temperature, 9.15, 9.16
Resonance neutron flux, 9.20
  utilization, 9.73
Rhodium, cross sections, 3.69
  neutron capture, 3.25

Samarium poisoning, 11.7, 11.46–11.48, 11.70–11.72
  maximum, 11.72
Saturation activity, 3.62
Scalar flux, 5.4, 14.1, 14.5
Scattering, 2.48, 2.49, 5.9–5.12, 6.1–6.116, 14.7–14.9, *see also* Slowing down
  angle, 5.20
  average cosine, 5.22–5.24, 14.14

Scattering (*Continued*)
in C and L systems, 5.23, 5.25, 6.20
cross sections, 3.54–3.56
in hydrogen, 3.80–3.82
measurement, 3.59
values, 3.79
elastic, 2.49, 2.52–2.55, 3.10–3.13
mechanism, 6.3–6.11
energy change in, 6.12–6.16
average logarithmic, 6.21–6.24
inelastic, 2.49–2.51
isotropic, 5.9, 5.21, 5.23, 5.25, 6.18–
6.20, 14.24, 14.29
law, 6.17
potential, 2.53, 2.55
properties of nuclei, 6.24
resonance, 2.53–2.55
and Breit-Wigner formula, 2.54
spherically symmetric, *see* Scattering,
isotropic
Self-adjoint operator, 13.5, 13.6
Slowing down, 3.10–3.13, 6.30–6.116, *see
also* Scattering
continuous model, 6.117–6.122
in hydrogen, 6.32–6.43, 6.55
with capture, 6.80–6.88
leakage while, 7.27, 7.28, 7.30–7.33,
7.70
in mixtures, 6.69–6.75
in other media, 6.44–6.68
asymptotic case, 6.63–6.68
with capture, 6.89–6.116
Slowing down density, 6.40
experimental determination, 6.76–
6.79
in hydrogen, 6.40–6.43
in mixtures, 6.73, 6.74
in other media, 6.63–6.68
in reactor, 7.6–7.13, 7.22, 12.16,
12.17, 12.22, 12.27–12.29
spatial distribution, 6.117–6.159
plane source, 6.131–6.135,
6.149–6.154
point source, 6.136–6.140
Slowing down kernels, finite, 12.23–
12.25
Gaussian (age), 12.1–12.5
and critical equation, 12.53–
12.60
group-diffusion, 12.6–12.14
convolution of, 12.63–12.68

and critical equation, 12.61–
12.68
infinite, 12.1–12.14
Slowing down length, 6.142
Slowing down time, 6.129, 6.146, 6.147
and generation time, 7.35
Slow neutrons, 3.10
chain reaction, 4.56, 9.3
fission, 3.35, 4.36–4.45, *see also*
Fission
reactions, 3.30–3.35
alpha-particle emission, 3.29–3.34
gamma-ray emission, 3.21–3.28
proton emission, 3.34
Spherical harmonics, 14.13
Spin effect and binding energy, 1.40
and fission, 4.41, 4.45
Statistical distribution of excitation energy, 2.18–2.20
Statistical weight, 13.17, 13.18
Steady state, 5.2, 5.43, 7.2, 7.3, 7.18,
7.19, 12.39
Subcritical reactor, 4.71, 7.2, 7.18, 7.25,
7.32, 12.42
Supercritical reactor, 4.71, 7.25, 7.32,
12.42
Surface absorption term, 9.25–9.35
Surface tension effect, nuclear, 1.37
in fission, 4.33

Target nucleus, 2.10
Temperature coefficient, cross sections,
11.75
density, 11.74, 11.81–11.85
nuclear, 11.74–11.80, 11.85
Temperature effect, on age, 11.76, 11.82
on cross sections, 11.75
on diffusion length, 11.76, 11.82
on reactivity, 11.73–11.85
on reactor, 11.3–11.5, 11.73–11.85
on resonance integral, 9.15, 9.16
Thermal energy, 3.11
Thermal neutrons, 3.13, *see also* Slow
neutrons
chain reaction, 4.56, 9.3, 9.27
cross sections, 3.53
values, 3.79
energy of, 3.18
flux, *see* Neutron flux
Maxwell-Boltzmann distribution,
3.14–3.17

Thermal neutrons (*Continued*)
  speed of, 3.18
Thermal reactor, 4.55
Thermal utilization, 4.60
  in heterogeneous system, 9.46–9.66
  in homogeneous system, 9.23
Thermonuclear reactions, 2.5
Time behavior of reactors, 4.48–4.50,
  7.15–7.17, 10.1–10.52, 12.33–12.35
    and control, 4.72–4.77, 10.12
    and delayed neutrons, 10.13–10.52
      one group, 10.40–10.52
    and excess multiplication, 10.7–
      10.10
    and generation time, 4.49, 4.75,
      4.76, 10.9, 10.13, 10.14
    and prompt neutrons, 4.49, 10.1–
      10.12
    and reactivity, 10.24–10.52
      large, 10.46, 10.47
      negative, 10.48–10.52
      small, 10.43–10.45
Track length, 3.49
Transient periods, 10.28
Transport equation, diffusion approxima-
    tion, 14.17–14.29
  one-dimensional, 14.10–14.12
  one-velocity, 14.9
  solution, absorbing medium, 14.33–
    14.39
    nonabsorbing medium, 14.29–
    14.32
    rigorous, 14.41–14.46
Transport mean free path, 5.24–5.29,
  14.23
    and diffusion coefficient, 5.24,
      5.28
    experimental determination,
      5.42
    and extrapolation distance,
      5.39–5.41, 14.53–14.56
Transport theory, 5.3, 5.4, 14.1–14.56
  and boundary conditions, 14.47–
    14.56
  and diffusion coefficient, 5.22, 14.23
  and diffusion length, 14.40
  and diffusion theory, 5.4, 14.17–
    14.29, 14.32, 14.39, 14.45
    corrections, 5.20–5.29
  and extrapolation distance, 5.40,
    5.41, 14.53–14.56

and generalized Fick's law, 14.7–
  14.9
and neutron scattering, 14.7–14.9
Tritium formation, 3.39
Two-group treatment, control rod, 11.23–
  11.33
  perturbation theory, 13.24–13.26
  reflected reactor, 8.38–8.58

Uranium-233, fission, 3.35, 4.36, 4.42
  formation, 3.28
Uranium-235, fission, 3.35, 4.2, 4.36, 4.40,
  4.42, 4.56
  critical energy, 4.34, 4.36, 4.39
  cross section, 4.57
  energy of, 4.16–4.23
  excitation energy, 4.38
  yields, 4.13, 4.14
  in nature, 1.10
Uranium-238, fission, 3.37, 4.2, 4.36, 4.41,
  4.42
  critical energy, 4.34, 4.36, 4.39
  cross section, 4.57
  excitation energy, 4.38
  in nature, 1.10
  neutron capture, 3.26
Uranium isotopes, 1.10
Uranium, natural, 1.10
  chain reaction in, 4.56, 9.2–9.9
  cross sections, 4.57
  as fuel, 4.56, 4.64, 4.74, 9.2–9.9
  heterogeneous system, 9.24–9.111
    effective resonance integral, 9.30,
      9.31
    fast fission factor, 9.45, 9.76–9.86
    material buckling, 9.87–9.89
    experimental determination,
      9.90–9.111
    resonance escape probability,
      9.36–9.41, 9.43, 9.44, 9.67–
      9.75
    surface and volume absorption,
      9.25–9.35
    thermal utilization, 9.47–9.66
  homogeneous system, 9.10–9.23
    effective resonance integral, 9.22,
      9.23
    multiplication factor, 9.6
    resonance capture, 9.10–9.23
    resonance escape probability, 9.23
    thermal utilization, 9.23

Uranium-water system, 7.79–7.81
    critical equation, 12.67, 12.68
    slowing down kernels, 12.64–12.66

Vector flux, 5.3, 14.5
Volume absorption term, 9.25–9.35
Volume advantage factor, 9.17
    integrated, 9.26

Water, age in, 6.145
  albedo, 5.102
  diffusion properties, 5.91
  as moderator, 4.56
  resonance neutron constants, 9.71
  -uranium system, see Uranium
Water, heavy, age in, 6.145
  albedo, 5.102
  diffusion properties, 5.91

  as moderator, 4.56
  photoneutrons and shut-down, 4.80
  resonance neutron properties, 9.71
Wave equation, 5.44, 5.45
  solution, 5.46–5.61, 5.70–5.79, 7.37–7.59
Width, energy level, 2.26–2.30, 2.39–2.47
  partial, 2.27
  and resonance peak, 2.45

Xenon, concentration, 11.54–11.56
  after shut-down, 11.62–11.69
  equilibrium, 11.59
  maximum, after shut-down, 11.67
  during operation, 11.58
  poisoning, 11.7, 11.46–11.48, 11.57–11.61
  temperature effect, 11.80